GCSE
Additional Science
for AQA

Your Interactive Online Edition...

...includes this entire book, plus videos, animations and other brilliant digital features.
To access it, just go to **cgpbooks.co.uk/extras** and enter this unique code:

0735 0375 0805 9268

This code will only work once. If someone has used this book before you, they may have already claimed the Online Edition.

Published by CGP

Editors:
Katie Braid, Charlotte Burrows, Mary Falkner, Ben Fletcher, Christopher Lindle, Matteo Orsini-Jones, Rachael Rogers, Camilla Simson, Hayley Thompson, Megan Tyler, Rachel Ward, Karen Wells, Charlotte Whiteley, Sarah Williams.

ISBN: 978 1 84762 224 2

With thanks to Katherine Craig, Janet Cruse-Sawyer, Jane Ellingham, Ian Francis, Glenn Rogers and Jamie Sinclair for the proofreading.

With thanks to Laura Jakubowski for the copyright research.

Printed by Elanders Ltd, Newcastle upon Tyne.
Clipart from Corel®

Contents

Introduction

How Science Works

Biology 2

B2.1 Cells and Simple Cell Transport

B2.2 Tissues, Organs and Organ Systems

B2.3 Photosynthesis

B2.4 Organisms and Their Environment

B2.5 Proteins — Their Functions and Uses

B2.6 Aerobic and Anaerobic Respiration

B2.7 Cell Division and Inheritance

B2.8 Fossils and Speciation

Chemistry 2

C2.1 Structure and Bonding

C2.2 Structure, Properties and Uses of Substances

C2.3 Quantitative Chemistry and Analysis

C2.4 Rates of Reaction

C2.5 Exothermic and Endothermic Reactions

C2.6 Acids, Bases and Salts

C2.7 Electrolysis

Physics 2

P2.1 Forces and their Effects

P2.2 The Kinetic Energy of Objects

P2.3 Currents in Electrical Circuits

P2.4 Mains Electricity and Appliances

P2.5 Atomic Structure and Radioactivity

P2.6 Nuclear Fission and Nuclear Fusion

Controlled Assessment

Exam Help

Reference

How to use this book

Learning Objectives

- These tell you exactly what you need to learn, or be able to do, for the exam.
- There's a specification reference at the bottom that links to the AQA specification.

Learning Objectives:
- Know that the yield is the amount of product formed in a reaction.
- Know that the percentage yield is the yield of the reaction compared to the maximum theoretical yield, given as a percentage.
- H Know how to calculate percentage yields.
- Know that some reactions are reversible and can go in either direction.
- Know why percentage yield is never 100%.
- Understand why high yields are important for sustainable development.

Specification Reference C2.3, C2.3.3

5. Percentage Yield

Percentage yield is a good way of measuring how much of a chemical has been wasted during a reaction. Read on to find out how to calculate percentage yield and why it's important in the chemical industry.

What is percentage yield?

The amount of product you get in a reaction is known as the **yield**. The more reactant you start with, the higher the yield will be. But the **percentage yield** doesn't depend on the amount of reactant you started with — it's a percentage.

The percentage yield is a comparison between the amount of product you expect to get and the amount of product you actually get. It is always somewhere between 0 and 100%. A 100% yield means that you got all the product you expected to get. A 0% yield means that no reactants were converted into product, i.e. no product at all was made.

Calculating the percentage yield Higher

The predicted yield of a reaction can be calculated from the balanced reaction equation (see page 145). If you know the predicted yield of a reaction and the actual yield of a reaction, you can calculate the percentage yield using the following formula:

$$\text{percentage yield} = \frac{\text{actual yield (grams)}}{\text{predicted yield (grams)}} \times 100$$

Tip: The predicted yield is sometimes called the maximum theoretical yield.

Example **Higher**

If you reacted 24 g of calcium hydroxide with an excess of hydrochloric acid, you would expect to make 36 g of calcium chloride. If you actually only made 28.2 g of calcium chloride, then the percentage yield would be:

$$\%\text{ yield} = \frac{\text{actual yield}}{\text{predicted yield}} \times 100 = \frac{28.2}{36} \times 100 = 78.3\%$$

Tip: If you want to see how to calculate this predicted yield, have a look back at Example 2 on page 146.

Why percentage yields are never 100%

Even though no atoms are gained or lost in reactions, in real life, you never get a 100% yield. Some product or reactant always gets lost along the way — and that goes for big industrial processes as well as school lab experiments. There are several reasons for this.

Tip: Keeping the percentage yield as high as possible helps to make chemical reactions more environmentally friendly. See the next page for more.

148 Chemistry 2.3 Quantitative Chemistry and Analysis

Examples

These are here to help you understand the theory.

How Science Works

- How Science Works is a big part of GCSE Additional Science. There's a whole section on it at the front of the book.
- How Science Works is also covered throughout the book wherever you see this symbol.

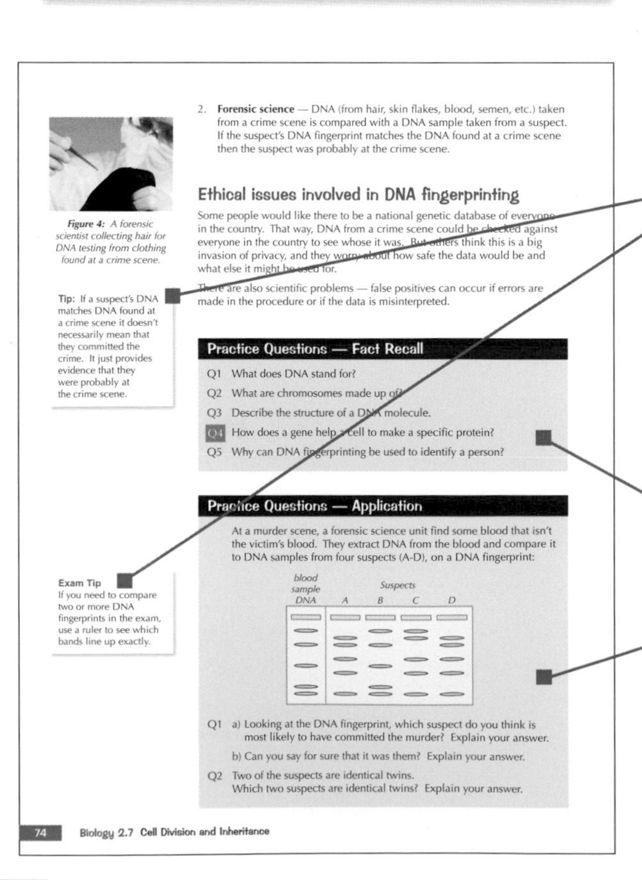

2. **Forensic science** — DNA (from hair, skin flakes, blood, semen, etc.) taken from a crime scene is compared with a DNA sample taken from a suspect. If the suspect's DNA fingerprint matches the DNA found at a crime scene then the suspect was probably at the crime scene.

Figure 4: A forensic scientist collecting hair for DNA testing from clothing found at a crime scene.

Ethical issues involved in DNA fingerprinting

Some people would like there to be a national genetic database of everyone in the country. That way, DNA from a crime scene could be checked against everyone in the country to see whose it was. But others think this is a big invasion of privacy, and they worry about how safe the data would be and what else it might be used for.

There are also scientific problems — false positives can occur if errors are made in the procedure or if the data is misinterpreted.

Tip: If a suspect's DNA matches DNA found at a crime scene it doesn't necessarily mean that they committed the crime. It just provides evidence that they were probably at the crime scene.

Practice Questions — Fact Recall

Q1 What does DNA stand for?
Q2 What are chromosomes made up of?
Q3 Describe the structure of a DNA molecule.
Q4 How does a gene help a cell to make a specific protein?
Q5 Why can DNA fingerprinting be used to identify a person?

Practice Questions — Application

At a murder scene, a forensic science unit find some blood that isn't the victim's blood. They extract DNA from the blood and compare it to DNA samples from four suspects (A-D), on a DNA fingerprint:

Q1 a) Looking at the DNA fingerprint, which suspect do you think is most likely to have committed the murder? Explain your answer.
b) Can you say for sure that it was them? Explain your answer.
Q2 Two of the suspects are identical twins. Which two suspects are identical twins? Explain your answer.

Exam Tip
If you need to compare two or more DNA fingerprints in the exam, use a ruler to see which bands line up exactly.

74 Biology 2.7 Cell Division and Inheritance

Tips and Exam Tips

- There are tips throughout the book to help you understand the theory.
- There are also exam tips to help you with answering exam questions.

Practice Questions

- There are a lot of facts to learn for GCSE Additional Science — fact recall questions test that you know them.
- Annoyingly, the examiners also expect you to be able to apply your knowledge to new situations — application questions give you plenty of practice at doing this.
- All the answers are in the back of the book.

Higher Exam Material

- Some of the material in this book will only come up in the exam if you're sitting the higher exam papers.
- This material is clearly marked with boxes that look like this:

- If you're sitting the foundation papers, you don't need to learn it.

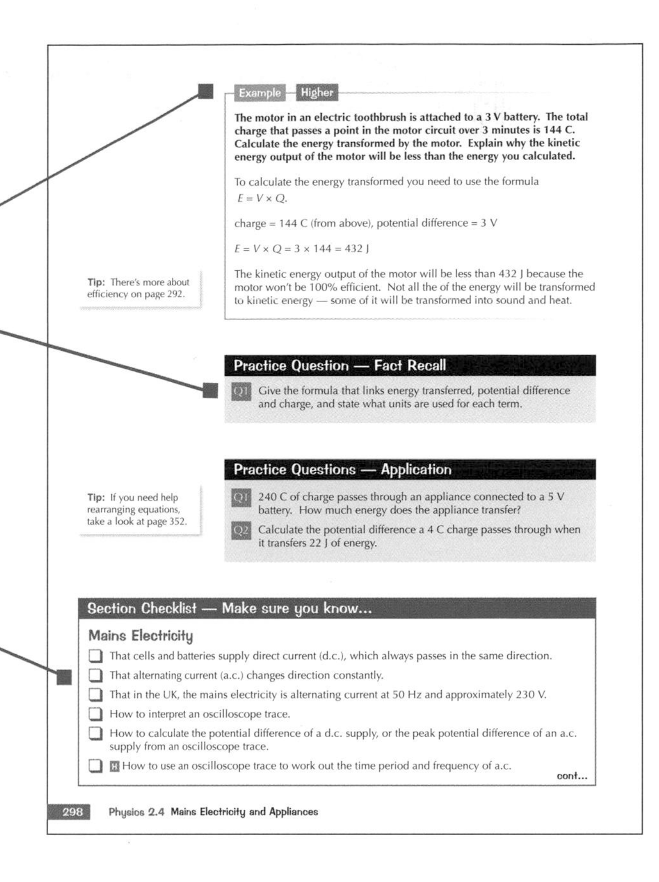

Example Higher

The motor in an electric toothbrush is attached to a 3 V battery. The total charge that passes a point in the motor circuit over 3 minutes is 144 C. Calculate the energy transformed by the motor. Explain why the kinetic energy output of the motor will be less than the energy you calculated.

To calculate the energy transformed you need to use the formula $E = V \times Q$.

charge = 144 C (from above), potential difference = 3 V

$E = V \times Q = 3 \times 144 = 432$ J

The kinetic energy output of the motor will be less than 432 J because the motor won't be 100% efficient. Not all the of the energy will be transformed to kinetic energy — some of it will be transformed into sound and heat.

Tip: There's more about efficiency on page 292.

Practice Question — Fact Recall

Q1 Give the formula that links energy transferred, potential difference and charge, and state what units are used for each term.

Practice Questions — Application

Q1 240 C of charge passes through an appliance connected to a 5 V battery. How much energy does the appliance transfer?

Q2 Calculate the potential difference a 4 C charge passes through when it transfers 22 J of energy.

Tip: If you need help rearranging equations, take a look at page 352.

Section Checklist — Make sure you know...

Mains Electricity

- ❑ That cells and batteries supply direct current (d.c.), which always passes in the same direction.
- ❑ That alternating current (a.c.) changes direction constantly.
- ❑ That in the UK, the mains electricity is alternating current at 50 Hz and approximately 230 V.
- ❑ How to interpret an oscilloscope trace.
- ❑ How to calculate the potential difference of a d.c. supply, or the peak potential difference of an a.c. supply from an oscilloscope trace.
- ❑ H How to use an oscilloscope trace to work out the time period and frequency of a.c.

cont...

298 Physics 2.4 Mains Electricity and Appliances

Section Checklist

Each section has a checklist at the end with boxes that let you tick off what you've learnt.

Glossary

There's a glossary at the back of the book full of all the definitions you need to know for the exam, plus loads of other useful words.

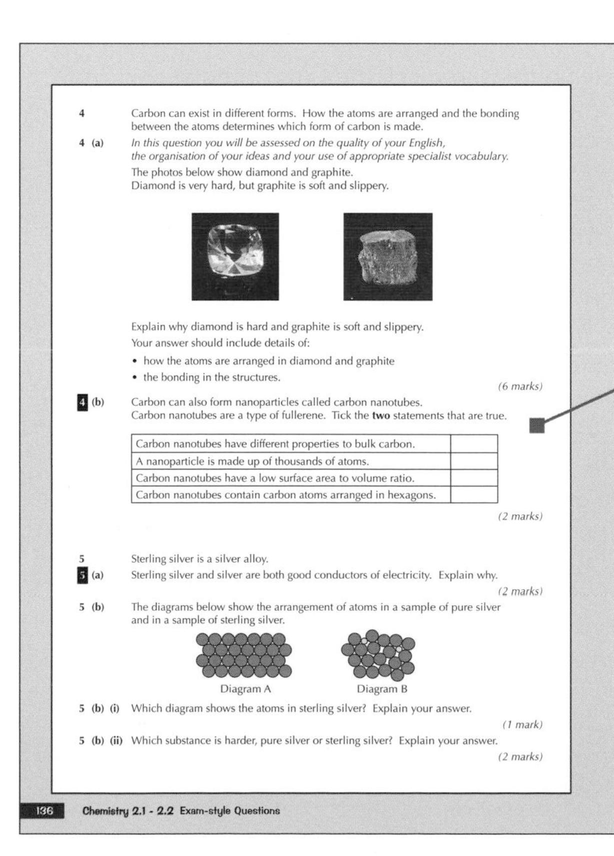

4 Carbon can exist in different forms. How the atoms are arranged and the bonding between the atoms determines which form of carbon is made.

4 (a) *In this question you will be assessed on the quality of your English, the organisation of your ideas and your use of appropriate specialist vocabulary.*
The photos below show diamond and graphite.
Diamond is very hard, but graphite is soft and slippery.

Explain why diamond is hard and graphite is soft and slippery.
Your answer should include details of:
- how the atoms are arranged in diamond and graphite
- the bonding in the structures.

(6 marks)

4 (b) Carbon can also form nanoparticles called carbon nanotubes.
Carbon nanotubes are a type of fullerene. Tick the **two** statements that are true.

Carbon nanotubes have different properties to bulk carbon.	
A nanoparticle is made up of thousands of atoms.	
Carbon nanotubes have a low surface area to volume ratio.	
Carbon nanotubes contain carbon atoms arranged in hexagons.	

(2 marks)

5 Sterling silver is a silver alloy.

5 (a) Sterling silver and silver are both good conductors of electricity. Explain why.

(2 marks)

5 (b) The diagrams below show the arrangement of atoms in a sample of pure silver and in a sample of sterling silver.

Diagram A Diagram B

5 (b) (i) Which diagram shows the atoms in sterling silver? Explain your answer.

(1 mark)

5 (b) (ii) Which substance is harder, pure silver or sterling silver? Explain your answer.

(2 marks)

136 Chemistry 2.1 - 2.2 Exam-style Questions

Exam-style Questions

- Practising exam-style questions is really important — there are some testing you on material from every section.
- They're the same style as the ones you'll get in the real exams.
- All the answers are in the back of the book, along with a mark scheme to show you how you get the marks.
- Higher-only questions are marked like this:

Controlled Assessment and Exam Help

There are sections at the back of the book stuffed full of things to help you with the controlled assessment and the exams.

1. The Scientific Process

Science is all about finding things out and learning things about the world we live in. This topic is all about the scientific process — how a scientist's initial idea turns into a theory that is accepted by the wider scientific community.

Learning Objectives:

- Know what a hypothesis and a prediction are and understand their roles in developing scientific ideas.
- Understand that scientists try to explain observations using evidence collected in investigations.
- Understand the importance of carrying out fair tests and collecting repeatable, reproducible and valid results.
- Understand why some decisions relating to science are not just based on scientific evidence but take other factors into account.

Specification Reference How Science Works

Hypotheses

Scientists try to explain things. Everything. They start by observing something they don't understand — it could be anything, e.g. planets in the sky, a person suffering from an illness, what matter is made of... anything.

Then, they come up with a **hypothesis** — a possible explanation for what they've observed. The next step is to test whether the hypothesis might be right or not — this involves gathering evidence (i.e. data from investigations).

The scientist uses the hypothesis to make a **prediction** — a statement based on the hypothesis that can be tested. They then carry out an investigation. If data from experiments or studies backs up the prediction, you're one step closer to figuring out if the hypothesis is true.

Tip: Investigations include lab experiments and studies.

Testing a hypothesis

Other scientists will use the hypothesis to make their own predictions, and carry out their own experiments or studies. They'll also try to reproduce the original investigations to check the results. And if all the experiments in the world back up the hypothesis, then scientists start to think it's true.

However, if a scientist somewhere in the world does an experiment that doesn't fit with the hypothesis (and other scientists can reproduce these results), then the hypothesis is in trouble. When this happens, scientists have to come up with a new hypothesis (maybe a modification of the old hypothesis, or maybe a completely new one).

Accepting a hypothesis

If pretty much every scientist in the world believes a hypothesis to be true because experiments back it up, then it usually goes in the textbooks for students to learn. Accepted hypotheses are often referred to as **theories**.

Our currently accepted theories are the ones that have survived this 'trial by evidence' — they've been tested many, many times over the years and survived (while the less good ones have been ditched). However... they never, never become hard and fast, totally indisputable fact. You can never know... it'd only take one odd, totally inexplicable result, and the hypothesising and testing would start all over again.

Example

Over time scientists have come up with different hypotheses about the layout of the Solar System.

About 500 years ago we thought the Solar System looked like this.

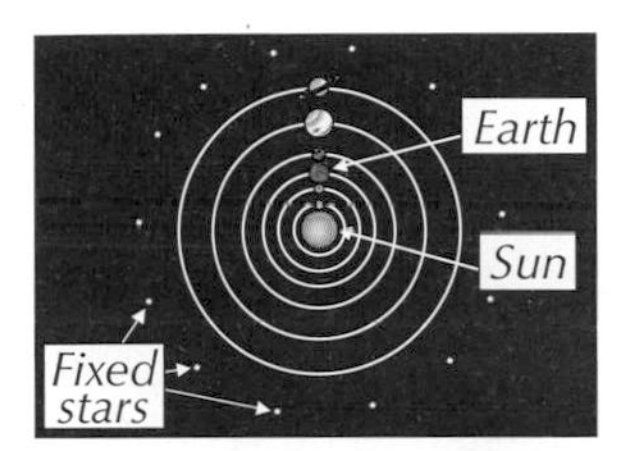

Then we thought it looked like this.

And now we think it's more like this.

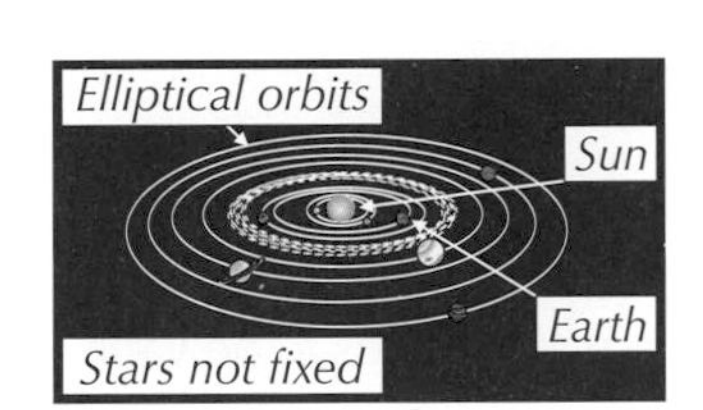

Tip: The different hypotheses on what the Solar System looks like are called different <u>models</u>. A model is a simplified description or a representation of an object or a concept.

Collecting evidence

If a hypothesis is going to get accepted, there needs to be good evidence for it. The way evidence is gathered can have a big effect on how trustworthy it is.

Results from experiments in laboratories are great. A lab is the easiest place to control variables so that they're all kept constant (except for the one you're investigating). This makes it easier to carry out a **fair test**. For things that you can't investigate in the lab (e.g. climate) you conduct scientific studies. As many of the variables as possible are controlled, to make it a fair test.

Tip: See page 7 for more on fair testing and variables.

Old wives' tales, rumours, hearsay, "what someone said", and so on, should be taken with a pinch of salt. Without any evidence they're not scientific — they're just opinions.

Sample size

Data based on small samples isn't as good as data based on large samples. A sample should be representative of the whole population (i.e. it should share as many of the various characteristics in the population as possible) — a small sample can't do that as well.

The bigger the sample size the better, but scientists have to be realistic when choosing how big.

Figure 1: *A scientist doing a laboratory experiment.*

Example

If you were studying how lifestyle affects people's weight. it'd be great to study everyone in the UK (a huge sample), but it'd take ages and cost a bomb. Studying a thousand people would be more realistic.

Quality of evidence

You can have confidence in the results if they can be repeated (during the same experiment) and other scientists can reproduce them too (in other experiments). If the results aren't **repeatable** or **reproducible**, you can't believe them.

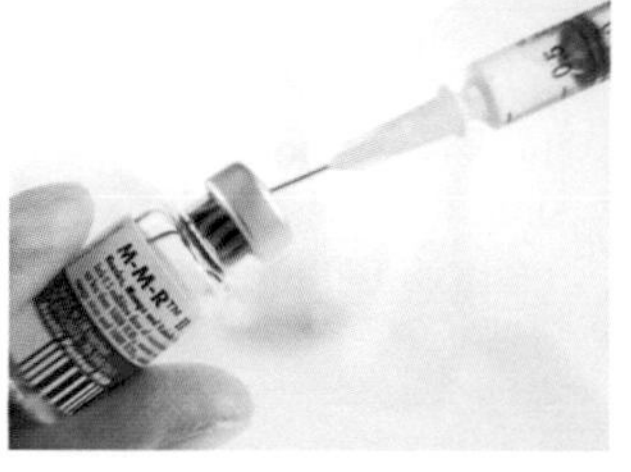

Figure 2: *The MMR vaccine.*

Example

In 1998, a scientist claimed that he'd found a link between the MMR vaccine (for measles, mumps and rubella) and autism. As a result, many parents stopped their children from having the vaccine — which led to a big rise in the number of children catching measles. However, no other scientist has been able to reproduce the results since. Health authorities have now concluded that the vaccine is safe to use.

If results are repeatable and reproducible, they're said to be **reliable**.

Getting valid evidence

Evidence also needs to be **valid**. Valid means that the data answers the original question.

Tip: To be valid, a result must also be repeatable and reproducible.

Example

Do mobile phones cause brain tumours?

Some studies have found that people who use mobile phones regularly are more likely to develop brain tumours. What they'd actually found was a **correlation** (relationship) between the variables "use of mobile phones" and "development of brain tumours" — they found that as one changed, so did the other.

Tip: See page 14 for more on correlation.

But this evidence is not enough to say that using a mobile phone causes brain tumours, as other explanations might be possible. For example, age, gender and family history can all increase the risk of developing a brain tumour. So these studies don't show a definite link and so don't answer the original question.

Communicating results

Once evidence is collected it can be shared with other people. It's important that the evidence isn't presented in a **biased** way. This can sometimes happen when people want to make a point, e.g. they overemphasise a relationship in the data. (Sometimes without knowing they're doing it.) And there are all sorts of reasons why people might want to do this.

Examples

- They want to keep the organisation or company that's funding the research happy. (If the results aren't what they'd like they might not give them any more money to fund further research.)

- Governments might want to persuade voters, other governments, journalists, etc.
- Companies might want to 'big up' their products. Or make impressive safety claims.
- Environmental campaigners might want to persuade people to behave differently.

There's also a risk that if an investigation is done by a team of highly-regarded scientists it'll be taken more seriously than evidence from less well known scientists. But having experience, authority or a fancy qualification doesn't necessarily mean the evidence is good — the only way to tell is to look at the evidence scientifically (e.g. is it repeatable, valid, etc.).

Issues created by science

Scientific knowledge is increased by doing experiments. And this knowledge leads to scientific developments, e.g. new technologies or new advice. These developments can create issues though. For example, particular scientific developments might be ignored if they could create political issues, or emphasised if they help a particular cause.

Example

Some governments were pretty slow to accept the fact that human activities are causing global warming, despite all the evidence. This is because accepting it means they've got to do something about it, which costs money and could hurt their economy. This could lose them a lot of votes.

Scientific developments can cause a whole host of other issues too.

Examples

- **Economic issues:** Society can't always afford to do things scientists recommend (e.g. investing heavily in alternative energy sources) without cutting back elsewhere.
- **Social issues:** Decisions based on scientific evidence affect people — e.g. should fossil fuels be taxed more highly (to invest in alternative energy)? Should alcohol be banned (to prevent health problems)? Would the effect on people's lifestyles be acceptable?
- **Environmental issues:** Chemical fertilisers may help us produce more food — but they also cause environmental problems.
- **Ethical issues:** There are a lot of things that scientific developments have made possible, but should we do them? E.g. clone humans, develop better nuclear weapons.

***Figure 3:** Dolly the sheep — the first mammal to be cloned. A great scientific advance but some people think that cloning animals is morally wrong.*

2. Limitations of Science

Science has taught us an awful lot about the world we live in and how things work — but science doesn't have the answer for everything.

Learning Objectives:

- Know that there are some things that haven't yet been explained by science because we don't have enough good evidence.
- Understand why some questions can't ever be answered by science alone.

Specification Reference
How Science Works

Questions science hasn't answered yet

We don't understand everything. And we never will. We'll find out more, for sure — as more hypotheses are suggested, and more experiments are done. But there'll always be stuff we don't know.

Examples

- Today we don't know exactly how many species exist on Earth. How many more have we yet to discover? How many of them will become extinct before we even discover evidence of their existence?
- We also don't know how life on Earth began. Did it all start in the sea? Maybe the first organic molecules were brought to Earth on a comet and it all started from there?

Figure 1: *The Earth. No one knows how Earth's first life forms came about.*

These are complicated questions. At the moment scientists don't all agree on the answers because there isn't enough repeatable, reproducible and valid evidence. But eventually, we probably will be able to answer these questions once and for all. All we need is more evidence. But by then there'll be loads of new questions to answer.

Questions science can't answer

There are some questions that all the experiments in the world won't help us answer — the "should we be doing this at all?" type questions.

Example

Think about embryonic screening (which allows you to choose an embryo with certain characteristics).

Some people think it's good because it can help reduce suffering — parents can choose not to have a baby that has a genetic disorder and would suffer a lot during its lifetime. It can cost a lot of money to treat people with genetic disorders, so destroying embryos with these disorders can save money.

Other people say it's bad. Some people think that destroying embryos that could have developed into humans is unethical. Some people also think that screening might lead to embryos being screened to pick the most 'desirable' one (e.g. an intelligent child) which can be considered unethical.

Tip: It's important that scientists don't get wrapped up in whether they can do something, before stopping to think about whether they should do it. Some experiments have to be approved by ethics councils before scientists are allowed to carry them out.

The question of whether something is morally or ethically right or wrong can't be answered by more experiments — there is no "right" or "wrong" answer. The best we can do is get a consensus from society — a judgement that most people are more or less happy to live by. Science can provide more information to help people make this judgement, and the judgement might change over time. But in the end it's up to people and their conscience.

3. Designing Investigations

To be a good scientist you need to know how to design a good experiment. That's what this topic is all about — how to make your experiment safe and how to make sure you get good quality results.

Learning Objectives:
- Know how to design fair investigations that allow good quality data to be collected.

Specification Reference
How Science Works

Making predictions from a hypothesis

Scientists observe things and come up with hypotheses to explain them (see page 2). To figure out whether a **hypothesis** might be correct or not you need to do an investigation to gather some evidence. The evidence will help support or disprove the hypothesis.

The first step is to use the hypothesis to come up with a **prediction** — a statement about what you think will happen that you can test.

Example

If your hypothesis is "as the speed of a car increases so does the amount of drag acting upon it", then your prediction might be "a car travelling at a high speed experiences a larger amount of drag than when it is travelling at a low speed".

Tip: Sometimes the words 'hypothesis' and 'prediction' are used interchangeably.

Investigations are used to see if there are patterns or relationships between two variables. For example, to see if there's a pattern or relationship between the variables 'speed the car is travelling at' and 'amount of drag'. The investigation has to be a **fair test** to make sure the evidence is **valid**.

Tip: See page 4 for more on valid evidence.

Ensuring it's a fair test

In a lab experiment you usually change one variable and measure how it affects the other variable. To make it a fair test everything else that could affect the results should stay the same (otherwise you can't tell if the thing you're changing is causing the results or not — the data won't be valid).

Tip: A variable is just something in the experiment that can change.

Example

You might change only the temperature of an enzyme-catalysed reaction and measure how this affects the rate of reaction. You need to keep the concentration of the reactants the same, otherwise you won't know if any change in the rate of reaction is caused by the change in temperature, or a difference in reactant concentration.

Figure 1: *Students measuring the rate of a chemical reaction.*

The variable you change is called the **independent variable**. The variable you measure is called the **dependent variable**. The variables that you keep the same are called **control variables**.

Example

In the rate of reaction example above, temperature is the independent variable, the rate of the reaction is the dependent variable and the concentration of reactants and volume of reactants are control variables.

Control experiments and control groups

To make sure no other factors are affecting the results, you also have to include a **control experiment** — an experiment that's kept under the same conditions as the rest of the investigation, but doesn't have anything done to it.

Example

You investigate antibiotic resistance in bacteria by growing cultures of bacteria on agar plates, then adding paper discs soaked in antibiotic.

If the bacteria are resistant to the antibiotic they will continue to grow. If they aren't resistant a clear patch will appear around the disc where they have died or haven't grown.

A disc that isn't soaked in antibiotic is included to act as a control. This makes sure any result is down to the antibiotic, not the presence of a paper disc.

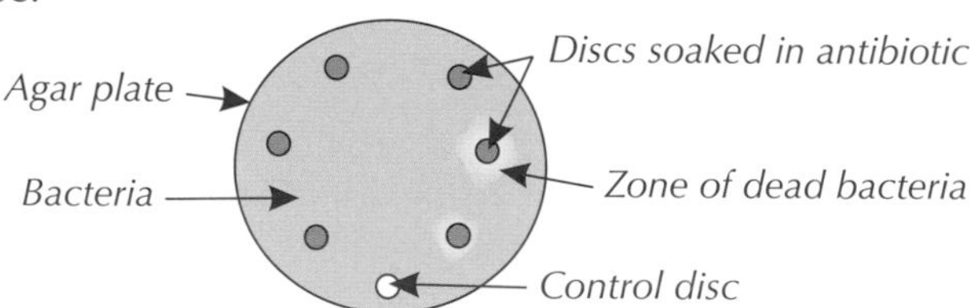

***Figure 2:** An investigation into antibiotic resistance.*

Tip: A study is an investigation that doesn't take place in a lab.

It's important that a study is a fair test, just like a lab experiment. It's a lot trickier to control the variables in a study than it is in a lab experiment though. Sometimes you can't control them all, but you can use a **control group** to help. This is a group of whatever you're studying (people, plants, lemmings, etc.) that's kept under the same conditions as the group in the experiment, but doesn't have anything done to it.

Example

If you're studying the effect of light on plant growth, one plant will be grown in the dark while another plant will be left to grow in daylight. The plants must be the same species and the other variables (e.g. temperature, water, nutrients) must all be kept the same.

The plant grown in the daylight is the control plant — if it grows normally then you know that light is the only variable affecting the other plant.

***Figure 3:** A seedling growing in daylight.*

Trial runs

It's a good idea to do a **trial run** (a quick version of your experiment) before you do the proper experiment. Trial runs are used to figure out the range (the upper and lower limit) of variable values used in the proper experiment. If you don't get a change in the dependent variable at the lower values in the trial run, you might narrow the range in the proper experiment. But if you still get a big change at the upper values you might increase the range.

Example

For an experiment investigating how temperature affects the rate of an enzyme-catalysed reaction, you might do a trial run with a temperature range of 20-50 °C. If there was no reaction at the lower end (e.g. 20-30 °C), you might narrow the range to 30-50 °C for the proper experiment.

Trial runs can also be used to figure out the intervals (gaps) between the values too. The intervals can't be too small (otherwise the experiment would take ages), or too big (otherwise you might miss something).

Tip: If you don't have time to do a trial run, you could always look at the data other people have got doing a similar experiment and use a range and interval values similar to theirs.

Example

If using 2 °C intervals doesn't give you much change in the rate of the reaction each time, you might decide to use 5 °C intervals, e.g 30, 35, 40, 45, 50 °C.

Trial runs can also help you figure out whether or not your experiment is repeatable.

Example

If you repeat it three times and the results are all similar, the experiment is repeatable.

Tip: Consistently repeating the results is crucial for checking that your results are repeatable.

Ensuring your experiment is safe

To make sure your experiment is safe you must identify all the **hazards**. A hazard is something that can potentially cause harm. Hazards include:

- Microorganisms: e.g. some bacteria can make you ill.
- Chemicals: e.g. sulfuric acid can burn your skin and alcohols catch fire easily.
- Fire: e.g. an unattended Bunsen burner is a fire hazard.
- Electricity: e.g. faulty electrical equipment could give you a shock.

Tip: You can find out about potential hazards by looking in textbooks, doing some internet research, or asking your teacher.

Scientists need to manage the risk of hazards by doing things to reduce them.

Examples

- If you're working with sulfuric acid, always wear gloves and safety goggles. This will reduce the risk of the acid coming into contact with your skin and eyes.
- If you're using a Bunsen burner, stand it on a heatproof mat. This will reduce the risk of starting a fire.

Figure 4: *Scientists wearing safety goggles to protect their eyes during an experiment.*

4. Collecting Data

Once you've designed your experiment, you need to get on and do it. Here's a guide to making sure the results you collect are good.

Learning Objectives:
- Know how to collect good quality data, taking repeatability, reproducibility, accuracy, precision and equipment selection and use into account.
- Understand what random errors, systematic errors and anomalous results are.

Specification Reference How Science Works

Getting good quality results

When you do an experiment you want your results to be **repeatable**, **reproducible** and as **accurate** and **precise** as possible.

To check repeatability you need to repeat the readings — you should repeat each reading at least three times. To make sure your results are reproducible you can cross check them by taking a second set of readings with another instrument (or a different observer). Checking your results match with secondary sources, e.g. other studies, also increases the reliability of your data.

Tip: For more on the mean see page 12.

Your data also needs to be accurate. Really accurate results are those that are really close to the true answer. Collecting lots of data and calculating a mean will improve the accuracy of your results. Your data also needs to be precise. Precise results are ones where the data is all really close to the mean (i.e. not spread out).

Tip: Sometimes, you can work out what result you should get at the end of an experiment (the theoretical result) by doing a bit of maths. If your experiment is accurate there shouldn't be much difference between the theoretical results and the result you actually get.

Example

Look at the data in this table. Data set 1 is more precise than data set 2 because all the data in set 1 is really close to the mean, whereas the data in set 2 is more spread out.

Repeat	Data set 1	Data set 2
1	12	11
2	14	17
3	13	14
Mean	13	14

Choosing the right equipment

When doing an experiment, you need to make sure you're using the right equipment for the job. The measuring equipment you use has to be sensitive enough to measure the changes you're looking for.

Example

If you need to measure changes of 1 ml you need to use a measuring cylinder that can measure in 1 ml steps — it'd be no good trying with one that only measures 10 ml steps, it wouldn't be sensitive enough.

Figure 1: *Different types of measuring cylinder and glassware — make sure you choose the right one before you start an experiment.*

The smallest change a measuring instrument can detect is called its **resolution**. For example, some mass balances have a resolution of 1 g, some have a resolution of 0.1 g, and some are even more sensitive.

Also, equipment needs to be calibrated so that your data is more accurate.

Example

Mass balances need to be set to zero before you start weighing things.

Tip: Calibration is a way of making sure that a measuring device is measuring things accurately — you get it to measure something you know has a certain value and set the device to say that amount.

Errors

Random errors

The results of your experiment will always vary a bit because of **random errors** — tiny differences caused by things like human errors in measuring. You can reduce their effect by taking many readings and calculating the mean.

Systematic errors

If the same error is made every time, it's called a **systematic error**.

Example

If you didn't fully empty a gas syringe (see page 162) before starting to take measurements from it, all your measurements would be too high (by the volume of gas left in the syringe at the beginning).

Tip: Repeating the experiment in the exact same way and calculating an average won't correct a systematic error.

Just to make things more complicated, if a systematic error is caused by using equipment that isn't zeroed properly it's called a **zero error**. You can compensate for some systematic and zero errors if you know about them though.

Tip: A zero error is a specific type of systematic error.

Example

If a voltmeter reads 0.2 V before you connect it up to your circuit, all of your measurements will be 0.2 V too high. This is a zero error. You can compensate for this by subtracting 0.2 V from all your readings.

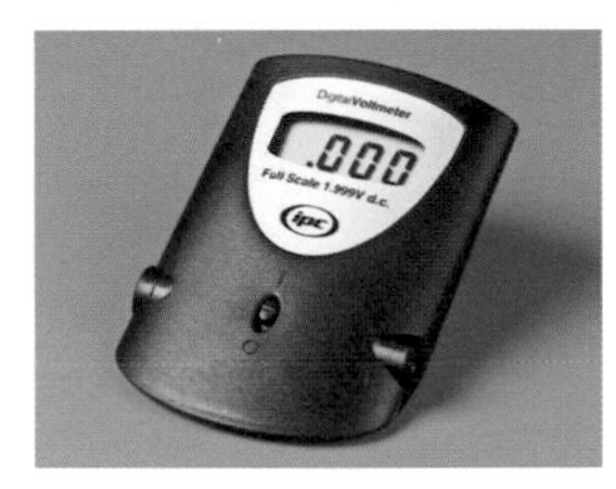

Figure 2: *A digital voltmeter that has been set to zero.*

Anomalous results

Sometimes you get a result that doesn't seem to fit in with the rest at all. These results are called **anomalous results** (or outliers).

Example

Look at the data in this table. The entry that has been circled is an anomalous result because it's much smaller than any of the other data values.

Experiment	1	2	3	4	5	6
Volume of gas produced (ml)	23	22	26	9	23	24

Tip: There are lots of reasons why you might get an anomalous result, but usually they're due to human error rather than anything crazy happening in the experiment.

You should investigate anomalous results and try to work out what happened. If you can work out what happened (e.g. you measured something totally wrong) you can ignore them when processing your results.

5. Processing and Presenting Data

Learning Objectives:
- Know why data is often organised into tables and understand the limitations of using tables to organise data.
- Be able to calculate ranges and means.
- Be able to select and draw an appropriate graph to display the data collected in an investigation.

Specification Reference
How Science Works

Once you've collected some data, you might need to process it, and then you'll need to present it in a way that you can make sense of.

Organising data

It's really important that your data is organised. Tables are dead useful for organising data. When you draw a table use a ruler, make sure each column has a heading (including the units) and keep it neat and tidy.

Annoyingly, tables are about as useful as a chocolate teapot for showing patterns or relationships in data. You need to use some kind of graph for that.

Processing your data

When you've done repeats of an experiment you should always calculate the **mean** (average). To do this add together all the data values and divide by the total number of values in the sample.

Tip: You should ignore anomalous results when calculating the mean and the range.

You might also need to calculate the **range** (how spread out the data is). To do this find the largest number and subtract the smallest number from it.

Example

Look at the data in this table. The mean and range of the data has been calculated for each test tube.

Test tube	Repeat (g)			Mean (g)	Range (g)
	1	2	3		
A	15	21	18	(15 + 21 + 18) ÷ 3 = 18	21 – 15 = 6
B	43	36	32	(43 + 36 + 32) ÷ 3 = 37	43 – 32 = 11
C	8	12	9	(8 + 12 + 9) ÷ 3 = 9.7	12 – 8 = 4

Plotting your data on a graph

One of the best ways to present your data after you've processed it is to plot your results on a graph. There are lots of different types of graph you can use. The type of graph you use depends on the type of data you've collected.

Tip: Categoric data is data that comes in distinct categories, for example, blood type, type of fuel, metals.

Bar charts

If either the independent or dependent variable is **categoric** you should use a bar chart to display the data.

You also use a bar chart if one of the variables is **discrete** (the data can be counted in chunks, where there's no in-between value, e.g. number of people is discrete because you can't have half a person).

There are some golden rules you need to follow for drawing bar charts:

- Draw it nice and big (covering at least half of the graph paper).
- Leave a gap between different categories.
- Label both axes and remember to include the units.
- If you've got more than one set of data include a key.
- Give your graph a title explaining what it is showing.

Tip: These golden rules will make sure that your bar chart is clear, easy to read and easy to understand if someone else looks at it.

Have a look at Figure 1 for an example of a pretty decent bar chart.

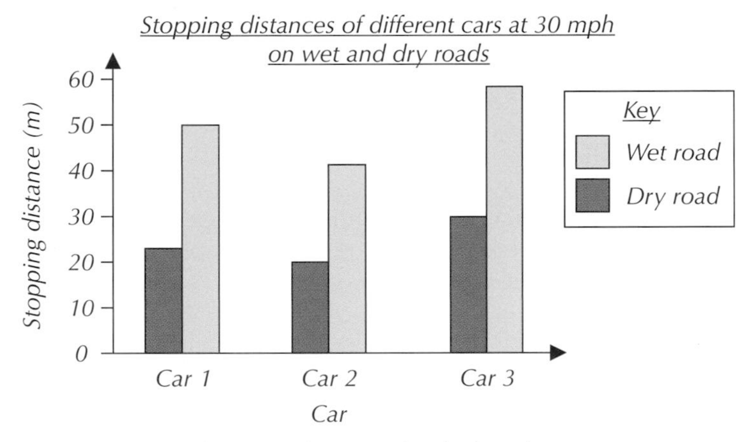

Figure 1: *An example of a bar chart.*

Line graphs

If the independent and the dependent variable are **continuous** (numerical data that can have any value within a range, e.g. length, volume, temperature) you should use a line graph to display the data. Here are the golden rules for drawing line graphs:

- Draw it nice and big (covering at least half of the graph paper).
- Put the independent variable (the thing you change) on the x-axis (the horizontal one).
- Put the dependent variable (the thing you measure) on the y-axis (the vertical one).
- Label both axes and remember to include the units.
- To plot the points, use a sharp pencil and make a neat little cross.
- Don't join the dots up. You need to draw a line of best fit (or a curve of best fit if your points make a curve). When drawing a line (or curve), try to draw the line through or as near to as many points as possible, ignoring anomalous results.
- If you've got more than one set of data include a key.
- Give your graph a title explaining what it is showing.

Exam Tip
You could be asked to draw a bar chart or a line graph in your exam. If so, make sure you follow the golden rules or you could end up losing marks.

See Figure 2 on the next page for an example of a pretty good line graph.

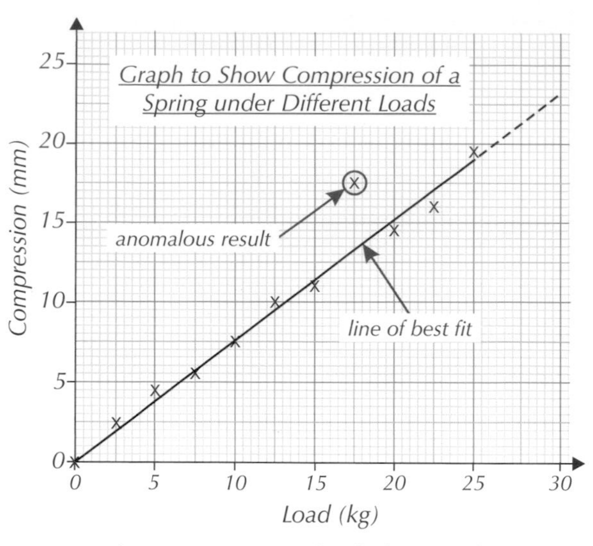

Figure 2: *An example of a line graph.*

Tip: If you're not in an exam, you can use a computer to plot your line graph and draw your line of best fit for you.

Scatter graphs

Scatter graphs are very similar to line graphs but they often don't have a line of best fit drawn on them. Like line graphs, scatter graphs can be used if the independent and dependent variables are continuous.

Tip: Scatter graphs can also be called scattergrams or scatterplots.

Correlations

Line graphs and scatter graphs are used to show the relationship between two variables (just like other graphs). Data can show three different types of **correlation** (relationship):

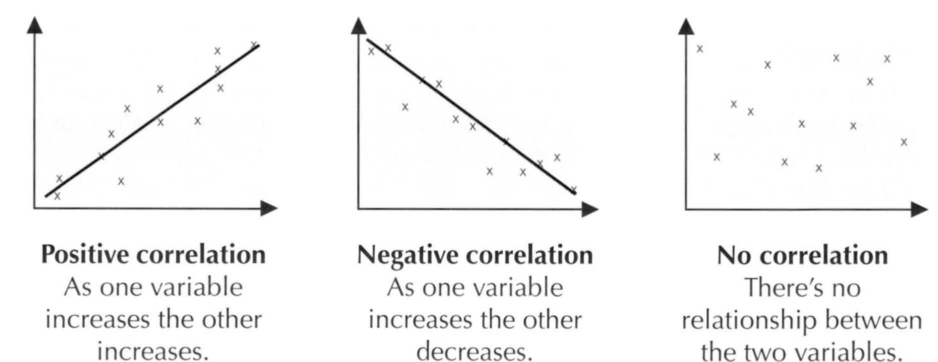

Positive correlation
As one variable increases the other increases.

Negative correlation
As one variable increases the other decreases.

No correlation
There's no relationship between the two variables.

Tip: If all of the points are very close to the line of best fit then it's said to be a strong correlation. If there is a general trend but all the points are quite far away from the line of best fit it's a weak correlation.

You also need to be able to describe the following relationships on line graphs.

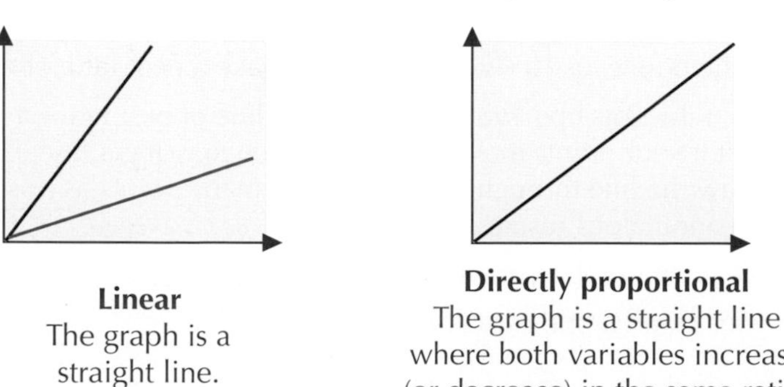

Linear
The graph is a straight line.

Directly proportional
The graph is a straight line where both variables increase (or decrease) in the same ratio.

Tip: On this graph the lines show positive linear relationships, but you can get linear relationships that show negative correlation too.

6. Drawing Conclusions

So... you've planned an amazing experiment, you've done the experiment, collected some data and have processed and presented your data in a sensible way. Now it's time to figure out what your data actually tells you.

Learning Objectives:

- Be able to draw conclusions based on the data available.
- Understand the difference between correlation and causation, and the possible reasons for correlation.
- Be able to evaluate investigations.

Specification Reference
How Science Works

How to draw conclusions

Drawing conclusions might seem pretty straightforward — you just look at your data and say what pattern or relationship you see between the dependent and independent variables.

But you've got to be really careful that your conclusion matches the data you've got and doesn't go any further. You also need to be able to use your results to justify your conclusion (i.e. back up your conclusion with some specific data).

Example

This table shows the heights of tomato plant seedlings grown for three weeks with different fertilisers.

Fertiliser	Mean growth (mm)
A	50.5
B	57.5
No fertiliser	40.5

The conclusion of this experiment would be that fertiliser B makes the seedlings grow taller than fertiliser A during the three week period.

The justification for this conclusion is that over the three week period fertiliser B made the tomato plants grow 7 mm more (on average) than fertiliser A.

You can't conclude that fertiliser B increases the growth of any other seedlings more than fertiliser A — the results might be completely different.

Correlation and causation

If two things are correlated (i.e. there's a relationship between them) it doesn't necessarily mean that a change in one variable is causing the change in the other — this is really important, don't forget it. There are three possible reasons for a correlation:

Tip: Causation just means one thing is causing another.

1. Chance

Even though it might seem a bit weird, it's possible that two things show a correlation in a study purely because of chance.

Example

One study might find a correlation between the size of the population of a fish species in a river and the distance from a power station that pumps warm water into the river. But other scientists don't get a correlation when they investigate it — the results of the first study are just a fluke.

Tip: Lots of things are correlated without being directly related. E.g. the level of carbon dioxide (CO_2) in the atmosphere and the amount of obesity have both increased over the last 100 years, but that doesn't mean increased atmospheric CO_2 is causing people to become obese.

2. They're linked by a third variable

A lot of the time it may look as if a change in one variable is causing a change in the other, but it isn't — a third variable links the two things.

Example

There's a correlation between the amount of petrol sold and the number of car accidents. This obviously isn't because buying petrol makes people become worse at driving and crash more often. Instead, they're linked by a third variable — the number of cars on the road (more cars on the road means that more petrol will be bought and also that more accidents are likely to happen).

Figure 1: Drinking too much alcohol can lead to liver damage.

3. Causation

Sometimes a change in one variable does cause a change in the other.

Example

There's a correlation between excessive consumption of alcoholic drinks and liver disease. This is because alcohol damages the liver.

You can only conclude that a correlation is due to cause when you've controlled all the variables that could, just could, be affecting the result. (For the drinking example above this would include things like age and exposure to other things that cause liver disease).

Evaluation

This is the final part of an investigation. Here you need to evaluate (assess) the following things about your experiment and the data you gathered.

- **Repeatability**: Did you take enough repeat readings of the measurements? Would you do more repeats if you were to do the experiment again? Do you think you'd get similar data if you did the experiment again?
- **Reproducibility**: Have you compared your results with other people's results? Were your results similar? Could other scientists gain data showing the same relationships that are shown in your data?
- **Validity**: Does your data answer the question you set out to investigate?

Once you've thought about these points you can decide how much confidence you have in your conclusion. For example, if your results are repeatable, reproducible and valid and they back up your conclusion then you can have a high degree of confidence in your conclusion.

1. Cell Structure

All living things are made of cells — they're the building blocks of every organism on the planet. But different organisms have different cell structures...

Learning Objectives:
- Know that most human and other animal cells have a nucleus, cytoplasm, cell membrane, mitochondria and ribosomes, and know the function of each of these parts.
- Know that plant and algal cells have the same parts as animal cells, plus a cell wall made of cellulose to strengthen the cell.
- Know that plant cells also usually have chloroplasts and a permanent vacuole.
- Know that yeast is a single-celled microorganism, and know the structure of a yeast cell.
- Know the structure of a bacterial cell.

Specification Reference B2.1.1

Animal cells

Most animal cells, including most human cells, have the following parts — make sure you know them all. The parts are labelled in Figure 1.

- **Nucleus** — contains genetic material that controls the activities of the cell.
- **Cytoplasm** — a gel-like substance where most of the chemical reactions happen. It contains enzymes (see p. 53) that control these chemical reactions.
- **Cell membrane** — holds the cell together and controls what goes in and out.
- **Mitochondria** — these are where most of the reactions for respiration take place (see p. 64). Respiration releases energy that the cell needs to work.
- **Ribosomes** — these are where proteins are made in the cell.

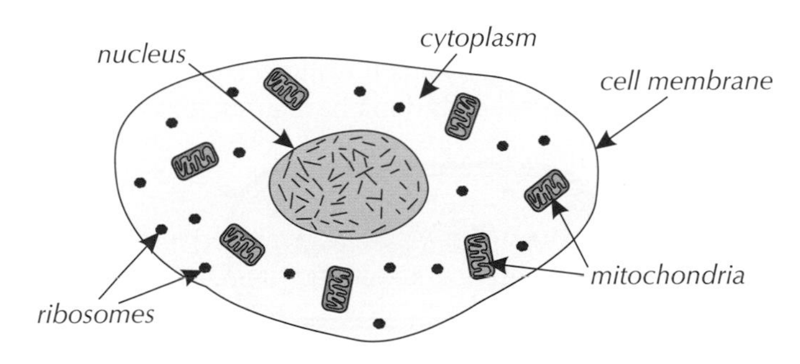

Figure 1: *The structure of a typical animal cell.*

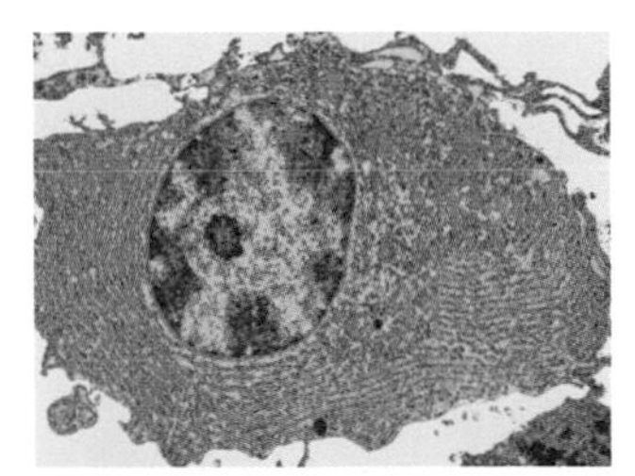

Figure 2: *A human cell seen under a microscope — the blue and yellow oval is the nucleus.*

Plant cells

Plant cells usually have all the bits that animal cells have, plus a few extra:

- **Cell wall** — a rigid structure made of cellulose. It supports and strengthens the cell. The cells of algae (e.g. seaweed) also have a rigid cell wall.
- **Permanent vacuole** — contains cell sap, a weak solution of sugar and salts.
- **Chloroplasts** — these are where photosynthesis occurs, which makes food for the plant (see page 33). They contain a green substance called **chlorophyll**, which absorbs the light energy needed for photosynthesis.

The parts of a typical plant cell are shown in Figure 4.

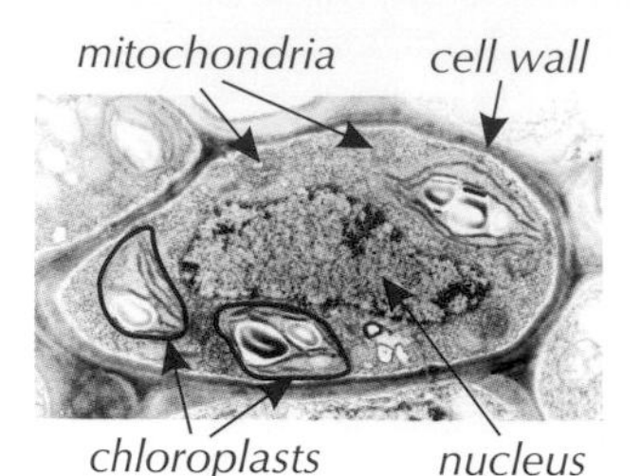

Figure 3: *A cross-section of a plant cell seen under a microscope.*

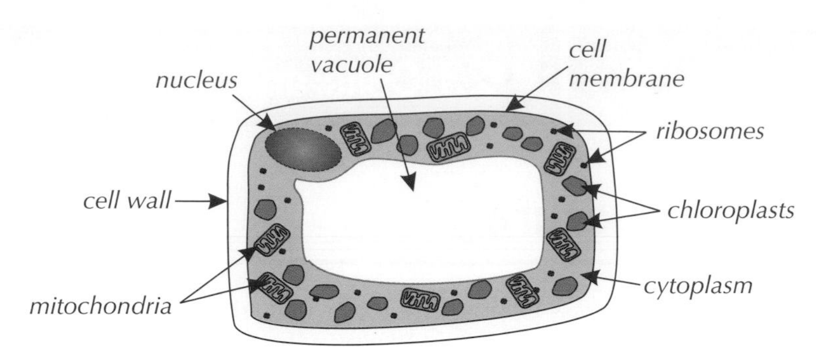

Figure 4: *The structure of a typical plant cell.*

Yeast cells

Yeast is a single-celled microorganism. A yeast cell has a nucleus, cytoplasm, and a cell membrane surrounded by a cell wall (see Figure 5).

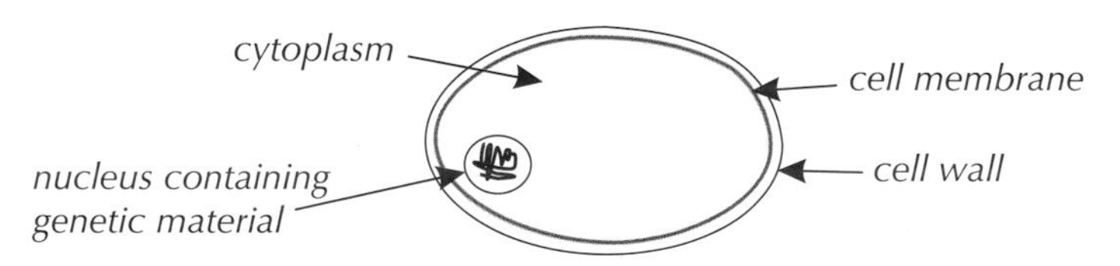

Figure 5: *The structure of a yeast cell.*

Tip: 'Genetic material' is just another word for 'genes', 'DNA' or 'chromosomes'.

Bacterial cells

Bacteria are also single-celled microorganisms. A bacterial cell has cytoplasm and a cell membrane surrounded by a cell wall. The genetic material floats in the cytoplasm because bacterial cells don't have a nucleus (see Figure 6).

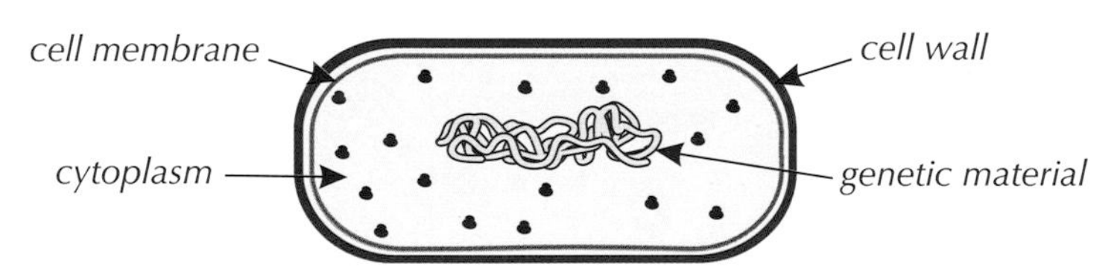

Figure 6: *The structure of a typical bacterial cell.*

Tip: The diagrams on this page and the previous one all show 'typical' cells. In reality the structure of a cell varies according to what job it does, so most cells won't look exactly like these.

Practice Questions — Fact Recall

Q1 Which part of an animal cell controls its activity?

Q2 Where do most of the chemical reactions take place in a cell?

Q3 What are mitochondria needed for in a cell?

Q4 Name three things that a plant cell usually has, that an animal cell doesn't.

Q5 Describe the structure of a yeast cell.

Q6 Give one difference between the structure of a yeast cell and the structure of a bacterial cell.

Exam Tip
You need to learn the functions of the cell parts, not just their names.

2. Specialised Cells

Not all cells in an organism do the same job. A cell's structure is related to the job it does, so cell structure can vary...

Learning Objectives:
- Understand that many cells are specialised — they perform a specific function.
- Be able to relate the structure of a cell to its function.

Specification Reference B2.1.1

What is a specialised cell?

A specialised cell is one that performs a specific function. Most cells in an organism are specialised. A cell's structure (e.g. its shape and the parts it contains) helps it to carry out its function — so depending on what job it does, a specialised cell can look very different to the cells you saw on pages 17-18.

Examples of specialised cells

In the exam, you could be asked to relate the structure of a cell to its function. The idea is that you apply your knowledge of cell structure (see previous topic) to the information you're given about the role of the cell in an organism. Don't panic — it's easier than it sounds. Here are a few examples to help you understand how cell structure and function are related:

1. Sperm and egg cells (animals)

Sperm and egg cells are specialised for reproduction. The main functions of an egg cell are to carry the female DNA and to nourish the developing embryo in the early stages, so the egg cell contains huge food reserves to feed the embryo.

The function of a sperm is to get the male DNA to the female DNA. It has a long tail and a streamlined head to help it swim to the egg. There are also lots of **mitochondria** (see p.17) in the cell to provide the energy it needs to do this.

Exam Tip
Energy is released by respiration, which mostly takes place in the mitochondria.
So any cell that needs lots of energy to do its job will have lots of mitochondria.

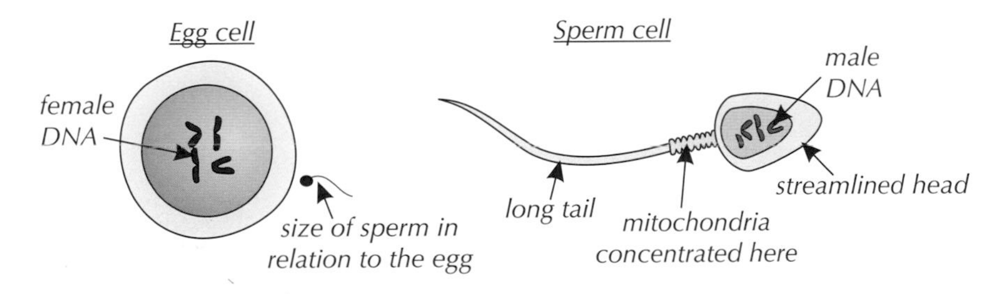

Figure 1: *An egg cell and a sperm cell.*

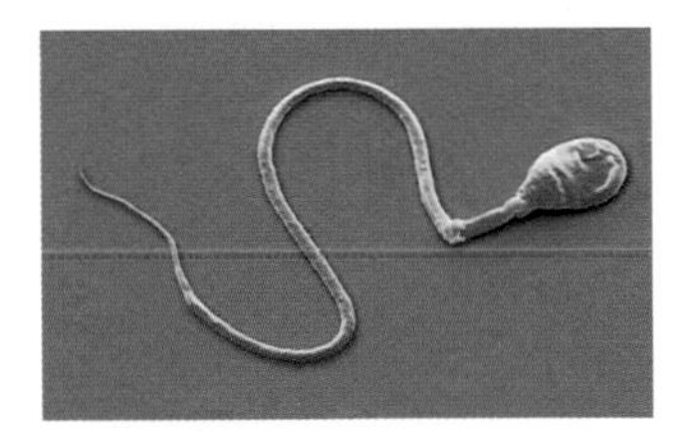

Figure 2: *A microscope image of a sperm cell. It's easy to see the streamlined head and tail.*

2. Red blood cells (animals)

Red blood cells are an important part of the blood — they are adapted to carry oxygen to every cell in the body. They have a biconcave shape (both sides of the cell curve inwards) which gives them a big surface area for absorbing oxygen — see Figure 3 (next page). This shape also helps them pass smoothly along capillaries (tiny blood vessels) to reach the body cells.

Tip: Similar to sperm cells, bacterial cells sometimes have long tail-like structures to help them swim.

Exam Tip
The concave shape of a red blood gives it a bigger surface area than if the cell was flat. Look:

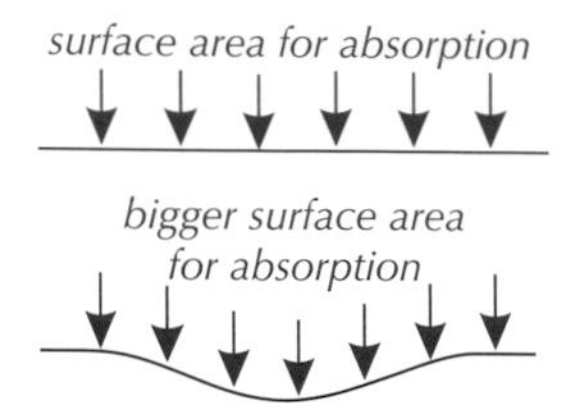

Folds or projections in the cell membrane would do the same thing. Any cell that absorbs molecules through its surface needs a big surface area — this helps it to absorb lots of molecules at once.

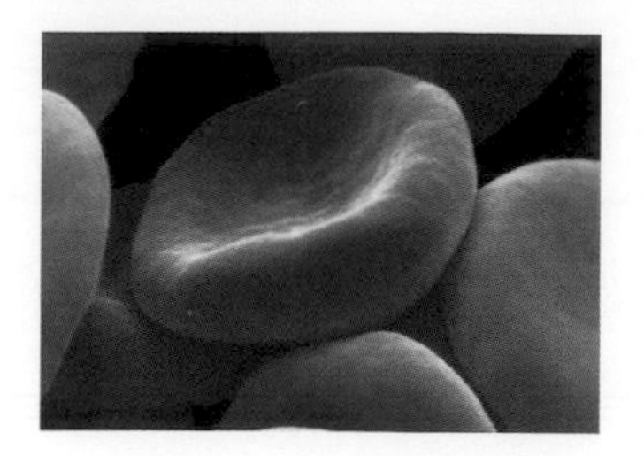

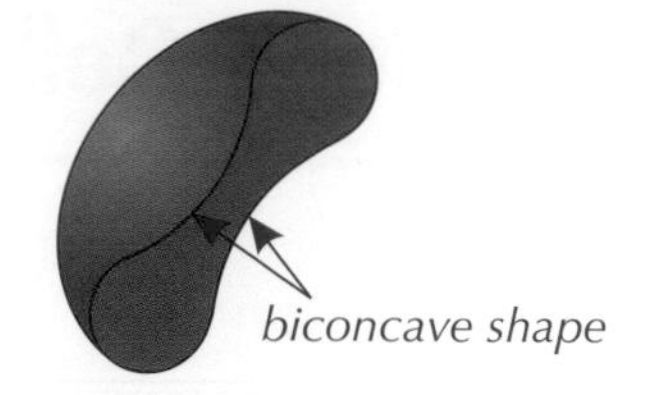

Figure 3: *A microscope image of red blood cells (left) and a cross-section through a red blood cell (right).*

Red blood cells are packed with haemoglobin — the pigment that absorbs the oxygen. And unlike a typical animal cell (see page 17), red blood cells have no nucleus to leave even more room for haemoglobin.

3. Palisade leaf cells (plants)

Palisade leaf cells are adapted for photosynthesis. They are grouped together at the top of a leaf where most of the photosynthesis happens (see Figure 4a).

They're packed with **chloroplasts** (see page 17), which absorb the light energy needed for photosynthesis. There are more chloroplasts crammed at the top of the cell, so they're nearer the light (see Figure 4b).

They're tall with long sides, which means there's more surface area exposed for absorbing carbon dioxide from the air in the leaf. They're also thin, which means that you can pack loads of them in at the top of a leaf.

Tip: Photosynthesis is the process in which plants use light energy from the sun to convert carbon dioxide and water into oxygen and glucose (food) — see page 33 for more.

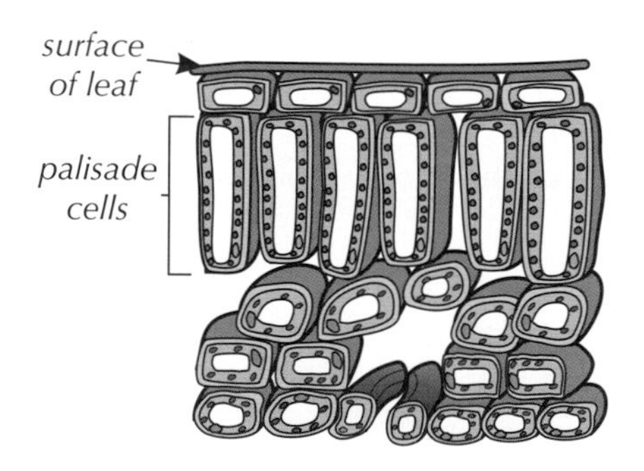

Figure 4a: *Cross section through a leaf showing the position of palisade cells.*

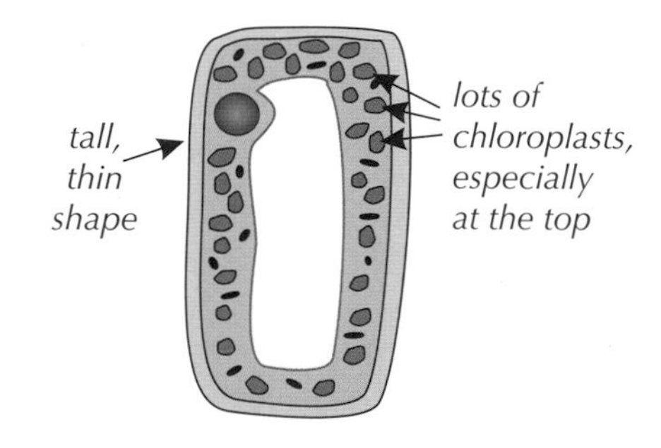

Figure 4b: *The structure of a palisade cell.*

Practice Questions — Application

Q1 The function of gastric chief cells is to secrete enzymes (proteins) into the stomach during digestion. Comment on the amount of ribosomes you'd expect to find in a gastric chief cell.

Tip: Think about the function of ribosomes — see page 17.

Q2 Root hair cells are specialised plant cells.
They absorb water and mineral ions from soil.

a) Which of the following diagrams (A-C) is most likely to show the correct structure of a root hair cell? Explain your answer.

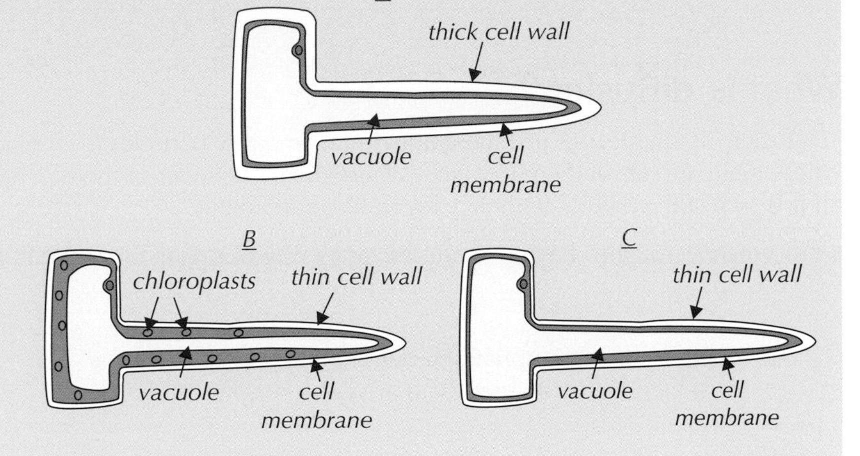

b) Suggest how the shape of a root hair cell makes it well adapted to its function.

Q3 A diagram of an epithelial cell from the small intestine is shown here:

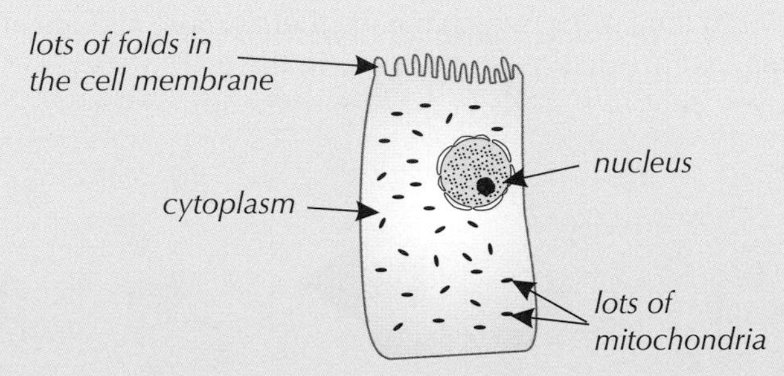

These cells line the inner surface of the small intestine and their function is to absorb food molecules as they move through the intestine. Sometimes this process requires energy.

Use this information and the diagram to suggest two ways in which the structure of these cells helps them to carry out their function.

Tip: To help with Q2 a), think about the job carried out by root hair cells and where they're found in the plant.

Tip: You're not expected to actually <u>know</u> the answer to these questions — just make sensible suggestions using the information given and your knowledge about cell structure from pages 17-18.

Tip: Look back at the examples on the last couple of pages if you're struggling with this one — the function of some of those cells involves absorption too.

3. Diffusion

Particles tend to move about randomly and end up evenly spaced. This is important when it comes to getting substances in and out of cells.

Learning Objectives:
- Know the definition of 'diffusion'.
- Know that dissolved substances (such as oxygen) can move in and out of a cell by diffusion.
- Understand that during diffusion, the net movement of substances will be from an area of higher concentration to an area of lower concentration.
- Understand that the rate of diffusion is faster when there is a greater difference in the concentration of particles.

Specification Reference B2.1.2

What is diffusion?

"Diffusion" is simple. It's just the gradual movement of particles from places where there are lots of them to places where there are fewer of them. That's all it is — just the natural tendency for stuff to spread out.

Unfortunately you also have to learn the fancy way of saying the same thing, which is this:

> Diffusion is the spreading out of particles from an area of high concentration to an area of low concentration.

Diffusion happens in both solutions and gases — that's because the particles in these substances are free to move about randomly. The simplest type is when different gases diffuse through each other.

Example

When you spray perfume, the smell of perfume diffuses through the air in a room:

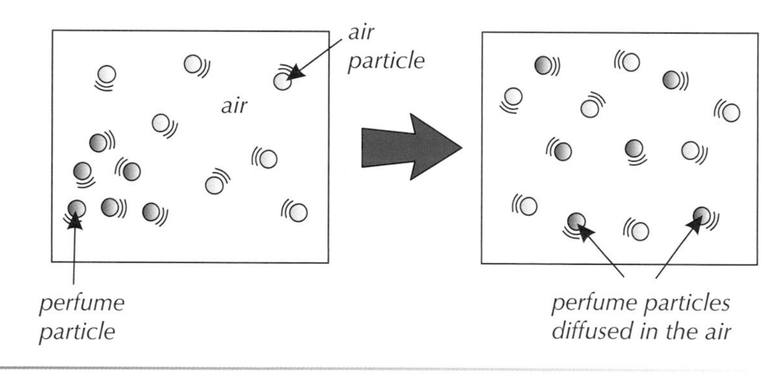

Figure 1: *The ink particles in this flask are diffusing into the water — they're moving from an area of high concentration (at the bottom of the flask) to an area of low concentration (higher up).*

Diffusion across cell membranes

Cell membranes are clever because they hold the cell together but they let stuff in and out as well. **Dissolved substances** can move in and out of cells by diffusion.

Only very small molecules can diffuse through cell membranes though — things like **oxygen** (needed for respiration — see page 64), glucose, amino acids and water. Big molecules like starch and proteins can't fit through the membrane (see Figure 2 on the next page).

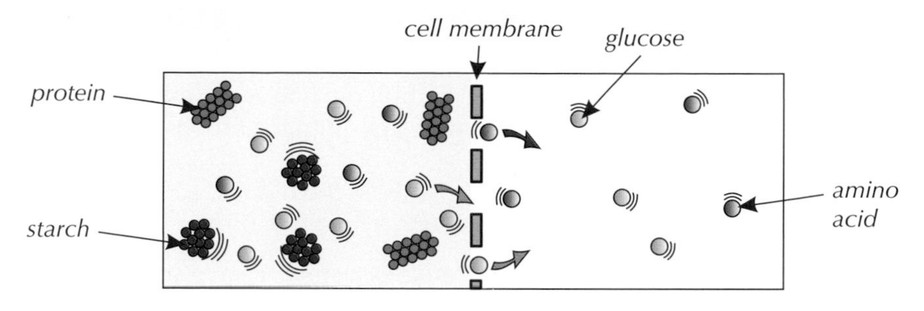

Figure 2: *Diagram to show diffusion across a cell membrane.*

Just like with diffusion in air, particles flow through the cell membrane from where there's a high concentration (a lot of them) to where there's a low concentration (not such a lot of them).

They're only moving about randomly of course, so they go both ways — but if there are a lot more particles on one side of the membrane, there's a **net** (overall) movement from that side.

Example

Particles are diffusing both in and out of this cell. However, the concentration of particles is higher inside the cell than outside, so the net movement of particles is out of the cell.

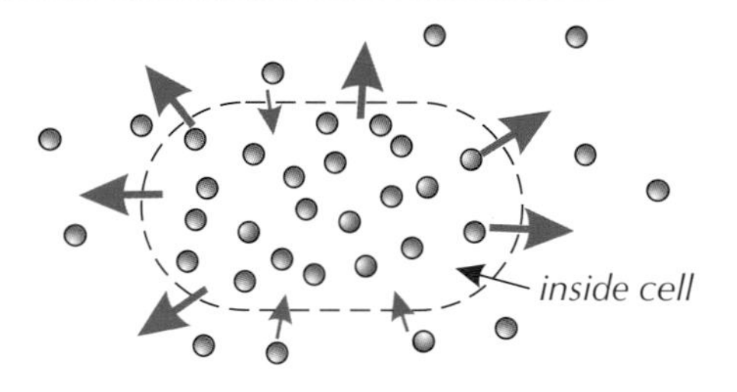

Exam Tip
If you're struggling to remember which way the particles move in diffusion, think of it like this: if you were in a really crowded place, you'd probably want to get out of there to somewhere with a bit more room. It's the same with particles — they always diffuse from an area of high concentration to an area of low concentration.

The rate of diffusion

The rate of diffusion is affected by the difference in concentration of the particles — the bigger the difference in concentration, the faster the diffusion rate.

Example

There will be a net movement of particles out of both Cell 1 and Cell 2 (shown below). However, the rate of diffusion will be faster out of Cell 1, because there's a bigger difference in the concentration of particles on either side of the cell membrane.

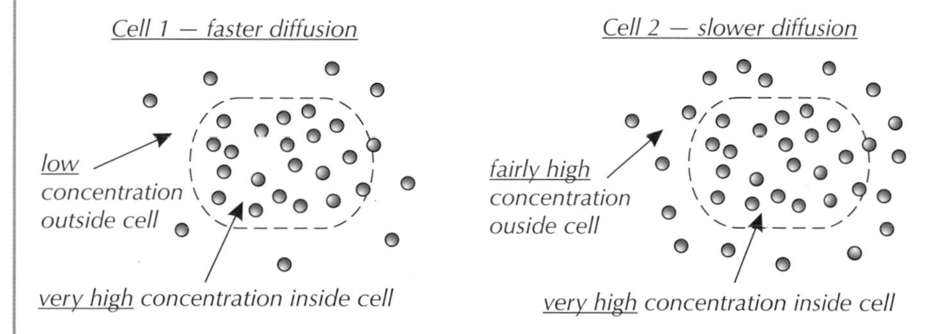

Practice Questions — Application

Q1 When cells respire they produce carbon dioxide as a waste product. The carbon dioxide diffuses from the cells into the bloodstream, so it can be removed from the body.
Is carbon dioxide concentration greater in the bloodstream or inside respiring cells? Explain your answer.

Q2 At a disco in a school hall, a DJ releases a short blast of smoke from a smoke machine at the front of the stage.

a) Explain how the smoke reaches the people standing at the opposite end of the hall from the stage.

b) Five minutes later the DJ sets the smoke machine off for a second time. Explain how the rate of diffusion of the smoke is now different from the first time the DJ set the smoke machine off.

Section Checklist — Make sure you know...

Cell Structure

- ❑ That most human and animals cells have: a nucleus (which contains the genetic material that controls the activities of a cell), cytoplasm (where most of the chemical reactions happen), a cell membrane (which controls what goes in and out of the cell), mitochondria (where most of the reactions for respiration happen), and ribosomes (where proteins are made in the cell).
- ❑ That in addition to all the parts that animal cells have, plant and algal cells have a cell wall made of cellulose to strengthen the cell.
- ❑ That most plant cells also have a permanent vacuole containing cell sap and chloroplasts which absorb the light energy needed for photosynthesis.
- ❑ That yeast is a single-celled organism, and that a yeast cell has a nucleus, cytoplasm, cell membrane and a cell wall.
- ❑ That a bacterial cell has cytoplasm, a cell membrane and a cell wall, and that its genetic material is not in a nucleus.

Specialised Cells

- ❑ That many cells are specialised to carry out a specific function.
- ❑ How to relate a cell's structure (its shape and the parts it contains) to its function.

Diffusion

- ❑ That diffusion is the spreading out of particles from an area of high concentration to an area of low concentration.
- ❑ That dissolved substances such as oxygen (which is needed for respiration) move in and out of a cell by diffusion, and that the net (overall) movement will be to an area of lower concentration.
- ❑ That the bigger the difference in concentration, the faster the diffusion rate.

1. Cell Organisation

Multicellular organisms (like humans) can have trillions of cells. To keep the organism going, those cells have to work together — which needs organisation.

How are cells organised?

Large **multicellular organisms** have different systems inside them for exchanging and transporting materials.

Example

Mammals have a breathing system — this includes the airways and lungs. The breathing system is needed to take air into and out of the lungs, so that oxygen and carbon dioxide can be exchanged between the body and the environment.

Exchange systems are made up of **specialised cells** (see page 19). The process by which cells become specialised for a particular job is called **differentiation**. Differentiation occurs during the development of a multicellular organism.

Specialised cells are organised to form tissues, which form organs, which form organ systems — there's more about each of these over the next few pages.

Tissues

You need to know what a tissue is:

> A tissue is a group of similar cells that work together to carry out a particular function.

A tissue can include more than one type of cell. Mammals (like humans), have several different types of tissue:

Examples

- **Muscular tissue**, which contracts (shortens) to move whatever it's attached to.
- **Glandular tissue**, which makes and secretes substances like enzymes (proteins that control chemical reactions, see p.53) and hormones (chemical messengers).
- **Epithelial tissue**, which covers some parts of the body, e.g. the inside of the gut.

Learning Objectives:

- Know that large multicellular organisms have systems that allow them to exchange substances.
- Understand that, as a multicellular organism is developing, cells differentiate to produce specialised cells.
- Know what a tissue is and understand the roles of muscular, glandular and epithelial tissue.
- Know what an organ is and understand why the stomach contains muscular, glandular and epithelial tissue.
- Know what an organ system is and understand the roles of the organs (the pancreas, salivary glands, stomach, small intestine, liver and large intestine) that make up the digestive system.

Specification Reference B2.2.1

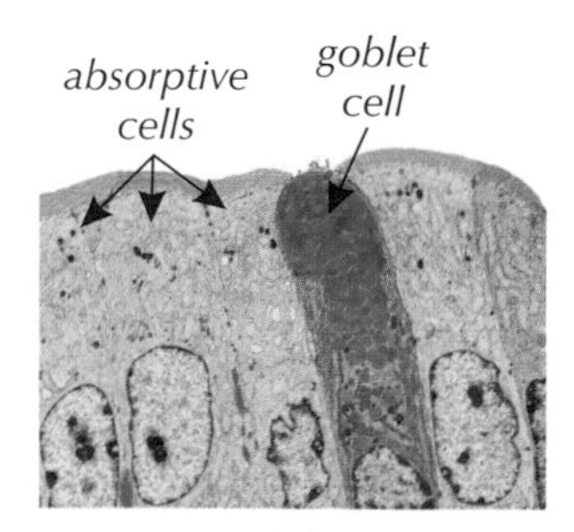

Figure 1: *Epithelial tissue in the small intestine. It contains absorptive cells and goblet cells.*

Organs

Tissues are organised into organs:

An organ is a group of different tissues that work together to perform a certain function.

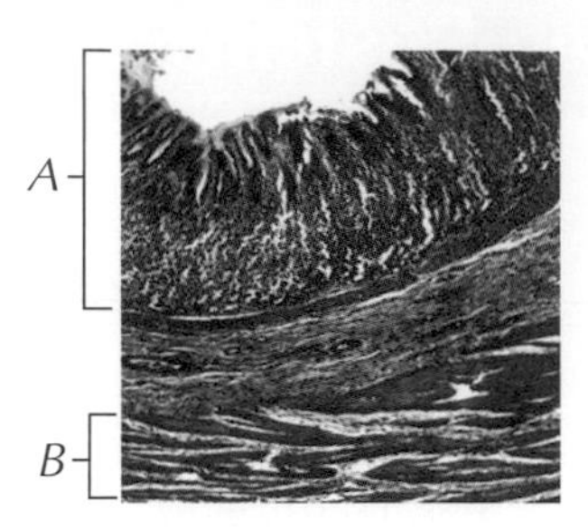

Figure 2: A cross-section through part of the stomach. There's glandular tissue at the top (A) and muscular tissue at the bottom (B).

Mammals have many different organs, which are made up of different tissues.

Example

The **stomach** is an organ made of these tissues:

- **Muscular tissue**, which moves the stomach wall to churn up the food.
- **Glandular tissue**, which makes digestive juices to digest food.
- **Epithelial tissue**, which covers the outside and inside of the stomach.

Tip: Digestive juices are secretions from the digestive system that help to break down food. They contain enzymes (see page 53).

Organ systems

Organs are organised into organ systems:

An organ system is a group of organs working together to perform a particular function.

Tip: There's more on the digestive system on pages 56-58.

Example

The **digestive system** is the organ system that breaks down food in humans and other mammals. It's also an exchange system — it exchanges materials with the environment by taking in nutrients and releasing substances such as bile (see page 58).

The digestive system (see Figure 3) is made up of these organs:

- **Glands** (e.g. the **pancreas** and **salivary glands**), which produce digestive juices.
- The **stomach**, where food is digested.
- The **liver**, which produces bile.
- The **small intestine**, where food is digested and soluble food molecules are absorbed.
- The **large intestine**, where water is absorbed from undigested food, leaving faeces.

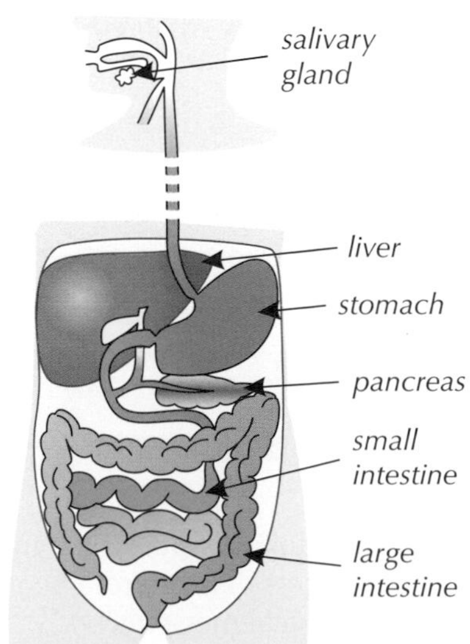

Figure 3: A diagram of the human digestive system.

Exam Tip
You need to learn the examples of muscular, glandular and epithelial tissue (see previous page), the stomach and the digestive system for your exam.

Size and scale

You need to have an understanding of the size and scale of all the structures that make up an organ system — from the tiny individual specialised cells to the organ system as a whole.

Example

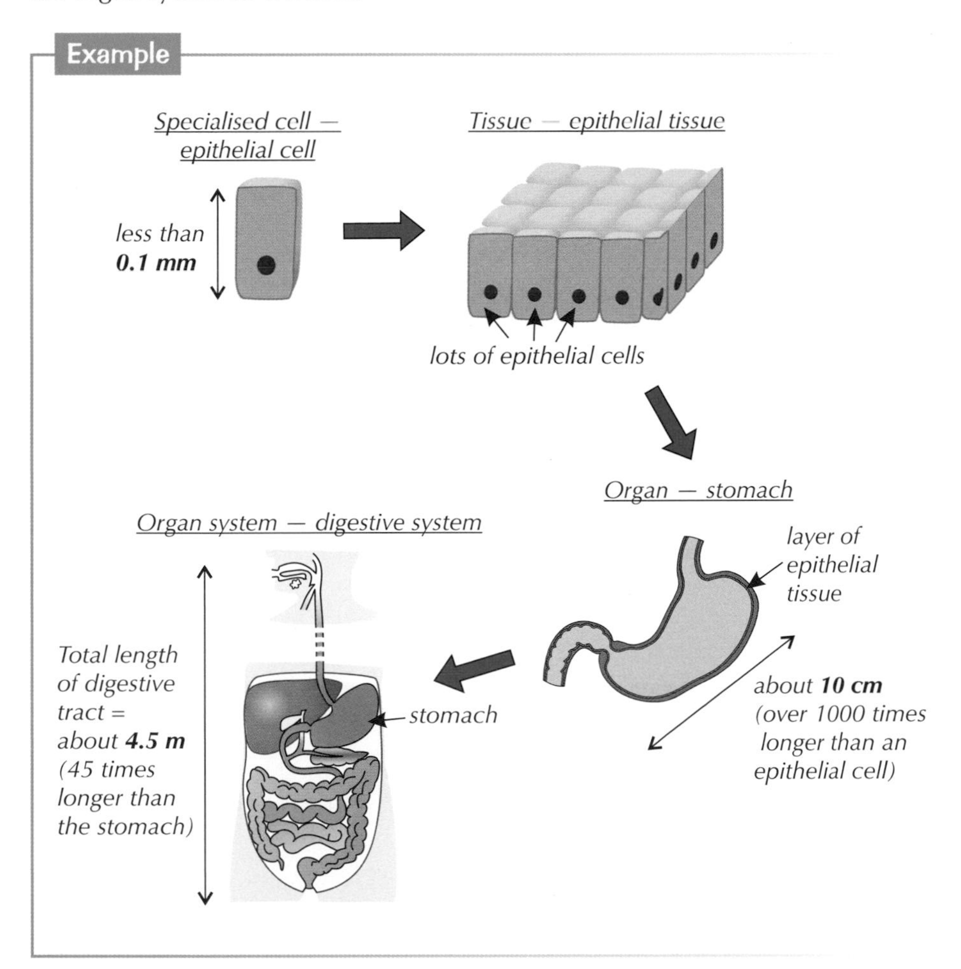

Exam Tip
You don't need to learn the lengths given in this example — they're just to give you an idea of size.

Tip: The digestive tract is the big long 'tube' which food passes through, including the small and large intestines. The intestines are all folded up, which is part of the reason why the digestive tract can be so long and yet still fit inside you.

Practice Questions — Fact Recall

Q1 a) Name the process by which cells become specialised for a particular function.

b) True or false? Cells become specialised for a particular function during the development of a multicellular organism.

Q2 a) What is a tissue?

b) Describe the role of glandular tissue.

c) Other than glandular tissue, name two types of tissue found in mammals.

Q3 What is an organ?

Q4 What term describes a group of organs which work together to perform a particular function?

Q5 Look at the diagram of the digestive system.

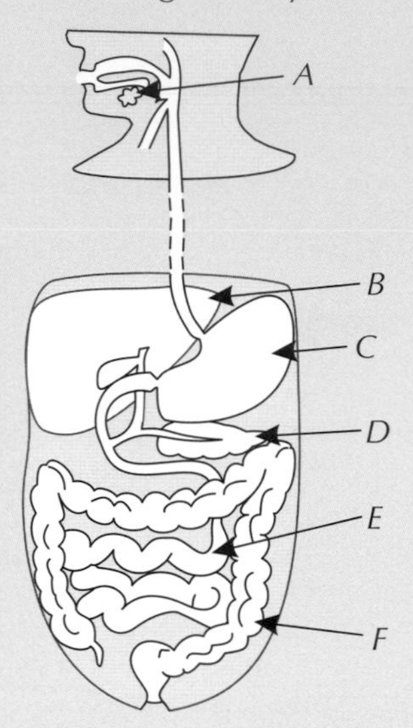

Write down the names of the organs labelled A-F and briefly say what each one does.

Exam Tip
You need to know where the organs of the digestive system are on a diagram for your exam, so make sure you can get them all right in Q5.

Practice Questions — Application

Q1 Cells in the hypophysis secrete thyroid-stimulating hormone into the blood. What type of tissue must the hypophysis contain? Explain your answer.

Q2 Blood is made up of specialised red blood cells and several different types of white blood cells. Is blood an example of a cell, tissue, organ or organ system? Explain your answer.

Q3 The fallopian tubes and uterus are part of the female reproductive system. A fallopian tube contains muscular and epithelial tissue. These work together to move a fertilised egg cell along the fallopian tube to the uterus (an organ).

a) Suggest why a fallopian tube has muscular tissue.

b) Is a fallopian tube a cell, tissue, organ or organ system? Explain your answer.

c) Rewrite the following list of structures in order of size. Start with the smallest:

uterus   reproductive system   egg cell   muscular tissue

Tip: The definitions of a tissue, an organ and an organ system should be really clear in your head. Take a look back at pages 25-26 if you're not sure of them.

2. Plant Tissues and Organs

You've just learnt about tissues and organs (see pages 25-26), but don't go thinking it's only animal cells that are organised this way — plant cells are organised into tissues and organs too.

Learning Objectives:
- Know that plants have organs including stems, roots and leaves.
- Understand the roles of epidermal tissue, mesophyll tissue, and xylem and phloem tissue in plants.

Specification Reference
B2.2.2

What organs do plants have?

Plants are made of organs such as stems, roots and leaves — see Figure 1.

- **Stems** support the plant, and assist in the transport of water and nutrients between the roots and the leaves.
- **Roots** absorb water and mineral ions for the plant, and hold the plant in place.
- **Leaves** are the main site of photosynthesis in a plant.

Figure 1: *A photograph showing the three types of plant organs.*

Tip: Photosynthesis is the process by which plants make their own food. See page 33 for more.

What tissues do plants have?

Plant organs are made of tissues such as:

- **Mesophyll tissue** — this is where most of the photosynthesis in a plant occurs.
- **Xylem** and **phloem** — these tissues transport things like water, mineral ions and sucrose around the plant.
- **Epidermal tissue** — this covers the whole plant.

Example

Leaves are made up of mesophyll tissue, xylem and phloem, and epidermal tissue as shown in Figures 2 and 3.

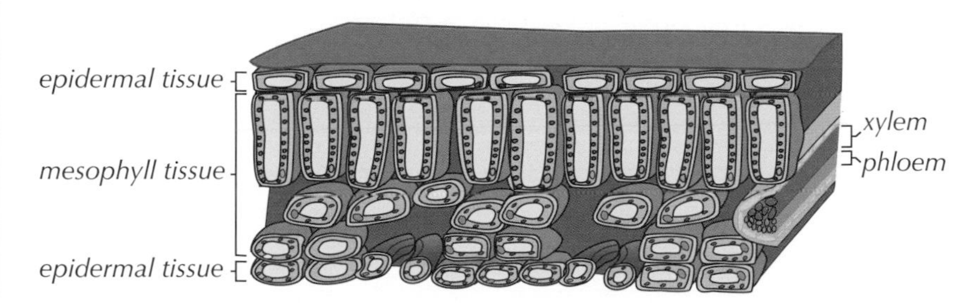

Figure 2: *Diagram showing the main tissues in a leaf.*

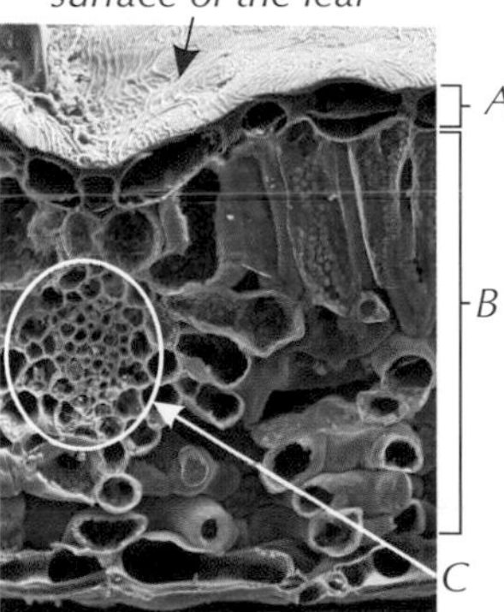

Figure 3: *A cross-section through a leaf, seen under a microscope. It shows the epidermal tissue (A), mesophyll tissue (B) and xylem and phloem tissue (C).*

Practice Questions — Fact Recall

Q1 Name three plant organs.

Q2 Name the plant tissue where photosynthesis occurs.

Q3 What is the function of xylem and phloem tissue?

Q4 What type of tissue covers a plant?

Section Checklist — Make sure you know...

Cell Organisation

- ❑ That large multicellular organisms contain systems that allow them to exchange substances.
- ❑ That when a multicellular organism is developing, its cells differentiate into specialised cells.
- ❑ That a tissue is a group of similar cells that work together to carry out a particular function and that a tissue can include more than one type of cell.
- ❑ That muscular tissue contracts (shortens) to make things move, glandular tissue makes and secretes enzymes and hormones, and epithelial tissue covers some parts of the body, e.g. the gut.
- ❑ That an organ is a group of different tissues that work together to perform a certain function.
- ❑ That the stomach is an organ which contains muscular tissue to churn food and glandular tissue to make digestive juices. It is covered with epithelial tissue on the inside and outside.
- ❑ That an organ system is a group of organs working together to perform a particular function.
- ❑ That the digestive system is an organ system containing glands such as the salivary glands and the pancreas (which produce digestive juices), the stomach (where food is digested), the small intestine (where food is digested and soluble food molecules are absorbed), the liver (which produces bile), and the large intestine (which absorbs water from undigested food leaving faeces).

Plant Tissues and Organs

- ❑ That plants have organs such as stems, roots and leaves.
- ❑ That plants have tissues such as mesophyll tissue (for photosynthesis), xylem and phloem (to transport water and other substances around the plant) and epidermal tissue (to cover the plant).

Exam-style Questions

1 This diagram shows the single-celled microorganism, *S. cerevisiae*.

1 (a) Look at the structures labelled A-D on the diagram.
Draw lines below to match each of the structures to the correct name.

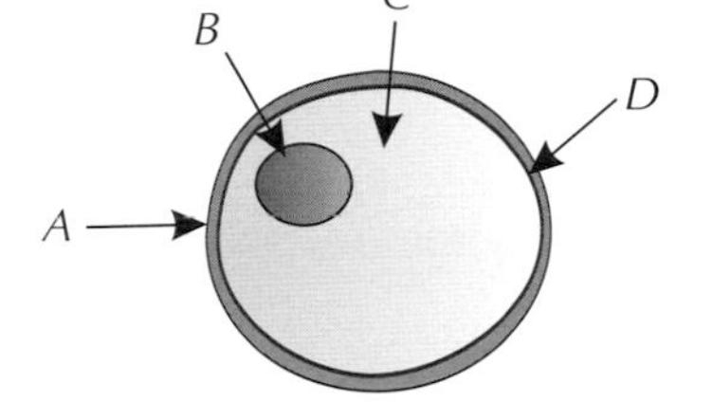

A	nucleus
B	cytoplasm
C	cell membrane
D	cell wall

(4 marks)

1 (b) Is *S. cerevisiae* a yeast or a bacterium? Give a reason for your answer.

(1 mark)

2 Some people with stomach cancer have an operation to completely remove their stomach.

2 (a) The diagram shows part of the digestive system of someone who has had their stomach removed.

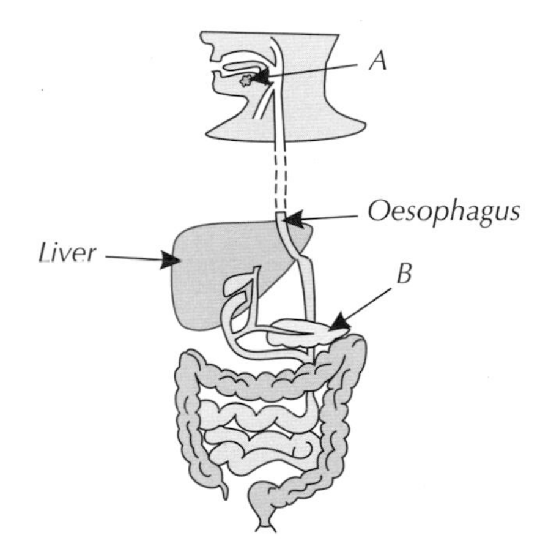

2 (a) (i) Name the organ that the oesophagus (food pipe) now joins directly on to.

(1 mark)

2 (a) (ii) Name the organs labelled **A** and **B** on the diagram and describe their role.

(3 marks)

2 (b) The stomach is made up of several different tissue types.
Name and describe the functions of **two** types of tissue in the stomach.

(4 marks)

3 The diagram shows three different types of neurone. These neurones work together to carry electrical signals around the body. The electrical signals travel along the neurones to body cells — they're passed onto the body cells at the branched endings of the motor neurones.

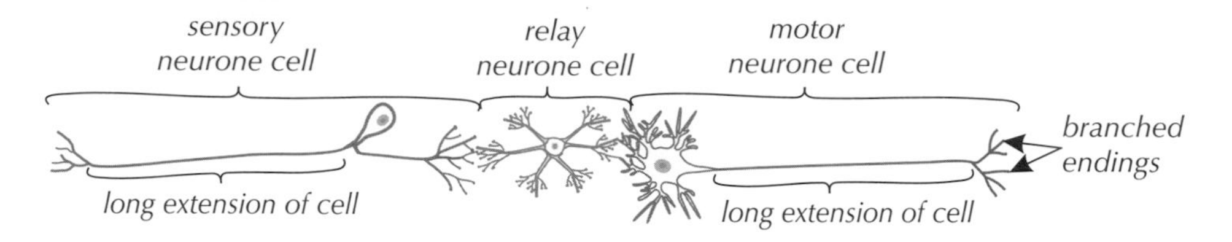

3 (a) A neurone is a specialised cell. What is a specialised cell?

(1 mark)

3 (b) Does the diagram as a whole represent a tissue, an organ or an organ system? Explain your answer.

(2 marks)

3 (c) By reading the information above and looking at the diagram, suggest **one** way in which the structure of a **motor neurone cell** helps it to carry out its function.

(1 mark)

4 The photograph below shows a cross section through a leaf.

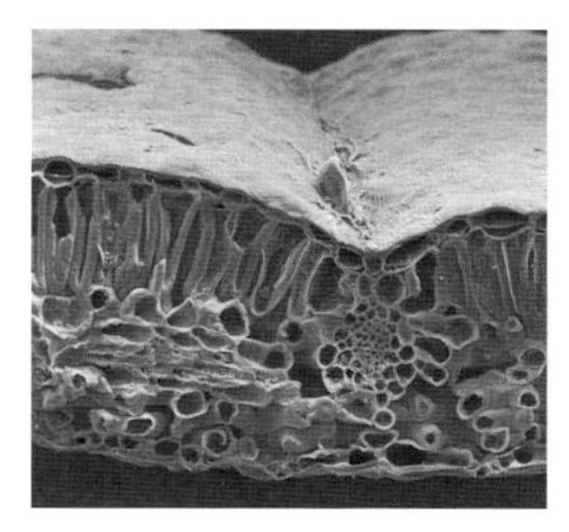

4 (a) What name is given to the tissue that covers the leaf?

(1 mark)

4 (b) Some of the cells in the photograph contain lots of chloroplasts. What plant tissue are these cells part of? Explain your answer.

(3 marks)

4 (c) (i) Carbon dioxide diffuses into leaf cells from the air spaces surrounding them. What does this tell you about the concentration of carbon dioxide inside the cells compared to in the air spaces? Explain your answer.

(2 marks)

4 (c) (ii) Throughout the day, the rate at which carbon dioxide diffuses into the leaf cells changes. Explain how a change in the concentration of carbon dioxide in the air spaces outside the cells could slow down the rate of diffusion.

(2 marks)

1. The Basics of Photosynthesis

Plants and algae make their own food using just light energy, a substance called chlorophyll, carbon dioxide from the air and water from the soil.

What is photosynthesis?

Photosynthesis is the process that produces 'food' in plants and algae. The 'food' it produces is **glucose** (a sugar). Plants use this glucose for a number of things, such as making cell walls and proteins (see page 42).

Where does photosynthesis happen?

Photosynthesis happens inside the **chloroplasts** in plant cells and algae. Chloroplasts contain a green substance called **chlorophyll**, which absorbs sunlight and uses its energy to convert carbon dioxide (from the air) and water (from the soil) into glucose. Oxygen is also produced as a by-product.

You need to learn the equation for photosynthesis:

$$\text{carbon dioxide} + \text{water} \xrightarrow{\text{light energy}} \text{glucose} + \text{oxygen}$$

Photosynthesis happens in the leaves of all green plants — this is largely what the leaves are for. Figure 2 shows a cross-section of a leaf showing the four raw materials (carbon dioxide, water, light energy and chlorophyll) needed for photosynthesis.

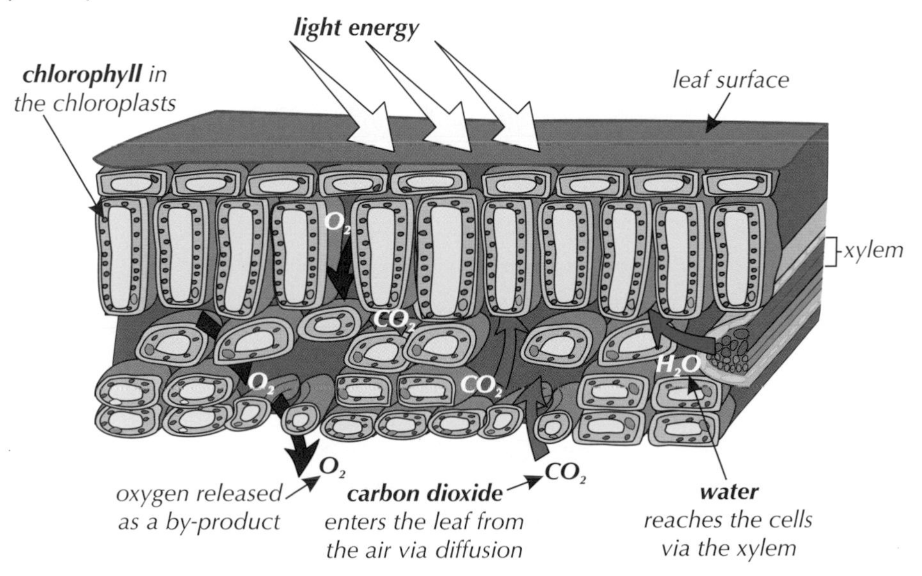

Figure 2: Diagram of a cross-section through a leaf, showing the four raw materials required for photosynthesis.

Learning Objectives:
- Know that the chloroplasts of plant cells and algae contain chlorophyll — a green substance which absorbs light energy.
- Know that during photosynthesis, the light energy absorbed by chlorophyll is used to convert carbon dioxide and water into glucose, and that oxygen is produced as a by-product.
- Know the word equation for photosynthesis.

Specification Reference B2.3.1

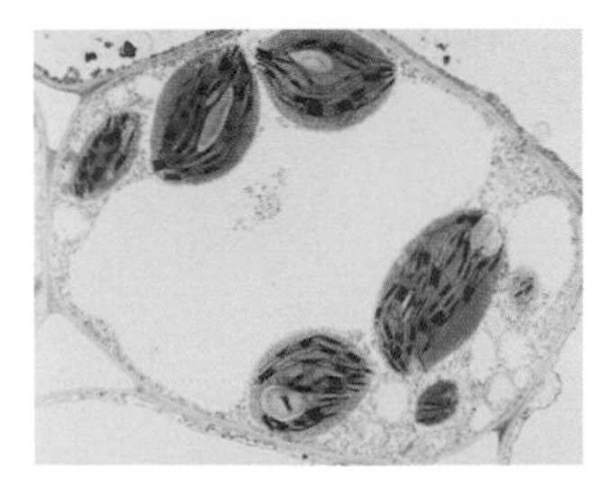

Figure 1: Microscope image of a plant cell. The chloroplasts (green structures) can be seen clearly.

Tip: Xylem is the tissue that transports water around a plant (see page 29).

Practice Questions — Fact Recall

Q1 Which product produced by photosynthesis is 'food' for the plant?

Q2 a) Name the parts of a plant cell that contain chlorophyll.

b) What role does chlorophyll play in photosynthesis?

Q3 Write out the word equation for photosynthesis.

Q4 Which gas is used in photosynthesis?

Q5 What is the by-product of photosynthesis?

Practice Questions — Application

Q1 Three identical plants were grown for a week. They were treated in exactly the same way, except they each received different amounts of sunlight per day, as shown in this table:

Plant	Hours of sunlight received per day
A	3
B	7
C	10

The plants didn't have any source of light other than sunlight.

Which plant do you think will have produced the most glucose after one week? Explain your answer.

Q2 A scientist studied three different types of plant cell (taken from the same plant) under a microscope. She recorded the average number of chloroplasts she found in each type of cell, as shown in this table:

Type of plant cell	Average number of chloroplasts
1	20
2	0
3	51

Suggest which type of plant cell (1-3) is likely to have the highest rate of photosynthesis. Explain your answer.

2. The Rate of Photosynthesis

Photosynthesis doesn't always happen at the same rate — factors such as light intensity, carbon dioxide level and temperature can all affect the rate.

Learning Objectives:

- Understand that light intensity, the availability of carbon dioxide and temperature all interact to affect the rate of photosynthesis, and that any one of these can be the limiting factor of photosynthesis.
- Understand that a low light intensity, low carbon dioxide level and low temperature can all limit the rate of photosynthesis.
- Be able to interpret data showing factors affecting the rate of photosynthesis.

Specification Reference B2.3.1

Limiting factors in photosynthesis

The rate of photosynthesis is affected by the intensity of light, the volume of carbon dioxide (CO_2), and the temperature. All three of these things need to be at the right level to allow a plant to photosynthesise as quickly as possible. If any one of these factors is too high or too low, it will become the **limiting factor**. This just means it's the factor which is stopping photosynthesis from happening any faster.

Which factor is limiting at a particular time depends on the environmental conditions:

Examples

- At night there's much less light than there is during the day, so light intensity is usually the limiting factor at night.
- In winter it's usually cold, so a low temperature is often the limiting factor.
- If it's warm enough and bright enough, the amount of CO_2 is usually limiting.

Tip: Plants also need water for photosynthesis, but when a plant is so short of water that it becomes the limiting factor in photosynthesis, it's already in such trouble that this is the least of its worries.

Investigating the rate of photosynthesis

To investigate the effect of different factors on photosynthesis, the rate of photosynthesis needs to be measured. There are different ways to do this:

Example

You can investigate the rate of photosynthesis of a water plant like Canadian pondweed. With this type of plant you can easily measure the amount of oxygen produced in a given time to show how fast photosynthesis is happening (remember, oxygen is made during photosynthesis). You could either count the bubbles given off, or if you want to be a bit more accurate you could collect the oxygen in a gas syringe as shown in Figure 1.

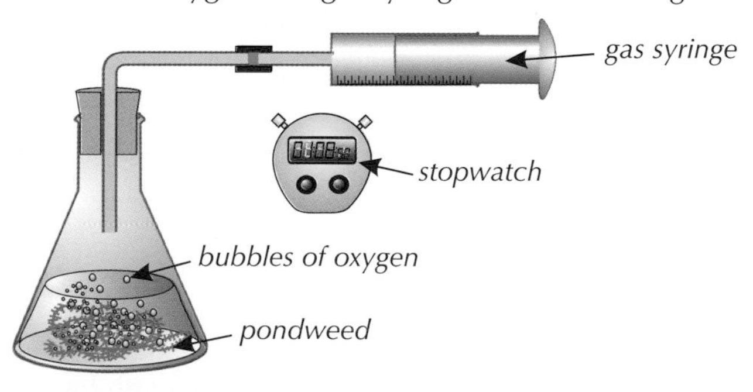

Figure 1: Diagram showing the experimental set up used to measure the rate of photosynthesis in water plants.

Figure 2: Pondweed giving off oxygen bubbles as a by-product of photosynthesis.

Controlling variables

HOW SCIENCE WORKS

Generally, you'll only be investigating one factor that affects the rate of photosynthesis at a time, so you have to try and keep all the other variables constant, so that it's a fair test.

Tip: The variables in these experiments include all of the limiting factors of photosynthesis.

Examples

- Use a bench lamp to control the intensity of the light (careful not to block the light with anything).
- If your plant's in a flask, keep the flask in a water bath to help keep the temperature constant.
- There's not much you can do to keep the carbon dioxide level constant — you may just have to use a large container for your plant, and do the experiments as quickly as you can, so that the plant doesn't use up too much of the carbon dioxide in the container.

Tip: For more on designing investigations and controlling variables see pages 7-8.

Interpreting data on the rate of photosynthesis

You need to be able to interpret data showing how different factors affect the rate of photosynthesis.

1. Effect of light intensity

Light provides the energy needed for photosynthesis. As you can see from Figure 3, as the light level is raised, the rate of photosynthesis increases steadily — but only up to a certain point. Beyond that, it won't make any difference because then it'll be either the temperature or the carbon dioxide level which is the limiting factor.

Tip: If you're using a bench lamp to control light intensity and you just plot the rate of photosynthesis against "distance of lamp from the beaker", you get a weird-shaped graph. To get a graph like the one in Figure 3, you either need to measure the light intensity at the beaker using a light meter or do a bit of nifty maths with your results.

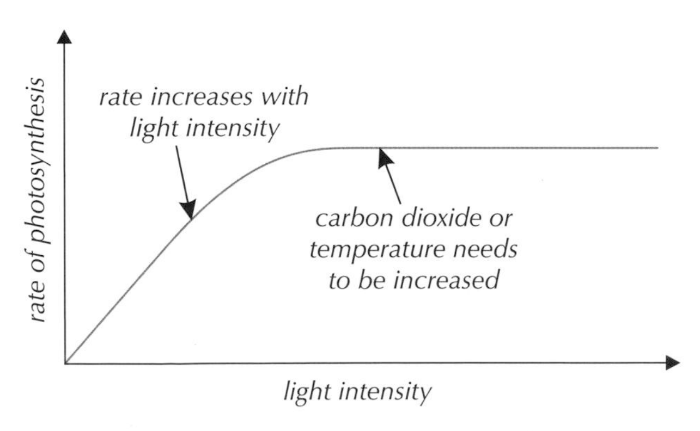

Figure 3: *Graph showing how light intensity affects the rate of photosynthesis.*

Remember, photosynthesis hasn't stopped when the graph levels off — it's just not increasing anymore.

2. Effect of carbon dioxide level

Carbon dioxide is one of the raw materials needed for photosynthesis.
As with light intensity the amount of carbon dioxide will only increase the rate of photosynthesis up to a point. After this the graph flattens out showing that carbon dioxide is no longer the limiting factor (see Figure 4).

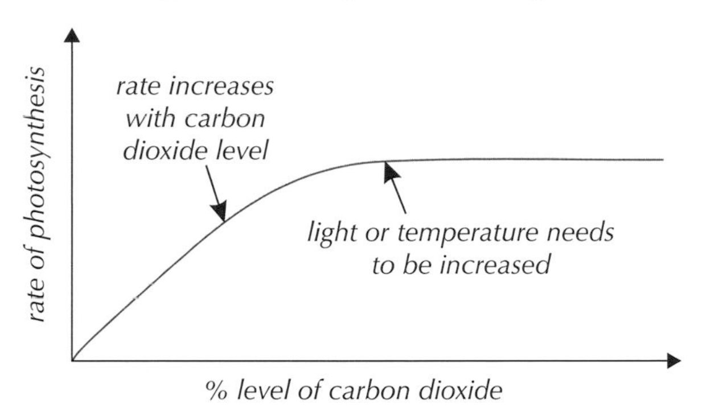

Figure 4: *Graph showing how carbon dioxide level affects the rate of photosynthesis.*

Tip: If you're investigating the rate of photosynthesis using a plant in water, you can increase the CO_2 level by dissolving sodium hydrogen carbonate in the water. This gives off carbon dioxide.

As long as light and carbon dioxide are in plentiful supply then the factor limiting photosynthesis must be temperature.

3. Effect of temperature

Enzymes are proteins which increase the speed of chemical reactions in living things — so enzymes increase the rate of photosynthesis in plant and algal cells. The speed at which enzymes work is affected by temperature.

Tip: You can read more about enzymes on pages 53-55.

Usually, if the temperature is the limiting factor in photosynthesis it's because it's too low — the enzymes needed for photosynthesis work more slowly at low temperatures. But if the plant gets too hot, the enzymes it needs for photosynthesis and its other reactions will be damaged. This happens at about 45 °C (which is pretty hot for outdoors, although greenhouses can get that hot if you're not careful). Figure 5 shows the effect of temperature on the rate of photosynthesis.

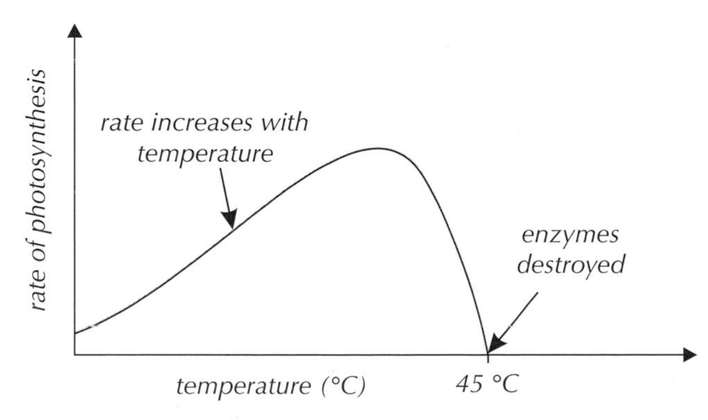

Figure 5: *Graph showing how temperature affects the rate of photosynthesis.*

Practice Question — Fact Recall

Q1 The rate of photosynthesis is affected by limiting factors.

a) What is meant by a 'limiting factor' of photosynthesis?

b) Give three factors that can affect the rate of photosynthesis.

Practice Questions — Application

Q1 Complete the table to show what is most likely to be the limiting factor of photosynthesis in the environmental conditions listed.

Environmental conditions	Most likely limiting factor
Outside on a cold winter's day.	
In an unlit garden at 1:30 am, in the UK, in summer.	
On a windowsill on a warm, bright day.	

Q2 Peter was investigating the rate of photosynthesis in pondweed. He put equally sized samples of pondweed from the same plant in two separate flasks containing different solutions. The solution in flask A had a lower carbon dioxide concentration than the solution in flask B. Peter put the flasks an equal distance away from a light source and gradually increased the intensity of the light throughout the experiment. He kept both flasks at a constant temperature of 25 °C. During the experiment Peter measured the amount of gas produced in each flask using a gas syringe. His results are shown on the graph:

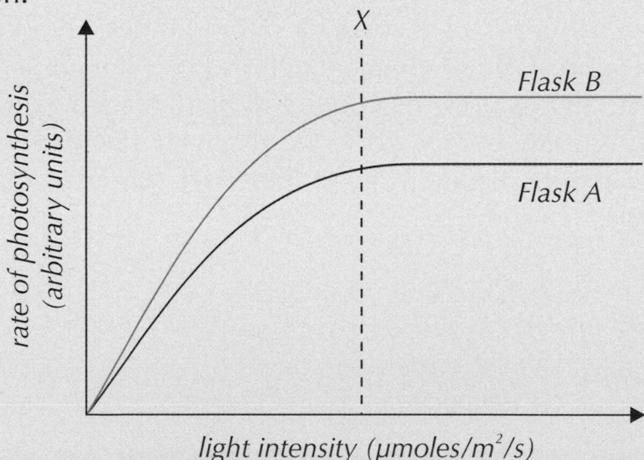

a) What gas did Peter collect in order to measure the rate of photosynthesis?

b) Give two things that Peter did to make the experiment a fair test.

c) Peter thinks that the limiting factor before point X in his experiment is light. Why does he think this?

HOW SCIENCE WORKS

d) Both graphs level off after point X. Suggest why Flask A levels off at a lower point than Flask B. Explain your answer.

Exam Tip
μmoles/m²/s is a unit used to measure light intensity. Don't panic if you see unfamiliar units in the exam — just focus on what the axis is showing you, e.g. here it's light intensity.

3. Artificially Controlling Plant Growth

As you've read on the last few pages, different factors affect the rate of photosynthesis. Farmers and other plant growers can use this knowledge to try and increase the rate of growth in their plants.

Learning Objectives:
- Understand that the temperature, light intensity and carbon dioxide concentration in a plant's environment can be managed artificially in order to increase the rate of photosynthesis.
- Be able to evaluate the benefits of using artificial environments to control plant growth.

Specification Reference B2.3.1

Greenhouses

If you know the ideal conditions for photosynthesis, then you can create an environment which maximises the rate of photosynthesis, which in turn maximises the rate of plant growth, (plants use some of the glucose produced by photosynthesis for growth — see page 42). The most common way to artificially create the ideal environment for plants is to grow them in a greenhouse. Commercial growers (people who grow plants to make money, such as farmers) often grow large quantities of plants in commercial greenhouses. The following conditions can easily be managed in a greenhouse:

1. Temperature

Greenhouses help to trap the Sun's heat, (see Figure 1) and make sure that the temperature doesn't become limiting.

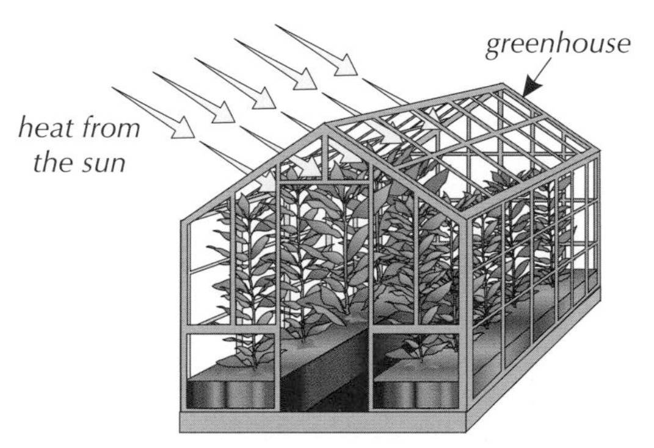

Figure 1: *Greenhouses trap the Sun's heat.*

Figure 2: *Lettuces growing in a commercial greenhouse.*

Temperature can be controlled in other ways too:

Examples

- In winter, a farmer might use a heater in their greenhouse to keep the temperature at the ideal level.
- In summer, greenhouses could get too hot, so farmers might use shades and ventilation to cool things down.

2. Light

Light is always needed for photosynthesis, so farmers often supply artificial light after the Sun goes down to give their plants more quality photosynthesis time.

Figure 3: *Lamps in greenhouses supply light so plants can continue to photosynthesise at night.*

3. Carbon dioxide concentration

Farmers can also increase the level of carbon dioxide in the greenhouse. A fairly common way is to use a paraffin heater to heat the greenhouse. As the paraffin burns, it makes carbon dioxide as a by-product.

4. General health of plants

Keeping plants enclosed in a greenhouse also makes it easier to keep them free from pests and diseases. The farmer can add fertilisers to the soil as well, to provide all the minerals needed for healthy growth.

Greenhouse costs

Controlling the conditions in a greenhouse costs money — but if the farmer can keep the conditions just right for photosynthesis, the plants will grow much faster and a decent crop can be harvested much more often, which can then be sold.

It's important that a farmer supplies just the right amount of heat, light, etc. — enough to make the plants grow well, but not more than the plants need, as this would just be wasting money.

Interpreting data on artificial environments

In the exam you could be given some data about controlling photosynthesis in artificial environments (like greenhouses) and asked questions about it.

Example

A farmer normally grows his plants outside when the average air temperature is between 9 and 11 °C. The farmer wants to increase the growth rate of his plants, so he is considering getting a greenhouse. He finds some data on how temperature affects the rate of photosynthesis for the type of plants he grows. This is shown in the graph:

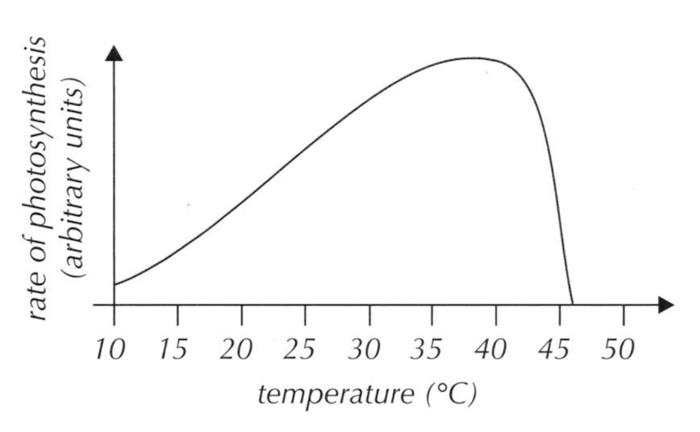

You could be asked to evaluate the benefits of growing plants in an artificial environment...
By looking at the graph you can see that the plants could photosynthesise faster if they were grown at temperatures higher than the average temperatures outside. If the farmer had a greenhouse he could control the temperature the plants were kept at, therefore increasing their rate of photosynthesis and growth. However, he would have to weigh up the cost of buying and running a greenhouse against this increased rate of growth.

You could be asked to make suggestions based on data from the graph...
For instance, you could be asked to suggest the best temperature for the farmer to keep his plants at and to explain why. Based on the graph, suggesting 37 °C would be a good idea, as this is the minimum temperature at which the rate of photosynthesis is highest. Keeping them at temperatures higher than this would just be a waste of money.

Exam Tip
If you get a question like this in the exam, remember that the aim of commercial farming is to make money. Farmers try to create conditions to increase photosynthesis (and therefore growth) but at a minimum cost.

Practice Questions — Fact Recall

Q1 Explain why some farmers grow plants in an artificial environment.

Q2 Farmers can control the light and temperature in a greenhouse. Give one other condition they can control in a greenhouse.

Practice Questions — Application

A farmer grew the same type of plant in two greenhouses, A and B. He used a paraffin heater in Greenhouse A and an electric heater in Greenhouse B. Electric heaters don't release any carbon dioxide, whereas carbon dioxide is released when paraffin is burnt.

For 8 weeks the farmer recorded the average height of the plants in each greenhouse. He also monitored the temperature in both greenhouses. Plants in both greenhouses were exposed to the same amount of light and given the same amount of water and nutrients. His results are shown below:

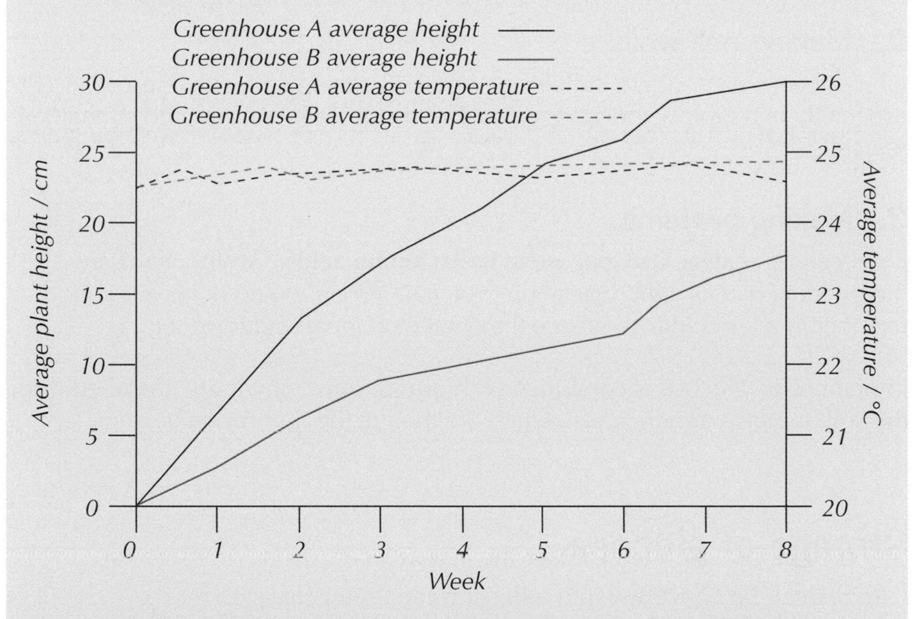

Q1 a) What was the average growth rate per week for the plants in Greenhouse A?

b) What was the average growth rate per week for the plants in Greenhouse B?

Q2 What factor do you think is responsible for the difference between the average growth rates of the plants in Greenhouse A compared to Greenhouse B. Explain your answer.

Q3 The farmer is trying to decide which type of heater to use on a permanent basis. Other than the effect on growth rate, suggest what else the farmer will need to consider when choosing a heater.

Exam Tip
In the exam you might see experiments using rate of plant growth or increase in plant mass as an indirect way of measuring the rate of photosynthesis. This is because some of the glucose produced by photosynthesis is used for growth in plants (see pages 42-43).

Tip: If you're stuck on Q2, have a look back at the pages on limiting factors of photosynthesis (35-37).

4. How Plants and Algae Use Glucose

As you know plants and algae photosynthesise to make 'food' in the form of glucose. They make use of this glucose in a number of ways...

Learning Objectives:
- Know that the glucose produced by photosynthesis can be used for respiration.
- Know that plants and algae can also use this glucose to make cellulose and proteins.
- Know that plants need to take nitrate ions from the soil to make proteins.
- Know that plants and algae use glucose to make lipids, which are stored.
- Know that plants can also store glucose as starch.

Specification Reference B2.3.1

What is glucose used for?

During photosynthesis, plants and algae convert carbon dioxide and water into glucose (see page 33). They use the glucose they produce for the following things:

1. Respiration

Plants and algae use some of the glucose they make for respiration. Respiration is a process which occurs in all living organisms — it's where energy is released from the breakdown of glucose (see page 64).
Plants and algae use this energy to convert the rest of the glucose into various other useful substances, which they can use to build new cells and grow. To produce some of these substances plants also need to gather a few minerals from the soil (e.g. nitrates — see below).

2. Making cell walls

Glucose is converted into **cellulose** for making strong cell walls (see page 17), especially in a rapidly growing plant. These cell walls support and strengthen the cells.

Figure 1: *Microscope image of a plant cell wall made up of strands of cellulose.*

3. Making proteins

Plant cells and algae use glucose to make **amino acids**. Amino acids are the building blocks which make up proteins. When amino acids are joined together in a particular sequence they make up a particular protein.

In plant cells, glucose is combined with **nitrate ions** (which are absorbed from the soil) to make amino acids, which are then made into proteins.

Storage of glucose

Glucose can be converted into other substances for storage:

Lipids

Plants and algae can convert some of the glucose they produce into lipids (fats and oils). Plants store lipids in seeds and algae store oil droplets in their cells.

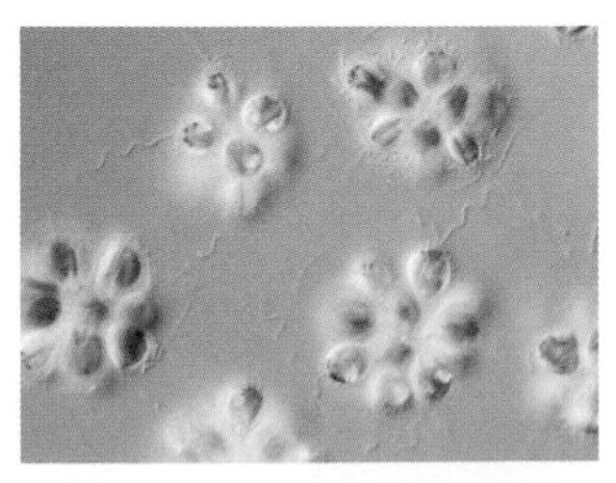

Figure 2: *Algal cells as seen under a microscope. The red dots are oil droplets.*

Example

Sunflower seeds contain a lot of oil — we get cooking oil and margarine from them.

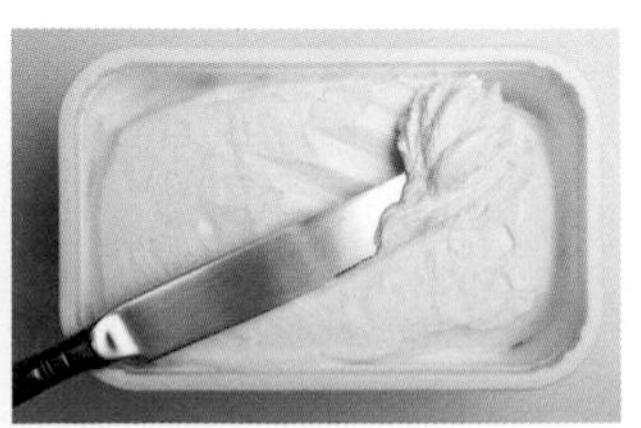

Starch

Plants and algae can convert glucose into starch. Glucose is stored as starch so it's ready for use when photosynthesis isn't happening as much, like in the winter. In plants starch is stored in roots, stems, seeds and leaves.

Example

Potato and parsnip plants store a lot of starch underground over the winter so a new plant can grow from it the following spring. We eat the swollen storage organs (see Figure 3).

Figure 3: *Potato plants that have just been dug up — the potatoes that we eat are starch stores for the plant.*

Starch is **insoluble** which makes it much better for storing than glucose — a cell with lots of glucose in would draw in loads of water and swell up.

Practice Questions — Fact Recall

Q1 By what process do plants and algae break down glucose in order to release energy?

Q2 What do plants and algae use cellulose for?

Q3 What do plants absorb from the soil to make proteins with?

Q4 Glucose can be stored as starch in plants and algae. How else is glucose stored?

Q5 Why is starch better for storage than glucose?

Section Checklist — Make sure you know...

The Basics of Photosynthesis

- ☐ That chlorophyll is a green substance found within the chloroplasts of plant cells and algae.
- ☐ That during photosynthesis, chlorophyll absorbs light energy, which is used to convert carbon dioxide (from the air) and water (from the soil) into glucose (a sugar).
- ☐ Know that oxygen is produced as a by-product of photosynthesis.
- ☐ That the word equation for photosynthesis is:

$$\text{carbon dioxide} + \text{water} \xrightarrow{\text{light energy}} \text{glucose} + \text{oxygen.}$$

The Rate of Photosynthesis

- ☐ That the rate of photosynthesis is affected by the interaction of light intensity, carbon dioxide concentration and temperature, and that any one of these three things can become the limiting factor of photosynthesis (the thing that stops it from happening any faster).
- ☐ That the rate of photosynthesis can be limited by low levels of light, low carbon dioxide levels or a low temperature.
- ☐ How to interpret data showing factors which affect the rate of photosynthesis.

Artificially Controlling Plant Growth

- ☐ That factors which affect the rate of photosynthesis (light intensity, carbon dioxide concentration and temperature) can be managed artificially (e.g. in a greenhouse) and that this is done in order to increase the rate of photosynthesis of plants.
- ☐ How to evaluate the benefits of growing plants in artificial environments.

How Plants and Algae Use Glucose

- ☐ That plants and algae use the glucose produced by photosynthesis for respiration, making cellulose (to strengthen cell walls) and for producing proteins.
- ☐ That plants need to absorb nitrate ions from the soil to make proteins.
- ☐ That plants and algae can store glucose as lipids (fats and oils) or as starch (which is insoluble).

1. Distribution of Organisms

Different environments will suit some organisms better than others. If the conditions within these environments change, then the type and number of organisms living there could change too...

Learning Objectives:
- Know that temperature, the availability of water, oxygen, carbon dioxide and nutrients, and amount of light are all factors that may affect the distribution of organisms.
- Be able to suggest reasons for the distribution of organisms in a habitat.

Specification Reference B2.4.1

Habitats and distribution

A **habitat** is the place where an organism lives, e.g. a playing field. **Distribution** is where organisms are found in a particular area, e.g. in a part of the playing field.

Factors affecting distribution

The distribution of organisms is affected by environmental factors such as:

- Temperature
- Availability of water
- Availability of oxygen
- Availability of carbon dioxide
- Availability of nutrients
- Amount of light

An organism might be more common in one area than another due to differences in environmental factors between the two areas.

Tip: Not all organisms are affected by all of these factors. For example, the availability of carbon dioxide and light doesn't really affect animals, but it does affect plants.

Example

- In a field, you might find that daisies are more common in the open, than under trees. This is because there's more light available in the open and daisies need light to survive (they use it for photosynthesis — see page 33).
- Some types of mayfly are more common in colder parts of a stream, as they can't tolerate the warmer temperatures in other parts of the stream.

Figure 1: *The distribution of daisies is affected by the amount of light available — so they grow well in an open field like this one.*

Practice Questions — Fact Recall

Q1 What is meant by the 'distribution' of organisms?

Q2 List six factors which could affect the distribution of organisms.

Learning Objectives:

- Understand that the distribution of organisms can be studied by random sampling with quadrats.
- Know what is meant by the terms 'mean', 'mode' and 'median'.
- Understand that the distribution of organisms across an area can be studied by sampling along a transect.
- Be able to evaluate methods used to collect environmental data, in terms of the validity of the methods used, and the reproducibility of the data produced, as evidence for environmental change.

Specification Reference B2.4.1

2. Studying Distribution

Some scientists are interested in studying the distribution of organisms, so that they can see how environmental changes affect it.
Right, enough talk — time to get your quadrat out...

Ways to study distribution

There are a couple of ways to study the distribution of organisms:

1. You can measure how common an organism is in two or more sample areas and compare them.
2. You can study how the distribution changes across an area e.g. from one edge of a field to another.

The data you collect can be used to provide evidence for environmental change. For instance, if the distribution of organisms across an area changes over time, this could be due to changes in the environment.

Example

The Dartford warbler is a species of bird. It has become more widely distributed in the UK in recent years — partly because warmer winters have allowed it to move further north and partly because there are now more areas of protected heathland for it to live in.

Studying distribution often involves the use of **quadrats** (see below) and **transects** (see page 48).

Tip: It's really important that the quadrats are placed randomly within the sample area (see page 49 for how to do this). Taking random samples improves the validity of the study.

Using quadrats

Quadrats are really useful for studying the distribution of small organisms that are slow-moving or that don't move around. A quadrat is a square frame enclosing a known area, e.g. 1 m^2 (see Figure 1). To compare how common an organism is in two sample areas, you can collect data using random sampling with a quadrat. Just follow these simple steps:

1. Place a quadrat on the ground at a random point within the first sample area.
2. Count all the organisms within the quadrat and record the results.
3. Repeat steps 1 and 2 as many times as you can.
4. Repeat steps 1 to 3 in the second sample area.
5. Finally compare the two sets of results. To do this you'll need to work out the average result for each sample area, which involves a bit of maths...

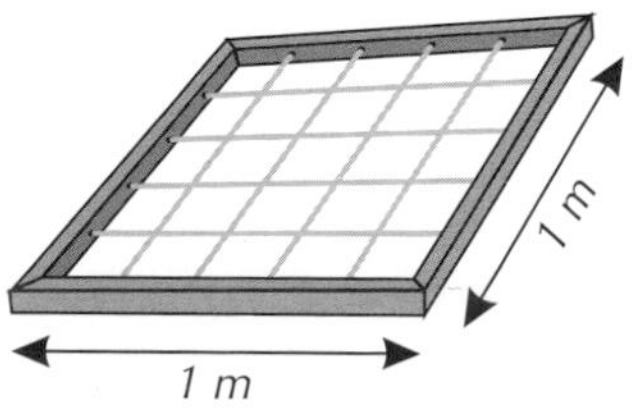

1 m

1 m

Figure 1: *A diagram of a 1 m^2 quadrat.*

Figure 2: *A student using a quadrat to gather data on the distribution of organisms.*

Working out averages

There are three averages you need to know how to work out — the mean, the mode and the median:

- **Mean** — you calculate this by adding together all the values in the data, and dividing that total by the number of values that you have.
- The **mode** is the most common value in a set of data.
- The **median** is the middle value in a set of data, when they're in order of size.

Examples

John counted the number of daffodils in 9 quadrats.
He recorded the following results: 5, 8, 2, 5, 9, 4, 11, 3, 7.

- **Mean:** work out the mean with this formula: $\frac{\text{total number of organisms}}{\text{number of quadrats}}$

  So the mean here is:

  $$\frac{5+8+2+5+9+4+11+3+7}{9} = \frac{54}{9} = \mathbf{6} \text{ daffodils per quadrat.}$$

- **Mode**: count how often each value occurs in the data to find the value that is most common — 5, 8, 2, 5, 9, 4, 11, 3, 7. 5 occurs most often in the data, so **5** is the mode.
- **Median**: put the numbers in order of size — 2, 3, 4, 5, 5, 7, 8, 9, 11, then find the middle value. Here the middle value is **5**, so that's the median.

Tip: If there are two middle numbers in a list of data, you just add them together and then divide by 2 to get the median. E.g. if you had the numbers 3, 4, 10, 19, the median would be **7**. (4 + 10 = 14, and then 14 ÷ 2 = **7**).

Population size

You can use the data you've gathered about an organism to work out the population size of the organism in the sample area. You need to:

1. Work out the mean number of organisms per m^2. (If your quadrat has an area of 1 m^2, this is the same as the mean number of organisms per quadrat.)
2. Then multiply the mean by the total area (in m^2) of the habitat.

Example

A field has an area of 800 m^2 and the mean number of daisies per m^2 is 22.
Calculate the population size of daisies in the field.

Size of the daisy population = mean number of daisies per m^2 × the total area
= 22 × 800
= **17 600 daisies**

Using transects

Tip: Transects can be used in any type of habitat, not just fields. For example, along a beach or in a stream.

You can use lines called transects (see Figure 3) to help find out how organisms (like plants) are distributed across an area — e.g. if an organism becomes more or less common as you move from a hedge towards the middle of a field.

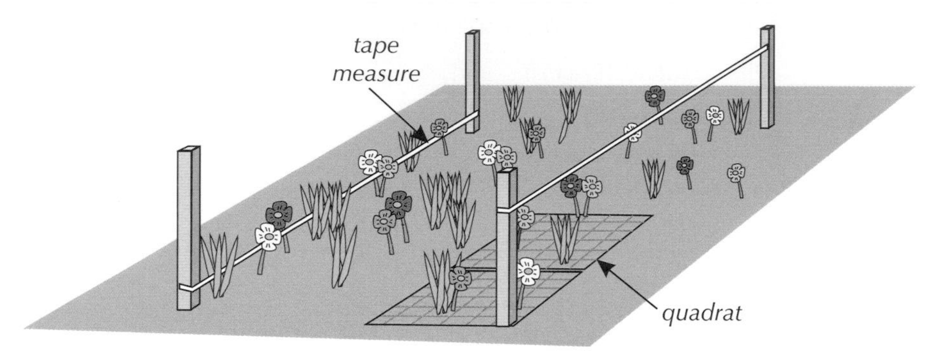

Figure 3: *A diagram showing two transects.*

Figure 4: *Students using a quadrat along a transect.*

Here's what to do:

1. Mark out a line in the area you want to study using a tape measure.
2. Then collect data along the line. You can do this by just counting all the organisms you're interested in that touch the line. Or, you can collect data by using quadrats. These can be placed next to each other along the line or at intervals, for example, every 2 m.

Reproducibility and validity

Tip: By collecting data about the distribution of organisms you are collecting environmental data.

The environmental data you gather when using quadrats and transects can provide evidence for environmental change. But you need to think carefully about the reproducibility and validity of your study:

Reproducibility

Tip: For more on reproducibility see page 4 and page 10 in 'How Science Works'.

You need to be confident that the results of your study could be reproduced. This means that someone else should be able to carry out the same study and get similar results to you.

One way to make your results more reproducible is to take a large sample size, e.g. use as many quadrats and transects as possible in your sample area. Bigger samples are more representative of the whole population (see page 3).

Tip: Repeatable means that if you conduct the experiment again, using the same method and equipment as in your original experiment, then you'll get the same results again.

Validity

For your results to be valid they must be repeatable and reproducible, and answer the original question (what you are trying to find out).

To answer the original question, you need to control all the variables. The question you want to answer is whether a difference in distribution between two sample areas (or across one area) is due to a difference in one environmental factor. If you've controlled all the other variables that could be affecting the distribution, you'll know whether a difference in distribution is caused by the environmental factor or not.

Tip: Have a look at page 4 for more information on validity.

If you don't control the other variables you won't know whether any correlation (relationship) you've found is because of chance, because of the environmental factor you're looking at or because of a different variable — the study won't give you valid data.

Example

A student found a correlation between the number of daisies in an area and the amount of light.

He found that there were more daisies growing in an area which received more light, than in an area where there was less light. However, he couldn't conclude that the amount of light caused the difference in the number of daisies because other variables, e.g. the availability of water, could have affected the results.

Unless the student could control these variables too, his results wouldn't be valid.

Exam Tip
In the exam you could be given an experiment and asked what variables were controlled. Think about what the experiment is trying to find out, and think of possible factors that could affect the results — these are the variables which need to be controlled.

Another way you can improve the validity of your results is to use random samples, e.g. randomly put down or mark out your quadrat or transect. You can do this by dividing the area you are going to study into a grid and using a random number generator, or drawing numbers out of a hat, to pick the coordinates of where you will place your quadrats or transect. If all your samples are in one spot, and everywhere else is different, the results you get won't be valid.

Tip: You must put your quadrat down in a random place before you start counting — don't just plonk it down on the first big patch of organisms that you see.

Practice Questions — Fact Recall

Q1 Describe how you would use random sampling with a quadrat to compare the distribution of organisms in two sample areas.

Q2 How do you calculate the mean of a set of data?

Q3 What is the mode value in a set of data?

Q4 What is the median value in set of data?

Q5 Describe one way in which a transect can be used to measure the distribution of organisms across an area.

Q6 Give one way you could increase the reproducibility of a study that involves collecting environmental data.

Practice Question — Application

Q1 Joanne read that bulrushes grow best in moist soil or in shallow water. She wanted to find out whether this was true, so she investigated the distribution of bulrushes in her garden. She used a transect (as shown in the diagram) and recorded the number of bulrushes in each quadrat as shown in the table.

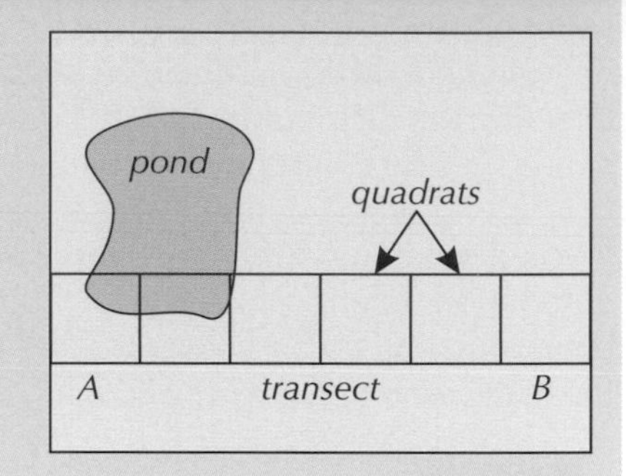

Quadrat	1	2	3	4	5	6
Number of Bulrushes	1	5	5	20	43	37

Tip: If you're asked to find the 'modal number' you need to find the mode.

a) i) Calculate the mean number of bulrushes per quadrat.

ii) Calculate the modal number of bulrushes per quadrat.

iii)Calculate the median number of bulrushes per quadrat.

b) Joanne started counting at quadrat 1 and moved along the transect in order, to quadrat 6. Assuming that the information Joanne read was correct, do you think quadrat 1 is at end A or end B of the transect? Explain your answer.

c) Joanne didn't control any of the variables which may have affected the growth of bulrushes in her garden. Explain how this affects the validity of her study.

d) A change to the drainage system in Joanne's garden means that the area of the pond is gradually decreasing in size. Suggest how the distribution of bulrushes in the garden may change in the future if the size of the pond continues to decrease.

Section Checklist — Make sure you know...

Distribution of Organisms

- ❑ That there are a number of environmental factors which can affect the distribution of organisms, including temperature and the availability of water, oxygen, carbon dioxide, nutrients and light.
- ❑ That the distribution of organisms varies in a habitat, and how to suggest reasons for this variation (often it's due to differences in environmental factors between different areas of the habitat).

Studying Distribution

- ❑ How random sampling with quadrats can be used to study the distribution of organisms.
- ❑ How to calculate the mean, mode and median of a set of data.
- ❑ How sampling along a transect can be used to show the distribution of organisms across an area.
- ❑ How to evaluate the methods used to collect environmental data, in terms of the validity of the methods used and the reproducibility of the data, as evidence of environmental change.

Exam-style Questions

1 A biology class were studying the distribution of organisms on a rocky shore line. Three students each set up a transect which ran from the water's edge up the shore, as shown in the diagram. All three students counted the number of limpets in each of the 50 cm × 50 cm quadrats. The number of limpets counted by each student are shown in the table.

Quadrat number	1	2	3	4	5	6	7
Student A Number of Limpets	18	65	70	55	30	10	0
Student B Number of Limpets	6	72	76	41	21	18	3
Student C Number of Limpets	14	83	84	57	26	16	1

1 (a) (i) Calculate the mean number of limpets found in quadrat 4.
Show your working.

(2 marks)

1 (a) (ii) Limpets need to stay moist in order to survive, but they are able to survive for a period of time without water by clamping down onto the surface of rocks — this helps to prevent them from drying out. Close to the water's edge, limpets have lots of competition from other species for space.

Use this information and the data above to describe the distribution of limpets along the shore line and suggest reasons for it.

(3 marks)

1 (a) (iii) One of the students thinks that they need to gather more data by setting up more transects. Explain why this would increase the reproducibility of their results.

(2 marks)

1 (b) During the class study, another group of students investigated the distribution of a type of starfish. They divided the area of shoreline they were interested in studying into two sample areas (A and B), and placed 20 quadrats at random in each area. The students' results showed that sample area A contained a higher number of starfish.

1 (b) (i) Why did the students place their quadrats randomly?

(1 mark)

1 (b) (ii) Suggest **two** environmental factors that could explain the difference in the distribution of starfish in the two sample areas.

(2 marks)

2 Tim read the following information in a science magazine:

> You can measure the rate of photosynthesis in plants by doing the following:
> Cut discs from a plant leaf and put them in a 0.2% sodium hydrogen carbonate solution (which serves as a source of carbon dioxide). Put the solution and leaf discs in a syringe and then remove all the air from the syringe — this removes any gases out of the air spaces in the leaf, which will cause the leaf discs to sink.
> Then put the syringe containing the leaf discs under a light source. As the leaf discs photosynthesise, their cells produce oxygen. The oxygen will fill the air spaces in the leaf — with enough oxygen in the air spaces they'll begin to float. You can use the time this takes as a measure of the rate of photosynthesis.

2 (a) (i) Where in a plant cell does photosynthesis take place?

(1 mark)

2 (a) (ii) Complete the word equation for photosynthesis:

carbon dioxide + ... $\xrightarrow{\text{.............................}}$ glucose + oxygen

(2 marks)

Tim decided to use the method described in the science magazine to investigate the effect of light intensity on the rate of photosynthesis. He conducted the experiment at three different light intensities. For each light intensity he cut 10 equally sized discs from a leaf, and set up the experiment as described in the magazine article. He then timed how long it took for all of the leaf discs to float to the surface in the syringe. His results are shown in this table:

Light intensity	Time it took for all discs to float (minutes)
A	18
B	9
C	11

2 (b) (i) Which light intensity do you think was the highest, A, B or C? Explain your answer.

(2 marks)

2 (b) (ii) Tim thinks that if he keeps increasing the light intensity, he will keep increasing the rate of photosynthesis. Is he right? Explain your answer.

(4 marks)

2 (b) (iii) Tim conducts the experiment again using light intensity A. This time he uses a solution containing 0.8% sodium hydrogen carbonate. Do you think it will take more or less than 18 minutes for all of the discs to float? Explain your answer.

(2 marks)

2 (c) *In this question you will be assessed on the quality of your English, the organisation of your ideas and your use of appropriate specialist vocabulary.*

The process of photosynthesis produces glucose. Describe as fully as you can how this glucose may be used by a plant.

(6 marks)

1. Proteins and Enzymes

Proteins are involved in all the processes and chemical reactions that keep us ticking over, so it's really important that you learn what they're all about...

What are proteins?

Proteins are large biological molecules, which are made up of long chains of smaller molecules called **amino acids**. These chains are folded into unique shapes that other molecules can fit into, allowing proteins to do their jobs.

Proteins have a variety of functions. They can act as:

- **Structural components of tissue**, like muscles.
  For example, myosin and actin are proteins that make up muscles.
- **Hormones**, for example insulin is a protein that works as a hormone.
- **Antibodies** — these lock onto foreign antigens (the unique molecules on a pathogen's surface) and kill invading cells.
- **Catalysts** — better known as enzymes. All enzymes are proteins.

Enzymes

Living things have thousands of different chemical reactions going on inside them all the time. These reactions need to be carefully controlled — to get the right amounts of substances.

You can usually make a reaction happen more quickly by raising the temperature. This would speed up the useful reactions but also the unwanted ones too... not good. There's also a limit to how far you can raise the temperature inside a living creature before its cells start getting damaged.

So... living things produce enzymes that act as **biological catalysts**. Enzymes reduce the need for high temperatures and we only have enzymes to speed up the useful chemical reactions in the body.

A catalyst is a substance which increases the speed of a reaction, without being changed or used up in the reaction.

Learning Objectives:

- Know what proteins are.
- Understand how the specific shape of a protein allows it to do its job.
- Know that the functions of proteins include being structural components of tissues, hormones, antibodies and catalysts.
- Know that all enzymes are proteins.
- Know that enzymes are biological catalysts.
- Understand how catalysts affect chemical reactions.
- Understand that enzymes have special shapes so they can catalyse reactions.
- Understand how high temperatures affect an enzyme's shape.
- Understand that different enzymes have different optimum pHs.

Specification Reference
B2.5.1, B2.5.2

Tip: All enzymes are proteins, but not all proteins are enzymes.

Tip: 'Biological' means related to living things. (Enzymes are biological catalysts because they're made by living things.)

Tip: It's the folding up of the long chains of amino acids, held together by bonds, that give an enzyme its unique shape.

Enzyme action

Enzymes have special shapes so that they can catalyse reactions. Chemical reactions usually involve substances either being split apart or joined together. Every enzyme has a unique shape that fits onto the substance involved in a reaction. Enzymes are really picky — they usually only catalyse one reaction. This is because, for the enzyme to work, the substance has to fit its special shape — see Figure 1.

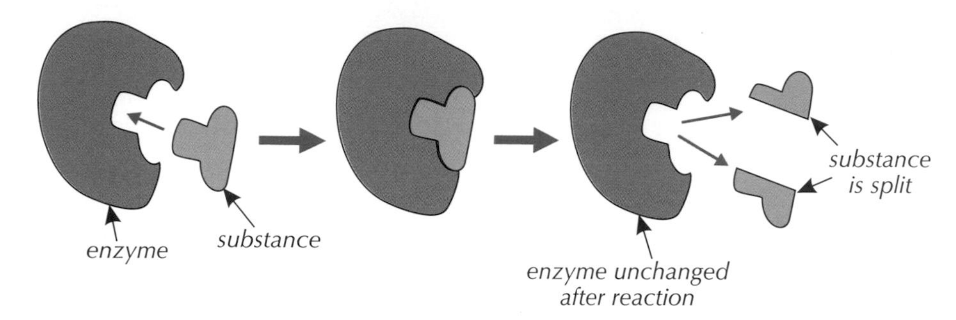

Figure 1: *Diagram to show how an enzyme works.*

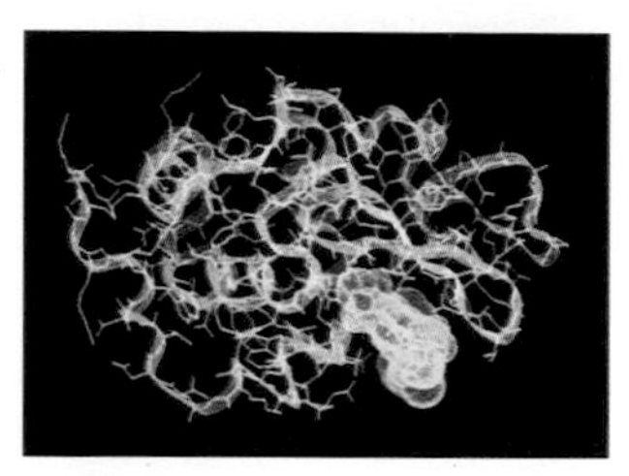

Figure 2: *Computer model of an enzyme bound to a substance (yellow) — they fit perfectly together.*

If the substance doesn't match the enzyme's shape, then the reaction won't be catalysed.

Optimum conditions for enzymes

Enzymes need the right conditions, such as the right temperature and pH, for them to work best — these are called **optimum conditions**.

Tip: Increasing the temperature increases the rate of a reaction because the reactants have more energy, so they move about more, and collide with each other more often.

Tip: If an enzyme is involved in speeding up a reaction, then the reaction is known as an 'enzyme-catalysed reaction'.

Temperature

Changing the temperature changes the rate of an enzyme-catalysed reaction. Like with any reaction, a higher temperature increases the rate at first. But if it gets too hot, some of the bonds holding the enzyme together break. This destroys the enzyme's special shape and so it won't work any more. It's said to be denatured.

Therefore enzymes have a temperature at which they are most active — this is called the optimum temperature (see Figure 3). Enzymes in the human body normally work best at around 37 °C.

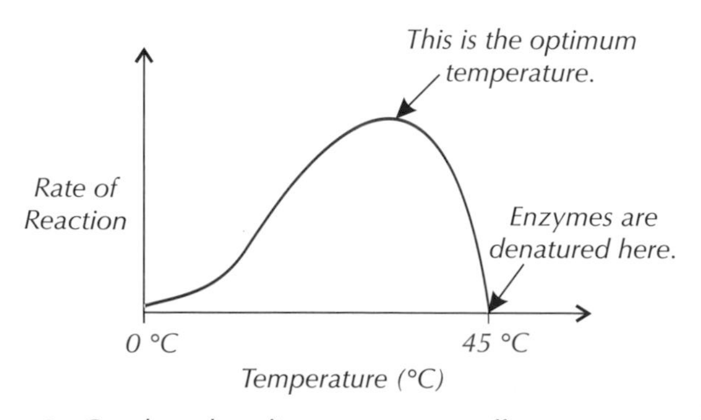

Figure 3: *Graph to show how temperature affects enzyme action.*

pH

The pH also affects enzymes. If it's too high or too low, the pH interferes with the bonds holding the enzyme together. This changes the shape and denatures the enzyme.

All enzymes have a pH that they work best at — this is called the optimum pH (see Figure 4).

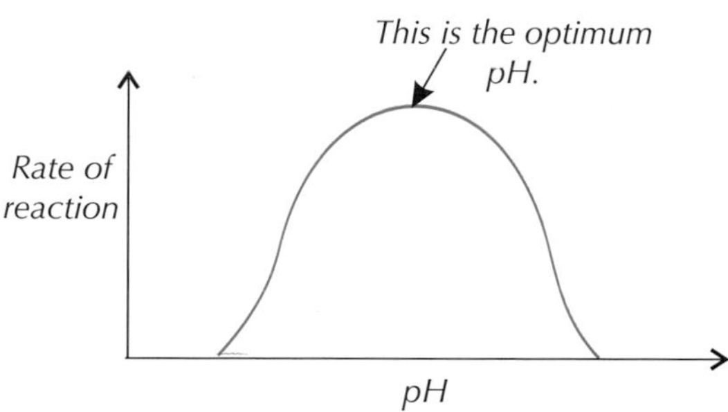

Figure 4: *Graph to show how pH affects enzyme action.*

The optimum pH is different for different enzymes depending on where they work.

Example

Pepsin is an enzyme used to break down proteins in the stomach (see page 58). It works best at pH 2, which means it's well-suited to the acidic conditions in the stomach.

Tip: A low pH means that an environment is acidic. A high pH means that it is alkaline.

Practice Questions — Fact Recall

Q1 a) What gives a protein its unique shape?

b) Why does a protein need to have a unique shape?

Q2 Give three functions of proteins.

Q3 What is a catalyst?

Q4 True or false? All enzymes work best at pH 7.

Practice Question — Application

Q1 Hexokinase is an enzyme found in the human body that's involved in respiration. It catalyses this reaction:

$$\text{glucose} \xrightarrow{\text{hexokinase}} \text{substance A}$$

Enzymes in the human body work best at 37 °C.

A scientist heats up hexokinase to 50 °C and adds it to some glucose. Suggest the effect this will have on the rate of the reaction compared to if the reaction was at 37 °C. Explain your answer.

Tip: Respiration is the process of breaking down glucose, which releases energy. There's loads more about it on page 64.

2. Digestion

Digestion involves loads of reactions where large food molecules are broken down into smaller ones. Lots of enzymes are needed to catalyse all these reactions, so the body creates the ideal conditions for these enzymes to work in.

Learning Objectives:
- Know that digestive enzymes work outside body cells — they're made in glands and the gut lining, then released into the gut to work.
- Know that digestive enzymes help break down large food molecules into smaller ones.
- Understand what amylase does, where it is made and where it works.
- Understand what proteases do, where they are made and where they work.
- Understand what lipases do, where they are made and where they work.
- Understand how the stomach creates the ideal conditions for enzymes to work there.
- Know where bile is produced, stored and released.
- Understand how bile creates the ideal conditions for enzymes to work in the small intestine.

Specification Reference B2.5.2

The digestive system

As you know from page 26, the digestive system is the organ system that breaks down food, so that nutrients can be absorbed into the body from the gut. (There's a reminder of what it looks like in Figure 1.)

Food is broken down in two ways:

- By mechanical digestion — this includes our teeth grinding down food and our stomach churning up food.
- By chemical digestion — where enzymes help to break down food.

You need to know all about how enzymes work in digestion.

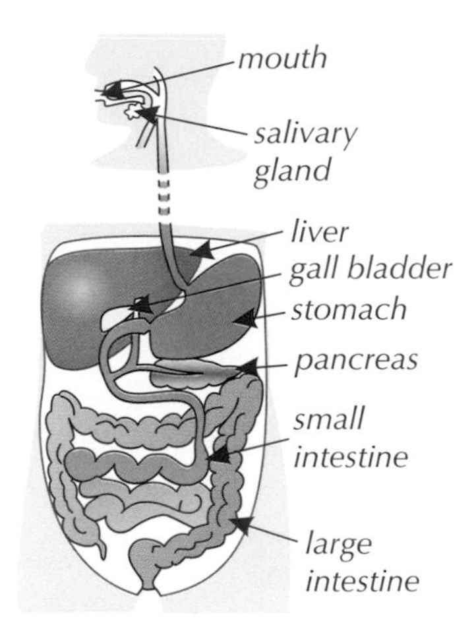

Figure 1: *The digestive system.*

Digestive enzymes

The enzymes involved in digestion work outside body cells. They're produced by specialised cells in glands and in the gut lining, and then released into the gut to mix with food molecules, such as starch, proteins and fats.

Starch, proteins and fats are big molecules. They're too big to pass through the walls of the digestive system. Sugars, amino acids, glycerol and fatty acids are much smaller molecules. They can pass easily through the walls of the digestive system. The digestive enzymes catalyse the breakdown of the big molecules into the smaller ones. Different digestive enzymes help to break down different types of food.

Amylase

Amylase is a digestive enzyme that catalyses the conversion of starch into sugars — see Figure 2.

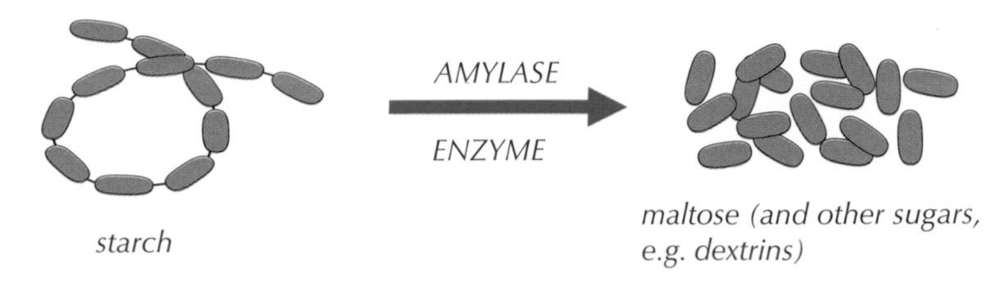

Figure 2: *Diagram to show the breakdown of starch by amylase.*

Amylase is made in the salivary glands, the pancreas and the small intestine. It works in the mouth and the small intestine.

Tip: Most absorption of food molecules happens in the small intestine (see page 26).

Tip: Enzymes produced by the salivary glands are released into the mouth. Enzymes produced by the pancreas are released into the small intestine.

Proteases

Protease enzymes are digestive enzymes that catalyse the conversion of proteins into amino acids — see Figure 3.

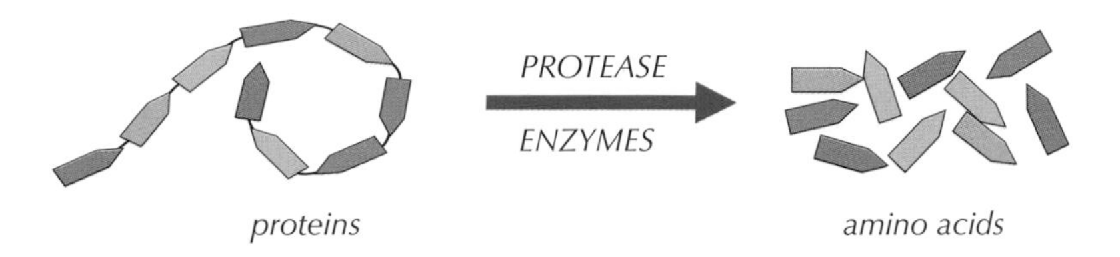

Figure 3: *Diagram to show the breakdown of proteins by proteases.*

Proteases are made in the stomach, the pancreas and the small intestine. They work in the stomach and the small intestine.

Lipases

Lipase enzymes are digestive enzymes that catalyse the conversion of lipids into glycerol and fatty acids — see Figure 4.

Tip: Lipids are fats and oils.

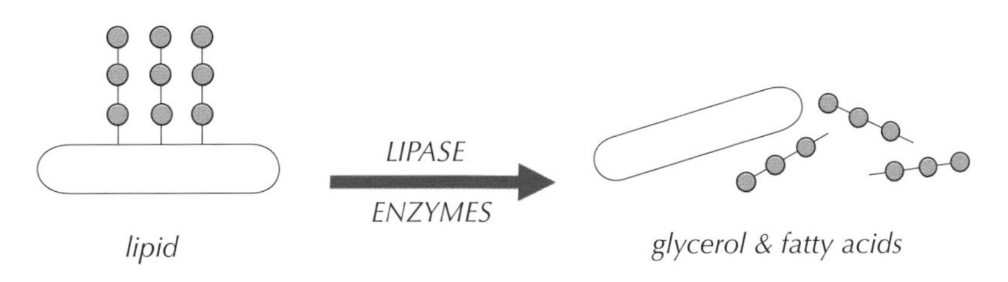

Figure 4: *Diagram to show the breakdown of lipids by lipases.*

Tip: Protease enzymes break down proteins. Lipase enzymes break down lipids.

Lipases are made in the pancreas and the small intestine. They work in the small intestine.

Summary of digestive enzymes

The table in Figure 5 summarises all the information you need to know about the digestive enzymes for your exam. Use Figure 5 to make sure you know exactly where each enzyme is made and where it works.

Enzyme(s) →	Amylase	Proteases	Lipases
Help(s) to break down...	Starch	Proteins	Lipids
...into...	Sugars	Amino acids	Glycerol and fatty acids
Made in the...	Salivary glands, pancreas and small intestine	Stomach, pancreas and small intestine	Pancreas and small intestine
Work(s) in the...	Mouth and small intestine	Stomach and small intestine	Small intestine

Figure 5: *Table summarising the key facts about amylase, proteases and lipases.*

Exam Tip
Make sure you can locate where different enzymes are made and work on a diagram of the digestive system — look back at Figure 1 on the previous page.

The stomach

The stomach is an organ in the digestive system. It pummels food with its muscular walls.

The stomach produces the protease enzyme, pepsin. It also produces **hydrochloric acid**. It produces hydrochloric acid for two reasons:

1. To kill bacteria.
2. To give the right pH for protease enzymes, such as pepsin, to work (pH 2 — acidic).

Bile

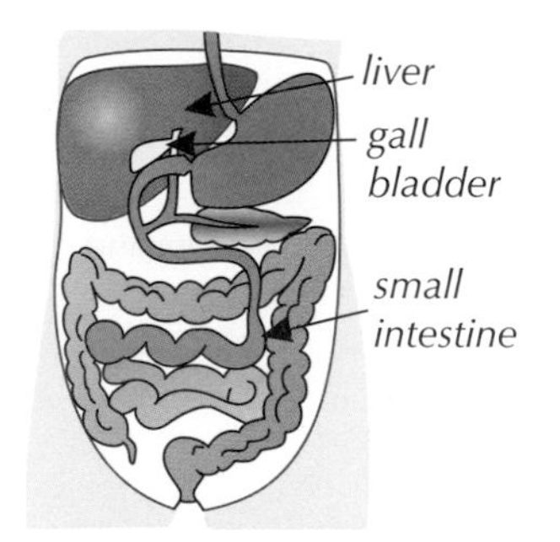

Figure 6: *Bile is produced in the liver, stored in the gall bladder and released into the small intestine.*

Bile is produced in the liver. It's stored in the gall bladder before it's released into the small intestine.

The hydrochloric acid in the stomach makes the pH too acidic for enzymes in the small intestine to work properly. Bile is alkaline — it neutralises the acid and makes conditions alkaline. The enzymes in the small intestine work best in these alkaline conditions.

Bile also emulsifies fats. In other words it breaks the fat into tiny droplets (see Figure 7). This gives a much bigger surface area of fat for the enzyme lipase to work on — which makes its digestion faster.

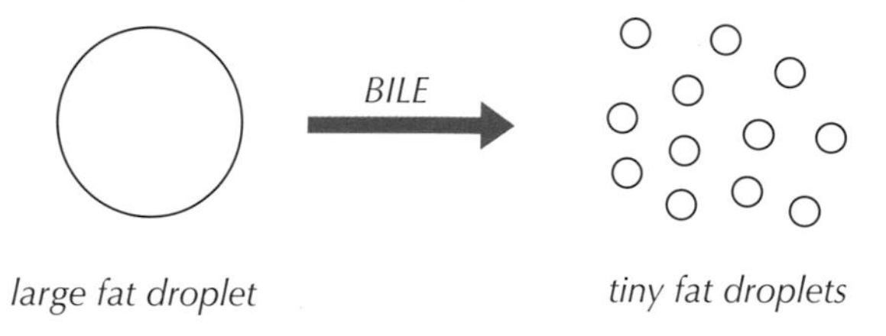

Figure 7: *Diagram to show the emulsification of fat by bile.*

Practice Questions — Fact Recall

Q1 In general, where are digestive enzymes produced?

Q2 True or false? Digestive enzymes build small molecules up into larger molecules.

Q3 Name the digestive enzyme produced in the salivary glands.

Q4 Where are protease enzymes involved in digestion produced?

Q5 Name the type of enzyme that catalyses the breakdown of lipids.

Q6 Describe how each of the following produce ideal conditions for enzymes to work in:

a) the stomach

b) bile

Practice Questions — Application

Q1 Here is a labelled diagram of the digestive system.

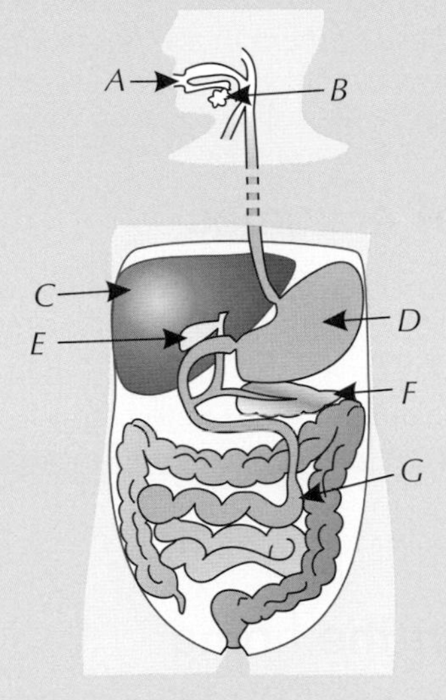

Complete this table using the appropriate letters from the diagram. (If there's more than one answer to the question, make sure you write down all the answers in the table.)

	Amylase	Proteases	Lipases	Bile
Made where?				
Work(s) where?				

Q2 An experiment was done to show how digestion in the stomach works. In the experiment, three equally sized pieces of meat were added to each of three test tubes. Then the test tubes were filled with equal volumes of the following substances:

Test tube 1 — hydrochloric acid (HCl acid)
Test tube 2 — pepsin
Test tube 3 — pepsin and hydrochloric acid (HCl acid)

The results are shown in the photograph:

Describe and explain what the results show.

Tip: Meat is a source of protein.

3. Enzymes in Home and Industry

Enzymes are really handy if you want to speed up chemical reactions. We humans have made good use of them in the home and in industry.

Learning Objectives:
- Know that some microorganisms produce enzymes that catalyse reactions outside of their cells.
- Understand how these enzymes are used in the home in biological detergents.
- Know the advantages and disadvantages of using these enzymes in the home in biological detergents, including that they are more effective at low temperatures than non-biological detergents.
- Understand how these enzymes are used in industry to produce baby foods, sugar syrup and slimming foods.
- Know the advantages and disadvantages of using these enzymes in industry, including that they reduce the need for reactions to be carried out at high temperatures and pressures, but they can be denatured and may be expensive.

Specification Reference B2.5.2

Mass production of enzymes

Some microorganisms produce enzymes which pass out of their cells and catalyse reactions outside them (e.g. to digest the microorganism's food). We can grow these microorganisms on a large scale and then harvest the enzymes they produce. The enzymes can then be used to catalyse useful reactions by adding them to products that we use at home or to industrial processes.

Uses of enzymes in the home

Detergents (e.g. washing powders) can be **biological** or **non-biological**. Non-biological detergents contain chemicals that break up stains on your clothes. Biological detergents contain the same chemicals as non-biological ones, but also contain a mixture of enzymes.

Biological detergents contain mainly protein-digesting enzymes (**proteases**) and fat-digesting enzymes (**lipases**). Because the enzymes break down animal and plant matter, they're ideal for removing stains like food or blood. Biological detergents are also more effective at working at low temperatures (e.g. 30 °C) than other types of detergents. Washing at lower temperatures is cheaper because less energy is used.

However, most biological detergents don't work well at high temperatures because the enzymes are denatured (see page 54). They might not work well in very acidic or alkaline tap water either — this is because the enzymes can be denatured at extremes of pH. Also, not everyone can use biological detergents because some of the enzymes can remain on clothes and can irritate sensitive skin.

Figure 1: *Biological washing powder is made up of granules, which contain enzymes that will break down stains.*

Uses of enzymes in industry

Enzymes are used in industrial processes to make lots of different products, such as:

Baby foods

The proteins in some baby foods are '**pre-digested**' using protein-digesting enzymes (**proteases**). This means the proteins are partially broken down, so they're easier for the baby to digest.

Sugar syrup

Carbohydrate-digesting enzymes (**carbohydrases**) can be used to turn starch syrup into sugar syrup (see Figure 2). Sugar syrup is used in lots of food products, such as sweets, jam and sports drinks.

Figure 2: *The conversion of starch syrup to sugar syrup.*

Slimming foods

Glucose syrup (a type of sugar syrup) can be turned into fructose syrup using an **isomerase** enzyme (see Figure 3). Fructose is sweeter than glucose, so you can use less of it — good for slimming foods and drinks.

Figure 3: *The conversion of glucose syrup to fructose syrup.*

Figure 4: *Microscope image of bacteria that produce the enzyme isomerase. By growing these bacteria we can get lots of isomerase, which we can use to make fructose syrup.*

Evaluating the use of enzymes in industry

Enzymes are really useful in industry. They speed up reactions without the need for high temperatures and pressures. You need to know the advantages and disadvantages of using them, so here are a few to get you started:

Advantages

1. They're specific, so they only catalyse the reaction you want them to.
2. Using lower temperatures and pressures means a lower cost as it saves energy.
3. Enzymes work for a long time, so after the initial cost of buying them, you can continually re-use them.
4. They are biodegradable and therefore cause less environmental pollution.

Tip: Remember that catalysts increase the speed of a reaction, without being changed or used up. Enzymes are biological catalysts — they don't get used up in a reaction, so you can continually re-use them.

Disadvantages

1. Enzymes can be denatured by even a small increase in temperature. They're also susceptible to poisons and changes in pH. This means the conditions in which they work must be tightly controlled.
2. Enzymes can be expensive to produce.
3. Contamination of the enzyme with other substances can affect the reaction.

Tip: Even tiny little changes in pH or temperature will stop enzymes working at maximum efficiency (see pages 54-55). Enzymes only catalyse one reaction too, so you need to use a different one for each reaction.

Practice Questions — Fact Recall

Q1 a) Name the two main types of enzymes that biological washing powders contain.

b) State what type of molecules each of the enzymes you mentioned in a) help to break down.

Q2 Give one disadvantage of using biological washing powders instead of non-biological detergents.

Q3 Some baby foods contain proteins that have been 'pre-digested'. Explain what this means.

Q4 Name the type of enzyme used to convert starch into sugar syrup.

Q5 What reaction does the enzyme isomerase catalyse?

Practice Questions — Application

Q1 Sarah and John are in a supermarket. They're each trying to decide whether to buy biological or non-biological washing powder. Sarah, who is prone to eczema, needs to put some bedsheets on a hot wash. John just has a normal clothes wash to do and is trying to save money.

Suggest which type of washing powder Sarah and John should each buy. Explain your answers.

Tip: Eczema is a skin condition that can make the skin sensitive.

Q2 A soft drink manufacturer makes a popular lemonade product called Lem-Fizz using glucose syrup. The manufacturer wants to start making a 'diet' version of the product called Diet Lem-Fizz.

a) Suggest what type of sugar syrup the manufacturer should use in Diet Lem-Fizz. Explain your answer.

b) Suggest how the sugar syrup in your answer to a) could be made.

Tip: Products with less sugar in them will have fewer calories.

Section Checklist — Make sure you know...

Proteins and Enzymes

- [ ] That proteins are large molecules made up of long chains of amino acids and that these chains of amino acids fold up to give each protein a special shape.
- [ ] That a protein's special shape allows other molecules to fit into it, which allows the protein to do its job.
- [ ] That proteins can be structural components of tissues (such as muscles), hormones, antibodies and catalysts.
- [ ] That all enzymes are proteins.
- [ ] That enzymes are biological catalysts.
- [ ] That catalysts speed up chemical reactions without being changed or used up themselves.

cont...

- [ ] That an enzyme can only catalyse a reaction when a substance fits into its special shape.
- [ ] That high temperatures denature enzymes (cause enzymes to lose their specific shapes).
- [ ] That enzymes have different optimum pHs — the pH they work best at.

Digestion

- [ ] That digestive enzymes work outside body cells — they're produced by specialised cells in glands and in the lining of the gut, then released into the gut where they work.
- [ ] That digestive enzymes catalyse the breakdown of large food molecules (e.g. carbohydrates, proteins and fats) into smaller food molecules (e.g. sugars, fatty acids and glycerol, and amino acids).
- [ ] That amylase helps break down starch into sugars. It is made in the salivary glands, pancreas and small intestine, and works in the mouth and small intestine.
- [ ] That proteases help break down proteins into amino acids. They are made in the stomach, pancreas and small intestine, and work in the stomach and small intestine.
- [ ] That lipases help break down lipids (fats and oils) into fatty acids and glycerol. They are made in the pancreas and small intestine, and work in the small intestine.
- [ ] That the stomach produces hydrochloric acid, creating acidic conditions which are ideal for protease enzymes (e.g. pepsin) to work there.
- [ ] That bile is produced in the liver, stored in the gall bladder and released into the small intestine.
- [ ] That bile neutralises stomach acid, creating alkaline conditions in the small intestine that are ideal for the enzymes that work there.

Enzymes in Home and Industry

- [ ] That some microorganisms produce enzymes that catalyse reactions outside their cells.
- [ ] That biological detergents contain proteases and lipases, which break down proteins and lipids.
- [ ] The advantages of biological detergents (e.g. they work better at low temperatures than non-biological detergents) and their disadvantages (e.g. they denature at high temperatures and extremes of pH, and can cause skin irritation).
- [ ] That proteases are used to pre-digest proteins in baby food.
- [ ] That carbohydrase enzymes can be used to make sugar syrup from starch syrup.
- [ ] That an isomerase enzyme can be use to make fructose syrup from glucose syrup and why it is better to use fructose syrup in slimming foods.
- [ ] That the advantages of using enzymes in industry are that they're specific, they allow reactions to be carried out at lower temperatures and pressures (which reduces costs), they work for a long time and are biodegradable.
- [ ] That the disadvantages of using enzymes in industry are that they can become denatured easily, they can be expensive and contamination can affect the reaction.

1. Aerobic Respiration

We, and other organisms, need energy to do... well... everything really. This energy comes from the reactions of respiration.

Learning Objectives:
- Know that the chemical reactions that occur inside cells (including those involved in respiration) are controlled by enzymes.
- Know that respiration using oxygen is called aerobic respiration.
- Know that aerobic respiration involves reactions that use glucose and oxygen to release energy.
- Know that aerobic respiration is happening all the time in all plants and animals.
- Know that the reactions of aerobic respiration happen mainly in mitochondria.
- Know the word equation for aerobic respiration.
- Know the ways in which energy released from respiration is used by organisms.

Specification Reference B2.6.1

Respiration and enzymes

The chemical reactions that occur inside cells are controlled by enzymes. All of the reactions involved in respiration are catalysed by enzymes. These are really important reactions, as respiration releases the energy that the cell needs to do just about everything.

Respiration is not breathing in and breathing out, as you might think. Respiration is the process of releasing energy from the breakdown of glucose — and it goes on in every cell in your body.

Respiration happens in plants too. All living things respire. It's how they release energy from their food.

Respiration is the process of releasing energy from glucose, which goes on in every cell.

What is aerobic respiration?

Aerobic respiration is respiration using oxygen. It's the most efficient way to release energy from glucose. Aerobic respiration goes on all the time in plants and animals.

Most of the reactions in aerobic respiration happen inside cell structures called **mitochondria** (see page 17).

You need to learn the overall word equation for aerobic respiration:

glucose + oxygen → carbon dioxide + water + ENERGY

Tip: You can also have anaerobic respiration, which happens without oxygen, but that doesn't release nearly as much energy as aerobic respiration — see page 68.

Energy from respiration

Organisms use the energy released from respiration to fuel all sorts of processes. You need to know about the following ways in which an organism may use energy from respiration:

1. Organisms use energy to build up larger molecules from smaller ones (like proteins from amino acids).

2. Animals use energy to allow their muscles to contract (which in turn allows them to move about).

3. Mammals and birds use energy to keep their body temperature steady (unlike other animals, mammals and birds keep their bodies constantly warm).

4. Plants use energy to build sugars, nitrates and other nutrients into amino acids, which are then built up into proteins.

Figure 1: *Animals, including humans, need energy from respiration to contract their muscles and move.*

Practice Questions — Fact Recall

Q1 What catalyses the reactions of respiration in a cell?

Q2 What is aerobic respiration?

Q3 Give three ways in which mammals use energy from respiration.

Q4 Plants use energy from respiration to make amino acids. Name two types of molecule that are needed in order to make amino acids.

Practice Questions — Application

Q1 Here is a photograph of a cell structure under a microscope.

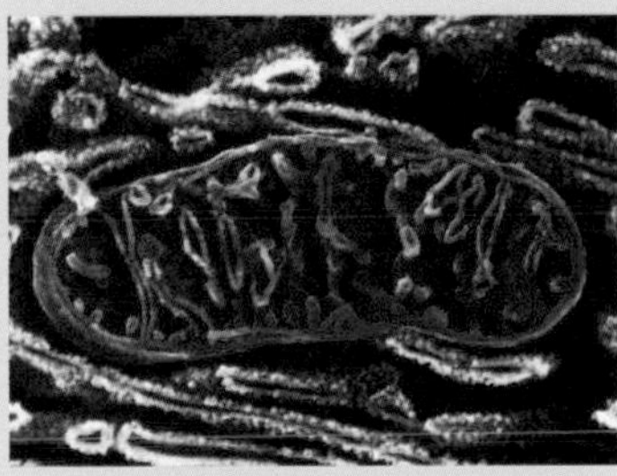

Most of the reactions of respiration take place in this cell structure. Suggest the name of the cell structure in this photograph.

Q2 This diagram shows the equation for aerobic respiration.

Glucose + [A] → carbon dioxide + [B] + [C]

a) What is A in the equation?

b) What is B in the equation?

c) What is C in the equation?

Exam Tip
Make sure you know the word equation for aerobic respiration off by heart, as it can get you easy marks in the exam.

2. Exercise

When we exercise we need to get more glucose and oxygen to our muscles for respiration. The body has some clever ways of doing this...

Learning Objectives:
- Understand how and why heart rate, and breathing rate and depth change when a human exercises.
- Be able to interpret data on exercise.
- Know that, during exercise, glucose can be released from glycogen that's stored in muscles.

Specification Reference B2.6.1

Energy for exercise

When we move we use our muscles. Muscles are made of muscle cells. These use oxygen to release energy from glucose (aerobic respiration — see page 64), which is used to contract the muscles.

When we do exercise we use our muscles more. An increase in muscle activity requires more glucose and oxygen to be supplied to the muscle cells. Extra carbon dioxide also needs to be removed from the muscle cells (because it's toxic at a high concentration). For this to happen the blood has to flow at a faster rate. Therefore physical activity:

- increases your breathing rate and makes you breathe more deeply to meet the demand for extra oxygen.
- increases the speed at which the heart pumps to make your blood flow more quickly, delivering more oxygen and glucose to cells for respiration, and taking more carbon dioxide away.

Fitness

When you're not exercising your heart rate is said to be at its resting level. During exercise your heart rate increases. Then, when you stop exercising, your heart rate returns to its resting level. The time it takes for this to happen is called the recovery period. When you're exercising your heart rate can be monitored and recorded, and the data shown on a graph.

Exam Tip
Your breathing rate can also be monitored and recorded during exercise. In the exam you might be given some data on heart rate or breathing rate during exercise and asked to say what is happening and why. So make sure you learn this page really well.

Example

This graph shows how a person's heart rate changes during exercise.

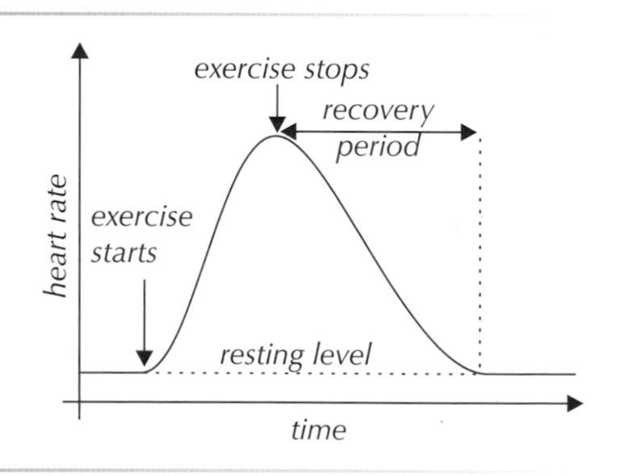

You need to know that the fitter you are:

- the lower your resting heart rate will be,
- the lower your increase in heart rate during exercise will be,
- and the shorter your recovery period will be.

Figure 1: A person having their breathing rate and heart rate recorded during exercise.

Glycogen

Some glucose from food is stored as glycogen. Glycogen's mainly stored in the liver, but each muscle also has its own store.

During vigorous exercise muscles use glucose rapidly, so some of the stored glycogen is converted back to glucose to provide more energy — see Figure 2.

Figure 2: *Diagram to show the conversion of glycogen to glucose in a muscle cell during exercise.*

Practice Questions — Fact Recall

Q1 Describe what happens to your breathing during exercise.

Q2 a) Some glycogen is stored in the liver. Where else is glycogen stored?

b) During vigorous exercise, describe and explain what happens to the glycogen at the place you answered in a).

Practice Questions — Application

Q1 Charlotte is working out on the cross trainer machine at the gym. She starts monitoring her heart rate whilst she is warming up and then as she's running. Her heart rate increases from 80 to 146 bpm. Explain why her heart rate has increased.

Tip: Beats per minute (bpm) is a unit used for measuring heart rate.

Q2 Samir is running in a race. His breathing rate is recorded at rest, at the end of the race and after the race. The results are shown in the table:

Time of record	Breathing rate (breaths per minute)
At rest, before race	16
At the end of the race	44
Eight minutes after the race	16

a) Describe the results shown in the table.

b) Explain the results shown in the table.

3. Anaerobic Respiration

When you're exercising hard, aerobic respiration isn't always enough to keep you going. Don't worry though, your body has another trick up its sleeve...

Learning Objectives:

- Understand why muscles may start to respire anaerobically during vigorous exercise.
- Know that anaerobic respiration is the incomplete breakdown of glucose to form lactic acid.
- H Know why anaerobic respiration releases less energy than aerobic respiration.
- Understand that the creation of lactic acid in muscles can cause muscle fatigue and know how this lactic acid can be removed.
- H Understand how an oxygen debt occurs, what it means and why it must be repaid.

Specification Reference B2.6.2

What is anaerobic respiration?

When you do vigorous exercise and your body can't supply enough oxygen to your muscles, they start doing anaerobic respiration instead of aerobic respiration.

Anaerobic respiration is the incomplete breakdown of glucose, which produces **lactic acid**. It takes place in the absence of oxygen. Here is the word equation for the process:

glucose → energy + lactic acid

Comparison to aerobic respiration Higher

Unfortunately anaerobic respiration does not release nearly as much energy as aerobic respiration because glucose is not completely broken down. However, it's useful in emergencies — it means that you can keep on using your muscles for a while longer.

Tip: "Anaerobic" just means "without oxygen".

Lactic acid

Anaerobic respiration causes lactic acid to build up in the muscles, which gets painful. It also causes **muscle fatigue** — the muscles get tired and they stop contracting efficiently. After you've finished exercising the blood flowing through your muscles will remove the lactic acid.

Figure 1: *Immediately after a race an athlete will still be breathing hard and have a high heart rate in order to replace their oxygen debt.*

Oxygen debt Higher

After resorting to anaerobic respiration, when you stop exercising you'll have an "oxygen debt". In other words you have to "repay" the oxygen that you didn't get to your muscles in time, because your lungs, heart and blood couldn't keep up with the demand earlier on.

This means you have to keep breathing hard for a while after you stop, to get more oxygen into your blood. Blood flows through your muscles to remove the lactic acid by oxidising it to carbon dioxide (CO_2) and water.

While high levels of CO_2 and lactic acid are detected in the blood (by the brain), the pulse and breathing rate stay high to try and rectify the situation.

Practice Questions — Fact Recall

Q1 Explain when the body uses anaerobic respiration.

Q2 Describe what anaerobic respiration is.

Q3 a) What is muscle fatigue?

b) What can muscle fatigue be caused by?

Q4 What is an oxygen debt?

Section Checklist — Make sure you know...

Aerobic respiration

- ❑ That enzymes catalyse the reactions that occur inside cells (including respiration reactions).
- ❑ That aerobic respiration is respiration using oxygen and that it involves reactions that use glucose and oxygen to release energy.
- ❑ That aerobic respiration is happening all the time in animals and plants, and that most of the respiration reactions happen in the mitochondria.
- ❑ The word equation for aerobic respiration: glucose + oxygen → carbon dioxide + water + ENERGY.
- ❑ That the energy released from respiration is used by organisms to make larger molecules from smaller ones, for muscle contraction (animals), to maintain a constant body temperature (mammals and birds), and to make amino acids from sugars, nitrates and other molecules, which can then be made into proteins (plants).

Exercise

- ❑ That, during exercise, a person's breathing rate and depth will increase to get oxygen into the body.
- ❑ That, during exercise, a person's heart rate increases, so that blood flow to their muscles increases in order to supply them with more oxygen and glucose, and take away carbon dioxide (CO_2).
- ❑ How to interpret data on exercise.
- ❑ That glycogen is stored in muscles and that, during exercise, it can be converted back to glucose for energy.

Anaerobic respiration

- ❑ That muscles will start to respire anaerobically if they can't get enough oxygen to respire aerobically.
- ❑ That anaerobic respiration is the incomplete breakdown of glucose, which forms lactic acid. It takes place in the absence of oxygen.
- ❑ H That anaerobic respiration releases less energy than aerobic respiration because glucose is not fully broken down. It takes place in the absence of oxygen.
- ❑ That the build up of lactic acid can cause muscle fatigue (muscles become tired and don't contract efficiently), but it will eventually be removed from the muscles by blood flow.
- ❑ H That an oxygen debt occurs after anaerobic respiration — you have to 'repay' the oxygen you didn't manage to get to your muscles in time, in order to oxidise the lactic acid to CO_2 and water.

Exam-style Questions

1 Enzymes are needed for many processes in the body.

1 (a) (i) What type of biological molecule is an enzyme? Circle the correct answer.

a lipid a hormone a protein an amino acid

(1 mark)

1 (a) (ii) What is the function of an enzyme?

(1 mark)

1 (b) *In this question you will be assessed on the quality of your English, the organisation of your ideas and your use of appropriate specialist vocabulary.*

One of the processes in the body that requires enzymes is digestion.
Describe the action, production and release of different types of enzymes in digestion.

(6 marks)

2 A food manufacturer is choosing an isomerase enzyme to catalyse the reaction of glucose syrup into fructose syrup at his factory.

The graph below shows the activity of two isomerase enzymes (A and B) at different temperatures.

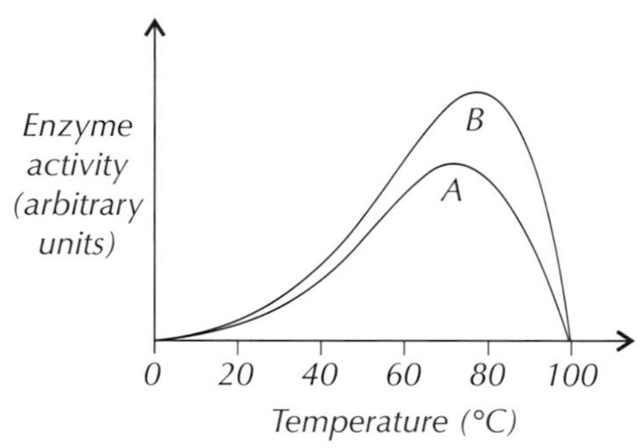

2 (a) (i) Which isomerase enzyme should the manufacturer use? Explain your answer.

(1 mark)

2 (a) (ii) The manufacturer is also deciding on the right conditions for the reaction.
Explain why the reaction should not be carried out at temperatures above 80 °C.

(2 marks)

2 (b) The manufacturer makes slimming foods.
Explain why he uses fructose syrup instead of glucose syrup in his products.

(2 marks)

2 (c) Other types of enzymes are also used in the food industry, such as proteases that are used to make baby food. Give **three** advantages of using enzymes in industry.

(3 marks)

3 A student wants to find out how his heart rate changes during exercise. The exercise he chooses is to run on a running machine for five minutes. He records his heart rate before the run, immediately after he stops running and one minute after he has stopped. He repeats the exercise three times. His results are shown in this table:

Time of record	Heart rate (beats per minute)		
	1st go	2nd go	3rd go
At rest, before run	72	71	72
At the end of the run	151	163	154
One minute after the run	131	142	129

3 (a) (i) Calculate the student's mean heart rate at the end of his runs.

(2 marks)

3 (a) (ii) At one minute after each run, the student's heart rate still hadn't reached its resting level. Explain why the student's heart rate remained high one minute after each run.

(5 marks)

3 (b) Respiration gives the student energy to contract his muscles and run. Give **two** other ways the student's body will use energy from respiration.

(2 marks)

4 A scientist is investigating the reactions of aerobic and anaerobic respiration.

4 (a) (i) What is the word equation for aerobic respiration?

(2 marks)

4 (a) (ii) When do animals respire?

(1 mark)

4 (b) In a cell, energy is present in the form of a molecule called ATP. The scientist conducts an experiment to find out how much ATP each type of respiration releases per glucose molecule. His results are shown in this table:

Type of respiration	Number of ATP molecules released per glucose molecule
Aerobic	32
Anaerobic	2

Describe and explain the difference in release of energy between aerobic and anaerobic respiration shown in the table.

(2 marks)

Learning Objectives:
- Know that genetic information is found in chromosomes.
- Know that long molecules of DNA (deoxyribonucleic acid) form chromosomes and that DNA has a double helix structure.
- Know that genes are small sections of DNA.
- H Understand that genes tell cells which combination of amino acids to put together, which in turn determines the protein they produce.
- Know that everybody's DNA is unique (with the exception of identical twins).
- Understand that DNA fingerprinting is a technique used to identify a person based on their DNA.

Specification Reference
B2.7.1, B2.7.2

1. DNA

DNA is a pretty important molecule because it's what makes us unique. This means that DNA tests can be used to identify people. Therefore it's really important that you learn all about it...

Chromosomes, DNA and genes

DNA stands for **deoxyribonucleic acid**. It contains all the instructions to put an organism together and make it work. It's found in the **nucleus** of animal and plant cells, in really long molecules called **chromosomes** (see Figure 1).

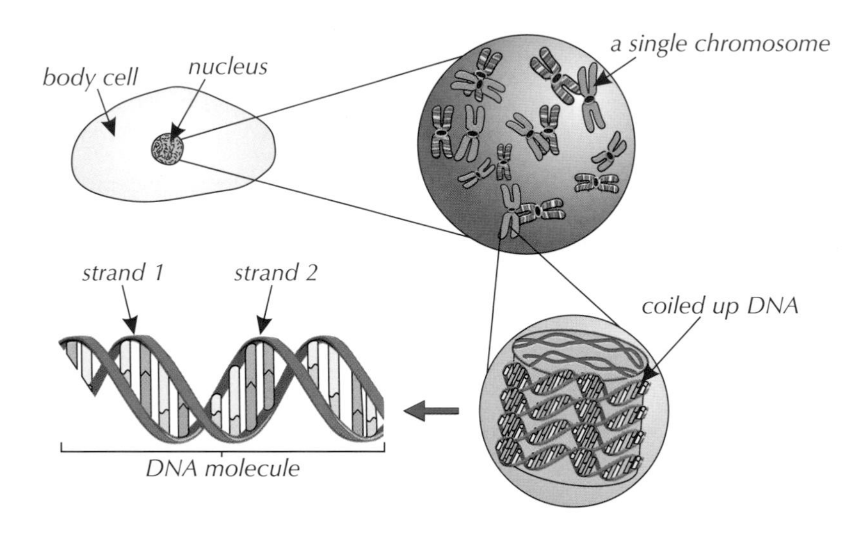

***Figure 1:** Diagram showing the structure of DNA and where it is found in a cell.*

As you can see from Figure 1, DNA has a **double helix** structure. This means that it's made up of two separate strands that are coiled around each other to form a spiral.

A **gene** is a section of DNA. Genes are found on chromosomes.

Tip: You might remember learning about genes and chromosomes in Biology 1 — however, there's a bit more you need to know now.

Genes and proteins Higher

A gene contains the instructions needed to make a specific **protein**.
Cells make proteins by stringing amino acids together in a particular order.
Different proteins have a different number and order of amino acids.
Only 20 amino acids are used, but they make up thousands of different proteins. Genes simply tells cells in what order to put the amino acids together (see Figure 2, on the next page).

Tip: H Amino acids are the building blocks that make up proteins.

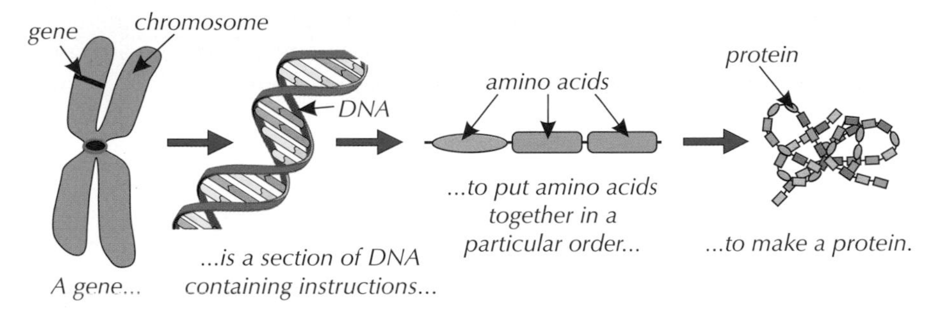

Figure 2: H *Diagram showing how a gene codes for a protein.*

DNA also determines what proteins the cell produces, e.g. haemoglobin, keratin. That in turn determines what type of cell it is, e.g. red blood cell, skin cell.

Tip: H Another way of saying a gene contains the instructions for a protein is to say a gene 'codes for' a protein.

DNA fingerprinting

Almost everyone's DNA is unique. The only exceptions are **identical twins**, where the two people have identical DNA, and clones.

Tip: A clone is an exact (genetically identical) copy of an organism.

DNA fingerprinting (or genetic fingerprinting) is a way of cutting up a person's DNA into small sections and then separating them. This produces a DNA fingerprint — a pattern of bands on a gel (see Figure 3). Every person's genetic fingerprint has a unique pattern (unless they're identical twins or clones of course). This means you can tell people apart by comparing DNA samples.

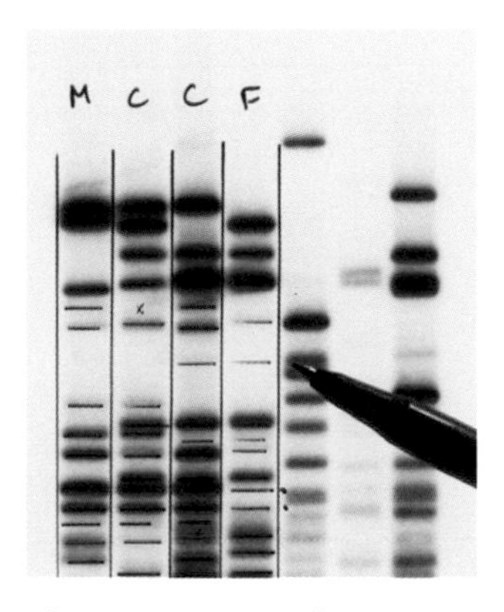

Figure 3: *A DNA fingerprint.*

Uses of DNA fingerprinting

DNA fingerprinting has some useful applications:

1. **Paternity testing** — to see if a man is the father of a particular child. The DNA fingerprint of the child is compared to the DNA fingerprint of the possible father. If lots of bands on the DNA fingerprints match, then that man is most probably the child's father.

Example

This DNA fingerprint shows that Male 2 is most likely to be the father of this child, as more of his bands match the child's than male 1.

Two bands from Male 1's DNA fingerprint match the child's (bands 17 and 20), whereas six bands from Male 2's DNA fingerprint match the child's (bands 21, 22, 23, 24, 27 and 29).

Child	Male 1	Male 2
1, 2, 3, 4, 5, 6, 7, 8, 9, 10	11, 12, 13, 14, 15, 16, 17, 18, 19, 20	21, 22, 23, 24, 25, 26, 27, 28, 29, 30

Tip: Half of the child's DNA fingerprint will match the mother's DNA fingerprint and half will match the father's, as we inherit half our DNA from our mum and half from our dad (see p.77).

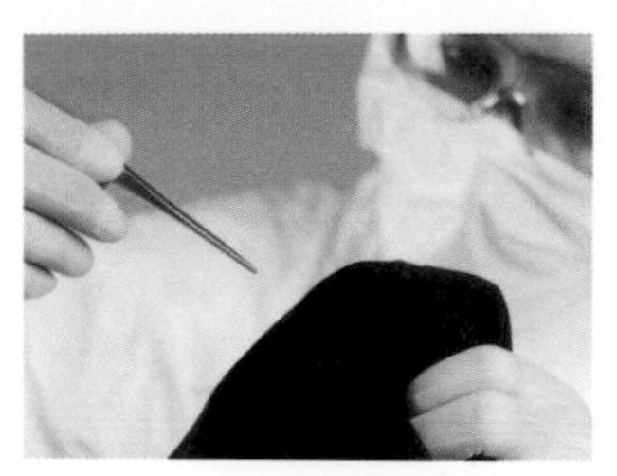

Figure 4: A forensic scientist collecting hair for DNA testing from clothing found at a crime scene.

Tip: If a suspect's DNA matches DNA found at a crime scene it doesn't necessarily mean that they committed the crime. It just provides evidence that they were probably at the crime scene.

2. **Forensic science** — DNA (from hair, skin flakes, blood, semen, etc.) taken from a crime scene is compared with a DNA sample taken from a suspect. If the suspect's DNA fingerprint matches the DNA found at a crime scene then the suspect was probably at the crime scene.

Ethical issues involved in DNA fingerprinting

Some people would like there to be a national genetic database of everyone in the country. That way, DNA from a crime scene could be checked against everyone in the country to see whose it was. But others think this is a big invasion of privacy, and they worry about how safe the data would be and what else it might be used for.

There are also scientific problems — false positives can occur if errors are made in the procedure or if the data is misinterpreted.

Practice Questions — Fact Recall

Q1 What does DNA stand for?

Q2 What are chromosomes made up of?

Q3 Describe the structure of a DNA molecule.

Q4 How does a gene help a cell to make a specific protein?

Q5 Why can DNA fingerprinting be used to identify a person?

Practice Questions — Application

At a murder scene, a forensic science unit find some blood that isn't the victim's blood. They extract DNA from the blood and compare it to DNA samples from four suspects (A-D), on a DNA fingerprint:

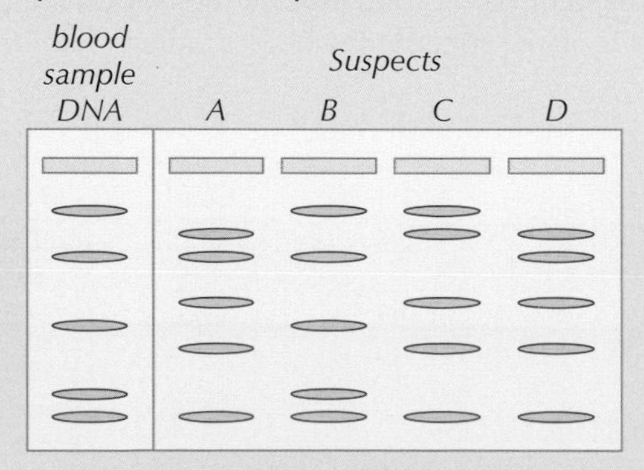

Exam Tip
If you need to compare two or more DNA fingerprints in the exam, use a ruler to see which bands line up exactly.

Q1 a) Looking at the DNA fingerprint, which suspect do you think is most likely to have committed the murder? Explain your answer.

b) Can you say for sure that it was them? Explain your answer.

Q2 Two of the suspects are identical twins.
Which two suspects are identical twins? Explain your answer.

2. Cell Division — Mitosis

Our body cells are able to make copies of themselves so that we can grow or repair any damaged tissue. It's pretty clever stuff...

Learning Objectives:

- Know that body cells contain two sets of chromosomes and that these chromosomes are found in pairs.
- Know that body cells divide by mitosis.
- Know that mitosis allows organisms to grow or to replace damaged cells.
- Know that organisms that reproduce asexually use mitosis to produce genetically identical offspring.
- Know that during mitosis, body cells copy their genetic material, and then undergo a single division to form two genetically identical cells.

Specification Reference B2.7.1

Body cells and chromosomes

Body cells normally have two copies of each chromosome — one from the organism's 'mother', and one from its 'father'. So, humans have two copies of chromosome 1, two copies of chromosome 2, etc.

Figure 1 shows the 23 pairs of chromosomes from a human cell. (The 23rd pair are a bit different — see page 83.)

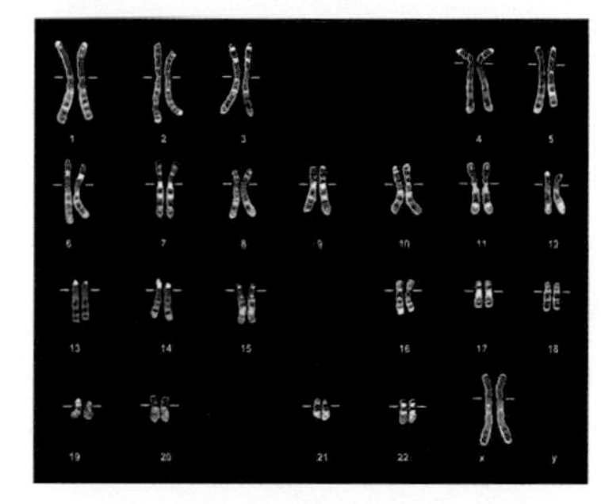

Figure 1: *The 23 pairs of chromosomes from a female human body cell.*

When a body cell divides to make a copy of itself, it needs to make new cells identical to the original cell — with the same number of chromosomes. This type of cell division is called **mitosis**:

> Mitosis is when a cell reproduces itself by splitting to form two identical offspring.

Uses of mitosis

Mitosis is used:

1. When plants and animals want to **grow**.
2. When plants and animals need to **replace cells** that have been damaged.
3. In **asexual reproduction** (see below).

Asexual reproduction

Some organisms reproduce by mitosis in a process called asexual reproduction.

Example

Figure 2: *Strawberry plant with runners (red stems).*

Strawberry plants form runners by mitosis (see Figure 2). These runners take root and become new plants. These new plants (the offspring) have exactly the same **alleles** as the parent — so there's no variation.

Tip: Alleles are different versions of the same gene. New plants formed from asexual reproduction are genetically identical, so they will have the same versions of genes, i.e. the same alleles.

What happens during mitosis?

Here are the steps involved in mitosis:

1. In a cell that's not dividing, the DNA is all spread out in long strings.
2. If the cell gets a signal to divide, it needs to duplicate its DNA — so there's one copy for each new cell. The DNA is copied and forms X-shaped chromosomes. Each 'arm' of the chromosome is an exact duplicate of the other.
3. The chromosomes then line up at the centre of the cell and cell fibres pull them apart. The two arms of each chromosome go to opposite ends of the cell.
4. Membranes form around each of the sets of chromosomes. These become the nuclei of the two new cells.
5. Lastly, the cytoplasm divides. You now have two new cells containing exactly the same DNA — they're identical.

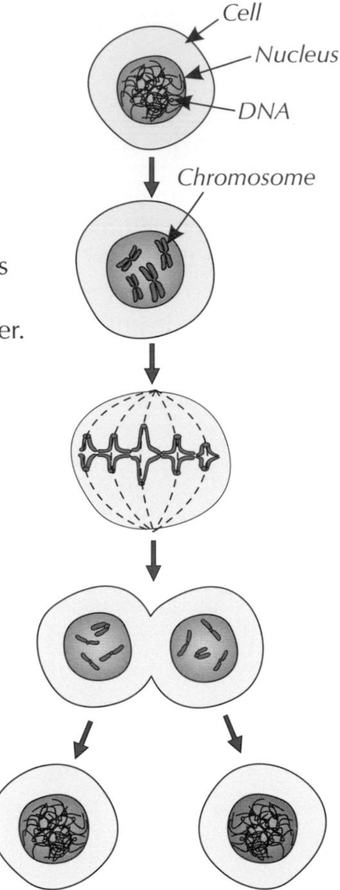

Figure 3: *Diagram showing the stages in mitosis.*

Tip: When a cell has copied its DNA, the left arm of an X-shaped chromosome has the same DNA as the right arm.

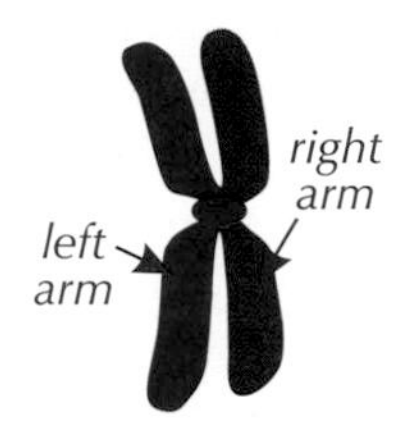

Tip: The key things to remember about mitosis are that when a body cell divides it copies its DNA first and then splits into two, to form two genetically identical daughter cells.

Practice Questions — Fact Recall

Q1 How many copies of each chromosome does a body cell have?

Q2 Give three uses of mitosis.

Q3 How many times does a body cell divide during mitosis?

Practice Questions — Application

This photograph shows the last stage in mitosis — two new daughter cells are forming.

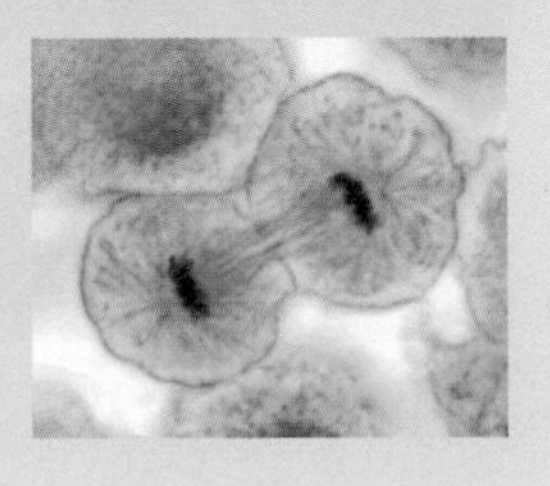

Q1 Will these new cells be genetically identical or genetically different to the parent cell?

Q2 How many sets of chromosomes will these cells have?

3. Cell Division — Meiosis

Another type of cell division. This one is different to mitosis though — it only happens in the cells of the reproductive organs and it produces sex cells.

Learning Objectives:
- Know that there is one set of chromosomes in gametes (sex cells).
- Know that at fertilisation, two gametes join, forming a body cell which contains two sets of chromosomes.
- Understand how sexual reproduction results in variation.
- Know that gametes are formed by meiosis.
- Know that meiosis occurs in cells in the reproductive organs (the ovaries and testes in humans).
- Know that, when two gametes have joined at fertilisation, the fertilised egg grows by mitosis.
- H Know that during meiosis, a cell copies its genetic material and then divides twice to form four gametes. These gametes each contain one set of chromosomes.

Specification Reference B2.7.1, B2.7.2

Sexual reproduction and gametes

During sexual reproduction, two cells called gametes (sex cells) combine to form a new individual.

Gametes only have one copy of each chromosome. This is so that you can combine one sex cell from the 'mother' and one sex cell from the 'father' and still end up with the right number of chromosomes in body cells.

Example

Human body cells have 46 chromosomes. The gametes (sperm and egg cells) have 23 chromosomes each. This means that when an egg and sperm combine at **fertilisation** you get a single body cell with 46 chromosomes again (see Figure 1).

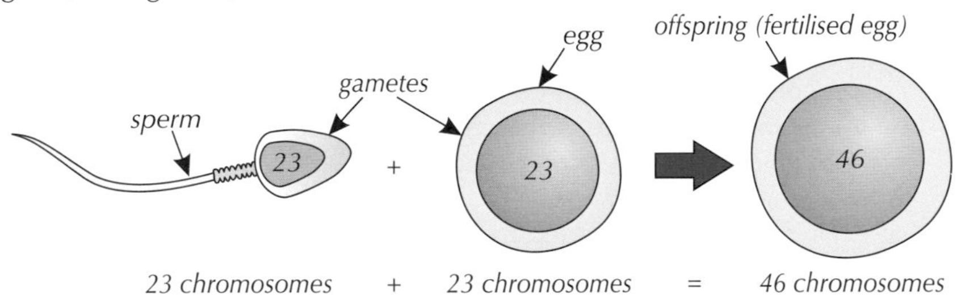

***Figure 1:** Diagram showing the change in number of chromosomes at fertilisation.*

The new individual will have a mixture of two sets of chromosomes — half from the mother and half from the father. This means he or she will have a mixture of two sets of genes (or two sets of alleles, see page 90).

The new individual will therefore inherit features from both parents, which is how sexual reproduction produces **variation**.

Meiosis

To make new cells which only have half the original number of chromosomes, cells divide by meiosis.

> Meiosis produces cells which have half the normal number of chromosomes.

Tip: To remind you that meiosis produces gametes, remember that they both have the word 'me' in them — meiosis and gametes.

In humans, it only happens in the **reproductive organs** (e.g. ovaries in females and testes in males) so these are where gametes are produced.

After two gametes join at fertilisation, the cell grows by repeatedly dividing by mitosis.

What happens during meiosis? Higher

Here are the steps involved in meiosis:

Figure 2: *Microscope image showing pairs of chromosomes being pulled apart during the first division in meiosis.*

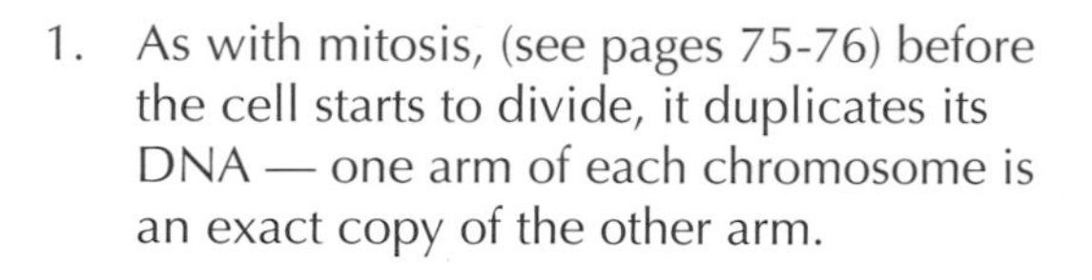

1. As with mitosis, (see pages 75-76) before the cell starts to divide, it duplicates its DNA — one arm of each chromosome is an exact copy of the other arm.

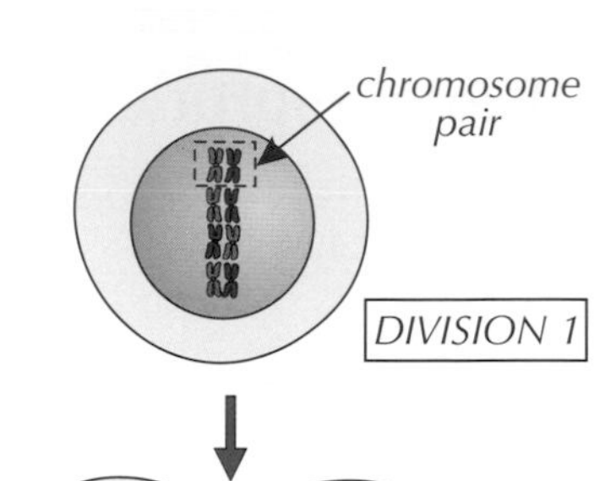

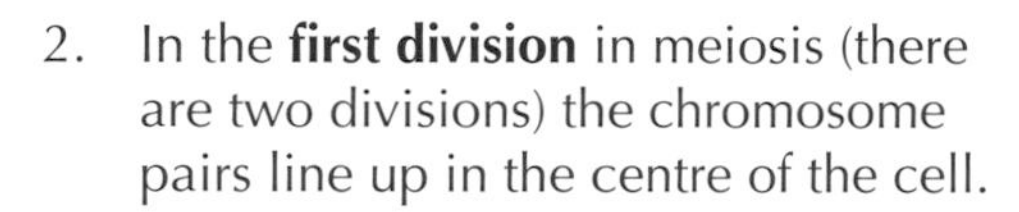

2. In the **first division** in meiosis (there are two divisions) the chromosome pairs line up in the centre of the cell.

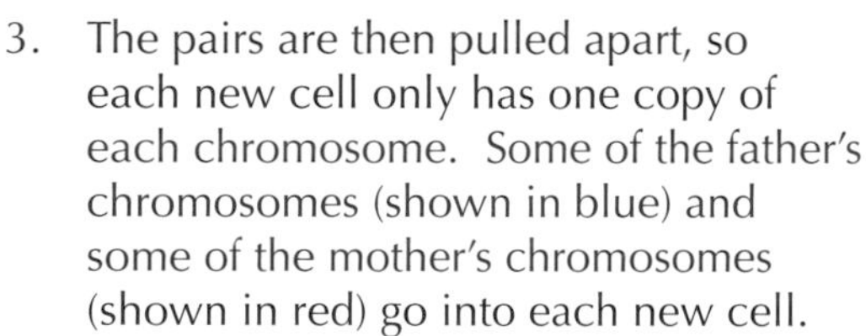

3. The pairs are then pulled apart, so each new cell only has one copy of each chromosome. Some of the father's chromosomes (shown in blue) and some of the mother's chromosomes (shown in red) go into each new cell.

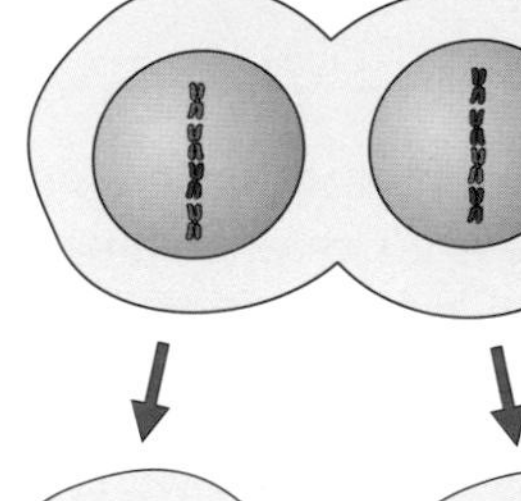

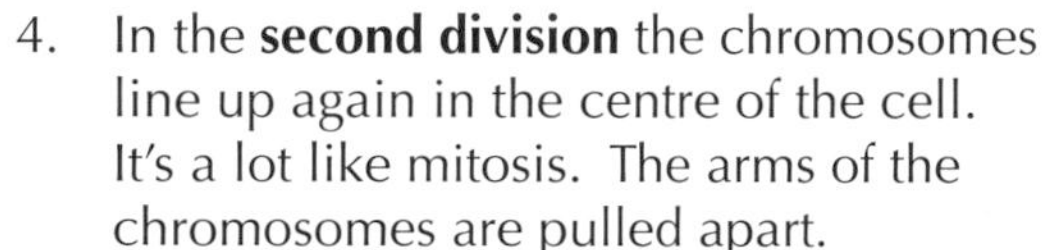

4. In the **second division** the chromosomes line up again in the centre of the cell. It's a lot like mitosis. The arms of the chromosomes are pulled apart.

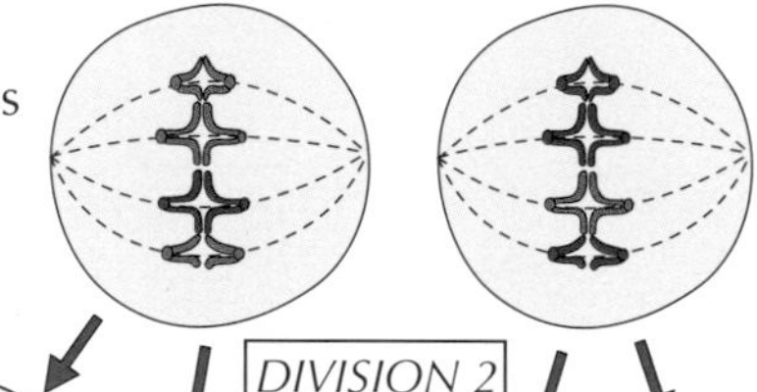

5. You get four gametes each with only a single set of chromosomes in it.

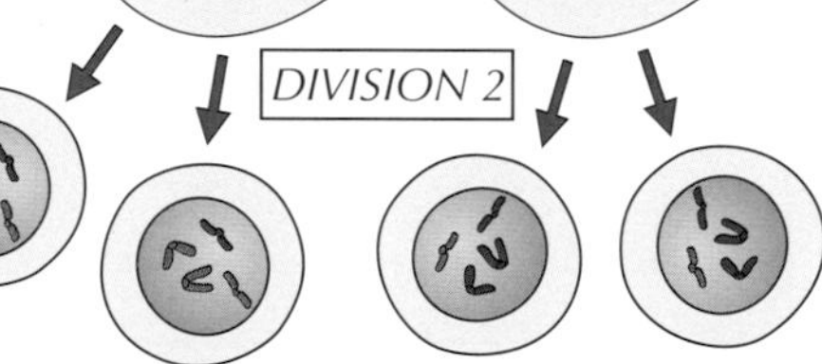

Figure 3: *Diagram showing the stages in meiosis.*

Tip: H Meiosis explains why you may be similar to, but not the same as, your siblings — you'll have different mixtures of your mother's and father's chromosomes. (Identical twins are an exception to this though, as they result from the splitting of a fertilised egg, so they always have the same combination of chromosomes.)

Comparing mitosis and meiosis Higher

Make sure you learn the key differences between mitosis and meiosis, as summarised in this table:

Question	Mitosis	Meiosis
Where does it occur?	in body cells	in cells in the reproductive organs only
What type of cells are produced?	body cells	gametes
How many cell divisions take place?	one	two
How many new cells are produced?	two	four
How many sets of chromosomes do the new cells have?	two	one

Exam Tip H
Questions asking about the differences between mitosis and meiosis often come up in the exam. Learning them now will make your life much easier.

Practice Questions — Fact Recall

Q1 How many sets of chromosomes do gametes contain?

Q2 Where are gametes produced?

Q3 Following fertilisation, how does the resulting cell grow?

Q4 How many cell divisions occur in meiosis?

Q5 How many new cells are produced when a cell divides by meiosis?

Q6 True or False? Gametes are all genetically identical.

Practice Questions — Application

Q1 As well as humans, there are other animals that reproduce by sexual reproduction. These animals have different numbers of chromosomes in their body cells and in their gametes, as shown in the table:

Type of animal cell	Number of chromosomes
Dog body cell	78
Cat egg cell	19
Horse sperm cell	32

Using your knowledge and the information provided in the table, suggest:

a) how many chromosomes there are in a dog sperm cell.

b) how many chromosomes there are in the body cell of a cat.

c) how many chromosomes there are in a horse egg cell.

Q2 Mary is learning about meiosis. She thinks that the gametes produced when a cell divides by meiosis will have half a set of chromosomes in them.

a) i) Why does this not happen when a cell divides by meiosis?

ii) Two gametes combine during fertilisation. If Mary was right, what would be wrong with the fertilised egg?

b) Mary keeps getting mitosis and meiosis confused. Give three differences between these two types of cell division.

Exam Tip
The words 'mitosis' and 'meiosis' look and sound very similar. Make sure that you know how to spell each one. You won't gain marks in the exam if the examiner can't tell which type of cell division you are talking about.

4. Stem Cells

All the cells in an organism originate from stem cells. Scientists are attempting to use these cells to do some pretty amazing things...

Learning Objectives:

- Know that most animal cells lose the ability to differentiate at an early stage but lots of plant cells never lose the ability to differentiate.
- Know that mature animals mainly use cell division to replace and repair cells.
- Know that human embryonic stem cells can differentiate into any type of human cell.
- Know that stem cells from adult bone marrow can be made to differentiate into different cell types.
- Know that it's possible to make stem cells from embryos differentiate into many different types of cell, e.g. nerve cells.
- Know that stem cells could be used to treat some medical conditions, e.g. paralysis.
- Be able to give informed opinions on the issues around using embryonic stem cells in medical research.

Specification Reference B2.7.1

Cell Differentiation

Differentiation is the process by which a cell becomes specialised for its job (see page 25). In most animal cells, the ability to differentiate is lost at an early stage, but lots of plant cells don't ever lose this ability. In animal embryos, cells divide to produce new cell types, but in mature animals, cells divide mainly to replace damaged cells.

What are stem cells?

Some cells are undifferentiated. They can develop into different types of cell depending on what instructions they're given. These cells are called stem cells (see Figure 1).

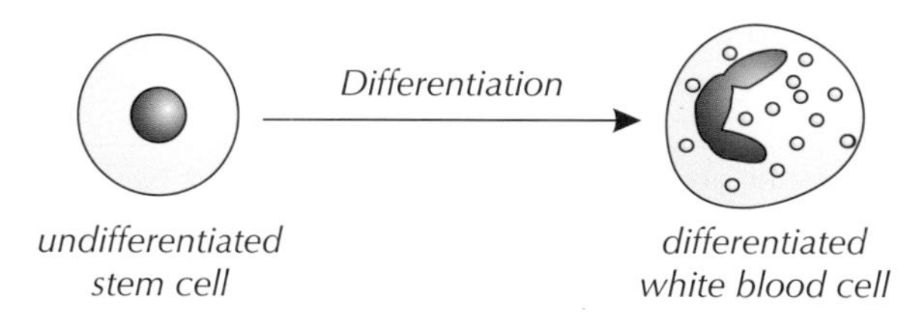

Figure 1: *Diagram showing stem cell differentiation.*

Stem cells are found in early human embryos. They're exciting to doctors and medical researchers because they have the potential to turn into any kind of cell at all. This makes sense if you think about it — all the different types of cell found in a human being have to come from those few cells in the early embryo.

Adults also have stem cells, but they're only found in certain places, like bone marrow. These aren't as versatile as embryonic stem cells — they can't turn into any cell type at all, only certain ones.

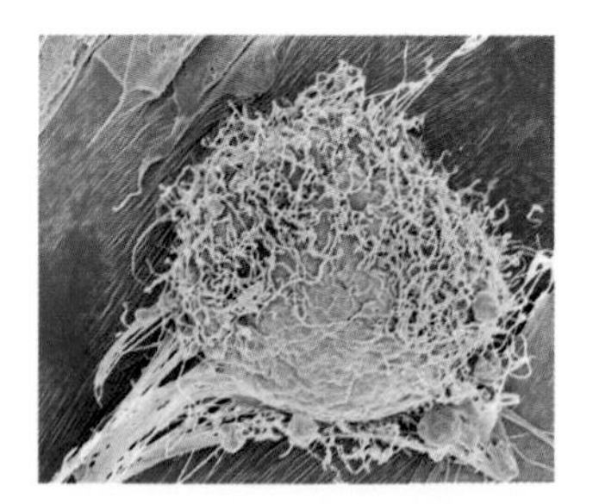

Figure 2: *Microscope image of a stem cell found in adult bone marrow.*

Adult stem cells in medicine

Medicine already uses adult stem cells to cure disease.

Example

People with some blood diseases (e.g. sickle cell anaemia — a disease which affects the shape of the red blood cells) can be treated by bone marrow transplants. Bone marrow is the tissue found inside bone. It contains stem cells that can turn into new blood cells to replace the faulty old ones.

Embryonic stem cells in medicine

Scientists can also extract stem cells from very early human embryos and grow them. These embryonic stem cells could be used to replace faulty cells in sick people in the future (see Figure 3).

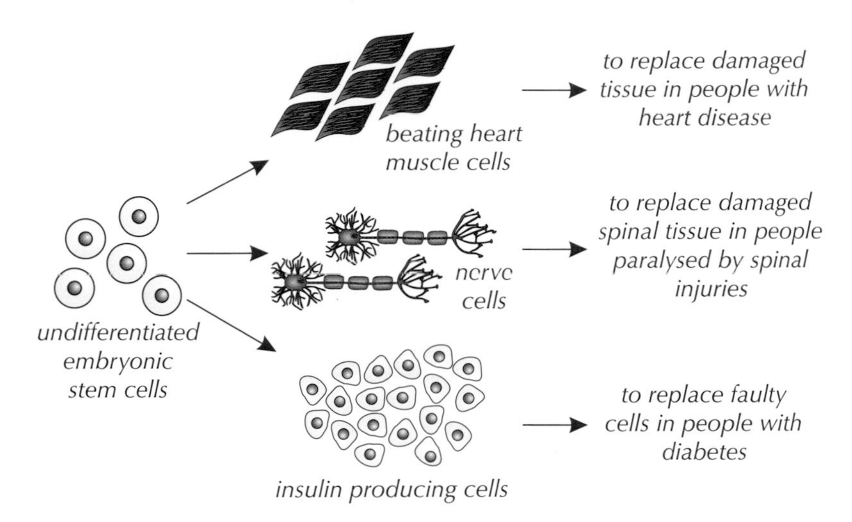

Figure 3: *Diagram showing some potential uses of embryonic stem cells in medicine.*

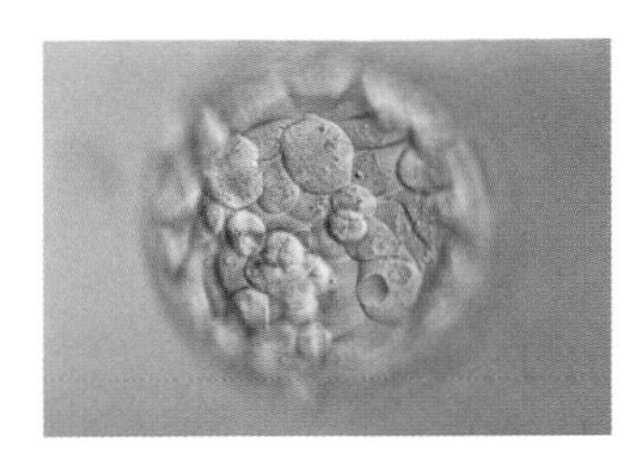

Figure 4: *Microscope image of a four-day old human embryo. Stem cells can be taken from the embryo at this stage.*

To get cultures of one specific type of cell, researchers try to control the differentiation of the stem cells by changing the environment they're growing in. So far, it's still a bit hit and miss — lots more research is needed.

Issues involved in stem cell research

Embryonic stem cell research has exciting possibilities, but it's also pretty controversial.

Some people are against it, because they feel that human embryos shouldn't be used for experiments since each one is a potential human life.

However, others think that curing patients who already exist and who are suffering is more important than the rights of embryos. One fairly convincing argument in favour of this point of view is that the embryos used in the research are usually unwanted ones from fertility clinics which, if they weren't used for research, would probably just be destroyed. But of course, campaigners for the rights of embryos usually want this banned too.

Campaigners for the rights of embryos feel that scientists should concentrate more on finding and developing other sources of stem cells, so people could be helped without having to use embryos. Some research has been done into getting stem cells from alternative sources. For example, some researchers think it might be possible to get cells from umbilical cords to behave like embryonic stem cells.

In some countries stem cell research is banned, but it's allowed in the UK as long as it follows strict guidelines.

Tip: Obtaining stem cells from an embryo destroys the embryo.

Exam Tip
Questions on the issues associated with the use of embryonic stem cells might crop up in the exam, so make sure you know arguments for and against the use of embryonic stem cells.

Practice Questions — Fact Recall

Q1 Describe the differences in the ability of plant and animal cells to differentiate.

Q2 What is a stem cell?

Q3 What type of cell can early embryonic stem cells turn in to?

Q4 Give one place where stem cells can be found in an adult human.

Practice Questions — Application

Q1 Alzheimer's disease is a condition which damages the neurones (nerve cells) in the brain. These neurones die, but are not replaced, leading to a decrease in the amount of neurones in the brain. Symptoms of Alzheimer's disease include memory loss, confusion and changes in personality.

a) Suggest a way in which embryonic stem cells could potentially be used to treat people with Alzheimer's disease.

b) Give another possible use of embryonic stem cells in medicine.

Q2 Embryonic stem cells used for medical research are mostly taken from embryos left over from fertility clinics, which would otherwise be destroyed. Suggest a reason why some people are happier with using these embryos for stem cell research, rather than creating embryos purely with the purpose of being used for research.

Exam Tip
It's important that you can look at something from the point of view of someone with different opinions to you.

Q3 Embryos begin to develop a nervous system 14 days after fertilisation. Some people think that it's morally acceptable to use an embryo for stem cell research before this point, as the embryo has no senses, so cannot be considered a life yet. Suggest a reason why some people may not agree with this view.

5. X and Y Chromosomes

We all know that there are loads of differences between males and females. It's all to do with two little chromosomes — X and Y.

Sex chromosomes

There are 22 matched pairs of chromosomes in every human body cell (see page 75). The 23rd pair are labelled XX or XY. They're the two chromosomes that decide whether you turn out male or female.

All **men** have an **X** and a **Y** chromosome: **XY**
The Y chromosome causes male characteristics.

All **women** have **two X** chromosomes: **XX**
The XX combination allows female characteristics to develop.

When making sperm, the X and Y chromosomes from the original male cell are drawn apart in the first division of meiosis (see page 78 for more on meiosis). There's a 50% chance each sperm cell gets an X chromosome and a 50% chance it gets a Y chromosome (see Figure 1).

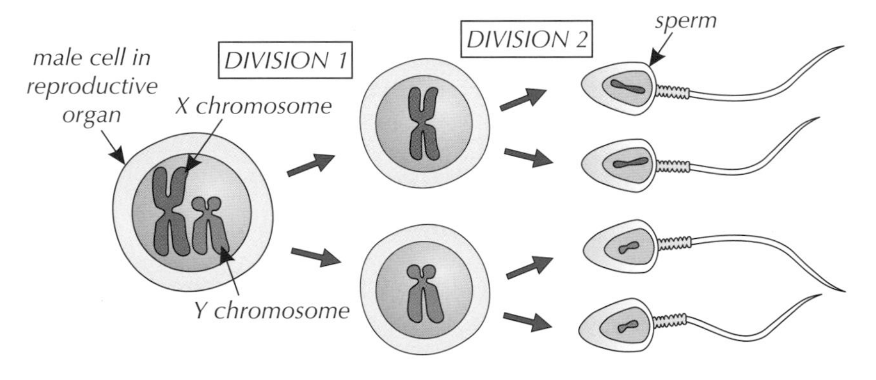

Figure 1: *Diagram showing sperm production by meiosis in males.*

A similar thing happens when making eggs. But the original cell has two X chromosomes (as it's from a female), so all the eggs end up with one X chromosome (see Figure 3).

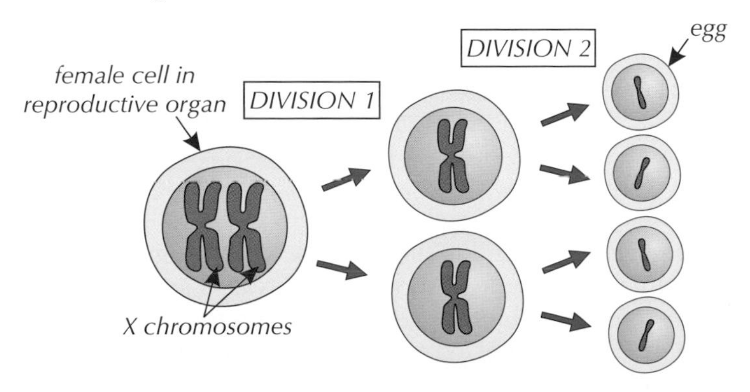

Figure 3: *Diagram showing egg production by meiosis in females.*

Learning Objectives:

- Know that the genes which determine sex are carried on just one of the 23 pairs of chromosomes found in human body cells — the sex chromosomes.
- Know that females have two of the same sex chromosome (XX) whereas males have two different sex chromosomes (XY).
- Be able to interpret genetic diagrams showing sex inheritance.
- **H** Be able to construct genetic diagrams showing sex inheritance.

Specification Reference B2.7.2

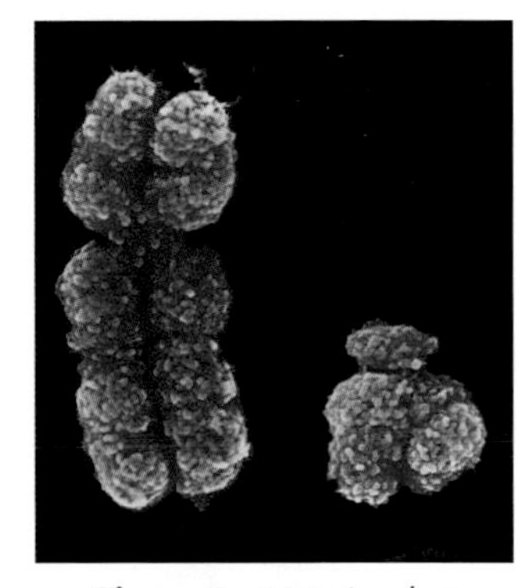

Figure 2: *Here's what the sex chromosomes actually look like. The Y chromosome (shown in blue) is smaller than the (pink) X chromosome.*

Sex inheritance and genetic diagrams

At fertilisation, the sperm fertilises the egg, and the chromosomes from the gametes combine, forming a new individual with the correct number of chromosomes (see page 77). Whether the individual is male or female depends on the combination of sex chromosomes it receives — this is sex inheritance.

Genetic diagrams can be used to show sex inheritance.

Interpreting genetic diagrams

You need to be able to interpret genetic diagrams showing sex inheritance.

Exam Tip
Most genetic diagrams you'll see in exams concentrate on a gene, instead of a chromosome. But the principle's the same. Don't worry — there are loads of other examples on pages 91-96.

Examples

Figure 4 is a type of genetic diagram called a Punnett square, showing sex inheritance. The pairs of letters in the middle show the possible combinations of the gametes.

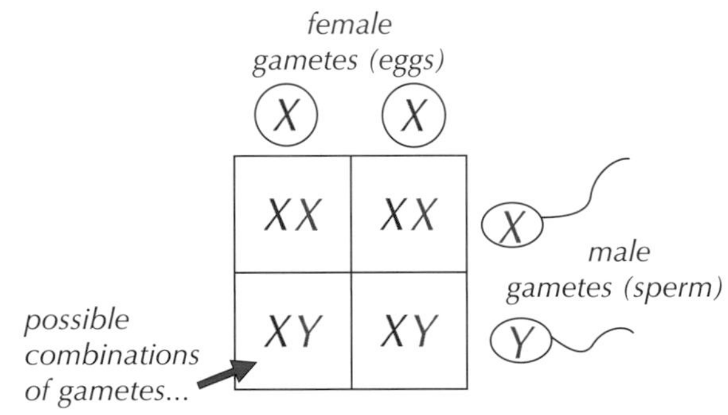

Figure 4: *Punnet square showing sex inheritance.*

Tip: Only one of these possible combinations would actually happen for any one offspring.

Figure 5 is another type of genetic diagram showing sex inheritance. The possible combinations of gametes are shown in the bottom circles.

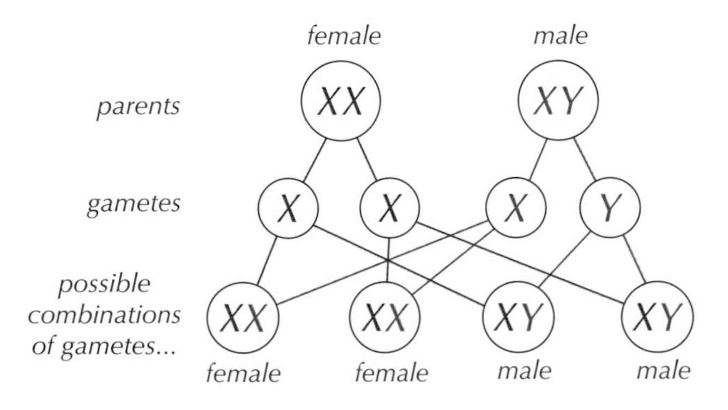

Figure 5: *Genetic diagram showing sex inheritance.*

Figure 6: *Having lots of sons doesn't increase the chances of having a daughter in the next pregnancy. There's still a 50:50 chance of having a boy or a girl at each pregnancy.*

You can use genetic diagrams to find the probability of getting a boy or a girl. Both Figure 4 and Figure 5 show two XX results and two XY results, so there's the same probability of getting a boy or a girl. This can also be written as a 50:50 ratio. Don't forget that this 50:50 ratio is only a probability at each pregnancy. If you had four kids they could all be boys.

Constructing genetic diagrams Higher

You need to be able to construct genetic diagrams to show sex inheritance.

Example 1 **Higher**

Drawing a Punnett square to show sex inheritance in humans.

1. First, draw a grid with four squares.
2. Put the possible gametes from one parent down the side, and those from the other parent along the top.
3. Then in each middle square you fill in the letters from the top and side that line up with that square — the pairs of letters in the middle show the possible combinations of the gametes.

Figure 7 shows these steps:

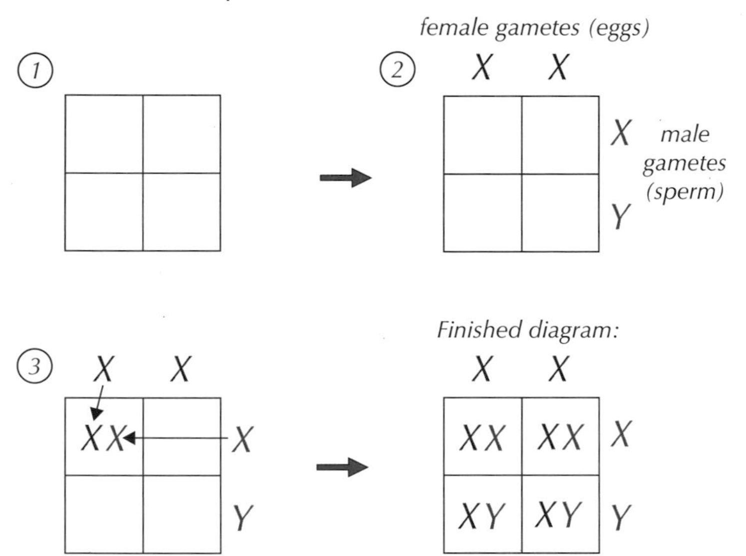

Figure 7: *How to draw a Punnett square to show sex inheritance in humans.*

Example 2 **Higher**

Drawing a different type of genetic diagram to show sex inheritance in humans.

1. Draw two circles at the top of the diagram to represent the parents. Put the female sex chromosomes in one and the male sex chromosomes in the other.

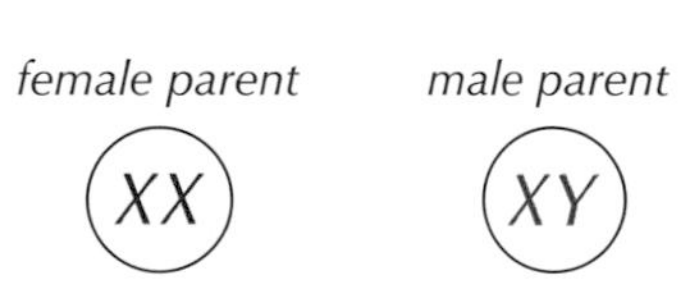

2. Draw two circles below each of the parent circles to represent the possible gametes. Put a single chromosome from each parent in each circle. Draw lines to show which chromosomes come from each parent.

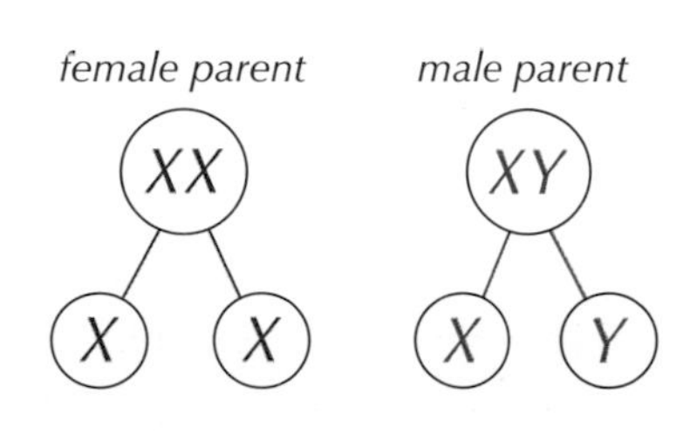

Tip: H Remember one gamete from the female combines with one gamete from the male during fertilisation. It's quite easy to get confused, so check you aren't drawing lines that put both the male's gametes or both the female's gametes into the same circle.

3. One gamete from the female combines with one gamete from the male during fertilisation, so draw criss-cross lines to show all the possible ways the X and Y chromosomes could combine.

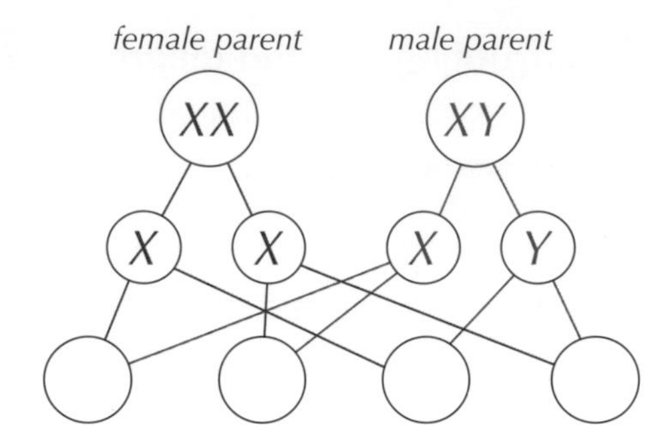

4. Then write the possible combinations of gametes in the bottom circles.

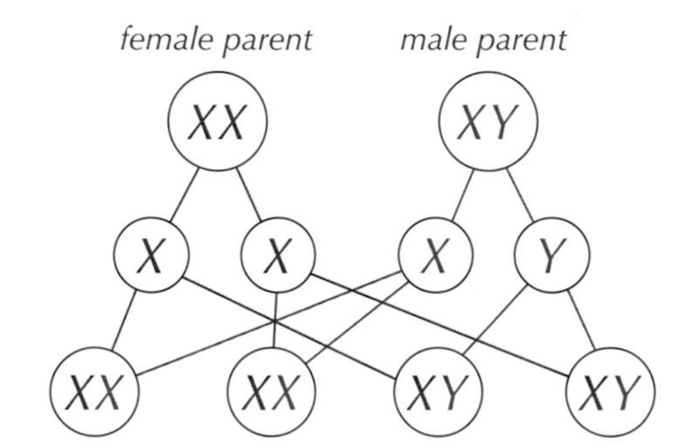

Practice Questions — Fact Recall

Q1 How many of the 23 pairs of human chromosomes determine sex?

Q2 True or False? All sperm cells carry the Y chromosome.

Q3 Who has the sex chromosome combination XX — males or females?

Practice Questions — Application

Rachael and her husband Henry are expecting their first child.

Q1 Complete this genetic diagram to show the possible combinations of sex chromosomes that the baby could have.

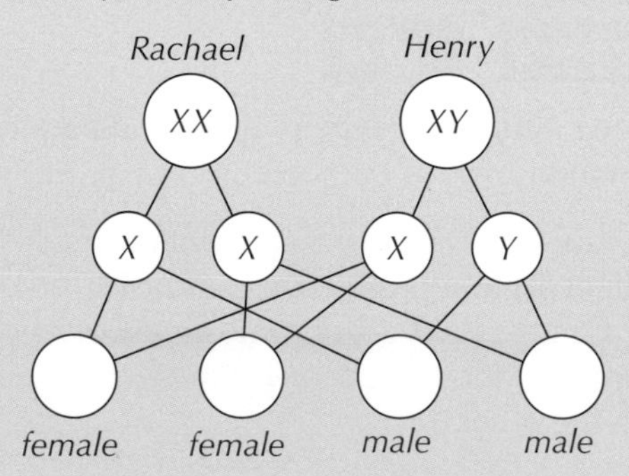

Q2 What is the probability that their child will be a boy?

Q3 If Rachael gets pregnant again, do her chances of having a boy change? Explain your answer.

Q4 Draw a Punnet square to show the possible combinations of sex chromosomes that Rachael and Henry's baby could have.

6. The Work of Mendel

We haven't always known as much about genetics and inheritance as we do now. The work of a monk called Gregor Mendel helped us on our way...

Learning Objectives:

- Understand how Mendel's work led him to develop the idea of inherited factors.
- Know that Mendel's inherited factors are what we now know as genes.
- Understand why Mendel's work was not appreciated until after he had died.

Specification Reference B2.7

Who was Gregor Mendel?

Gregor Mendel was an Austrian monk who trained in mathematics and natural history at the University of Vienna. On his garden plot at the monastery, Mendel noted how characteristics in plants were passed on from one generation to the next. The results of his research were published in 1866 and eventually became the foundation of modern genetics.

Figure 1: Gregor Mendel.

Mendel's work

Mendel did lots of experiments with pea plants. In one experiment he crossed two pea plants of different heights — a tall pea plant and a dwarf pea plant. The offspring produced were all tall pea plants (see Figure 2).

A tall pea plant and a dwarf pea plant are crossed...

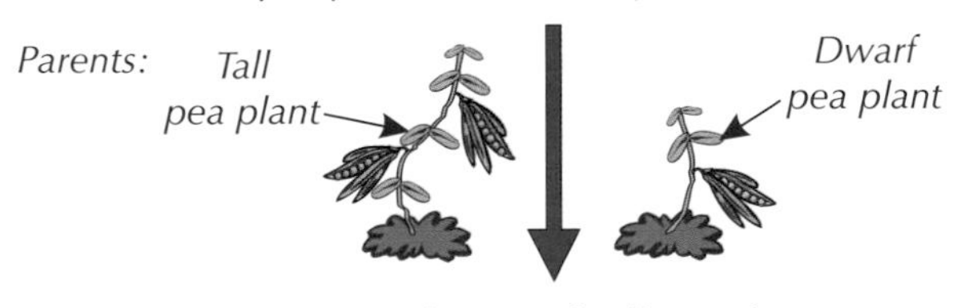

...resulting in all tall pea plants.

Figure 2: *Diagram of the first cross in Mendel's pea plant height experiment.*

Tip: 'Crossed' just means 'bred together'.

He then bred two of these tall pea plants together. The resulting offspring consisted of three tall pea plants and one dwarf pea plant (see Figure 3).

Tip: Genetic diagrams of these crosses are shown on the next page.

Two pea plants from the 1st set of offspring are crossed...

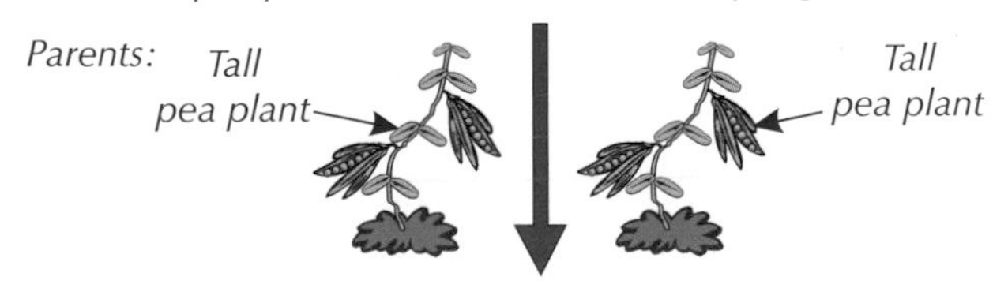

...resulting in three tall pea plants and one dwarf pea plant.

Figure 3: *Diagram of the second cross in Mendel's pea plant height experiment.*

Explaining Mendel's results

Tip: "Hereditary units" can also be called "inherited factors".

From his pea plant height experiment, Mendel had shown that the height characteristic in pea plants was determined by separately inherited "hereditary units" passed on from each parent.

This can be explained using genetic diagrams, where **T** represents the hereditary unit for tall plants and **t** represents the hereditary unit for dwarf plants.

First cross

Exam Tip

In Mendel's pea plant experiments he also investigated lots of other pea plant characteristics, such as flower colour:

So don't be put off if you have a question in the exam about one of Mendel's other experiments — just use what you've learnt here to answer the question.

As shown in Figure 4, in the first of Mendel's crosses, a tall and a dwarf pea plant are crossed together.

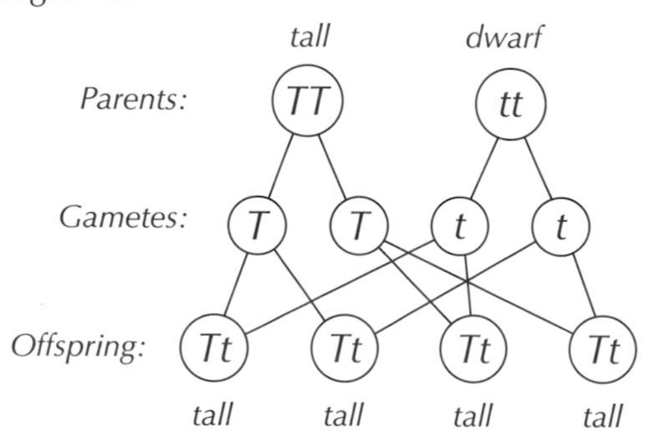

Figure 4: *Genetic diagram of the first cross in Mendel's pea plant height experiment.*

The resulting offspring are **Tt** — they are all tall plants, but they all carry the hereditary unit for dwarf plants.

Second cross

In the second cross, two tall pea plants from the first cross are crossed together (see Figure 5).

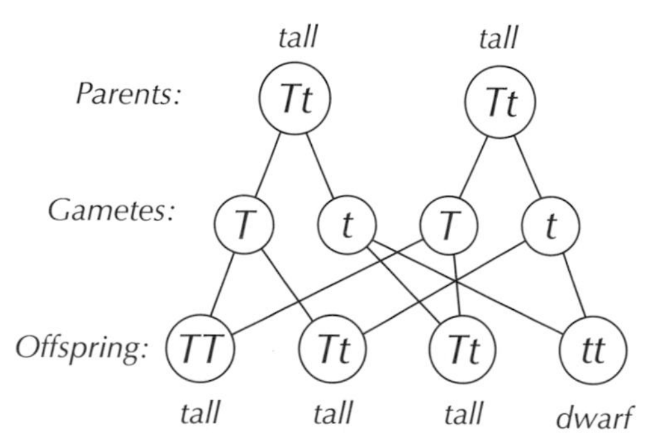

Figure 5: *Genetic diagram of the second cross in Mendel's pea plant height experiment.*

Tip: Figure 5 shows that when two tall (Tt) pea plants are crossed, there's a 3:1 ratio of tall:dwarf pea plants in the offspring. Or a 25% chance of getting a dwarf plant from this cross. There's more about ratios and probabilities on page 91.

The resulting offspring are **TT**, **Tt**, **Tt** and **tt** — this gives three tall plants and one dwarf plant.

The ratios of tall and dwarf plants in the offspring show that the hereditary unit for tall plants, **T**, is **dominant** over the hereditary unit for dwarf plants, **t**, i.e. plants with hereditary units for both types of plant (**Tt**) will be tall plants.

Mendel's conclusions

From all his experiments on pea plants, Mendel reached these three important conclusions about heredity in plants:

1. Characteristics in plants are determined by "hereditary units".
2. Hereditary units are passed on from both parents, one unit from each parent.
3. Hereditary units can be dominant or recessive — if an individual has both the dominant and the recessive unit for a characteristic, the dominant characteristic will be expressed.

We now know that the "hereditary units" are of course genes. But in Mendel's time nobody knew anything about genes or DNA, and so the significance of his work was not to be realised until after his death.

Exam Tip
Mendel is one of the great scientists, who found out really important things about genetics. In the exam don't get him mixed up with other great scientists, like Darwin.

Practice Questions — Fact Recall

Q1 What three important conclusions did Mendel come to about hereditary units in plants?

Q2 What name do we now give to Mendel's hereditary units?

Q3 Why didn't Mendel get any credit for his work while he was alive?

Practice Question — Application

Q1 Mendel did experiments on pea plants with different seed colours. From these experiments he found that there is a hereditary unit in pea plants that gives them green seeds and one that gives them yellow seeds. The hereditary unit for yellow pea seeds is dominant.

Tick or cross the boxes in the table to show which hereditary units pea plants with the following seed colours could have. (You can tick more than one option for each seed colour.)

Seed colour of pea plant	Type of hereditary unit		
	Just green	Just yellow	Both green and yellow
Green			
Yellow			

7. Alleles and Genetic Diagrams

The next few pages are all about how our genes determine our characteristics...

Learning Objectives:

- Know that some characteristics of an organism are controlled by just one gene.
- Know that 'alleles' is the term given to different forms of the same gene.
- Know that if two alleles of the same gene are present, then the allele for the characteristic displayed by the organism is dominant, and the allele for the characteristic that isn't displayed is recessive.
- H Understand and be able to use the terms 'heterozygous' and 'homozygous'.
- H Understand and be able to use the terms 'genotype' and 'phenotype'.
- Be able to predict and explain the outcomes of genetic diagrams showing monohybrid inheritance, for all combinations of dominant and recessive alleles of a gene.
- H Be able to construct genetic diagrams for monohybrid crosses.

Specification Reference B2.7.2

What are alleles?

Alleles are different versions of the same gene (see Figure 1). Gametes only have one allele, but all the other cells in an organism have two — because we inherit half of our alleles from our mother and half from our father. In genetic diagrams letters are usually used to represent alleles.

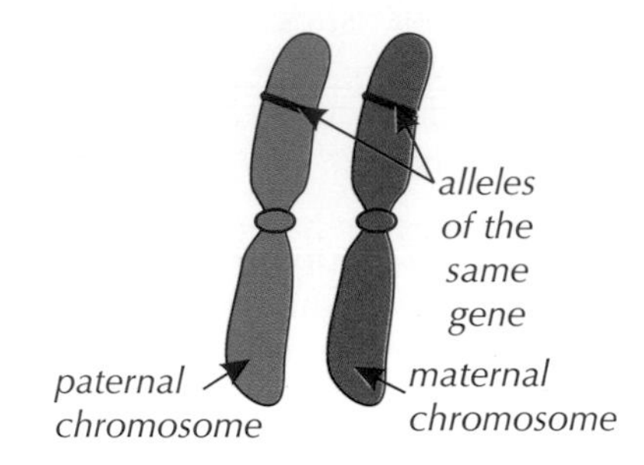

Figure 1: *Diagram showing two alleles for the same gene.*

Some characteristics of an organism are determined by single genes. Organisms can have two alleles for a particular gene that are the same, or they can have two alleles for a particular gene that are different. If the two alleles are different, only one can determine what characteristic is present. The allele for the characteristic that's shown is called the **dominant** allele (use a capital letter for dominant alleles — e.g. 'C'). The other one is called **recessive** (and you show these with small letters — e.g. 'c').

For an organism to display a recessive characteristic, both its alleles must be recessive (e.g. cc). But to display a dominant characteristic the organism can be either CC or Cc, because the dominant allele overrules the recessive one if the plant/animal/other organism has two different alleles.

Genetic terminology Higher

If you're a higher tier student, then you need to know the fancy words used to describe things to do with genetics. Learn these definitions:

- **Homozygous** — When an organism has two alleles for a particular gene that are the same, e.g. TT.
- **Heterozygous** — When an organism has two alleles for a particular gene that are different, e.g Tt.
- **Genotype** — What alleles you have, e.g. you could have the genotype Bb for hair colour.
- **Phenotype** — The characteristics you have, e.g. brown eyes, blonde hair, etc.

Monohybrid inheritance

Characteristics that are determined by a single gene can be studied using monohybrid crosses. This is where you cross two parents to look at just one characteristic. In the exam they could ask you about the inheritance of any characteristic controlled by a single gene, as the principle's always the same.

Genetic diagrams of monohybrid inheritance

Genetic diagrams allow you to see how certain characteristics are inherited. Remember Mendel's pea plant experiments? (If not, flick back to pages 87-89). Mendel also observed that pea plants produced peas that were either wrinkly or round. The inheritance of round or wrinkly peas is an example of monohybrid inheritance and can be shown using genetic diagrams.

Figure 2: The peas produced by pea plants can either be wrinkly (left) or round (right).

Example 1

The gene which causes wrinkly peas is recessive, so you can use a small 'r' to represent it. Round peas are due to a dominant gene, which you can represent with a capital 'R'. If you cross one pea plant which produces wrinkly peas (rr) and one that produces round peas (in this case RR), all of the offspring will produce round peas — but they'll have the alleles Rr.

Parents' characteristics: *round peas* *wrinkly peas*
Parents' alleles: *RR* *rr*
Gametes' alleles: *R* *R* *r* *r*
Possible alleles of offspring: *Rr* *Rr* *Rr* *Rr*
Possible characteristics of offspring: *round* *round* *round* *round*

Tip: In this example, a plant producing wrinkly peas must have 'rr' alleles. However, a plant producing round peas could have two possible combinations of alleles — RR or Rr.

You need to be able to use genetic diagrams to predict and explain the outcomes of monohybrid crosses between individuals for lots of different combinations of alleles. The outcomes are given as ratios and can be used to work out the probability of having offspring with a certain characteristic.

A 3:1 ratio in the offspring

A cross could produce a 3:1 ratio of certain characteristics in the offspring.

Example 2

If two of the offspring from Example 1 are now crossed, this is what you'll get in the next generation:

Parents' characteristics: *round peas* *round peas*
Parents' alleles: *Rr* *Rr*
Gametes' alleles: *R* *r* *R* *r*
Possible alleles of offspring: *RR* *Rr* *Rr* *rr*
Possible characteristics of offspring: *round* *round* *round* *wrinkly*

This gives a 3:1 ratio of plants producing round peas:plants producing wrinkly peas in this generation of offspring. This means there's a 1 in 4 or 25% chance of any new pea plant having wrinkly peas. Remember that "results" like this are only probabilities — they don't say definitely what'll happen.

Exam Tip
In the exam you might be given the results of a breeding experiment and asked to say whether a characteristic is dominant or recessive. To figure it out, look at the ratios of the characteristic in different generations. For example, in Example 2 here the 3:1 ratio of round to wrinkly peas shows that the round allele is dominant.

All the offspring are the same

More than one cross could result in all of the offspring showing the same characteristic. Here you have to do some detective work to find out what's gone on:

Example 3

Back to the pea plant example — if you cross a pea plant that produces round peas and has two dominant alleles (RR), with a pea plant that produces wrinkly peas (rr), all the offspring will produce round (Rr) peas:

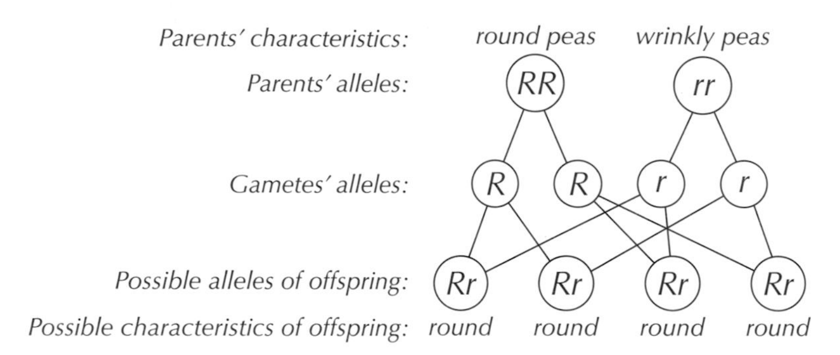

Tip: H The offspring of this cross are all heterozygous (Rr) — they have two different alleles for a particular gene.

This means there's a 100% probability of any new pea plant having round peas.

But, if you crossed a pea plant that produces round peas, and has two dominant alleles (RR), with a pea plant that produces round peas, but has a dominant and a recessive allele (Rr), you would also only get offspring that produce round peas:

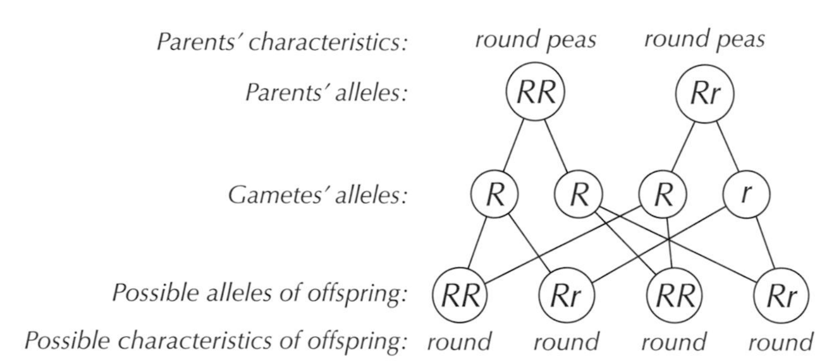

To find out which cross you'd done, you'd have to breed the offspring together and see what kind of ratio you got — then you'd have a good idea. If it was a 3:1 ratio of round to wrinkly in the offspring, it's likely that you originally had RR and rr plants (see Example 2 on the previous page).

A 1:1 ratio in the offspring

On the next page there's an example of when a cross produces a 1:1 ratio in the offspring — half the offspring are likely to show one characteristic and half are likely to show another characteristic. This time we're using cats with long and short hair. (Peas are a bit dull...).

Example

A cat's long hair is caused by a dominant allele 'H'. Short hair is caused by a recessive allele 'h'. A cat with long hair (Hh) was bred with another cat with short hair (hh):

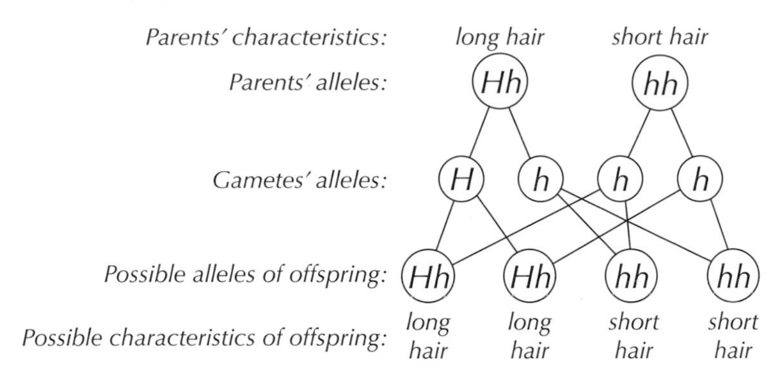

The cats had 8 kittens — 4 with long hair and 4 with short hair. This is a 1:1 ratio, which gives a 50% probability of a new cat being born to these parents having long hair.

Tip: H Half the offspring of this cross are homozygous (hh) — they have two alleles the same for a particular gene.

Constructing genetic diagrams Higher

You need to be able to construct genetic diagrams of monohybrid crosses.

Example **Higher**

Drawing a genetic diagram to show a cross between a pea plant with wrinkly peas (rr) and a pea plant with round peas (RR):

1. Draw two circles at the top of the diagram to represent the parents. Put the round pea genotype in one and the wrinkly pea genotype in the other.
2. Draw two circles below each of the parent circles to represent the possible gametes. Put a single allele from each parent in each circle.
3. One gamete from the female combines with one gamete from the male during fertilisation, so draw criss-cross lines to show all the possible ways the alleles could combine.
4. Then write the possible combinations of alleles in the offspring in the bottom circles.

These steps are illustrated here:

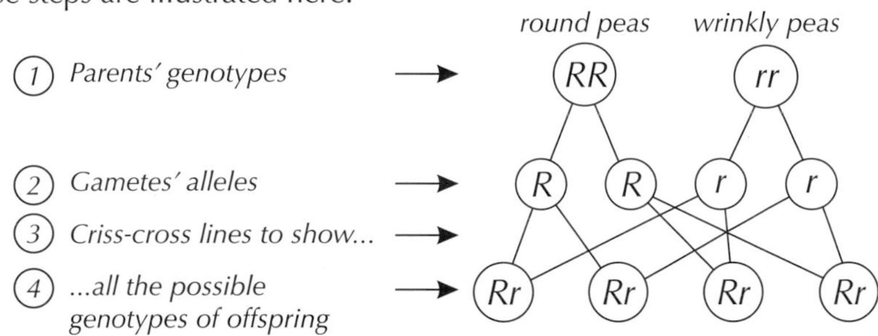

Exam Tip H
If you're asked to construct a genetic diagram in the exam you could also draw a Punnett square (see page 85).

Tip: H Remember, an organism's genotype is the alleles it has. Its phenotype is the characteristics it shows.

Practice Questions — Fact Recall

Q1 What are alleles?

Q2 What is a dominant allele?

Q3 What is meant by the term 'homozygous'?

Q4 What is meant by the term 'phenotype'?

Exam Tip H
Make sure you learn what the terms 'genotype', 'phenotype', 'homozygous' and 'heterozygous' mean. It'll help you pick up easy marks in the exam.

Practice Questions — Application

Q1 Charlotte has some guinea pigs with rough coats and some guinea pigs with smooth coats. The allele for a rough coat is represented by 'R'. The allele for a smooth coat is represented by 'r'. She crosses a rough coated guinea pig (RR) with a smooth coated guinea pig (rr). Here is a genetic diagram of the cross:

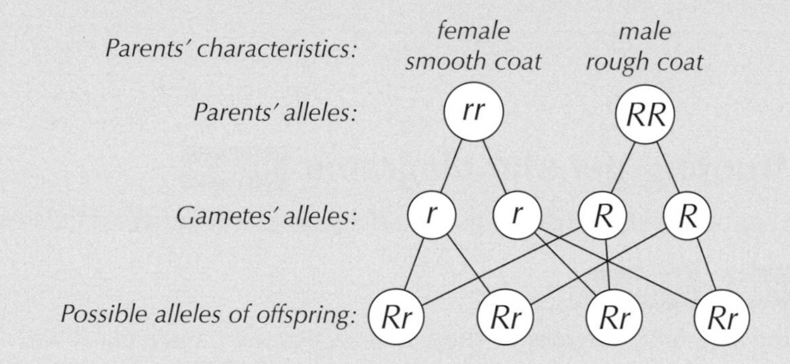

a) What type of coat will the offspring have?

b) i) Charlotte breeds two guinea pigs together that are both heterozygous for a rough coat. Construct a genetic diagram to show the possible genotypes their offspring could have.

ii) From the genetic diagram, what is the probability of the offspring having a smooth coat?

Q2 A female cat has the genotype Ss. 'S' is the allele for spots and is dominant. 's' is the allele for no spots and is recessive.

a) Is the cat homozygous or heterozygous for the spot allele?

b) What genotype would a cat without spots have?

c) What other possible genotype could a spotty cat have?

8. Genetic Disorders

It's not just an organism's characteristics that can be passed on to its offspring. Some disorders can be inherited too. These are known as genetic disorders.

What are genetic disorders?

Genetic disorders are disorders that are caused by an abnormal gene or chromosome, which can be inherited by an individual's offspring. You need to know about two genetic disorders — **cystic fibrosis** and **polydactyly**.

Cystic fibrosis

Cystic fibrosis is a genetic disorder of the cell membranes. It results in the body producing a lot of thick sticky mucus in the air passages (which makes breathing difficult) and in the pancreas.

The allele which causes cystic fibrosis is a recessive allele, carried by about 1 person in 25. Because it's recessive, people with only one copy of the allele won't have the disorder — they're known as **carriers** (they carry the faulty allele, but don't have any symptoms).

For a child to have the disorder, both parents must be either carriers or sufferers. There's a 1 in 4 chance of a child having the disorder if both parents are carriers. This is shown in Figure 1, where '**f**' is used for the recessive cystic fibrosis allele.

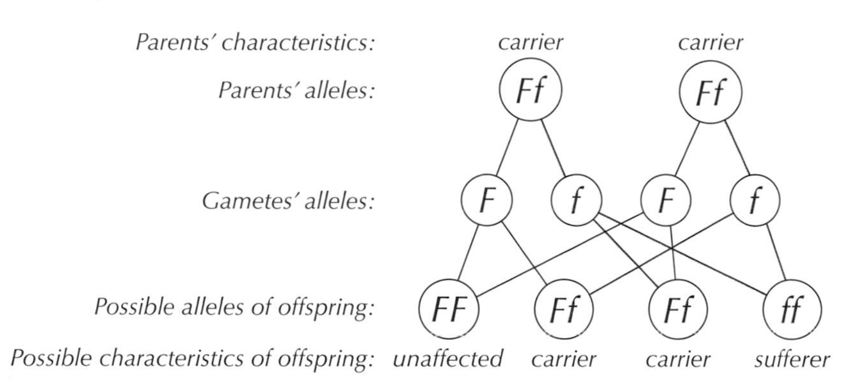

Figure 1: *Genetic diagram to show the inheritance of cystic fibrosis from two carriers.*

Polydactyly

Polydactyly is a genetic disorder where a baby's born with extra fingers or toes (see Figure 2). It doesn't usually cause any other problems so isn't life-threatening.

The disorder is caused by a dominant allele and so can be inherited if just one parent carries the defective allele. The parent that has the defective allele will be a sufferer too since the allele is dominant.

Learning Objectives:

- Know that some disorders are genetic, and what this means.
- Know that cystic fibrosis is a genetic disorder affecting the cell membranes.
- Understand that people will only be sufferers of cystic fibrosis if both their parents have the faulty allele because it's a recessive disorder.
- Know what a carrier is in relation to cystic fibrosis.
- Know that polydactyly is a genetic disorder that results in a person having extra fingers or toes.
- Understand that people will suffer from polydactyly if only one parent has the allele because it is a dominant disorder.
- Be able to interpret family trees.
- Know that embryos can be screened for genetic disorders and understand issues associated with this.

Specification Reference B2.7.3

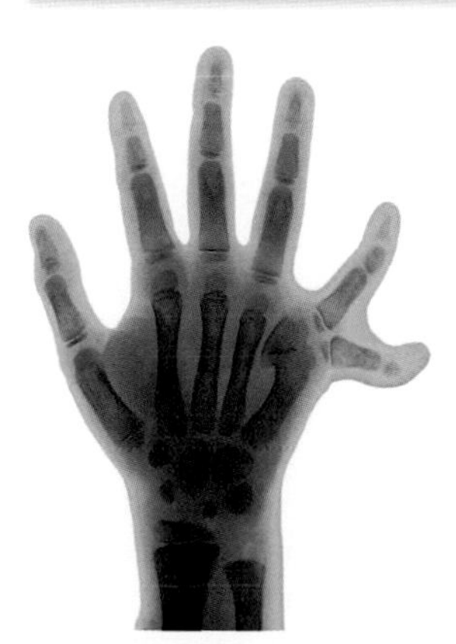

Figure 2: *X ray of a hand with an extra finger. This person is suffering from polydactyly.*

There's a 50% chance of a child having the disorder if one parent has the polydactyly allele. This is shown in Figure 3, where '**D**' is used for the dominant polydactyly allele.

Tip: Remember that there are no carriers for polydactyly. If you carry the faulty gene then you are a sufferer because the disorder is caused by a dominant allele, so you only need one copy to have the disorder.

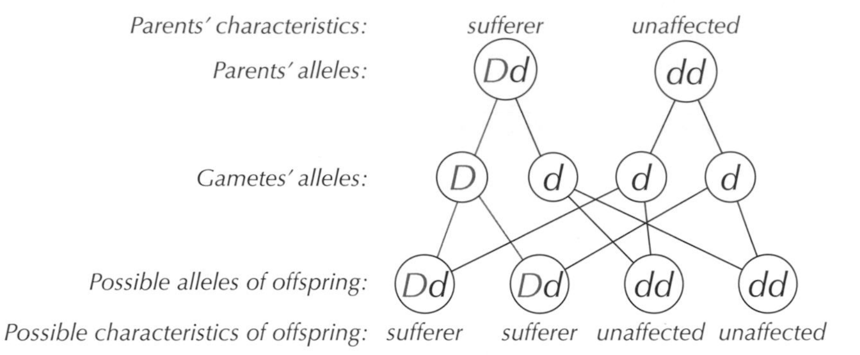

Figure 3: *Genetic diagram to show the inheritance of polydactyly from a sufferer and an unaffected individual.*

Family trees

In genetics, a family tree is a diagram, which shows how a characteristic (or disorder) is inherited in a group of related people. In the exam you might be asked to interpret a family tree.

Exam Tip
In the exam you might get a family tree showing the inheritance of a dominant allele — in this case there won't be any carriers shown.

Example

Here is a family tree for cystic fibrosis:

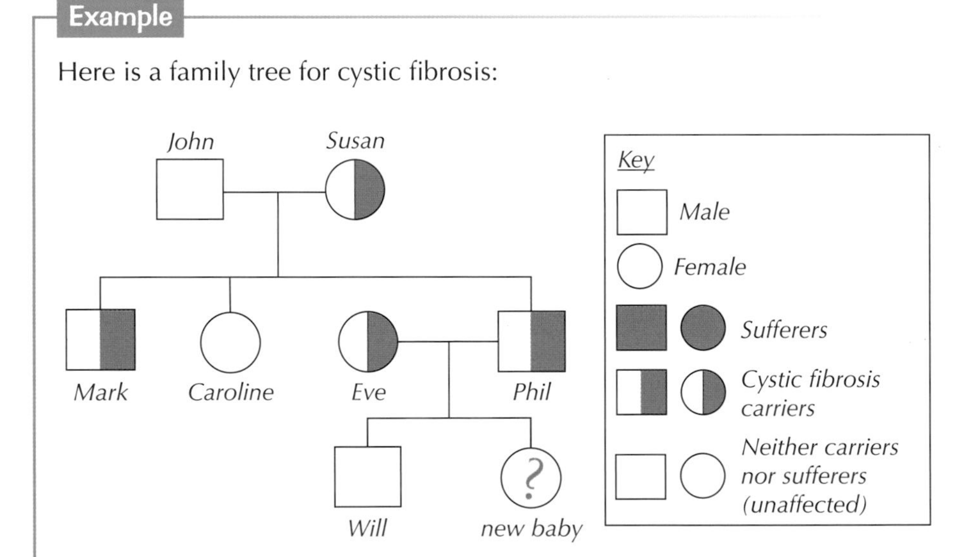

From the family tree, you can tell that:

1. The allele for cystic fibrosis isn't dominant because plenty of the family carry the allele but aren't sufferers.

2. There is a 25% chance that Eve and Phil's new baby will be a sufferer and a 50% chance that it will be a carrier, as Eve and Phil are carriers but not sufferers. This is because the case of the new baby is just the same as in the genetic diagram on the previous page — so the baby could be unaffected (FF), a carrier (Ff) or a sufferer (ff).

Exam Tip H
A good way to work out a family tree is to write the genotype of each person onto it.

Embryonic screening

Embryonic screening is a way of detecting genetic disorders, such as cystic fibrosis, in embryos. There are different methods used to do this:

1. **Pre-implantation genetic diagnosis (PGD).** During IVF, embryos are fertilised in a laboratory, and then implanted into the mother's womb. Before being implanted, it's possible to remove a cell from each embryo and analyse its genes (see Figure 4) — this is called pre-implantation genetic diagnosis (PGD). Embryos with 'healthy' alleles would be implanted into the mother — the ones with 'faulty' alleles destroyed.
2. **Chorionic villus sampling (CVS).** CVS is usually carried out between 10 and 13 weeks of pregnancy. It involves taking a sample of cells from part of the placenta and analysing their genes. The part of the placenta that's taken and the embryo develop from the same original cell — so they have the same genes. If the embryo is found to have a genetic disorder, the parents can decide whether or not to terminate (end) the pregnancy.

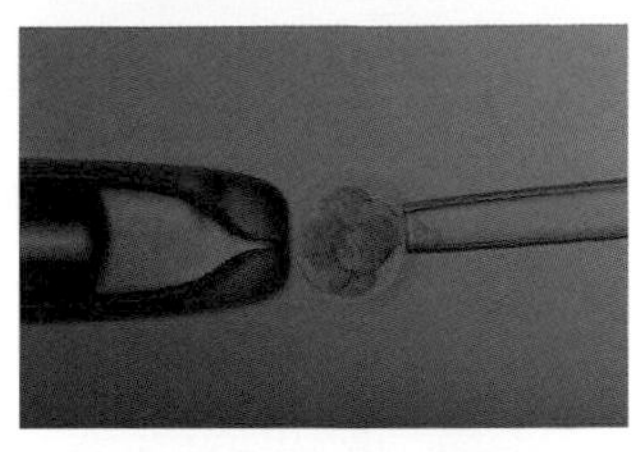

Figure 4: *A single cell being extracted from an embryo in order to be screened for genetic disorders.*

Tip: The placenta is an organ that attaches the embryo to the lining of the womb. It provides the developing embryo with nutrients and takes away waste.

Issues surrounding embryonic screening

There is a huge debate raging about embryonic screening. Here's why:

Arguments for screening

- It helps to stop people suffering from certain genetic disorders.
- Treating disorders costs the Government (and the taxpayers) a lot of money, so screening embryos could reduce healthcare costs.
- During IVF, most of the embryos are destroyed anyway — PGD just ensures that the selected one is healthy.
- If a genetic disorder is diagnosed through CVS, parents don't have to have a termination — but it does give them the choice.

Arguments against screening

- There may come a point where everyone wants to screen their embryos so they can pick the most 'desirable' one, e.g. they want a blue-eyed, blond-haired, intelligent boy.
- It implies that people with genetic problems are 'undesirable' — this could increase prejudice.
- After PGD, the rejected embryos are destroyed — they could have developed into humans, so some people think destroying them is unethical.
- There's a risk that CVS could cause a miscarriage. And if a genetic disorder is diagnosed through CVS, it could lead to a termination (abortion).

Tip: There are laws to stop embryonic screening going too far. At the moment, parents can't even select their baby's sex (unless it's for health reasons).

Many people think that screening isn't justified for genetic disorders that don't affect a person's health:

Example

Polydactyly causes a physical disfigurement but it isn't life-threatening, so lots of people don't agree with screening for it. In comparison, conditions such as cystic fibrosis are potentially life-threatening and so more people agree to screening for them.

Exam Tip
You could be given some data about screening for genetic disorders in the exam, and then asked questions about it. You'll just need to read the information given to you carefully, and apply what you know.

Practice Questions — Fact Recall

Q1 Name the genetic disorder that affects a person's cell membranes.

Q2 Is cystic fibrosis caused by a dominant or recessive allele?

Q3 What do sufferers of the genetic disorder polydactyly have?

Q4 Why would an embryo be screened before it is inserted into the mother's uterus during IVF?

Practice Questions — Application

Q1 If 'f' represents the recessive allele for cystic fibrosis and 'F' represents the dominant allele:

a) give the alleles a carrier of cystic fibrosis would have.

b) give the alleles that a sufferer of cystic fibrosis would have.

Q2 The family tree below shows the inheritance of the genetic disorder polydactyly in a family.

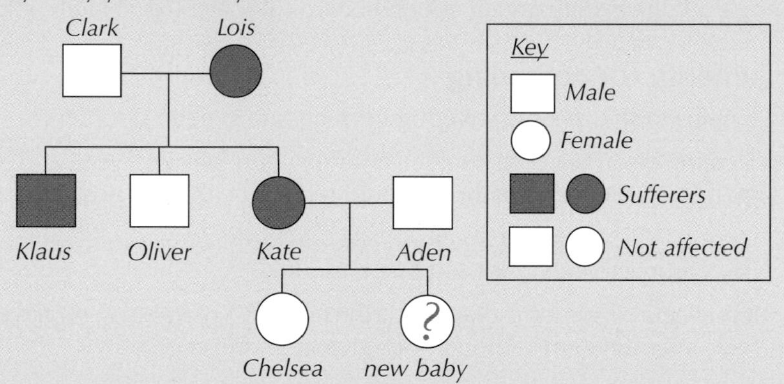

Using the family tree, answer the following questions:

a) From the diagram, how do you know that the allele for polydactyly is dominant?

b) If the new baby was a girl with polydactyly, what symbol would she have on the family tree?

For the following questions, use 'D' to represent the allele for polydactyly and 'd' to represent the allele for a non-sufferer.

c) Give the genotype of the following individuals:

i) Clark ii) Kate

d) Lois has the genotype Dd. Draw a Punnet square to show the inheritance of the polydactyly allele from parents Lois and Clark.

e) Kate and Aden are having a baby.

i) Draw a genetic diagram to show the inheritance of polydactyly from Kate and Aden.

ii) What is the probability the new baby will have polydactyly?

Section Checklist — Make sure you know...

DNA

- ☐ That our chromosomes are made up of long molecules of DNA (deoxyribonucleic acid) and so they contain our genetic information.
- ☐ That DNA has a double helix structure and that genes are small sections of DNA.
- ☐ H That our genes determine the proteins a cell produces by telling the cell what order to put amino acids together in.
- ☐ That (apart from identical twins), a person's DNA is unique and, as a result of this, a technique called DNA fingerprinting can be used to identify an individual based on their DNA.

Cell Division — Mitosis

- ☐ That body cells contain two sets of chromosomes and that these chromosomes are found in pairs.
- ☐ That body cells divide by mitosis, allowing organisms to grow and replace damaged cells.
- ☐ That some organisms (e.g. strawberry plants) reproduce asexually using mitosis and that the offspring have the same genes as the parent.
- ☐ That when a cell divides by mitosis it first copies its genetic material and then divides once, producing two cells which are genetically identical.

Cell Division — Meiosis

- ☐ That gametes only contain one set of chromosomes and that at fertilisation they combine to form a body cell containing two sets of chromosomes.
- ☐ How sexual reproduction results in variation — the offspring inherits alleles from both parents.
- ☐ That gametes are produced when cells divide by meiosis in the reproductive organs (testes or ovaries in humans).
- ☐ That once two gametes have joined at fertilisation, the fertilised egg grows by mitosis.
- ☐ H That when a cell divides by meiosis, it first copies its genetic information, and then divides twice to produce four gametes that are genetically different.

Stem Cells

- ☐ That most animal cells lose the ability to differentiate (become specialised for a particular job) early on, but lots of plants don't ever lose this ability. In mature animals, cell division is mainly used for growth and repair.
- ☐ That embryonic stem cells are found in early human embryos and can be made to differentiate into any type of cell. This means they could potentially be used to treat many medical conditions by replacing damaged or dead cells, such as nerve cells in people with paralysis.
- ☐ That adult stem cells can be taken from bone marrow and made to differentiate into certain types of cell. Adult stem cells already have some uses in medicine, e.g. in bone marrow transplants.
- ☐ How to give informed opinions on the use of embryos as a source of stem cells for medical research.

cont...

X and Y Chromosomes

- ❑ That on one of the 23 pairs of chromosomes in a human body cell are the genes that determine sex, and that these chromosomes are called sex chromosomes — females have two XX sex chromosomes and males have an X sex chromosome and a Y sex chromosome.
- ❑ How to predict the outcome of genetic diagrams showing sex inheritance.
- ❑ **H** How to construct genetic diagrams showing sex inheritance.

The Work of Mendel

- ❑ How Mendel's experiments with pea plants led him to develop the idea of hereditary units/inherited factors and what that meant — characteristics are determined by separate units, that organisms receive one unit from each parent and that these units can be dominant or recessive.
- ❑ That what Mendel called inherited factors are what we now know as genes.
- ❑ That Mendel's work was not appreciated until after his death because people were not aware of things like genes and DNA at the time.

Alleles and Genetic Diagrams

- ❑ That some characteristics of an organism are controlled by just one gene and that different forms of the same gene are called alleles.
- ❑ That if an individual has two different alleles for a characteristic, that the allele for the characteristic that is displayed is dominant, and the other allele is recessive.
- ❑ **H** That if an organism has two alleles for a gene that are the same, then it is homozygous. If the two alleles for the gene are different then it's heterozygous.
- ❑ **H** That 'genotype' means the alleles an organism has (e.g. Gg, bb) and that 'phenotype' means the characteristics an organism has (e.g. blue eyes, blonde hair).
- ❑ That a monohybrid cross is where you cross two parents to look at one characteristic inherited by a single gene. And how to predict and explain the outcomes of genetic diagrams for all combinations of dominant and recessive alleles in monohybrid crosses.
- ❑ **H** How to construct genetic diagrams of monohybrid inheritance.

Genetic Disorders

- ❑ That genetic disorders are inherited disorders.
- ❑ That cystic fibrosis is a genetic disorder of the cell membranes caused by a recessive allele. This means both of a sufferer's parents must have the faulty allele for the sufferer to inherit the condition. If a person inherits just one faulty allele for cystic fibrosis then they will be a carrier.
- ❑ That polydactyly is a genetic disorder where people have extra fingers and toes, and it's caused by a dominant allele. This means anyone who inherits a single polydactyly allele from one of their parents will have the condition.
- ❑ How to interpret family trees.
- ❑ What embryonic screening is and the issues surrounding it.

Exam-style Questions

1 DNA fingerprinting can be used to identify the father of a child.

DNA samples are taken from a child and from men who may be the father of the child (Males 1-4). A DNA fingerprint is produced from the samples, as shown here:

Child	*Male 1*	*Male 2*	*Male 3*	*Male 4*
1	7	13	19	25
2	8	14	20	26
3	9	15	21	27
4	10	16	22	28
5	11	17	23	29
6	12	18	24	30

1 (a) Which man is most likely to be the child's father? Explain your answer.

(2 marks)

1 (b) Which of the bands in the child's DNA fingerprint would match the mother's DNA fingerprint? Explain your answer.

(3 marks)

2 Kaye and Mark are expecting a baby.

2 (a) Kaye has dimples in her cheeks, but Mark does not.
The presence of dimples is thought to be caused by a dominant allele represented by the letter **D**. The recessive allele is represented by the letter **d**. Kaye is heterozygous for the dimples gene.

2 (a) (i) Draw a genetic diagram to show the possible inheritance of the dimples gene by the baby.

(2 marks)

2 (a) (ii) What is the probability that the baby will have dimples?

(1 mark)

Kaye and Mark have found out that they are expecting baby boy.

2 (b) What combination of sex chromosomes will the baby have?

(1 mark)

2 (c) Explain why the baby will be genetically different to both Kaye and Mark.

(3 marks)

3 Mitosis and meiosis are types of cell division.

3 (a) Tick the boxes to say whether the following statements apply to mitosis or meiosis.

Statement	Mitosis	Meiosis
Only occurs in the reproductive organs.		
It produces gametes.		
It produces body cells.		

(3 marks)

3 (b) A cell divides by mitosis once every half hour.

3 (b) (i) Starting with one cell, calculate how many cells there will be after 2 hours.

(2 marks)

3 (b) (ii) Will the offspring be genetically identical or genetically different to the original parent cell?

(1 mark)

4 Family trees can show the inheritance of characteristics, such as cystic fibrosis.

4 (a) What is cystic fibrosis?

(2 marks)

This family tree shows the inheritance of the cystic fibrosis in a family.

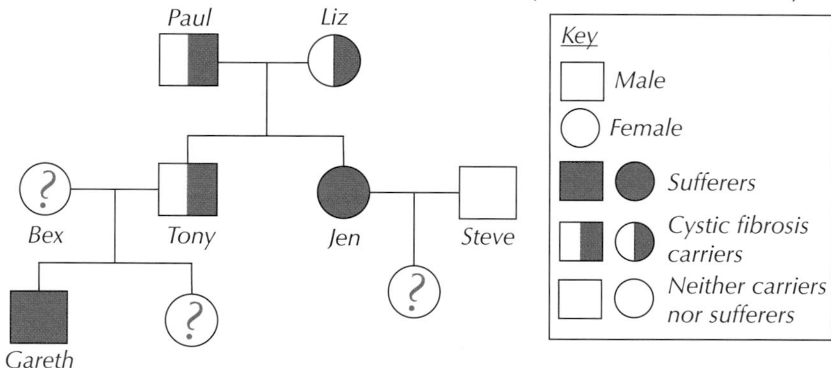

4 (b) Is Gareth heterozygous or homozygous for the cystic fibrosis allele? Explain your answer

(1 mark)

4 (c) Looking at the family tree, could Jen and Steve have a child with cystic fibrosis? Draw a genetic diagram to help you explain your answer. In your genetic diagram use **f** to represent the allele for cystic fibrosis and **F** to represent the healthy allele.

(4 marks)

4 (d) Bex and Tony have a child with cystic fibrosis. However, Bex doesn't suffer from cystic fibrosis. Therefore, what combination of alleles must Bex have for the cystic fibrosis gene? Explain your answer.

(3 marks)

1. Fossils

Fossils might sound a bit dull, but they're actually dead interesting. Without them, we wouldn't know that dinosaurs ever existed.

What are fossils?

Fossils are the remains of organisms from many years ago, which are found in rocks. Fossils provide the evidence that organisms lived ages ago. They also show how life on Earth **evolved** — by comparing fossils with species that are alive today, we can see that many of today's species have developed from much simpler organisms over millions of years.

How do fossils form?

Fossils form in rocks in one of three ways:

1. From gradual replacement by minerals

Things like teeth, shells, bones, etc., which don't **decay** easily, can last a long time when buried. They're eventually replaced by minerals as they decay, forming a rock-like substance shaped like the original hard part (see Figures 1 and 2).

The surrounding sediments also turn to rock, but the fossil stays distinct inside the rock and eventually someone digs it up. Most fossils are made this way.

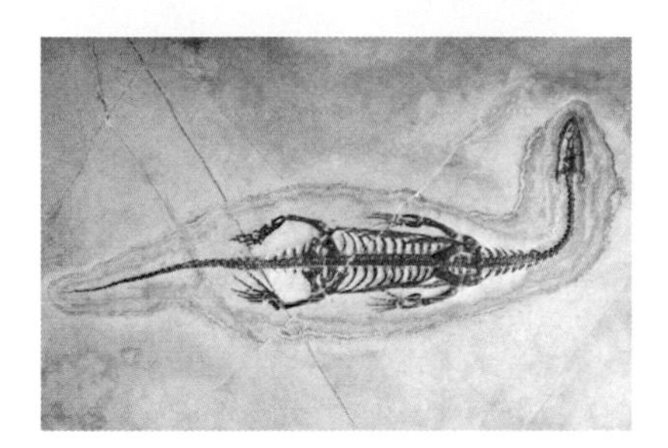

Figure 1: *Fossil of a reptile skeleton, dug out of the rock in China.*

Figure 2: *Fossils of ammonite shells. Ammonites were ancient marine organisms.*

2. From casts and impressions

Sometimes, fossils are formed when an organism is buried in a soft material like clay. The clay later hardens around it and the organism decays, leaving a **cast** of itself. An animal's burrow (see Figure 3, next page) or a plant's roots can be preserved as casts. Things like footprints can also be pressed into soft materials, leaving an impression when the material hardens (see Figure 4, next page).

Learning Objectives:
- Know what fossils are.
- Know that fossils provide evidence for the existence of early organisms.
- Know that fossils show how life on Earth evolved.
- Understand the main ways in which fossils form.
- Understand why scientists have different views on how life on Earth began.
- Understand why there are so few fossils of early organisms.

Specification Reference B2.8.1

Tip: When organisms die, they usually get broken down (digested) by microorganisms such as bacteria and fungi. This process is known as decay. Decay can take place at different rates. Very occasionally, it doesn't happen at all (see next page).

Tip: The soft tissue of this reptile (Figure 1) and the soft bodies of the ammonites (Figure 2) decayed away quickly, so they haven't formed part of the fossils.

***Figure 3:** Fossilised burrows made in the sea bed by small organisms millions of years ago.*

***Figure 4:** The footprint of an early human-like primate, preserved in hardened volcanic ash.*

3. From preservation in places where no decay happens

The microbes involved in decay need the right conditions in order to break down material — that means plenty of oxygen (for aerobic respiration, see p. 64), enough moisture, and the right temperature and pH for their enzymes to work properly (see pages 54-55). If the conditions aren't right, decay won't take place and the dead organism's remains will be preserved.

Tip: As it happens, the conditions needed for decay are usually right — so it's very rare for dead organisms to be preserved in this way.

Examples

- In amber (a clear yellow 'stone' made from fossilised tree sap) and tar pits there's no oxygen or moisture so decay microbes can't survive (see Figure 5).
- In glaciers it's too cold for the decay microbes to work.
- Peat bogs are too acidic for decay microbes. Whole human bodies have been preserved as fossils in peat bogs (see Figure 6).

***Figure 5:** Fossil of a midge, preserved in amber.*

***Figure 6:** Photo of the 'Tollund Man'. This well preserved fossil of a man was discovered in a bog.*

Tip: The 'Tollund Man' lived over 2000 years ago. He was so well preserved in the bog that scientists were able to tell what he ate for his last meal from the contents of his stomach (barley gruel, yum).

The origins of life on Earth

There are various **hypotheses** suggesting how life first came into being, but no one really knows the answer.

Maybe the first life forms came into existence in a primordial swamp (or under the sea) here on Earth. Maybe simple organic molecules were brought to Earth on comets — these could have then become more complex organic molecules, and eventually very simple life forms.

Tip: 'Primordial' means 'original' or 'first'. So primordial swamps were the first swamps.

Tip: Organic molecules are molecules containing carbon, e.g. amino acids.

These hypotheses can't be supported or disproved because there's a lack of **valid** and **reliable evidence**. There's a lack of evidence because:

- Scientists believe many early organisms were soft-bodied, and soft tissue tends to decay away completely, without forming fossils.
- Fossils that did form millions of years ago may have been destroyed by **geological activity**, e.g. the movement of tectonic plates may have crushed fossils already formed in the rock.

This means that the **fossil record** is incomplete — in other words, we don't have fossils of every organism or even every type of organism that has ever lived.

Tip: Validity and reliability are explained on page 4.

Tip: Tectonic plates are the large 'pieces' of rock that make up the Earth's crust.

Practice Questions — Fact Recall

Q1 What is a fossil?

Q2 What do fossils provide evidence of?

Q3 Explain why there is a lack of valid and reliable evidence to support any hypothesis about how life on Earth began.

Practice Question — Application

Q1 Suggest how each of the following fossils was formed:

A

Fossilised animal burrows preserved in rock.

B

A fossilised snail shell.

C

A fossilised leaf imprint in rock.

D

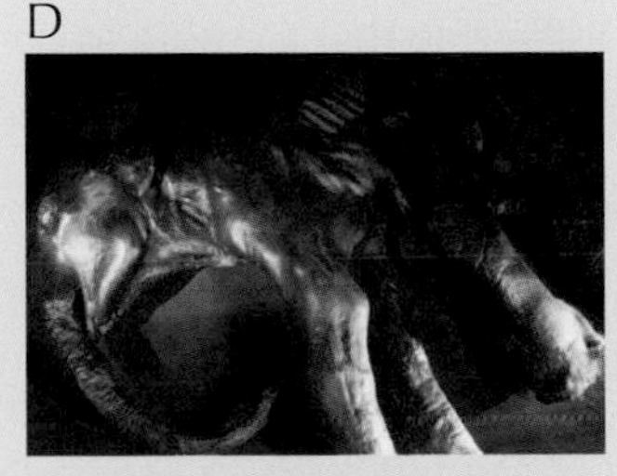

A fossilised baby mammoth, found in frozen ground in Siberia.

2. Extinction and Speciation

Life on Earth is changing all the time — species die out and new ones emerge. It's all to do with extinction and speciation...

Learning Objectives:
- Know the six main causes of extinction.
- Know that the formation of new species is called speciation.
- Know that speciation starts with the isolation of populations.
- H Understand how genetic variation and natural selection lead to speciation — populations can no longer interbreed to produce fertile offspring.

Specification Reference B2.8.1

What is extinction?

The fossil record contains many species that don't exist any more — these species are said to be **extinct**. Dinosaurs and mammoths are extinct animals, with only fossils to tell us they existed at all.

Why do species become extinct?

Species become extinct for these reasons:

- The environment changes too quickly (e.g. destruction of habitat).
- A new predator kills them all (e.g. humans hunting them).
- A new disease kills them all.
- They can't compete with another (new) species for food.
- A catastrophic event happens that kills them all (e.g. a volcanic eruption or a collision with an asteroid).
- A new species develops (this is called speciation — see below).

Tip: If an environment changes too rapidly, a species may not be able to evolve quickly enough to survive. If so, the species will eventually die out.

Example

Dodos (a type of large, flightless bird) are now extinct. Humans not only hunted them, but introduced other animals which ate all their eggs, and also destroyed the forest where they lived — they really didn't stand a chance.

Tip: If lots of species die out at the same time (e.g. due to a catastrophic event), it's known as a mass extinction.

Figure 1: An artist's impression of the dodo.

Speciation

A **species** is a group of similar organisms that can reproduce to give fertile offspring (offspring that are able to breed themselves). **Speciation** is the development of a new species.

Isolation

Isolation is where populations of a species are separated. This can happen due to a physical barrier. E.g. floods and earthquakes can cause barriers that geographically isolate some individuals from the main population. Isolation can eventually lead to speciation.

Example

The chimpanzee and bonobo are two separate species of ape that evolved from a common ancestor. It's thought that two populations of the ancestor became isolated from each other when the Congo River formed.

The population to the north of the river became chimpanzees and the population to the south became bonobos (see Figure 2).

Congo river

● = chimp ● = bonobo

Figure 2: Diagram to show the isolation, and so speciation, of chimp and bonobo populations.

Natural selection Higher

When two populations are isolated due to a physical barrier, conditions on either side of the barrier will be slightly different, e.g. the climate may be different. Because the environment is different on each side, different characteristics will become more common in each population due to natural selection. Here's how:

1. Each population shows variation because they have a wide range of **alleles**.
2. In each population, individuals with characteristics that make them better adapted to their environment have a better chance of survival and so are more likely to breed successfully.
3. So the alleles that control the beneficial characteristics are more likely to be passed on to the next generation.

Tip: H Alleles are different forms of a gene. See page 90 for more.

Eventually, individuals from the different populations will have changed so much that they won't be able to breed with one another to produce fertile offspring. This means the two groups have become separate species — in other words, speciation has occurred.

The whole process is shown in Figure 3.

Tip: H Populations can sometimes split up into more than two groups — this could result in the formation of several new species.

Key:
● = individual organism
● = individual organism of new species

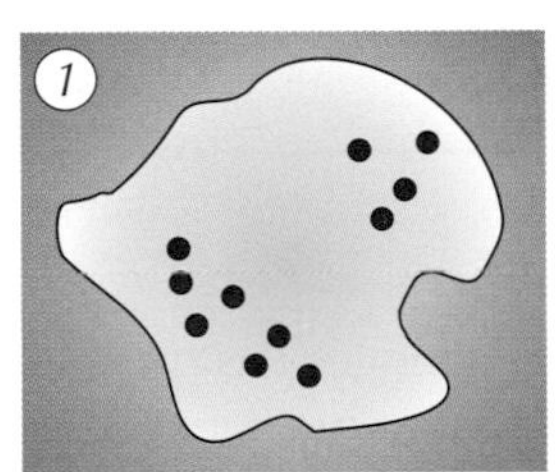

Two populations of the same species.

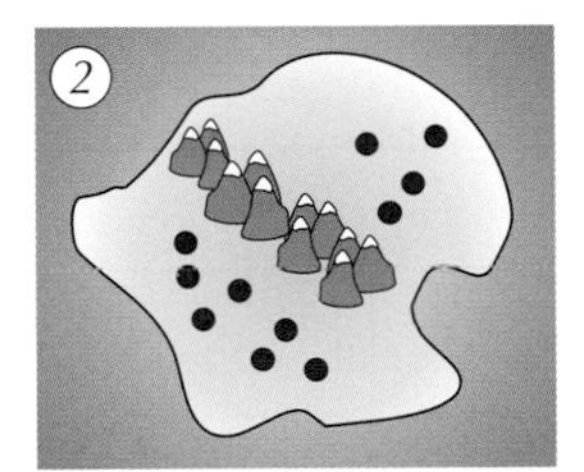

Physical barriers separate populations.

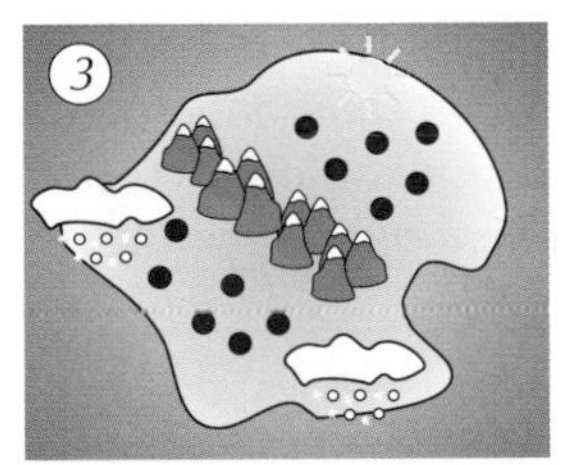

Populations adapt to new environments.

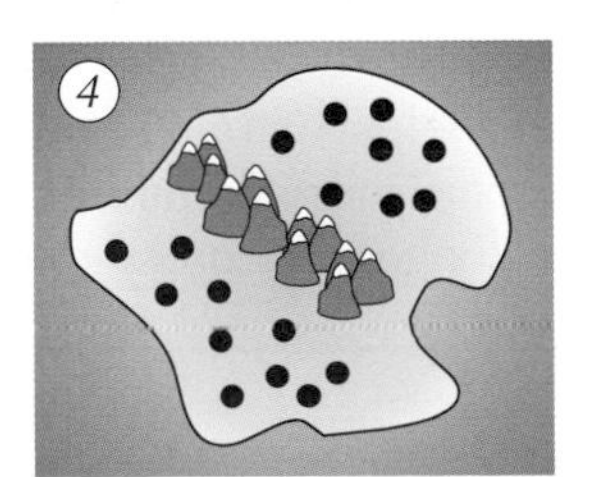

Development of a new species.

Figure 3: *H Diagram to show how speciation occurs.*

Exam Tip H
In the exam, you could be asked to apply your knowledge of how speciation occurs to explain the formation of any new species. So make sure you know the main stages involved — isolation, then genetic variation and natural selection lead to speciation.

Practice Questions — Fact Recall

Q1 Give two ways in which a species may become extinct.

Q2 What is speciation?

Q3 Describe one way in which populations of a species may become isolated from one another.

Q4 Why do populations of the same species show variation?

Q5 How can you tell that speciation has taken place?

Section Checklist — Make sure you know...

Fossils

- ☐ That fossils are the remains of organisms from many years ago, which are found in rocks.
- ☐ That fossils provide evidence that organisms lived long ago and show how species evolved.
- ☐ That fossils can be made when hard body parts (that don't decay easily) are gradually replaced by minerals, from casts and impressions, and from preservation in places where no decay happens.
- ☐ That there are various hypotheses as to how life on Earth began, but that these can't be supported or disproved because there's not enough valid and reliable evidence.
- ☐ That there's a lack of valid and reliable evidence because there are so few fossils of early organisms — their soft bodies decayed easily and didn't form fossils, and geological activity has destroyed many fossils that did form.

Extinction and Speciation

- ☐ The reasons why species become extinct — the environment changes too quickly, a new predator or disease appears, they can't compete with other species, a catastrophic event happens (e.g. a volcanic eruption or an asteroid collision) which kills them or a new species develops.
- ☐ That speciation is the formation of a new species and that it can happen when populations become geographically isolated.
- ☐ H How, following isolation, genetic variation and natural selection can lead to speciation: each isolated population has different alleles; natural selection causes different characteristics, and therefore different alleles, to become more common in each population; eventually, the populations become so different they can no longer interbreed to produce fertile offspring.

Exam-style Questions

1 The photograph below shows part of the Grand Canyon in Arizona, USA.
The canyon is several kilometres wide and nearly two kilometres deep in places.

Two closely-related, but separate squirrel species live either side of the canyon.
They are thought to be descended from a single original squirrel species, present in the area before the canyon formed.

1 (a) Use your knowledge of speciation to explain how the two separate squirrel species formed.

(5 marks)

1 (b) A bird species is found on both sides of the canyon.
Suggest why the formation of the canyon did not cause the bird species to form two separate species.

(2 marks)

1 (c) Fossils of shelled organisms are often found in the Grand Canyon.

1 (c) (i) Suggest how these fossils may have formed.

(2 marks)

1 (c) (ii) Why didn't the soft bodies of these shelled organisms form part of the fossils?

(1 mark)

1 (c) (iii) Give **one** way in which some fossils can be destroyed over time.

(1 mark)

Learning Objectives:
- Know that when atoms of more than one element are chemically joined together a compound is formed.
- Understand that bonding occurs when electrons are transferred or shared between atoms.
- Know that bonding occurs so that the outer shells of atoms are filled.

Specification Reference C2.1.1

1. Bonding in Compounds

Bonding is a really important topic in chemistry, and there are a couple of different types that you need to know about. But fret not, all the information that you need is coming your way.

What is a compound?

A **compound** is a substance that's formed when atoms of two or more elements are chemically combined. For example, carbon dioxide is a compound formed from a chemical reaction between carbon and oxygen. It's difficult to separate the two original elements out again.

Types of bonding

The two main types of bonding that you need to know about are **ionic bonding** (see pages 111-115) and **covalent bonding** (see pages 116-119). Both types of bonding occur because atoms prefer to have full outer shells of electrons, rather than part-filled shells.

A full outer shell gives an atom a stable electronic structure, just like a noble gas. Most atoms don't have a full outer shell though, so they either need to lose, gain or share electrons to achieve it.

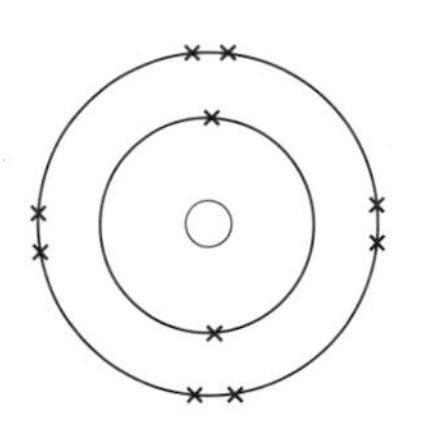

Figure 1: *The electronic structure of neon. Neon is a noble gas so has a full outer shell of electrons.*

Atoms can gain electrons from other atoms (this is part of ionic bonding), or by sharing electrons (covalent bonding). Atoms can lose electrons by giving them up to other atoms (also part of ionic bonding). Ionic and covalent bonding are covered in more detail over the next few pages. For now, the important things to remember are:

- Atoms can form bonds by transferring electrons or sharing electrons.
- They do this so that they can achieve a stable electronic structure — a full outer shell of electrons.

Practice Questions — Fact Recall

Q1 What is a compound?

Q2 Name two types of bonding.

Q3 Why do atoms form chemical bonds?

Q4 Chemical bonds are formed when electrons are transferred between atoms. Give one other way that a chemical bond can be formed.

2. Ionic Bonding

There's loads to know about ionic bonding — what it is, how it works, the charges on ions, representing ions, working out formulae... So best crack on...

What is ionic bonding?

Ionic bonding is a strong electrostatic attraction between oppositely charged ions that holds ions in an ionic compound together. Electrostatic attraction is the force of attraction between negatively charged ions and positively charged ions. Here's how ionic bonding works...

All the metal atoms over at the left-hand side of the periodic table, for example, sodium, potassium and calcium, have just one or two electrons in their outer shell (highest energy level). They're keen to get rid of them, because then they'll have full shells, which is how they like it.

On the other side of the periodic table, the non-metal elements in Group 6 and Group 7, such as oxygen and chlorine, have outer shells which are nearly full. They're keen to gain that extra one or two electrons to fill the shell up.

When metals react with non-metals, electrons are transferred from the metal atoms to the non-metal atoms. The metal atoms lose electrons to become positively charged ions with a full outer shell of electrons. The non-metal atoms gain electrons and become negatively charged ions with a full outer shell of electrons. The oppositely charged ions are strongly attracted to each other, and this strong electrostatic attraction holds the ions together. This is known as ionic bonding.

Example

- A potassium atom has one electron in its outer shell.
- A chlorine atom has seven electrons in its outer shell.
- Potassium and chlorine react to form the compound potassium chloride, which is held together by ionic bonding.
- The potassium ion and the chloride ion both have full outer shells.

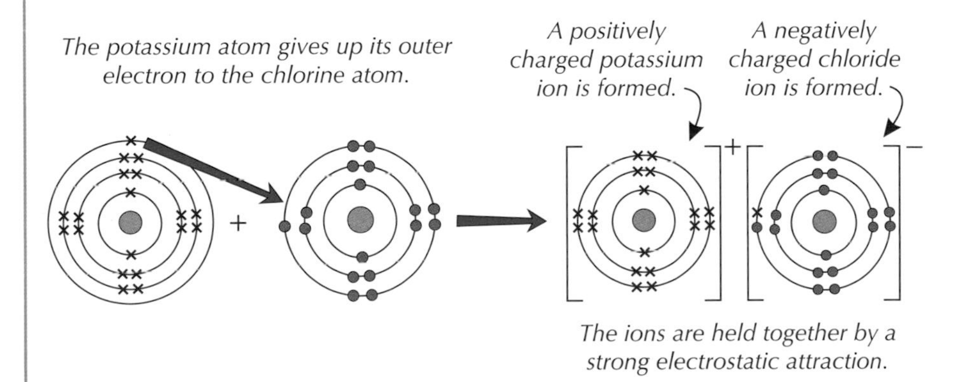

Figure 1: *The formation of potassium chloride.*

Learning Objectives:

- Know that ionic bonding involves the transfer of electrons between atoms, so that ions with stable electronic structures are formed.
- Know that when atoms lose electrons they form positive ions and when they gain electrons they form negative ions.
- Be able to work out the charge on an ion from its group in the periodic table.
- Know that the alkali metals will react with halogens to form ionic compounds made up of oppositely charged ions with single charges.
- Be able to work out the formulae of ionic compounds.
- Be able to draw the electronic structures of sodium, chloride, magnesium, oxygen and calcium ions.
- Know ionic compounds are giant structures of ions held together in a lattice, and that the electrostatic forces holding the ions together act in all directions.

Specification Reference
C2.1, C2.1.1

Charges on ions

The elements that most readily form ions are those in Groups 1, 2, 6 and 7. The charge on an ion depends on the number of electrons that have been lost or gained — and that depends on the number of electrons in their outer shell.

Tip: Each electron has a charge of 1^- and each proton has a charge of 1^+. The overall charge on an ion depends on the number of protons and the number of electrons that the ion contains.

Examples

- Group 1 elements (the alkali metals) have one electron in their outer shell. So when they form an ion they lose one electron, which gives them a charge of 1^+. For example, K^+, Na^+, Li^+.
- Group 2 elements have two electrons in their outer shell. So they need to lose two electrons to achieve a stable electronic structure. This means they form ions with a charge of 2^+. For example, Be^{2+}, Ca^{2+}, Mg^{2+}.
- Group 7 elements (the halogens) have seven electrons in their outer shell. So when they form an ion they gain one electron, which gives them a charge of 1^-. For example, Cl^-, F^-.
- Group 6 elements have six electrons in their outer shell. So they need to gain two electrons to achieve a stable electronic structure. This means they form ions with a charge of 2^-. For example, O^{2-}.

The positive and negative charges we talk about, (for example Na^+ for sodium), just tell you what type of ion the atom will form in a chemical reaction. In sodium metal there are only neutral sodium atoms, Na. The Na^+ ions will only appear if the sodium metal reacts with something.

Formulae of compounds

Any of the positive ions mentioned above can combine with any of the negative ions to form an ionic compound. Only elements at opposite sides of the periodic table will form ionic compounds.

Tip: The reaction of an alkali metal with a halogen is the classic example of ionic bonding, so make sure you know how it works.

Example

- Group 1 elements will react with Group 7 elements to form ionic compounds.
- The metal ion in these ionic compounds has a single positive charge.
- The non-metal ion in the compound has a single negative charge.

The overall charge of any compound is zero. So all the negative charges in the compound must balance all the positive charges. You can use the charges on the individual ions present to work out the formula of the ionic compound.

Example 1

Sodium chloride contains Na^+ and Cl^- ions.

Because a sodium ion has a 1^+ charge and a chloride ion has a 1^- charge only one of each ion is needed to balance out the charges.

$$(+1) + (-1) = 0$$

So the formula for sodium chloride is NaCl.

Example 2

Magnesium chloride contains Mg^{2+} (+2) and Cl^- (–1) ions.

Because a chloride ion only has a 1^- charge we will need two of them to balance out the 2^+ charge of a magnesium ion.

$$(+2) + (-1) + (-1) = 0$$

This gives us the formula $MgCl_2$.

Exam Tip
In the exam, you could be given the chemical symbols and ionic charges for certain elements and be asked to write the formulae of the compound they form, so make sure you know how to do it. The important thing to remember is that the charges must balance.

Representing ionic structures

A useful way of representing ions is by drawing out their electronic structure. Just use a big square bracket and a + or – to show the charge. You need to know how to draw the ions that form sodium chloride, magnesium oxide and calcium chloride. Here they are:

1. Sodium chloride

Sodium chloride consists of sodium ions and chloride ions.

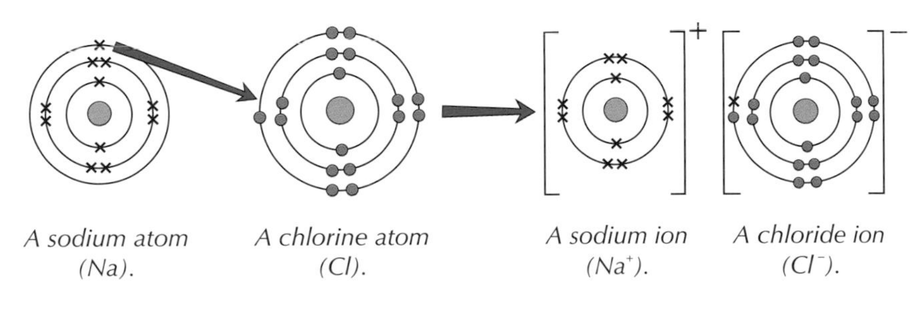

Figure 2: *A representation of the electronic structures of the ions in sodium chloride.*

Exam Tip
Don't forget to include the charge when you're drawing the electronic structures of ions — you won't get all the marks without it.

2. Magnesium oxide

Magnesium oxide consists of magnesium ions and oxygen ions.

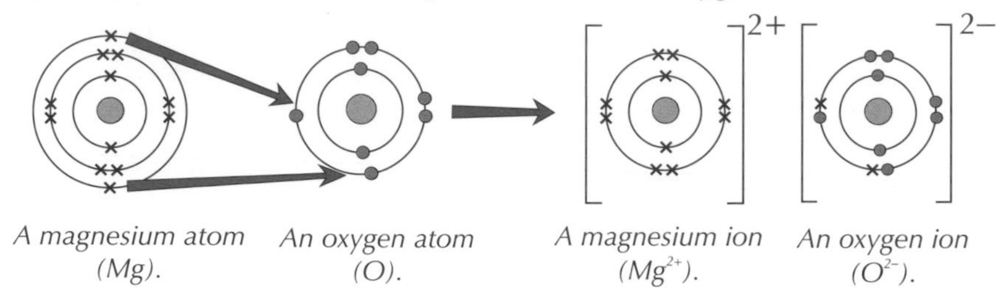

Figure 3: *A representation of the electronic structures of the ions in magnesium oxide.*

The formula of magnesium oxide is MgO — the charge on one magnesium ion (2^+) balances out the charge on one oxygen ion (2^-).

Tip: The electrons in the oxygen ion are represented by dots AND crosses, so that you can see which electrons have been transferred from the magnesium atom. You don't have to draw ions like this though — once the electrons have been transferred it doesn't matter where they came from, so you could draw all the electrons in an ion as dots or all as crosses if you wanted to.

3. Calcium chloride

Calcium chloride consists of calcium ions and chloride ions.

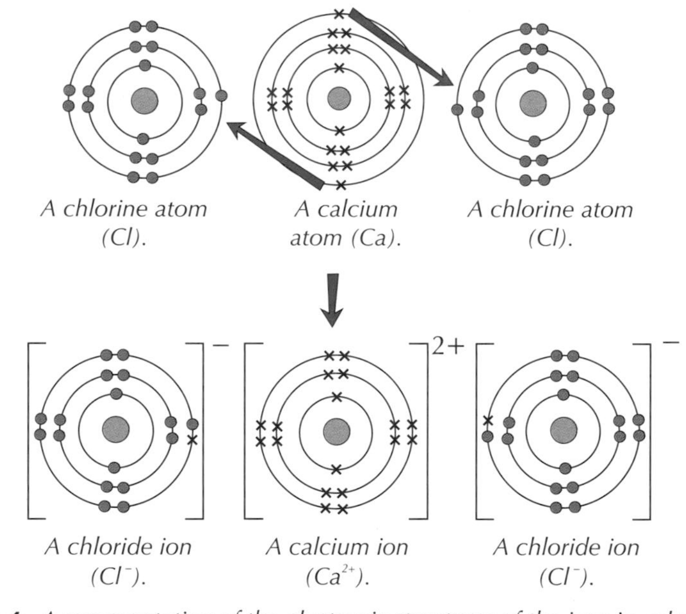

Figure 4: *A representation of the electronic structures of the ions in calcium chloride.*

Tip: A chlorine atom is just called 'chlorine'. But when chlorine is part of an ionic compound, we say that there are 'chloride ions' present. It's quite common for the names of ions to be slightly different from the elements.

The structure of ionic compounds

Ionic compounds are giant structures made of ions. The ions are held together in a lattice (a closely-packed regular arrangement). The strong electrostatic forces of attraction between the ions act in all directions.

Figure 5: *Crystals of salt.*

Example

A single crystal of sodium chloride (salt) is one giant ionic lattice, which is why salt crystals tend to be cuboid in shape. The Na^+ and Cl^- ions are held together in a regular lattice.

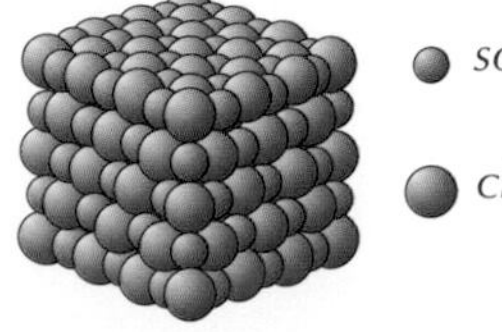

Practice Questions — Fact Recall

Q1 What is ionic bonding?

Q2 Which groups in the periodic table contain elements that have outer shells of electrons that are almost full?

Q3 Do metals form positively charged ions or negatively charged ions?

Q4 Do non-metal atoms gain or lose electrons to become ions?

Q5 What is the charge on an ion of a Group 1 element?

Q6 What is the charge on an ion of a Group 7 element?

Q7 Draw the electronic structure of:

a) a chloride ion.

b) a magnesium ion.

c) an oxygen ion.

d) a calcium ion.

Q8 Describe the structure of an ionic compound.

Tip: You can use the periodic table on the inside of the back cover to help you answer these questions.

Practice Questions — Application

Q1 What ions would the following elements form? Give the chemical symbol and the charge on the ion.

a) Rubidium

b) Bromine

c) Barium

d) Sulfur

Q2 Write the formulae of the ionic compounds listed below.

a) Sodium bromide

b) Calcium fluoride

c) Sodium oxide

d) Calcium oxide

Tip: Before working out the formula of a compound, you need to work out the charge on each of the ions in the compound.

Q3 Potassium reacts with iodine to form potassium iodide.

a) What ions are formed during this reaction? (Give the chemical symbols and the charges).

b) What is the formula of potassium iodide?

c) Describe, in terms of electron transfer, the reaction between potassium and iodine.

Q4 Describe, in terms of electrons and bonding, the formation of magnesium chloride from magnesium and chlorine. Include details of electronic structures, electron transfer and electrostatic attraction in your answer.

3. Covalent Bonding

Learning Objectives:

- Know that a covalent bond is a shared pair of electrons and that covalent bonds are very strong.
- Be able to represent the bonding in the simple molecules H_2, Cl_2, HCl, CH_4, NH_3, H_2O and O_2.
- Know that macromolecules such as silicon dioxide and diamond are giant covalent structures.

Specification Reference C2.1, C2.1.1

Ionic bonding — done. Next up is covalent bonding, which is all about atoms sharing their electrons. There are a fair few diagrams coming your way over the next few pages and yes — you do need to know them all.

What is covalent bonding?

Some elements bond ionically (see page 111) but others form **covalent bonds**. A covalent bond is a shared pair of electrons. Covalent bonds are very strong bonds and are formed when atoms share electrons with each other so that they've got full outer shells (highest energy levels). They only share electrons in their outer shells and both atoms involved in the bond end up with the electronic structure of a noble gas.

Each covalent bond provides one extra shared electron for each atom. Each atom involved has to make enough covalent bonds to fill up its outer shell. See Figure 1 for a reminder of how many electrons each shell can hold.

Shell	Max. number of electrons
1st	2
2nd	8
3rd	8

***Figure 1:** Table showing the number of electrons each shell (energy level) can hold.*

Simple molecules

Simple molecules are molecules made up of just a few atoms. You need to know the bonding in seven different simple molecules. Here they are:

1. Hydrogen (H_2)

Hydrogen atoms have just one electron. They only need one more to complete the first shell, so they often form **single covalent bonds** to achieve this (see Figure 2).

Tip: In a molecule of hydrogen there are two hydrogen atoms joined by one pair of electrons. This single shared pair of electrons is a <u>single covalent bond</u>.

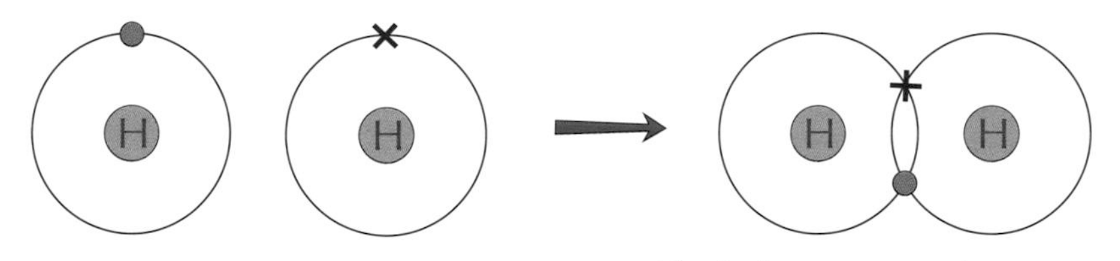

***Figure 2:** The formation of a covalent bond between hydrogen atoms.*

You can show the covalent bond by drawing out the electronic structure of the hydrogen atoms (as in Figure 2), but there are also other ways that the covalent bond can be represented — see Figure 3.

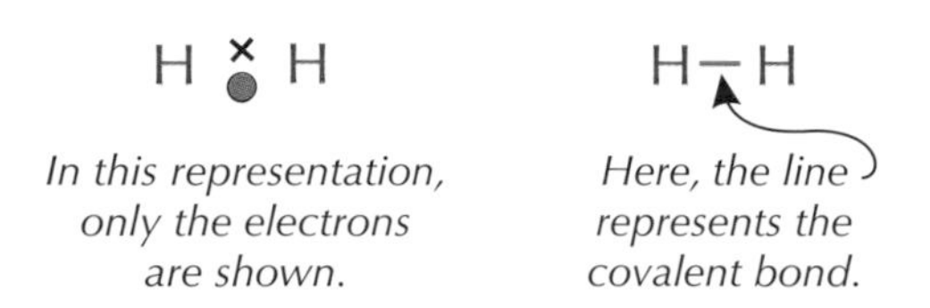

***Figure 3:** Representations of covalent bonding in hydrogen.*

2. Chlorine (Cl_2)

Chlorine atoms need one more electron to gain a stable electronic structure. So, two chlorine atoms each share one of their electrons to form a chlorine molecule containing one shared pair of electrons — a single covalent bond.

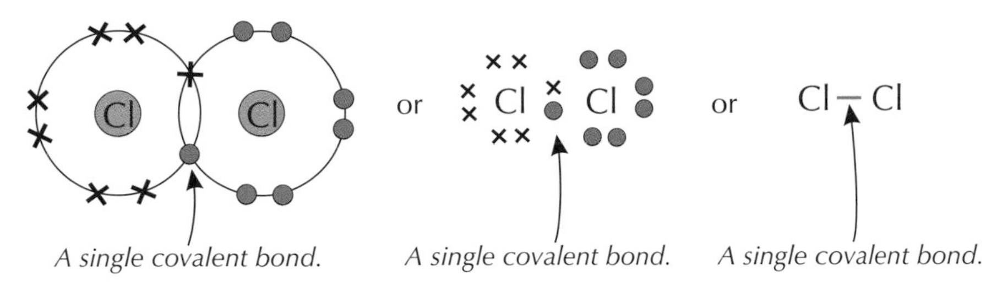

Figure 4: *Representations of covalent bonding in chlorine.*

Tip: You don't need to show all the electrons in the atoms when drawing covalent bonding — just the ones in the outer shell.

3. Hydrogen chloride (HCl)

The bonding in hydrogen chloride is very similar to the bonding in H_2 and Cl_2. Again, both atoms only need one more electron to complete their outer shells, so they share one pair of electrons and one single covalent bond is formed.

Tip: Hydrogen chloride dissolves in water to form hydrochloric acid.

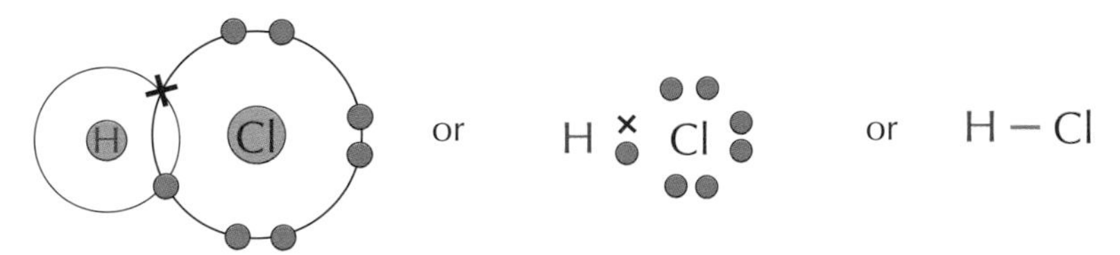

Figure 5: *Representations of covalent bonding in hydrogen chloride.*

4. Methane (CH_4)

Carbon has four outer electrons, which is half a full shell. So it forms four covalent bonds to make up its outer shell. Hydrogen atoms only need to form one covalent bond to achieve a full outer shell. So a carbon atom will form covalent bonds with four hydrogen atoms to form a CH_4 molecule (methane).

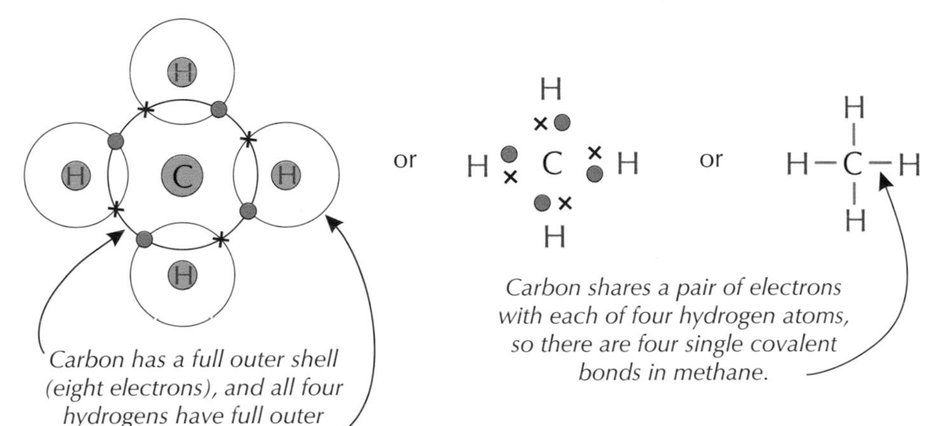

Figure 6: *Representations of covalent bonding in methane.*

Tip: The diagrams where covalent bonds are shown using dots and crosses are imaginatively called 'dot and cross diagrams'. The diagrams where lines are used to show covalent bonds are called displayed formulae.

5. Ammonia (NH_3)

Nitrogen has five outer electrons so it needs to form three covalent bonds to make up the extra three electrons needed. Hydrogen needs one extra electron, so a single covalent bond is formed between nitrogen and each of three hydrogen atoms.

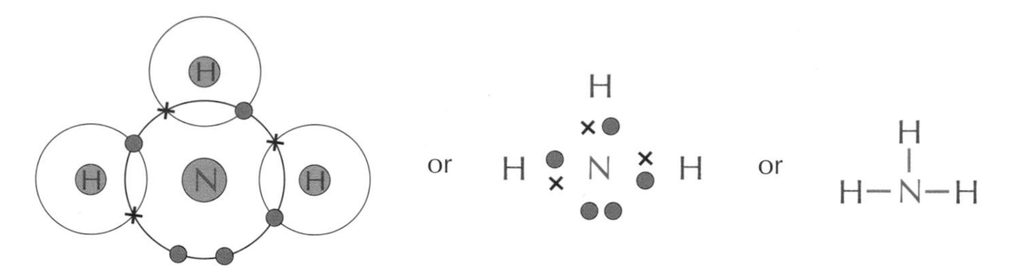

Figure 7: Representations of covalent bonding in ammonia.

6. Water (H_2O)

Oxygen atoms have six outer electrons. They sometimes form ionic bonds by taking two electrons from other atoms to complete their outer shell. However they'll also form covalent bonds and share two electrons instead. In water molecules, the oxygen shares electrons with two hydrogen atoms to form two single covalent bonds.

Exam Tip
Always check you've got the bonding right by counting the number of electrons each atom has in its outer shell. If it's not got a full outer shell you've gone wrong somewhere.

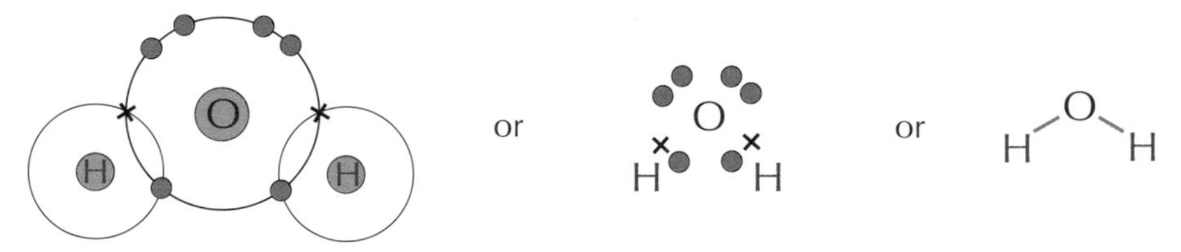

Figure 8: Representations of covalent bonding in water.

7. Oxygen (O_2)

In oxygen gas, an oxygen atom shares two electrons with another oxygen atom to get a full outer shell. So there are two pairs of electrons shared between two oxygen atoms. This is called a **double covalent bond**.

Tip: If an atom shares one pair of electrons with one atom and another pair of electrons with another atom then there are two single bonds. You get double bonds when two atoms share two pairs of electrons with each other.

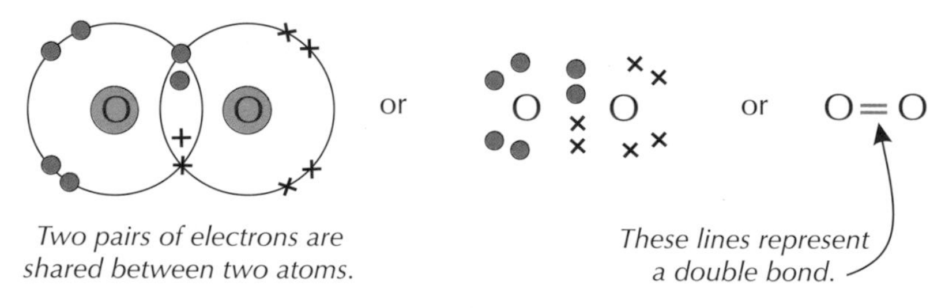

Figure 9: Representations of covalent bonding in oxygen.

Macromolecules

All the molecules on the previous couple of pages are simple molecules, as they're only made up of a few atoms. But covalent bonding can also lead to giant structures called **macromolecules**.

> **Tip:** There's more on macromolecules such as silicon dioxide and diamond on pages 124 and 125.

Examples

- Silicon dioxide (SiO_2) is a macromolecule formed when many silicon and oxygen atoms are covalently bonded to form a giant covalent structure.
- Diamond is a macromolecule formed from many covalently bonded carbon atoms.

Figure 10: A molecular model showing the giant covalent structure of diamond.

Practice Questions — Fact Recall

Q1 What is a covalent bond?

Q2 Name the molecules shown by the dot and cross diagrams below.

a) H Cl

b)

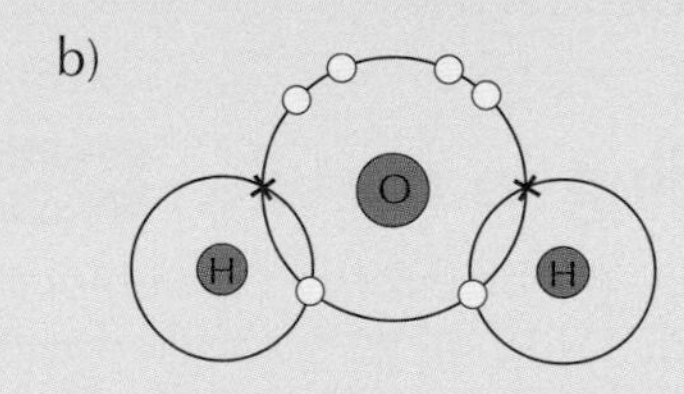

Q3 Draw dot and cross diagrams to represent the following molecules.

a) hydrogen b) chlorine c) methane

Q4 Using displayed formulae, draw the bonding in the molecules below.

a) chlorine b) ammonia c) oxygen

Q5 What is a double covalent bond?

Q6 Name two macromolecules.

Practice Questions — Application

Q1 An element, 'A', has 3 shells of electrons. Its 3rd shell contains seven electrons. 'A' covalently bonds to hydrogen. Describe and explain the bonding in the molecule that is formed.

Q2 a) Which of the molecules below contains a double covalent bond? Explain your answer.

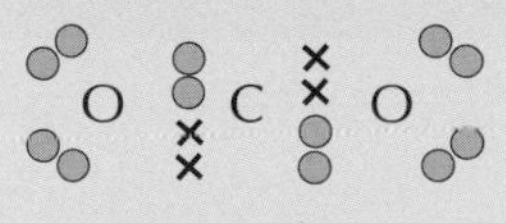

Molecule A

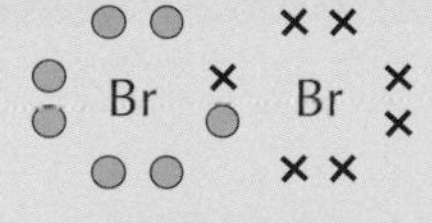

Molecule B

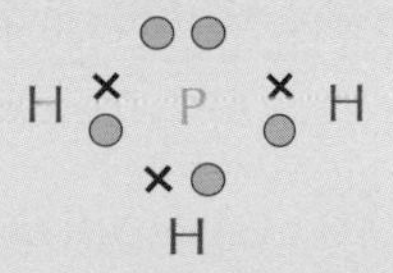

Molecule C

b) Draw the displayed formula of the molecule that contains the double bond.

Learning Objectives:

- Know that metals are giant structures.
- Know how the atoms in a metal are arranged.
- H Know that electrons from the outer shells of metal atoms are delocalised.
- H Understand how these delocalised electrons hold the metal atoms together.
- H Be able to draw diagrams to represent the bonding in metals.

Specification Reference C2.1, C2.1.1

4. Metallic Bonding

Metallic bonding is the final type of bonding in this section and, luckily for you, there's not a huge amount that you need to know. For now that is...

The structure of metals

Metals consist of a giant structure. The atoms in a metal are arranged in a regular pattern (see Figure 1). Metals are said to have giant structures because they have lots of atoms. Exactly how many depends on how big the piece of metal is.

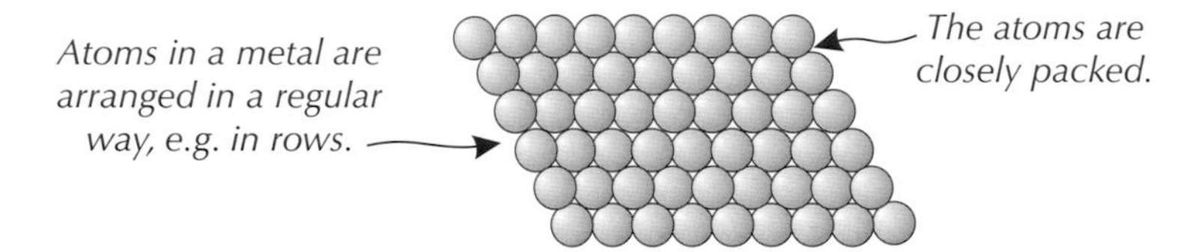

Figure 1: *The structure of a metal.*

Bonding in metals Higher

In metals, the electrons in the outer shells of the atoms are **delocalised**. This means that they aren't associated with a particular atom or bond — they're free to move through the whole structure (see Figure 2). There are strong forces of electrostatic attraction between the positive metal ions and the negative electrons, and these forces hold the metal structure together.

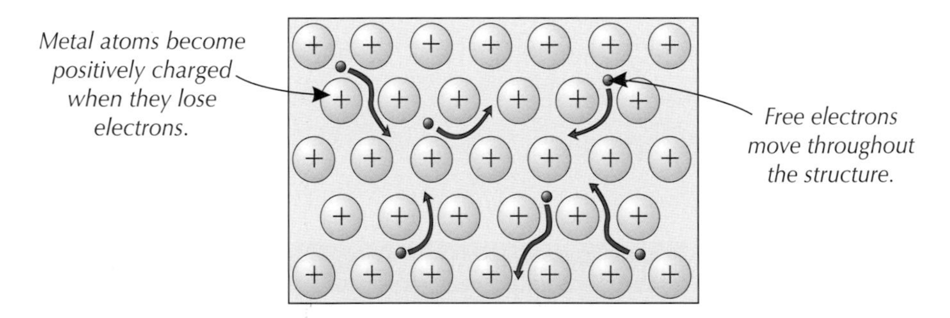

Figure 2: *Delocalised electrons within a giant metallic structure.*

Practice Questions — Fact Recall

Q1 Describe the structure of a metal.

Q2 What are delocalised electrons?

Q3 a) What type of forces hold the particles in a metal together?

b) Why do these forces exist in a metal?

Section Checklist — Make sure you know...

Bonding in Compounds

- [ ] That a compound is a substance that's formed from atoms of two or more elements, chemically bonded together.
- [ ] That atoms bond together in order to achieve a full outer shell of electrons (like noble gases).
- [ ] That atoms can achieve a full outer shell of electrons through ionic bonding or covalent bonding.

Ionic Bonding

- [ ] That ionic bonding is a strong electrostatic attraction between oppositely charged ions.
- [ ] That metal atoms can lose electrons to form positively charged ions with stable electronic structures and non-metal atoms can gain electrons to form negatively charged ions with stable electronic structures.
- [ ] How to work out the charge on an ion from the position of the element in the periodic table.
- [ ] That alkali metals and halogens react to form ionic compounds containing one metal ion with a single positive charge and one non-metal ion with a single negative charge.
- [ ] How to work out the formulae of ionic compounds from the chemical symbols and charges on ions.
- [ ] How to represent the electronic structures of sodium ions, chloride ions, magnesium ions, oxygen ions and calcium ions.
- [ ] That ionic compounds are giant structures and that the ions are held together in a regular arrangement (a lattice) by electrostatic forces that act in all directions.

Covalent Bonding

- [ ] That a covalent bond is a shared pair of electrons, and that covalent bonds are very strong.
- [ ] That atoms form covalent bonds by sharing one or more of their electrons with another atom.
- [ ] That atoms need to make enough covalent bonds to fill their outer electron shell.
- [ ] That a single covalent bond is formed when two atoms share one pair of electrons and a double covalent bond is formed when two atoms share two pairs of electrons.
- [ ] How to represent the covalent bonds in hydrogen, water, chlorine, hydrogen chloride, methane, ammonia, water and oxygen using dot and cross diagrams and displayed formulae.
- [ ] That macromolecules like silicon dioxide and diamond are giant covalent structures.

Metallic Bonding

- [ ] That metals are giant structures, with atoms arranged in a regular pattern.
- [ ] **H** That metallic structures have delocalised electrons that are free to move through the structure.
- [ ] **H** That the delocalisation of electrons gives rise to positive metal ions and that the strong electrostatic attraction between the delocalised electrons and the positive ions holds the structure together.

1. Ionic Compounds

The last section was about the different types of bonding that hold substances together. This section is all about how the bonding affects the properties of a substance, and therefore the uses. First up — ionic compounds.

Learning Objectives:
- Know that ions in an ionic compound are arranged in a giant ionic lattice and held together by strong electrostatic forces.
- Know why ionic compounds have high melting and boiling points.
- Know why ionic compounds can conduct electricity when they are melted or dissolved in water.

Specification Reference C2.2.2

Melting point and boiling point

Ionic compounds have a regular arrangement of ions called a giant ionic lattice. Ionic compounds all have high melting points and high boiling points due to the strong electrostatic attraction between the ions. It takes a large amount of energy to overcome this attraction. When ionic compounds melt, the ions are free to move and they'll carry electric current — see Figure 1.

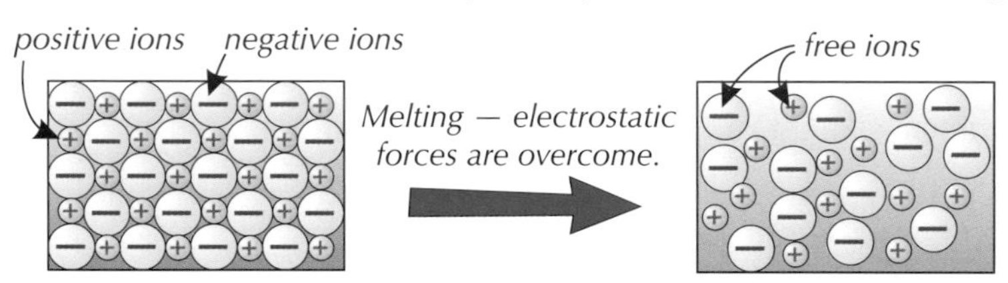

Figure 1: *A particle diagram of an ionic compound when solid and melted.*

Tip: Remember, an electrostatic attraction is the force of attraction between oppositely charged ions.

Solubility

Ionic compounds dissolve easily in water. The ions separate and are all free to move in the solution, so they'll carry electric current — see Figure 2.

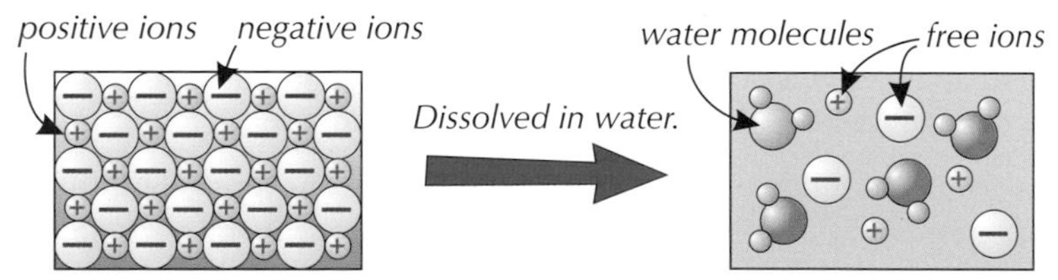

Figure 2: *A particle diagram of an ionic compound when solid and in solution.*

Tip: Have a look back at pages 111-114 for more on ionic compounds and the bonding that holds the ions together.

Practice Questions — Fact Recall

Q1 Do ionic compounds have high melting points or low melting points? Explain your answer.

Q2 Ionic compounds conduct electricity when they are dissolved in water. Explain why.

2. Covalent Substances

There are two very different types of covalent substances — simple molecules and macromolecules. The properties of these types of substances are different, because the bonding in them is different. All will be explained...

Simple molecules

Substances with covalent bonds can be **simple molecules** — molecules made up of only a few atoms. Hydrogen, chlorine, hydrogen chloride, methane, ammonia, water and oxygen are all examples of simple molecules.

Properties of simple molecules

All simple molecular substances have similar properties.

Examples

- They have low melting and boiling points.
- They are mostly gases or liquids at room temperature (because they have relatively low melting and boiling points). But they can be solids.
- They don't conduct electricity — there are no ions or free electrons so there's nothing to carry an electrical charge.

Bonding in simple molecular substances

In molecular substances, atoms form very strong covalent bonds to make small molecules of several atoms. By contrast, the forces of attraction between these molecules (**intermolecular forces**) are very weak (see Figure 1).

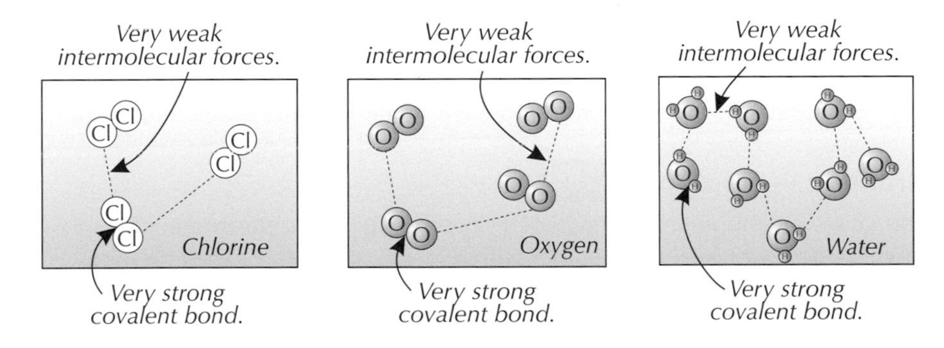

Figure 1: H *The bonding within and between simple molecules.*

It's the intermolecular forces that get broken when simple molecular substances melt or boil — not the much stronger covalent bonds. Because the intermolecular forces are weak, not much energy is needed to overcome them, and the molecules are easily parted from each other. That's why simple molecular substances have low melting and boiling points.

Learning Objectives:

- Know the general properties of simple molecular substances.
- H Be able to explain, in terms of intermolecular forces, why simple molecular substances have low melting and boiling points.
- Know that diamond, graphite and silicon dioxide are giant covalent structures (macromolecules).
- Understand why macromolecules have high melting points.
- Be able to explain, in terms of its bonding, why diamond is hard.
- Know that graphite is slippery because it consists of layers of covalently bonded atoms that are free to slide over each other.
- H Be able to explain why graphite is slippery in terms of intermolecular forces.
- H Be able to explain why graphite is a good conductor.

Specification Reference
C2.2.1, C2.2.3

Tip: Covalent substances contain covalent bonds.
A covalent bond is a shared pair of electrons.
See pages 116-119 for more on covalent bonding.

Giant covalent structures (macromolecules)

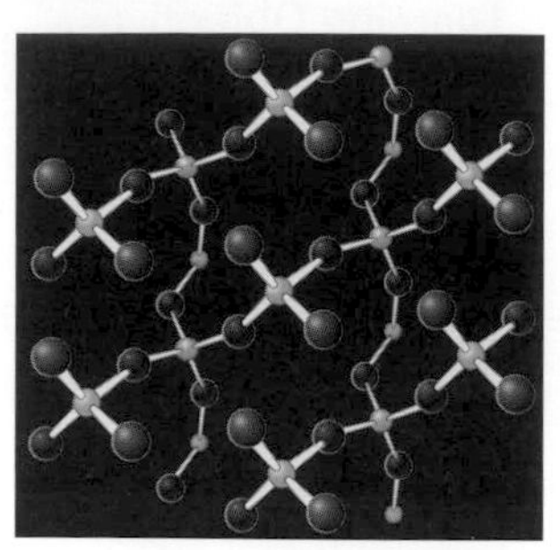

Figure 2: The structure of silicon dioxide. Silicon dioxide, sometimes called silica, is what sand is made of. Each grain of sand is one giant structure of silicon and oxygen.

Giant covalent structures are similar to giant ionic structures (lattices) except that there are no charged ions. All the atoms are bonded to each other by strong covalent bonds. A lot of energy is needed to overcome these bonds and this means that giant molecules have very high melting and boiling points. Most don't conduct electricity — not even when molten. The main examples of macromolecules are diamond and graphite, which are both made only from carbon atoms, and silicon dioxide (silica — see Figure 2).

Diamond

In diamond, each carbon atom forms four covalent bonds in a very rigid giant covalent structure (see Figure 3). This structure makes diamond the hardest natural substance, so it's used for drill tips.

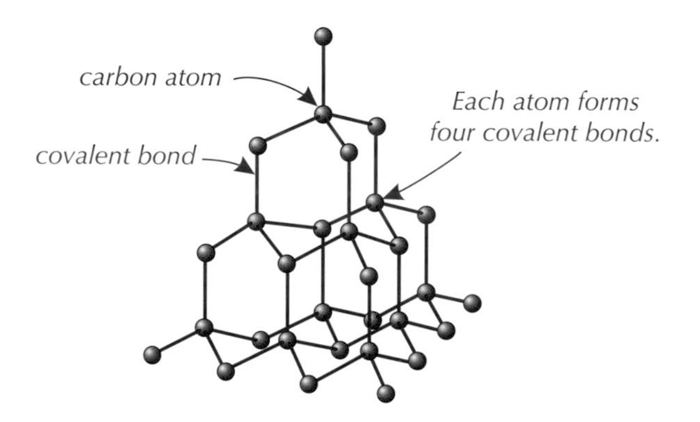

Figure 3: *The structure of diamond.*

Figure 4: *A cut, polished and sparkly diamond.*

Graphite

Graphite — the basics

In graphite, each carbon atom only forms three covalent bonds. This creates layers of carbon atoms (see Figure 6 on the next page). The layers are free to slide over each other because there are no covalent bonds between them. The layers can even be rubbed off onto paper (that's how a pencil works). Because the layers aren't covalently bonded to each other, graphite is soft and slippery.

Exam Tip
If you're doing the Foundation exam you just need to know the basics about graphite. If you're taking Higher you'll need to learn the basics and the more in-depth stuff too. Sorry!

Graphite — in-depth Higher

The layers in graphite are held loosely together by weak **intermolecular forces**. These are easily overcome, which is why the layers can slide over each other, making graphite soft and slippery.

Carbon atoms have four electrons in their outer electron shells, so they need four more to achieve a full outer shell. Usually, carbon forms four covalent bonds, but in graphite each carbon atom only forms three covalent bonds. The outer shell electrons that don't form covalent bonds are **delocalised**. This means they are free to move throughout the structure (just like the delocalised electrons in metals — see page 120). Because one electron from each carbon atom is delocalised, graphite is a good conductor of heat and electricity.

Figure 5: *Graphite. Not as nice as diamond :(*

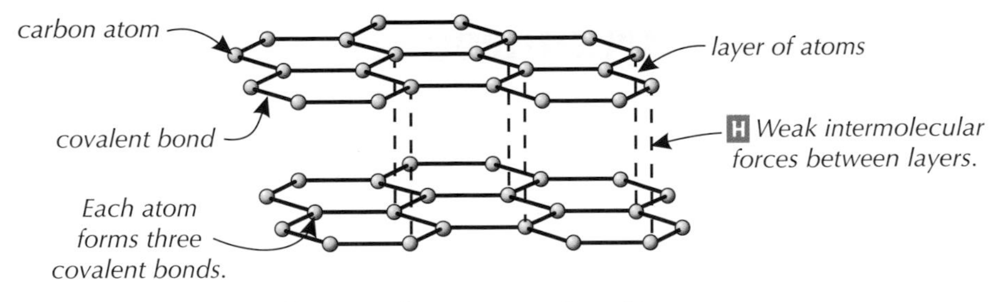

Figure 6: *The structure of graphite.*

Tip: Figure 6 only shows a tiny section of the structure of graphite. In reality, the outer carbon atoms are bonded to more carbon atoms and the overall structure is much bigger.

Practice Questions — Fact Recall

Q1 What is a simple molecule?

Q2 What type of bonding holds atoms in a simple molecule together?

Q3 Give three examples of simple molecular substances.

Q4 Simple molecular substances have low melting points. Explain why.

Q5 Diamond has a high melting point. Explain why.

Q6 Which statement(s) below describe(s) the structure of graphite?

a) Each carbon atom is covalently bonded to four other atoms.

b) The layers are held together by weak intermolecular forces.

c) Electrons not involved in covalent bonding are delocalised.

d) The structure is very hard.

Q7 What properties does graphite have that are unusual for a non-metal?

Practice Questions — Application

Q1 Diamonds can be used as cutting tools. What property of diamond makes it suitable for use as a cutting tool?

Q2 Graphite can be used as a lubricant. What property of graphite makes it suitable for use as a lubricant?

Tip: A lubricant is a substance that reduces friction, allowing things to move more smoothly.

Q3 The table below shows the melting points of graphite, oxygen and diamond (under certain conditions), and whether they conduct electricity or not.

Substance	Melting Point	Conducts Electricity?
A	3500 °C	No
B	3500 °C	Yes
C	–218 °C	No

a) Which substance (A, B or C) is graphite?

b) Which substance (A, B or C) is oxygen?

c) Which substance (A, B or C) is diamond?

Learning Objectives:

- Know that the atoms in a metal are arranged in layers.
- Know that these layers can slide over each other, which allows metals to be bent and made into different shapes.
- H Know that metals have delocalised electrons that are free to move throughout the metal.
- H Know that the delocalised electrons make metals good conductors of heat and electricity.
- Know what an alloy is and why alloys are harder than pure metals.

Specification Reference C2.2.4

3. Metallic Structures

Metals are up next, and once again you need to know about how the bonding in metals (see page 120) affects their properties.

Properties of metals

Malleability

Metals consist of atoms held together in a regular structure. The atoms form layers that are able to slide over each other — see Figure 1. This allows metals to be bent and shaped (they are malleable).

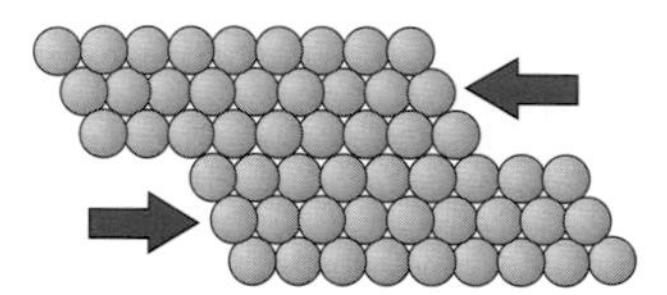

Figure 1: *Layers of atoms in a metal sliding over each other.*

Conductivity Higher

Metals have delocalised electrons that are free to move through the whole structure (see page 120 for more). Because of this, they are good conductors of heat and electricity. The electrons carry the current and the heat energy through the structure.

Alloys

Pure metals often aren't quite right for certain jobs. So scientists mix two or more metals together — creating an **alloy** with the properties they want. Different elements have different sized atoms. So when another metal is mixed with a pure metal, the new metal atoms will distort the layers of metal atoms, making it more difficult for them to slide over each other (see Figure 2). This makes alloys harder than pure metals.

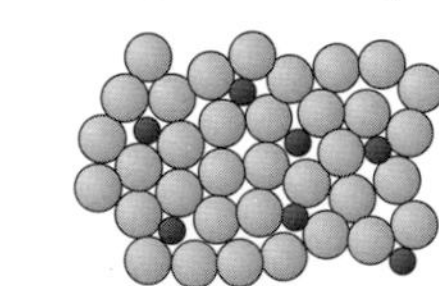

Figure 2: *Distorted layers of atoms in an alloy.*

Practice Questions — Fact Recall

Q1 Explain why metals can be easily bent.

Q2 Metals are good conductors of heat. Explain why.

Q3 Why are alloys harder than pure metals?

4. New Materials

Nowadays, we don't have to rely only on materials that occur naturally — we can make new materials. The great thing about this is that we can design them to have exactly the properties we want.

Learning Objectives:

- Know that a shape memory alloy is a material whose shape can be changed, but that will return back to its original shape when heated.
- Know some uses of shape memory alloys.
- Know what nanoparticles are and that they can have different properties to the bulk material.
- Know that nanoparticles have a high surface area to volume ratio.
- Know some of the uses of nanoparticles.
- H Know that fullerenes are nanoparticles made up of hexagonal rings of carbon atoms.
- H Know some of the uses of fullerenes.

Specification Reference C2.2.3, C2.2.4, C2.2.6

Smart materials

Smart materials behave differently depending on the conditions, for example, the temperature. **Shape memory alloys** are a type of smart material — their shape can be changed, but they'll return to their original shape when heated (see Figure 1).

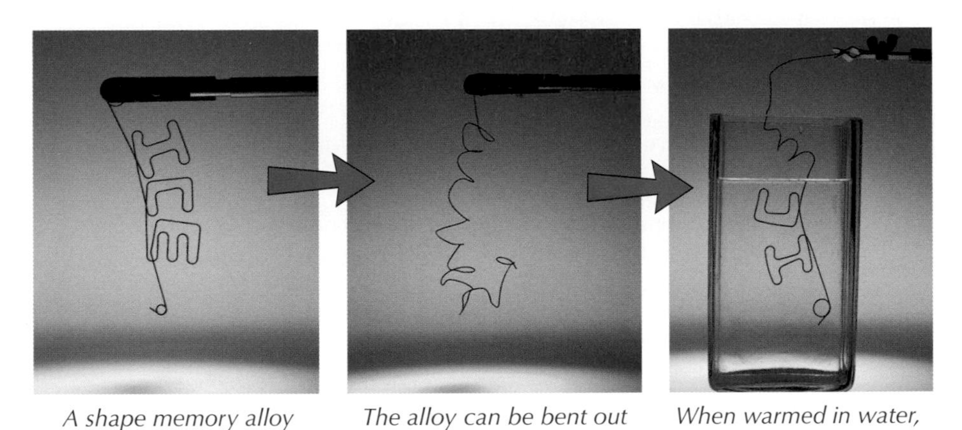

A shape memory alloy in its original shape. *The alloy can be bent out of its original shape.* *When warmed in water, the alloy starts to take on its original shape again.*

***Figure 1:** A shape memory alloy.*

Example

Nitinol is a shape memory alloy. It's a metal alloy (about half nickel, half titanium) but when it's cool you can bend it and twist it like rubber. Bend it too far, though, and it stays bent. If you then heat it above a certain temperature, it goes back to its "remembered" shape.

It's really handy for glasses frames (see Figure 2). If you accidentally bend them, you can just pop them into a bowl of hot water and they'll jump back into shape.

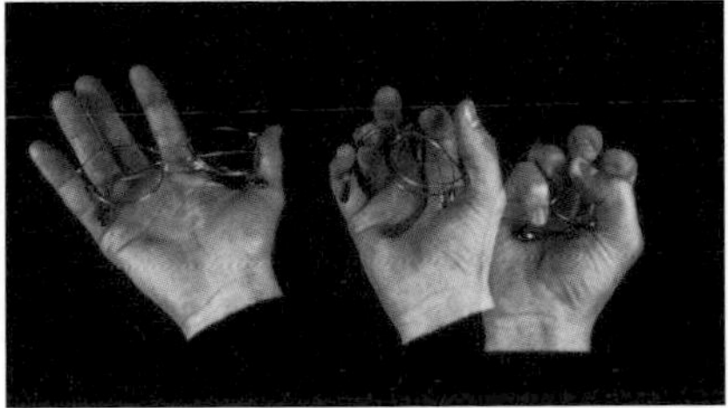

Figure 2: *Nitinol glasses.*

Nitinol is also used for dental braces. In the mouth it warms and tries to return to a 'remembered' shape, and so it gently pulls the teeth with it.

Nanoparticles

Really tiny particles, 1–100 nanometres across, are called '**nanoparticles**'. Nanoparticles contain roughly a few hundred atoms. A nanoparticle has very different properties from the 'bulk' chemical that it's made from.

Tip: 1 nm is really, really small. It's the same as 0.000 000 001 m.

Example

Silver nanoparticles can kill bacteria, so they're added to the polymer fibres used to make surgical masks. Normal silver particles are much bigger and can't kill bacteria.

Using nanoparticles is known as nanoscience. Many new uses of nanoparticles are being developed.

Examples

- Nanoparticles have a huge surface area to volume ratio, so they could help make new industrial catalysts.
- You can use nanoparticles to make sensors to detect one type of molecule and nothing else. These highly specific sensors are already being used to test water purity.
- Nanotubes can be used to make stronger, lighter building materials.
- New cosmetics, e.g. sun tan cream and deodorant, have been made using nanoparticles. The small particles do their job but don't leave white marks on the skin.
- New lubricant coatings are being developed using nanoparticles. These coatings reduce friction a bit like ball bearings and could be used in all sorts of places from artificial joints to gears.
- Nanotubes conduct electricity, so they can be used in tiny electric circuits for computer chips.

Tip: Nanotubes are tiny tube shaped nanoparticles.

Fullerenes **Higher**

Fullerenes are a type of nanoparticle — they're molecules of carbon, shaped like hollow balls or closed tubes. The carbon atoms are arranged in hexagonal rings (see Figure 3). Different fullerenes contain different numbers of carbon atoms.

Tip: Fullerenes always contain hexagonal rings of carbon atoms, but they can also contain rings with different numbers of carbon atoms, e.g. pentagonal rings.

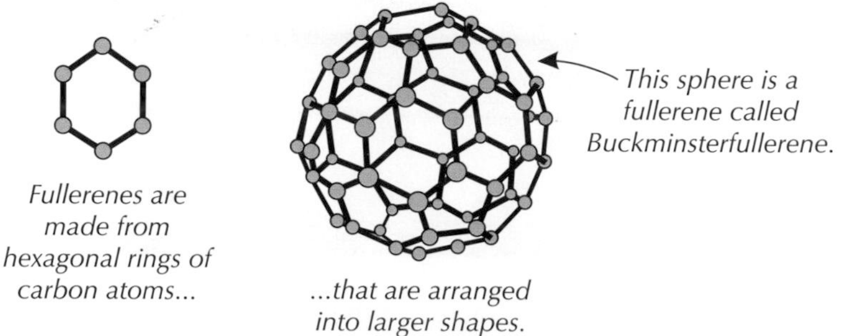

Figure 3: *The structure of fullerenes.*

Uses of fullerenes Higher

- Fullerenes can be used in lubricants and as catalysts (see previous page).
- Fullerenes could one day be used in medicine. They're absorbed more easily by the body than most particles. This means they could deliver drugs right into the cells where they're needed.
- Carbon nanotubes are a type of fullerene — they're teeny tiny hollow carbon tubes that are only a few nanometres across (see Figures 4 and 5). All those covalent bonds make carbon nanotubes very strong. They can be used to reinforce materials, such as graphite in tennis rackets.

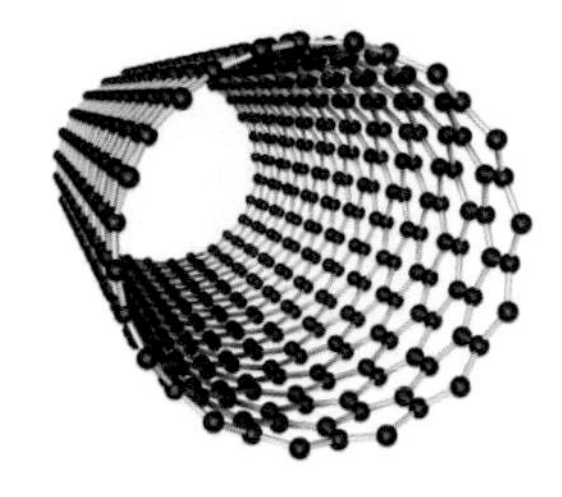

Figure 4: *A model of a carbon nanotube.*

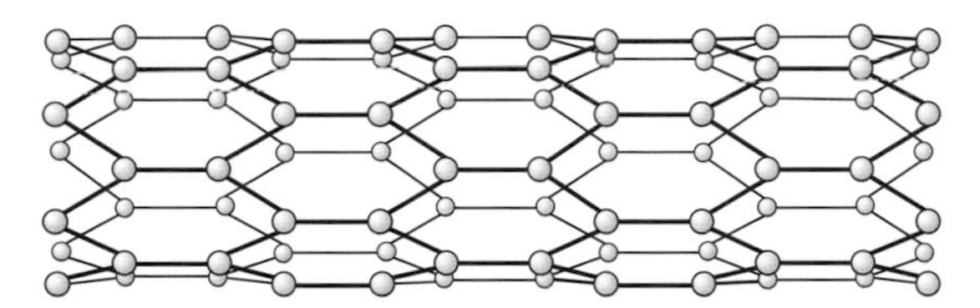

Figure 5: *A nanotube.*

Practice Questions — Fact Recall

Q1 Which sentence below is true?

a) Shape memory alloys return to their original shape when cooled.

b) Shape memory alloys can 'remember' and return to a variety of different shapes, depending on their temperature.

c) When heated, shape memory alloys return to their original shape.

Q2 Name one shape memory alloy.

Q3 How big (in nanometres) are nanoparticles?

Q4 Give three uses of nanoparticles.

Q5 Fullerenes are made from carbon atoms arranged into a particular shape. Which of the diagrams below shows the arrangement of carbon atoms found in all fullerenes?

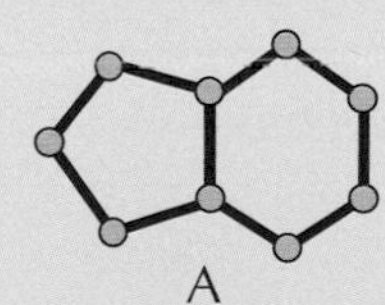

A

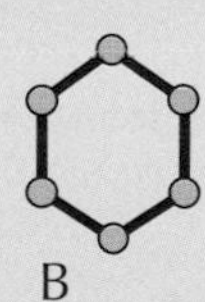

B

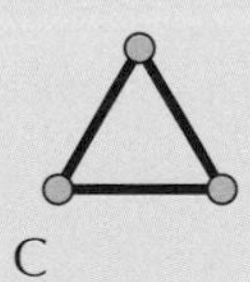

C

Q6 Give two uses of fullerenes.

5. Polymers

Polymers are mighty useful things, and there's loads to know about them. Here's all the stuff that you need to know...

Learning Objectives:
- Know that there are no cross-links between polymer chains in thermosoftening polymers.
- Know that thermosetting polymers are made up of polymer chains with cross-links between them.
- Know that thermosetting polymers don't melt when they are heated.
- H Know that the intermolecular forces between polymer chains in thermosoftening polymers are weak and that this allows the polymer to be softened and remoulded repeatedly.
- Know that the reactants and the reaction conditions when a polymer is formed affect the properties of the polymer.
- Be able to link the properties of polymers to their uses.

Specification Reference C2.2, C2.2.5

Types of polymers

Polymers are very large molecules formed when many small molecules, called monomers, join together. Strong covalent bonds hold the atoms together in long chains. You need to know about two different types of polymers — **thermosoftening polymers** and **thermosetting polymers**.

1. Thermosoftening polymers

Thermosoftening polymers are made of individual tangled chains of polymers (see Figure 1).

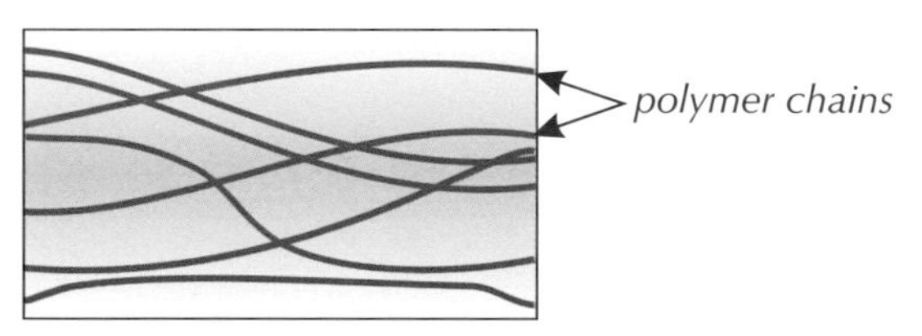

Figure 1: *Polymer chains in a thermosoftening polymer.*

2. Thermosetting polymers

Thermosetting polymers have cross-links between their polymer chains (see Figure 2). These mean that the polymer doesn't melt when it's heated. When the polymer reaches a certain temperature it just burns instead.

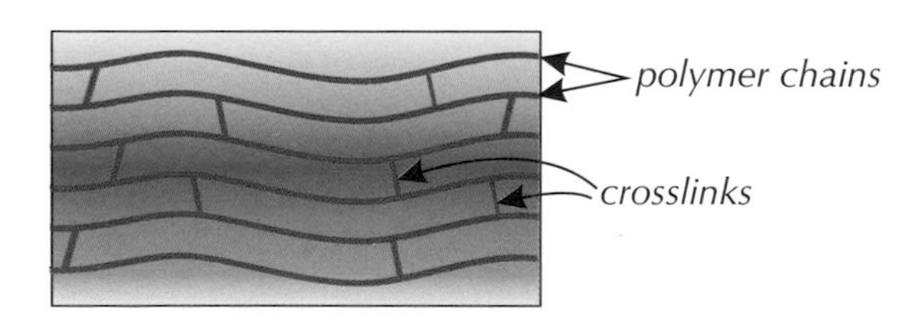

Figure 2: *Polymer chains in a thermosetting polymer.*

Intermolecular forces in polymers Higher

It's the bonds or the intermolecular forces between different polymer chains that determine the properties of a polymer.

The cross-links between the polymer chains in thermosetting polymers are very strong. They hold the chains firmly together in a solid structure. They make thermosetting polymers tough — they're strong, hard and rigid.

Figure 3: *A telephone made of Bakelite — the first thermosetting polymer in widespread use.*

Thermosoftening polymers don't have cross-linking between chains. The chains are held together by weak intermolecular forces, and are free to slide over each other. The forces between the chains are really easy to overcome, so it's dead easy to melt the plastic. When it cools, the polymer hardens into a new shape. You can melt these polymers and remould them as many times as you like. This makes it relatively easy to recycle thermosoftening polymers.

Exam Tip
Thermosetting polymers are set in one shape and won't melt. Thermosoftening polymers can be softened and re-shaped.

Properties of polymers

The starting materials and reaction conditions will both affect the properties of a polymer.

Example

Two types of polythene can be made using different conditions:

Low density (LD) polythene is made by heating ethene to about 200 °C under high pressure. It's flexible and is used for bags and bottles.

High density (HD) polythene is made at a lower temperature and pressure (with a catalyst). It's more rigid and is used for water tanks and drainpipes.

Tip: Polythene is also known as poly(ethene).

Uses of polymers

The use of a polymer depends on its properties. You might get exam questions where you have to relate the properties of polymers to their uses.

Example

Choose from the table the polymer that would be best suited for making:

1. a disposable cup for hot drinks,
2. clothing,
3. a measuring cylinder.

Give reasons for each choice.

Polymer	Cost	Resistance to chemicals	Melting point	Transparency	Rigidity	Can be made into fibres
W	High	High	High	Low	High	No
X	Low	Low	Low	Low	Low	Yes
Y	High	High	High	High	High	No
Z	Low	Low	High	High	High	No

Answers:
1. Z — low cost (disposable) and high melting point (for hot drinks).
2. X — flexible (essential for clothing) and able to be made into fibres (clothing is usually woven).
3. Y — transparent and resistant to chemicals (you need to be able to see the liquid inside and the liquid and measuring cylinder mustn't react with each other).

Tip: Plastics are polymers. That's why plastics can be used for so many different things — there are lots of different types, all with different properties.

Practice Questions — Fact Recall

Q1 Give the name of the type of polymer that's made up of polymer chains with cross-links between the chains.

Q2 Which type of polymer will melt when it is heated — a thermosetting polymer or a thermosoftening polymer?

Q3 Explain the difference in the properties of thermosetting polymers and thermosoftening polymers in terms of the forces between the polymer chains.

Q4 The reactants used to make a polymer affect the properties of the polymer. Give one other factor that affects the properties of a polymer.

Q5 Give the names of two types of polythene.

Practice Questions — Application

Q1 Melamine resin is a polymer used to make kitchenware such as plates, ladles and spatulas. Suggest whether melamine resin is a thermosetting or thermosoftening polymer. Give a reason for your answer.

Q2 Polystyrene softens when it's heated above 100 °C. It can then be moulded to make lots of different products, including test-tubes and petri dishes. Suggest what type of polymer polystyrene is. Give a reason for your answer.

Q3 The table shows some of the properties of four different polymers.

Polymer	Properties
LD polythene	Soft, flexible, waxy.
Polyvinyl chloride	Strong, hard, rigid.
Expanded polystyrene	Poor conductor of heat, good shock absorber, lightweight.
Poly(methyl methacrylate)	Hard, transparent, shatter-resistant.

Using the information in the table, suggest a polymer that would be suitable for each of the uses listed below. Give reasons for your choices.

a) A packaging material for glassware.

b) A protective barrier for spectators at an ice-hockey game.

c) Insulation material in a house.

d) Pipes for sewage.

Tip: You can use each polymer in Q3 once, more than once, or not at all in your answers.

Section Checklist — Make sure you know...

Ionic Compounds

- ❑ That ionic compounds are giant lattices of ions held together by strong electrostatic forces.
- ❑ That a lot of energy is needed to overcome these electrostatic forces and melt or boil the compound, so ionic compounds have high melting points and boiling points.
- ❑ That melted or dissolved ionic compounds can conduct electricity because the ions are free to move.

Covalent Substances

- ❑ That simple molecules have low melting points, low boiling points and don't conduct electricity.
- ❑ H That the intermolecular forces in simple covalent substances are very weak and not much energy is needed to overcome them, so simple covalent substances have low melting and boiling points.
- ❑ That all the atoms in macromolecules are joined by strong covalent bonds and large amounts of energy are needed to break these bonds, so macromolecules have very high melting points.
- ❑ Why diamond is very hard and why graphite is soft and slippery.
- ❑ H That each carbon atom in graphite provides one delocalised electron, and that these delocalised electrons allow graphite to conduct heat and electricity.

Metallic Structures

- ❑ That metals can be bent and shaped because the layers of metal atoms can slide over each other.
- ❑ H That metals have delocalised electrons, which allows them to conduct electricity.
- ❑ That alloys are harder than pure metals because atoms of another element are added, disrupting the layers and stopping them from sliding over each other.

New Materials

- ❑ That shape memory alloys can be bent out of shape but will return to their original shape on heating.
- ❑ That nanoparticles are tiny particles with a high surface area to volume ratio and that they have different properties to the bulk material.
- ❑ Some of the uses of nanoparticles, e.g. as catalysts, in computers, as lubricants and in cosmetics.
- ❑ H What fullerenes are and some uses of fullerenes, e.g. in drug delivery and strengthening materials.

Polymers

- ❑ That thermosoftening polymers are made of individual chains of polymers tangled together and that thermosetting polymers have cross-links between their polymer chains.
- ❑ That thermosetting polymers don't melt when heated.
- ❑ H That thermosoftening polymers soften when heated because they only have weak intermolecular forces between their polymer chains, which are easily overcome.
- ❑ That the reactants and reaction conditions used when a polymer is made determine its properties.

Exam-style Questions

1 Different substances have different structures.

1 (a) Draw a straight line from each structure listed below to the name of the substance that has that structure.

Structure	Substance
Giant ionic	Silicon dioxide
Simple molecular	Sodium chloride
Giant covalent	Ammonia
Giant metallic	Aluminium

(4 marks)

1 (b) The structure of a substance affects its properties. The melting point, boiling point and electrical conductivity of four substances were tested. The results are shown in the table below.

Substance	Melting point (°C)	Boiling point (°C)	Good electrical conductor?
A	–218.4	–182.96	No
B	1535	2750	Yes
C	1410	2355	No
D	801	1413	When molten

Use the words in the box to complete the sentences below.
You can use each structure once, more than once or not at all.

giant ionic	simple molecular	giant covalent	giant metallic

1 (b) (i) Substance A has a .... structure.

1 (b) (ii) Substance B has a .... structure.

1 (b) (iii) Substance C has a .... structure.

1 (b) (iv) Substance D has a .... structure.

(4 marks)

2 Lithium chloride is formed from the reaction between potassium and chlorine. The diagrams below show the electronic structures of lithium and chlorine atoms.

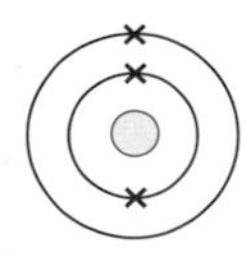

Lithium atom

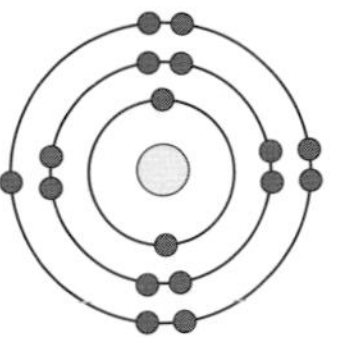

Chlorine atom

2 (a) Chlorine (Cl_2) is a gas at room temperature.

2 (a) (i) Name the type of bonding found in chlorine gas.

(1 mark)

2 (a) (ii) Explain, as fully as you can, why chlorine is a gas at room temperature.

(3 marks)

2 (b) The electronic structures of lithium and chlorine change when they react together.

2 (b) (i) Describe and explain the changes in the electronic structures of lithium and chlorine when they react.

(3 marks)

2 (b) (ii) Draw a diagram to show the electronic structures of the particles formed during the reaction of lithium and chlorine.

(2 marks)

2 (b) (iii) Give the chemical formula of lithium chloride.

(1 mark)

2 (c) Lithium chloride has a high melting point. Explain why.

(2 marks)

3 Polycaprolactone is a biodegradable polymer with a melting point of 60 °C.

3 (a) Circle the correct term in the box below.

Polycaprolactone is a

thermosetting polymer.
thermosoftening polymer.

3 (b) The atoms in a polymer chain are held together by covalent bonds.

3 (b) (i) Explain, as fully as you can, what happens when a covalent bond is formed.

(2 marks)

3 (b) (ii) Covalent bonds are very strong but polycaprolactone has a relatively low melting point. Explain why.

(2 marks)

3 (c) Urea formaldehyde is a thermosetting polymer. Explain why this makes it difficult to recycle.

(3 marks)

3 (d) Polymers are macromolecules. Give the name of **one** other macromolecule.

(1 mark)

4 Carbon can exist in different forms. How the atoms are arranged and the bonding between the atoms determines which form of carbon is made.

4 (a) *In this question you will be assessed on the quality of your English, the organisation of your ideas and your use of appropriate specialist vocabulary.*

The photos below show diamond and graphite.
Diamond is very hard, but graphite is soft and slippery.

Explain why diamond is hard and graphite is soft and slippery.

Your answer should include details of:

- how the atoms are arranged in diamond and graphite
- the bonding in the structures.

(6 marks)

4 (b) Carbon can also form nanoparticles called carbon nanotubes. Carbon nanotubes are a type of fullerene. Tick the **two** statements below that are true.

Carbon nanotubes have different properties to bulk carbon.	
A nanoparticle is made up of thousands of atoms.	
Carbon nanotubes have a low surface area to volume ratio.	
Carbon nanotubes contain carbon atoms arranged in hexagons.	

(2 marks)

5 Sterling silver is a silver alloy.

5 (a) Sterling silver and silver are both good conductors of electricity. Explain why.

(2 marks)

5 (b) The diagrams below show the arrangement of atoms in a sample of pure silver and in a sample of sterling silver.

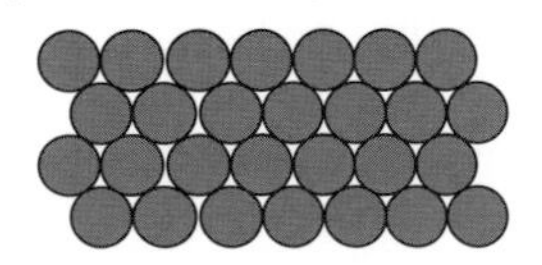

Diagram A

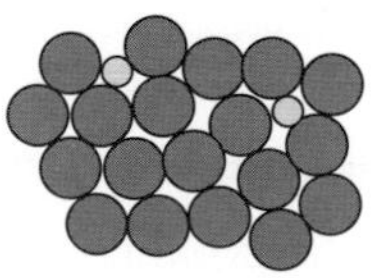

Diagram B

5 (b) (i) Which diagram shows the atoms in sterling silver? Explain your answer.

(1 mark)

5 (b) (ii) Which substance is harder, pure silver or sterling silver? Explain your answer.

(2 marks)

1. Atoms and Isotopes

By now, you should know that everything is made up of atoms and that atoms are made up of protons, neutrons and electrons. Time to find out a bit more...

Atomic number and mass number

In the periodic table, atoms are represented by chemical symbols with two numbers next to them. The bottom number is the **atomic number** — this tells you how many protons there are in the atom. The top number is the **mass number** — this is the total number of protons and neutrons in the atom (see Figure 1).

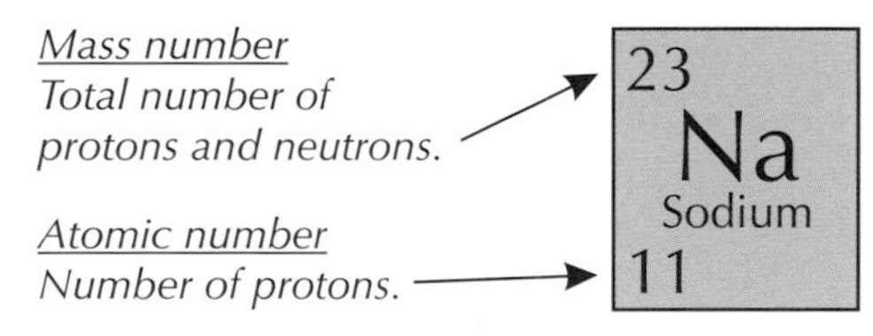

Figure 1: *The mass and atomic numbers of the element sodium.*

Atoms of the same element all have the same number of protons — so atoms of different elements will have different numbers of protons.

Finding the number of neutrons

To find the number of neutrons in an atom, you just subtract the atomic number from the mass number.

Example

Sodium (above) has an atomic number of 11 (it contains 11 protons).
It has a mass number of 23 (there are 23 protons and neutrons altogether).
So an atom of sodium contains 23 – 11 = 12 neutrons.

Relative masses of protons, neutrons and electrons

Electrons aren't counted in the mass number because their relative mass is very small — see Figure 2.

Particle	Relative mass
Proton	1
Neutron	1
Electron	very small

Figure 2: *Table showing the relative masses of protons, neutrons and electrons.*

Learning Objectives:

- Know that atoms can be represented as chemical symbols with a mass number and an atomic number.
- Know that the mass number is the total number of protons and neutrons in an atom.
- Know the relative masses of protons, neutrons and electrons.
- Know that isotopes are atoms that have the same number of protons but different numbers of neutrons.

Specification Reference C2.3.1

Tip: The actual masses of protons and neutrons are tiny, so chemists use relative mass instead to make life simpler. The masses of protons and neutrons are very similar, so they are each given a relative mass of 1.

Isotopes

Exam Tip
Examiners love to ask you about isotopes, so make sure you know what isotopes are and how to spot them.

Isotopes are different atomic forms of the same element, which have the same number of protons but a different number of neutrons. Isotopes must have the same atomic number but different mass numbers. If they had different atomic numbers, they'd be different elements altogether.

Example

Carbon-12 and carbon-14 are an important pair of isotopes. They each have 6 protons (and so an atomic number of 6). But carbon-12 has 6 neutrons (giving it a mass number of 12), while carbon-14 has 8 neutrons (giving it a mass number of 14) — see Figure 3.

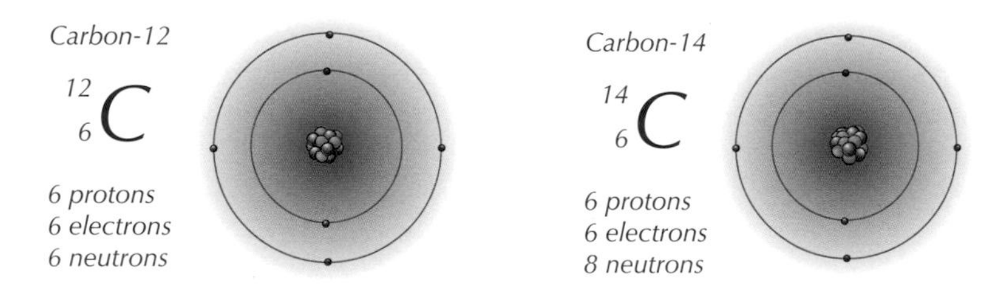

Figure 3: *The atomic structures of carbon-12 and carbon-14.*

Practice Questions — Fact Recall

Q1 a) What does the atomic number tell you about an atom?

b) What does the mass number tell you about an atom?

Q2 How would you find the number of neutrons in an atom from the mass number and the atomic number?

Q3 What is the relative mass of:

a) a proton. b) an electron. c) a neutron.

Q4 What is an isotope?

Exam Tip
If you're ever asked what an isotope is, it's fine to start your answer "Isotopes are...". It's really hard to explain it if you don't start with a plural.

Practice Questions — Application

Q1 Write down how many protons and neutrons each of the following atoms have:

a) $^{16}_{8}O$ b) $^{27}_{13}Al$ c) $^{51}_{23}V$ d) $^{108}_{47}Ag$

Q2 Which of these is the chemical symbol of an isotope of $^{35}_{17}Cl$?

A: $^{37}_{17}Cl$ B: $^{35}_{16}Cl$ C: $^{36}_{16}Cl$ D: $^{17}_{35}Cl$

2. Relative Formula Mass

Relative atomic masses and relative formula masses sound a lot scarier than they actually are. Give these pages a read and you should have got to grips with them in no time...

Learning Objectives:

- Know the term 'relative atomic mass'.
- H Know that relative atomic mass tells you how heavy the atoms of an element are compared to atoms of carbon-12.
- Know what is meant by the term 'relative formula mass'.
- Be able to calculate the relative formula mass for a compound.
- Know how relative formula mass is linked to moles.

Specification Reference C2.3.1

Relative atomic mass

Relative atomic mass (A_r) is a way of comparing the masses of atoms of different elements. The relative atomic mass is usually just the same as the **mass number** of the element in the periodic table.

Examples

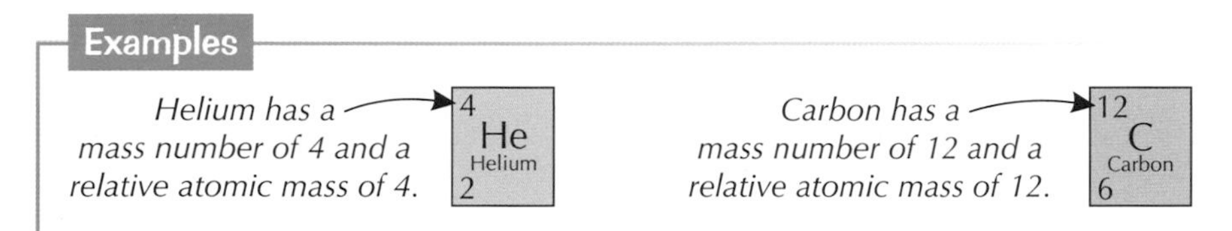

More on relative atomic mass Higher

The relative atomic mass of an element is just how heavy atoms of that element are compared with the mass of an atom of carbon-12. Carbon-12 has an A_r of exactly 12 by definition (scientists decided it would be that) — the relative atomic masses of all the other elements were set relative to it.

When an element has more than one stable **isotope**, the relative atomic mass is an average value of all the different isotopes (taking into account how much there is of each isotope).

Tip: See page 138 for a recap of isotopes.

Example **Higher**

Chlorine has two stable isotopes — chlorine-35 and chlorine-37. There's lots more chlorine-35 around than chlorine-37, so the average relative atomic mass of chlorine turns out to be about 35.5.

Calculating relative formula mass

The **relative formula mass** (M_r) of a compound is just all the relative atomic masses of the atoms in that compound added together.

Examples

- Magnesium chloride ($MgCl_2$) contains one atom of magnesium and two atoms of chlorine. Magnesium has a relative atomic mass of 24 and chlorine has a relative atomic mass of 35.5, so the relative formula mass of magnesium chloride is 24 + (2 × 35.5) = 95.
- Iron oxide (Fe_2O_3) contains two atoms of iron and three atoms of oxygen. Iron has an A_r of 56 and oxygen has an A_r of 16, so the relative formula mass of iron oxide is (2 × 56) + (3 × 16) = 160

Exam Tip
You can get the A_r of any element from the periodic table, though if you need to use them in an exam question they'll usually be given to you.

Tip: The relative atomic mass of chlorine is multiplied by 2 here because there are two chlorine atoms in $MgCl_2$.

***Figure 1:** Carbon has an A_r of 12, so one mole of carbon weighs exactly 12 g.*

Tip: If you're finding the number of moles of an element, you can always use A_r instead of M_r in the equation.

Exam Tip
You could be expected to rearrange equations like this in the exam. There's more on how to rearrange equations on page 352.

The mole

The relative mass (A_r or M_r) of a substance in grams is known as one **mole** of that substance.

Examples

- Iron (Fe) has an A_r of 56. So one mole of iron weighs exactly 56 g.
- Nitrogen gas (N_2) has an M_r of 2 × 14 = 28. So one mole of N_2 weighs exactly 28 g.

You can convert between moles and grams using this formula:

$$\text{Number of moles} = \frac{\text{Mass in g (of element or compound)}}{M_r \text{ (of element or compound)}}$$

Example 1

How many moles are there in 42 g of carbon?

The A_r of carbon is 12, so the number of moles in 42 g of carbon is:

$$\text{Moles} = \frac{\text{mass}}{A_r} = \frac{42}{12} = 3.5 \text{ moles}$$

Example 2

How much would 0.8 moles of sulfuric acid (H_2SO_4) weigh in grams?

The M_r of sulfuric acid is (2 × 1) + 32 + (4 × 16) = 98.

Rearrange the formula to find mass (multiply both sides by M_r):

mass = moles × M_r = 0.8 × 98 = 78.4 g

So 0.8 moles of sulfuric acid would weigh 78.4 g

Practice Questions — Fact Recall

Q1 What is the relative atomic mass (A_r) of an element?

Q2 Explain why relative atomic masses aren't always whole numbers.

Q3 Describe how you would work out the relative formula mass (M_r) of a compound.

Q4 What equation can you use to convert between moles and grams?

Practice Questions — Application

Use the periodic table on the back cover to help answer these questions.

Q1 Find the relative atomic masses of the following elements:

a) Beryllium (Be) b) Phosphorus (P)

c) Zinc (Zn) d) Copper (Cu)

Q2 What is the relative formula mass of:

a) Oxygen (O_2) b) Potassium hydroxide (KOH)

c) Nitric acid (HNO_3) d) Calcium carbonate ($CaCO_3$)

Q3 How many moles are there in each of the following?

a) 19.5 g of potassium (K)

b) 23.4 g of sodium chloride (NaCl)

c) 76.8 g of sulfur dioxide (SO_2)

d) 31.9 g of copper sulfate ($CuSO_4$)

Q4 How much would the following weigh in grams?

a) 0.8 moles of nickel (Ni)

b) 0.5 moles of magnesium oxide (MgO)

c) 1.6 moles of ammonia (NH_3)

d) 1.4 moles of calcium hydroxide ($Ca(OH)_2$)

Figure 2: *One mole of a variety of compounds.*

Learning Objectives:

- Know how to calculate the percentage of an element in a compound.
- H Know how to work out the empirical formula of a compound.

Specification Reference C2.3.3

3. Formula Mass Calculations

If you're not all that fond of maths, then brace yourself. This topic is all about the calculations you can do using the relative formula mass of a compound.

Calculating percentage mass

The percentage mass is a way of saying what proportion of the mass of a compound is due to atoms of a particular element.

Example

The percentage mass of carbon (C) in methane (CH_4) is 75%. This means that 75% of the mass of methane is made up of carbon atoms — so if you have 100 g of methane, it will contain 75 g of carbon.

Tip: Methane only contains carbon and hydrogen. So once you know that 75% of its mass is made up of carbon atoms, you can also say that 25% of its mass must be made up of hydrogen atoms.

If you know the molecular formula of a compound, you can work out the percentage mass of a particular element within that compound using this formula:

$$\text{Percentage mass of an element in a compound} = \frac{A_r \times \text{No. of atoms (of that element)}}{M_r \text{ (of the whole compound)}} \times 100$$

Example 1

Find the percentage mass of magnesium in magnesium oxide, MgO.

The A_r of magnesium = 24 and the A_r of oxygen = 16.

So the M_r of MgO = 24 + 16 = 40

$$\% \text{ Mass of Mg} = \frac{A_r \text{ of Mg} \times \text{No. of Mg atoms}}{M_r \text{ of MgO}} \times 100 = \frac{24}{40} \times 100 = 60\ \%$$

This means that magnesium makes up 60% of the mass of magnesium oxide.

Example 2

Find the percentage mass of sodium in sodium carbonate, Na_2CO_3.

The A_r of sodium = 23, the A_r of carbon = 12 and the A_r of oxygen = 16.

So the M_r of Na_2CO_3 = (2 × 23) + 12 + (3 × 16) = 106

$$\% \text{ Mass of Na} = \frac{A_r \text{ of Na} \times \text{No. of Na atoms}}{M_r \text{ of } Na_2CO_3} \times 100 = \frac{23 \times 2}{106} \times 100 = 43.4\ \%$$

This means that sodium makes up 43.4% of the mass of sodium carbonate.

Finding the empirical formula Higher

The **empirical formula** of a compound gives the simplest possible whole number ratio of atoms of each element within that compound. It's slightly different to the **molecular formula** of a compound, which gives you the actual number of atoms of each element within the compound. Often, the empirical and molecular formulae of a compound will be the same.

Example — Higher

The molecular formula of sodium hydroxide is NaOH.

This can't be simplified so NaOH is also the empirical formula.

But occasionally they're different.

Example — Higher

The molecular formula of glucose is $C_6H_{12}O_6$.

This can be simplified to CH_2O, which is the empirical formula of glucose.

Tip: The molecular formula is always a multiple of the empirical formula. In the case of glucose, you multiply the empirical formula by six to get the molecular formula.

If you know the actual mass or the percentage mass of each element that's in a compound, you can find its empirical formula. Here's what you do:

1. List all the elements in the compound (there's usually only two or three).
2. Underneath them, write their masses or percentages.
3. Divide each mass or percentage by the A_r of that particular element.
4. Take each of these numbers and divide them by the smallest answer from step 3. This will give you the ratio of the elements in the compound.
5. If any of your answers are not whole numbers, you'll need to multiply everything up to get the lowest possible whole number ratio.

Tip: Step 5 may look a bit tricky, but it's simple really. For example, if one of your Step 4 answers ends in a half, it just means multiplying them all by 2.

Example 1 — Higher

A compound contains 26.1% carbon, 4.3% hydrogen and 69.6% oxygen by mass. Find the empirical formula of this compound. (A_r for carbon = 12, A_r for hydrogen = 1, A_r for oxygen = 16)

1. List the three elements in the compound:	C	H	O
2. Write out the experimental percentages given in the question:	26.1	4.3	69.6
3. Divide each percentage by the A_r of that element:	$\frac{26.1}{12} = 2.2$	$\frac{4.3}{1} = 4.3$	$\frac{69.6}{16} = 4.4$
4. Divide by the smallest answer (2.2 in this case):	$\frac{2.2}{2.2} = 1$	$\frac{4.3}{2.2} = 2$	$\frac{4.4}{2.2} = 2$

5. This is a whole number ratio.

So the empirical formula must be CH_2O_2.

Tip: You might need to round your answers in step 4 to the nearest whole number of atoms. For example, 4.3 ÷ 2.2 is actually 1.9545... but that's close enough that you can round it to 2.

Tip: You need to know that doing an experiment like this is the only way of getting the data you need to find the formula of a compound. You might know that rust is iron oxide, but is it FeO, or Fe_2O_3? An experiment to determine the empirical formula will tell you for certain.

Example 2 — Higher

Find the empirical formula of the iron oxide produced when 44.8 g of iron reacts with 19.2 g of oxygen. (A_r for iron = 56, A_r for oxygen = 16)

Step	Fe	O
1. List the two elements in iron oxide:	Fe	O
2. Write out the experimental masses given in the question:	44.8	19.2
3. Divide each mass by the A_r of that element:	$\frac{44.8}{56} = 0.8$	$\frac{19.2}{16} = 1.2$
4. Divide by the smallest number (0.8 in this case):	$\frac{0.8}{0.8} = 1$	$\frac{1.2}{0.8} = 1.5$
5. Multiply to get the lowest whole number ratio (in this case multiply by 2).	2	3

So the empirical formula must be Fe_2O_3.

Practice Questions — Fact Recall

Q1 Which formula would you use to calculate the percentage mass of an element in a compound?

Q2 What is the empirical formula of a compound?

Q3 Describe how you would find the empirical formula of a compound from experimental masses.

Practice Questions — Application

Use the periodic table on the back cover to help answer these questions.

Q1 Find the percentage mass of:

a) hydrogen (H) in hydrochloric acid (HCl).

b) sodium (Na) in sodium hydroxide (NaOH).

c) aluminium (Al) in aluminium oxide (Al_2O_3).

d) oxygen (O) in copper hydroxide ($Cu(OH)_2$).

Q2 Find the empirical formula of the nitrogen oxide produced when 5.6 g of nitrogen reacts with 12.8 g of oxygen.

Q3 A hydrocarbon contains 80% carbon and 20% hydrogen by mass. Find the empirical formula of this hydrocarbon.

Q4 Find the empirical formula of the compound that contains 10.8 g of carbon, 2.4 g of hydrogen and 9.6 g of oxygen.

Q5 Find the empirical formula of the compound that contains 52.3% iron, 44.9% oxygen and 2.8% hydrogen by mass.

Tip: Make sure you've got a calculator handy to help you with these calculations.

4. Calculating Masses in Reactions

If you know the mass of one reactant in a reaction, you can use the symbol equation for that reaction and a nifty bit of maths to work out the mass of product you should get. Here's what you do...

Learning Objective:

- **H** Know how to calculate masses of reactants and products from balanced symbol equations.

Specification Reference C2.3.3

How to calculate the mass of a product Higher

If you want to work out the mass of product you would expect to make from a certain mass of reactant, you need to follow these steps:

1. Write out the balanced equation for the reaction.
2. Find the M_r of the reactant and the product that you're interested in.
3. Apply the rule: Divide to get one, then multiply to get all:
   - Divide both relative formula masses by the M_r of the reactant — this tells you how much product would be formed from 1 g of the reactant.
   - Multiply this by the amount of reactant given in the question to find out how much product would be formed from that much reactant.

Example 1 Higher

What mass of magnesium oxide is produced when 60 g of magnesium is burned in air?

1. The balanced symbol equation for this reaction is:

$$2Mg + O_2 \rightarrow 2MgO$$

2. The reactant you've got is 2Mg. The product you want is 2MgO.

The M_r of 2Mg = 2 × 24 = 48
The M_r of 2MgO = 2 × (24 + 16) = 80

1. Apply the rule: divide to get one, then multiply to get all.
   - First, you need to know how much magnesium oxide can be made from 1 g of magnesium. So start by dividing both relative formula masses by the M_r of the reactant (that's the magnesium).

÷ 48 48 g of magnesium reacts to give 80 g of magnesium oxide. ÷ 48
1 g of magnesium reacts to give 1.67 g of magnesium oxide.

   - The question asks you to find the mass of magnesium oxide produced when 60 g of magnesium is burned in air. So now you need to multiply both sides by 60.

× 60 1 g of magnesium reacts to give 1.67 g of magnesium oxide. × 60
60 g of magnesium reacts to give 100 g of magnesium oxide.

So there you have it — 60 g of Mg will produce 100 g of MgO.

Tip: Make sure you include the numbers in front of the symbols when you're working out the relative masses of the products and reactants.

***Figure 1:** Magnesium burning in air.*

Example 2 **Higher**

What mass of calcium chloride ($CaCl_2$) is produced when 24 g of calcium hydroxide ($Ca(OH)_2$) reacts with an excess of hydrochloric acid (HCl)?

1. The balanced symbol equation for this reaction is:

$$Ca(OH)_2 + 2HCl \rightarrow CaCl_2 + 2H_2O$$

2. The reactant you've got is $Ca(OH)_2$. The product you want is $CaCl_2$.

The M_r of $Ca(OH)_2 = 40 + (2 \times (16 + 1)) = 74$
The M_r of $CaCl_2 = 40 + (2 \times 35.5) = 111$

3. Apply the rule, divide to get one, then multiply to get all.

- First divide both relative formula masses by the M_r of $Ca(OH)_2$:

÷ 74 — 74 g of $Ca(OH)_2$ reacts to give 111 g of $CaCl_2$. — ÷ 74
1 g of $Ca(OH)_2$ reacts to give 1.5 g of $CaCl_2$.

- Then multiply both sides by 24:

× 24 — 1 g of $Ca(OH)_2$ reacts to give 1.5 g of $CaCl_2$. — × 24
24 g of $Ca(OH)_2$ reacts to give 36 g of $CaCl_2$.

So 24 g of $Ca(OH)_2$ will produce 36 g of $CaCl_2$.

Tip: The mass of product is called the yield of a reaction — see page 148 for more.

How to calculate the mass of a reactant **Higher**

You can use the same basic method to find how much reactant you'd need to use to make a certain mass of product. The only difference is in Step 3 — this time you divide both relative formula masses by the M_r of the product. This tells you how much reactant you would need to form 1 g of product. Then you just multiply everything by the mass of product given in the question.

Example **Higher**

How much zinc carbonate ($ZnCO_3$) would need to decompose to form 24.2 g of zinc oxide (ZnO)?

1. The balanced symbol equation for this reaction is:

$$ZnCO_3 \rightarrow ZnO + CO_2$$

2. The reactant you want is $ZnCO_3$. The product you've got is ZnO.

The M_r of $ZnCO_3 = 65 + 12 + (3 \times 16) = 125$
The M_r of $ZnO = 65 + 16 = 81$

3. Apply the rule, divide to get one, then multiply to get all.

- This time, you want to know how much zinc carbonate you would need to produce 1 g of zinc oxide. So start by dividing both relative formula masses by the M_r of the product (zinc oxide).

Exam Tip
In the exam, you might be expected to know the equation for a reaction (if it's one you've studied), or you might be given the balanced symbol equation in the question.

÷ 81 (125 g of $ZnCO_3$ reacts to give 81 g of ZnO.) ÷ 81

1.54 g of $ZnCO_3$ reacts to give 1 g of ZnO.

- Now all you have to do is multiply both sides by 24.2 to find how much zinc carbonate you would need to make 24.2 g of zinc oxide.

× 24.2 (1.54 g of $ZnCO_3$ reacts to give 1 g of ZnO.) × 24.2

37.3 g of $ZnCO_3$ reacts to give 24.2 g of ZnO.

So, 37.3 g of $ZnCO_3$ would need to decompose to form 24.2 g of ZnO.

Practice Questions — Application

Use the periodic table on the back cover to help answer these questions.

Q1 Calculate the mass of potassium chloride (KCl) that will be formed if 36.2 g of potassium bromide (KBr) reacts with an excess of chlorine. The balanced symbol equation for this reaction is:

$$2KBr + Cl_2 \rightarrow 2KCl + Br_2$$

Q2 Calculate the mass of aluminium chloride ($AlCl_3$) that will be made if 15.4 g of hydrochloric acid (HCl) reacts with an excess of aluminium. The balanced symbol equation for this reaction is:

$$6HCl + 2Al \rightarrow 2AlCl_3 + 3H_2$$

Q3 28.5 g of calcium carbonate ($CaCO_3$) reacts with an excess of sulfuric acid (H_2SO_4) to form calcium sulfate ($CaSO_4$), carbon dioxide (CO_2) and water (H_2O). Calculate the mass of calcium sulfate that will be formed in this reaction.

Tip: For Q3 you need to write and balance the symbol equation yourself — but all the information you need is given in the question.

Q4 Calculate the mass of potassium hydroxide (KOH) that would be needed to form 25.0 g of potassium nitrate (KNO_3) in this reaction:

$$HNO_3 + KOH \rightarrow KNO_3 + H_2O$$

Q5 Ethanol (C_2H_6O) can be made from ethene (C_2H_4) using this reaction:

$$C_2H_4 + H_2O \rightarrow C_2H_6O$$

Calculate the amount of ethene that would be needed to make 60.0 g of ethanol using this reaction.

Q6 Iron oxide (Fe_2O_3) can be reduced with carbon to form iron (Fe) and carbon dioxide, as shown by the equation below.

$$2Fe_2O_3 + 3C \rightarrow 4Fe + 3CO_2$$

Calculate the amount of iron oxide needed to form 32.0 g of iron.

Tip: You should be familiar with a lot of these reactions — they're all covered elsewhere in this book.

5. Percentage Yield

Percentage yield is a good way of measuring how much of a chemical has been wasted during a reaction. Read on to find out how to calculate percentage yield and why it's important in the chemical industry.

Learning Objectives:

- Know that the yield is the amount of product formed in a reaction.
- Know that the percentage yield is the yield of the reaction compared to the maximum theoretical yield, given as a percentage.
- H Know how to calculate percentage yields.
- Know that some reactions are reversible and can go in either direction.
- Know why percentage yield is never 100%.
- Understand why high yields are important for sustainable development.

Specification Reference C2.3, C2.3.3

What is percentage yield?

The amount of product you get in a reaction is known as the **yield**. The more reactant you start with, the higher the yield will be. But the **percentage yield** doesn't depend on the amount of reactant you started with — it's a percentage.

The percentage yield is a comparison between the amount of product you expect to get and the amount of product you actually get. It is always somewhere between 0 and 100%. A 100% yield means that you got all the product you expected to get. A 0% yield means that no reactants were converted into product, i.e. no product at all was made.

Calculating the percentage yield Higher

The predicted yield of a reaction can be calculated from the balanced reaction equation (see page 145). If you know the predicted yield of a reaction and the actual yield of a reaction, you can calculate the percentage yield using the following formula:

$$\text{percentage yield} = \frac{\text{actual yield (grams)}}{\text{predicted yield (grams)}} \times 100$$

Tip: The predicted yield is sometimes called the maximum theoretical yield.

Example — Higher

If you reacted 24 g of calcium hydroxide with an excess of hydrochloric acid, you would expect to make 36 g of calcium chloride. If you actually only made 28.2 g of calcium chloride, then the percentage yield would be:

$$\%\text{ yield} = \frac{\text{actual yield}}{\text{predicted yield}} \times 100 = \frac{28.2}{36} \times 100 = 78.3\%$$

Tip: If you want to see how to calculate this predicted yield, have a look back at Example 2 on page 146.

Why percentage yields are never 100%

Even though no atoms are gained or lost in reactions, in real life, you never get a 100% yield. Some product or reactant always gets lost along the way — and that goes for big industrial processes as well as school lab experiments. There are several reasons for this.

Tip: Keeping the percentage yield as high as possible helps to make chemical reactions more environmentally friendly. See the next page for more. (HOW SCIENCE WORKS)

1. The reaction is reversible

A **reversible reaction** is one where the products of the reaction can themselves react to produce the original reactants. Reversible reactions can be represented like this:

$$A + B \rightleftharpoons C + D$$

Example

The breakdown of ammonium chloride into ammonia and hydrogen chloride is a good example of a reversible reaction. Here's the equation:

ammonium chloride $\rightleftharpoons$ ammonia + hydrogen chloride

The ammonia and hydrogen chloride that form when ammonium chloride breaks down can react with each other to reform the ammonium chloride.

If a reaction is reversible, it means that the reactants will never be completely converted to products because the reaction goes both ways. Some of the products are always reacting together to change back to the original reactants. This will mean a lower yield.

Figure 1: *Copper sulfate crystals being filtered from copper sulfate solution — some liquid and some solid will be lost in this process.*

2. Product is lost when it's separated from the reactants

When you filter a liquid to remove solid particles, you nearly always lose a bit of liquid or a bit of solid. So, some of the product may be lost when it's separated from the reaction mixture. This will also result in a lower yield.

3. Unexpected reactions may be happening

Things don't always go exactly to plan. Sometimes there can be other unexpected reactions happening which use up the reactants. This means there's not as much reactant to make the product you want.

Sustainable development

HOW SCIENCE WORKS

Thinking about product yield is important for sustainable development. Sustainable development is about making sure that we don't use resources faster than they can be replaced — there needs to be enough for future generations too.

Tip: Sustainable development is all about making sure we can continue to use important resources in the distant future.

There are a few things that can be done to help make industrial processes sustainable:

- Use reactions with high percentage yields. Using a reaction with a low percentage yield uses up resources and wastes a lot of chemicals.
- Use reactions that don't require much energy. When you save energy you don't need to burn as much fuel — this means that you use up less fossil fuels and create less pollution.
- Use raw materials that come from renewable sources. The more that we use reactants and fuels from non-renewable sources (like fossil fuels), the faster we'll run out of them.

Tip: A low percentage yield isn't so much of a problem if you can recycle any unreacted chemicals.

Example

Ethanol can be made either by hydrating ethene or by fermenting sugar.

- Hydrating ethene isn't very sustainable because the ethene comes from non-renewable crude oil. The reaction is done at a high temperature, so it uses lots of energy. The overall percentage yield is high though.
- Fermenting sugar is more sustainable because sugar comes from plants, so it's a renewable resource. The reaction works at a much lower temperature too, so it uses less energy. But the percentage yield is low.

Practice Questions — Fact Recall

Q1 What is the yield of a reaction?

Q2 What is the percentage yield of a reaction?

Q3 Give the formula that you would use to calculate the percentage yield of a reaction.

Q4 Give three reasons why percentage yields are never 100%.

Q5 Explain why high percentage yields are important for sustainable development.

Practice Questions — Application

Q1 Look at the reaction below:

$$N_2 + 3H_2 \rightleftharpoons 2NH_3$$

Use information from the equation to explain why the percentage yield of this reaction will not be 100%.

Q2 A scientist has developed a new way of making a certain chemical. His new method has a higher percentage yield than the old method and works at a lower temperature. Explain why the new method will be better for the environment than the old method.

Q3 The predicted yield of a reaction was 34.6 g of iron. The actual yield was 28.6 g of iron. Calculate the percentage yield of this reaction.

Q4 A scientist performed an experiment that involved reacting sodium hydroxide with sulfuric acid. She expected to get 41.9 g of sodium sulfate, but actually only got 33.4 g of sodium sulfate. Calculate the percentage yield of this reaction.

Q5 A reaction produced 10.3 g of copper sulfate. The predicted yield of the reaction was 15.2 g of copper sulfate. Calculate the percentage yield of this reaction.

Q6 A student worked out that his experiment should make 8.45 g of sodium chloride. He actually only ended up with 4.27 g of sodium chloride. Calculate the percentage yield of his experiment.

6. Chemical Analysis

This topic is all about how substances can be analysed to find out what they're made up of. Often, the best way to analyse substances is to use instrumental methods — this basically means getting a machine to do it for you.

Learning Objectives:

- Know that food additives can be identified using chemical analysis.
- Know how paper chromatography is used to identify dyes in artificial colourings.
- Know that instrumental methods (using machines) can be used to analyse substances.
- Know why instrumental methods are usually better than manual methods.
- Know how gas chromatography-mass spectrometry (GC-MS) works.
- H Know that a mass spectrometer can be used to find out the relative molecular mass of a substance.

Specification Reference C2.3.2

Paper Chromatography

Chemical analysis is used to identify the different additives that are present in foods. For example, if you know that a food colouring is made up of a mixture of dyes, you can use a technique called **paper chromatography** (see Figure 1) to find out which dyes are in it. Here's what you do:

- Extract the colour from the food sample by placing it in a small cup with a few drops of solvent (can be water, ethanol, salt water, etc.).
- Put a spot of the coloured solution on a pencil baseline on some filter paper. (Don't use pen because it might dissolve and confuse everything.)
- Put the paper in a beaker with some solvent — but keep the baseline above the level of the solvent.
- The solvent seeps up the paper, taking the dyes with it. Different dyes form spots in different places.

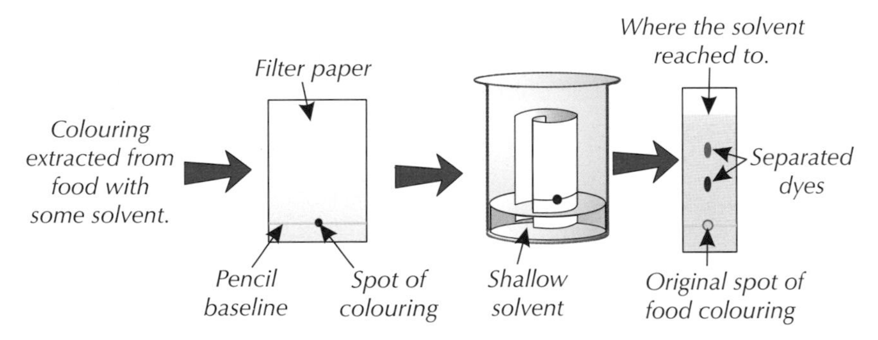

***Figure 1:** The process of paper chromatography.*

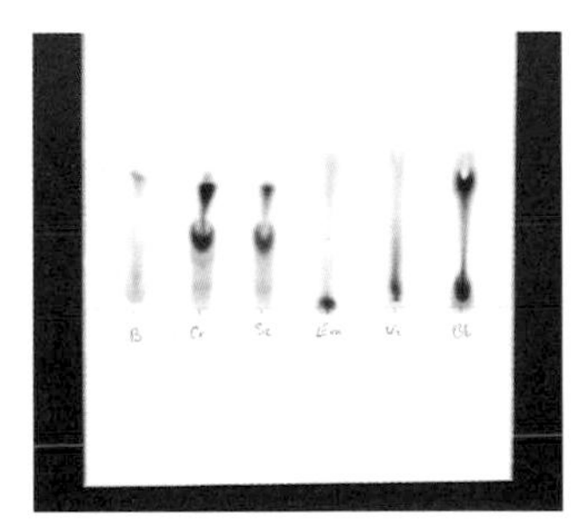

***Figure 2:** Paper chromatography being used to analyse dyes.*

Analysing the results

The piece of filter paper you get at the end, with the separated spots on, is called a chromatogram. A chromatogram gives you information about:

- What dyes different colourings contain. Each dye will move up the paper at a different rate and form a spot at a different distance from the baseline. So if you test two different colourings and they both contain a spot that's moved the same distance, it's likely to be the same dye.
- How many dyes a colouring contains. Be careful though — four spots means at least four dyes, not exactly four. It could be five, if two of the dyes have travelled such similar distances that their spots have joined up.

Tip: You couldn't get four spots from three dyes though — one dye can't split into two spots.

Example

On the chromatogram in Figure 1, the original spot of colouring has separated into two spots (a blue one and a pink one). This shows that the food colouring contains at least two different dyes (but it may be more).

Instrumental methods

You can identify elements and compounds using **instrumental methods** — this just means using machines. There are a number of advantages to using instrumental methods, instead of analysing substances manually:

- They are very sensitive — they can detect even the tiniest amounts of substances, which is really handy if your sample is small.
- They are very fast and tests can be automated, so using instrumental methods saves a lot of time.
- They are very accurate — machines don't make mistakes like people do.

Gas chromatography

A good example of an instrumental method that is commonly used in chemistry labs is **gas chromatography** (see Figure 3). Gas chromatography can separate out a mixture of compounds and help you identify the substances present. Here's how it works:

Tip: Each substance has its own retention time. You can identify substances by looking up their retention times in a database. Or you could run samples of pure substances through your machine to find their retention times.

- A gas is used to carry a mixture of substances through a column (tube) packed with a solid material.
- The substances travel through the column at different speeds, so they're separated.
- The time each substance takes to reach the detector is called its retention time. It can be used to help identify the substance.
- The recorder draws a gas chromatogram (see Figure 3).

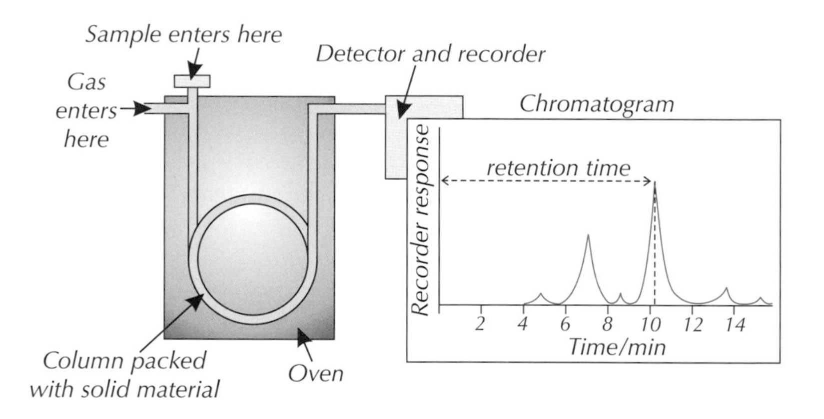

***Figure 3:** The process of gas chromatography.*

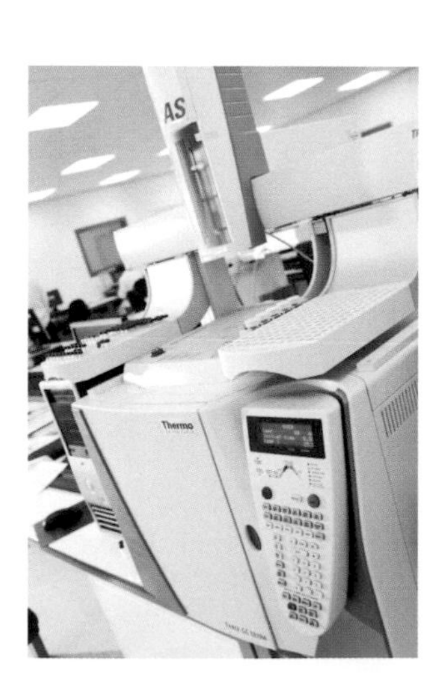

***Figure 4:** A gas chromatography machine.*

The number of peaks on the chromatogram shows the number of different substances in the sample.

Example

On the chromatogram in Figure 3, there are six peaks, so the mixture being analysed must contain six different substances.

The gas chromatography column can also be linked to a mass spectrometer. This process is known as GC-MS (Gas Chromatography-Mass Spectrometry). The mass spectrometer can be used to identify the substances leaving the column and can accurately detect very small quantities.

Analysing mass spectrometry results **Higher**

A mass spectrometer can be used to accurately identify the separated substances leaving a gas chromatography column, because it tells you the relative molecular mass of each one. You can work out the relative molecular mass of the substances from the graphs that the mass spectrometer draws. You just read off the value of the molecular ion peak (see Example below).

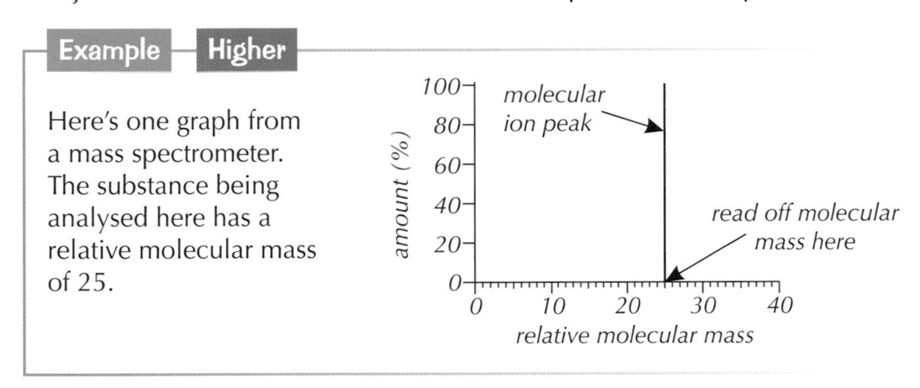

Practice Questions — Fact Recall

Q1 Describe how you could use paper chromatography to separate the dyes in some food colouring.

Q2 Give three advantages of using instrumental methods to analyse substances.

Q3 Describe how gas chromatography can be used to separate mixtures.

Q4 When a gas chromatography column is linked to a mass spectrometer, what information is obtained from the mass spectrometer?

Practice Questions — Application

Q1 Paper chromatography was used to analyse the dyes in some food colouring. The result is shown on the right. How many dyes does this colouring contain? Explain your answer

A: Three or less. B: Exactly three. C: Three or more

Q2 A mixture was analysed using gas chromatography. The results are shown on the right.

a) How many substances does this mixture contain?

b) What is the retention time of the tallest peak to the nearest minute?

Recorder response

2 4 6 8 10 12 14

Time/min

Section Checklist — Make sure you know...

Atoms and Isotopes

- ❑ That atoms have a mass number (which tells you the total number of protons and neutrons in the atom) and an atomic number (which tells you the number of protons in the atom).
- ❑ That protons and neutrons have a relative mass of 1, while the relative mass of an electron is tiny.
- ❑ That isotopes have the same number of protons but different numbers of neutrons.

Relative Formula Mass

- ❑ **H** That the relative atomic mass (A_r) of an element is the average mass of atoms of that element measured relative to the mass of one atom of carbon-12.
- ❑ What relative formula mass (M_r) is and how to calculate it using relative atomic masses.
- ❑ That the relative formula mass (A_r for elements or M_r for compounds) of a substance in grams is known as one mole of that substance.
- ❑ How to convert mass to moles and vice versa using the equation moles = mass (in g) ÷ M_r.

Formula Mass Calculations

- ❑ How to calculate the percentage mass of an element in a compound.
- ❑ **H** How to work out the empirical formula of a compound from masses or percentage masses.

Calculating Masses in Reactions

- ❑ **H** How to calculate the masses of reactants used or products made in a reaction.

Percentage Yield

- ❑ That yield is the amount of product formed in a reaction and percentage yield is a comparison between the amount of product expected and the amount of product actually obtained.
- ❑ **H** How to calculate percentage yields.
- ❑ That in reversible reactions the products can react with each other to form the reactants.
- ❑ The reasons why percentage yields are never 100%.
- ❑ That high percentage yields, low energy needs and renewable reactants make reactions sustainable.

Chemical Analysis

- ❑ How paper chromatography can be used to separate and identify dyes in artificial colourings.
- ❑ What instrumental methods are and some advantages of using instrumental methods.
- ❑ How GC-MS can be used to separate and identify the compounds in a substance.
- ❑ **H** That the mass spectrometer in GC-MS tells you the relative molecular mass of the compounds.

Exam-style Questions

1 A scientist is making some sodium hydroxide (NaOH) from calcium hydroxide ($Ca(OH)_2$) and sodium carbonate (Na_2CO_3).

When calcium hydroxide and sodium carbonate are mixed, the following reaction occurs.

$$Ca(OH)_{2(aq)} + Na_2CO_{3(s)} \rightarrow CaCO_{3(s)} + 2NaOH_{(aq)}$$

1 (a) The scientist starts with 25.0 g of sodium carbonate.

1 (a) (i) How many moles are there in 25.0 g of sodium carbonate?

(2 marks)

1 (a) (ii) Calculate the mass of sodium hydroxide the scientist could expect to form if he reacts 25.0 g of sodium carbonate with an excess of calcium hydroxide.

(2 marks)

1 (b) The scientist separated the sodium hydroxide solution from the solid calcium carbonate using filter paper.

Next he crystallised the solution and weighed the solid sodium hydroxide crystals. He found that he had only made 10.4 g of sodium hydroxide.

1 (b) (i) Use the information above and your answer from (a) part (ii) to calculate the percentage yield of this reaction.

(If you were unable to answer (a) part (ii), use a value of 22.4 g for the expected yield of sodium hydroxide — this is not the correct answer.)

(2 marks)

1 (b) (ii) Even if all of the sodium carbonate is converted to sodium hydroxide, the yield of this reaction will never be 100%. Suggest **one** reason why.

(1 mark)

1 (b) (iii) Suggest **one** reason why chemical companies try to avoid using reactions that have low percentage yields.

(1 mark)

2 A chemist is using gas chromatography linked to mass spectrometry (GC-MS) to analyse a mixture of substances. Her results are shown below.

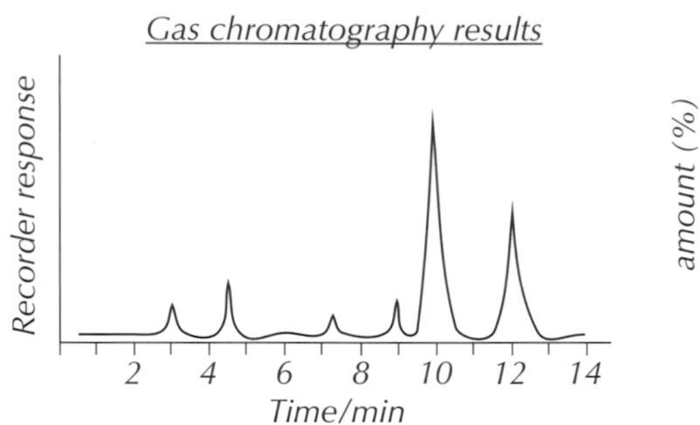

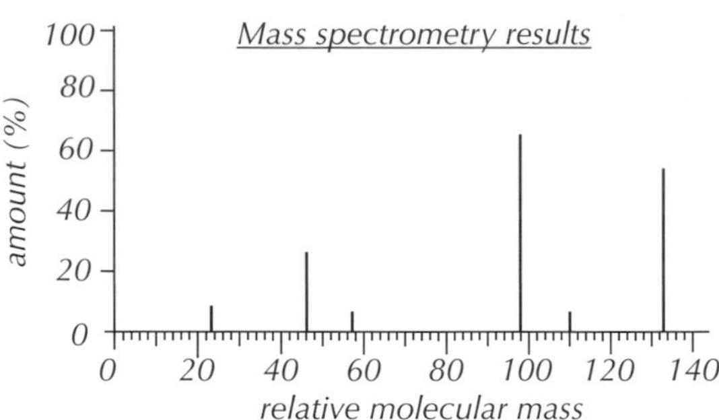

The table below contains information on some of the compounds that might be in this mixture.

Compound	Molecular Formula	Retention time (min)
Phosphoric acid	H_3PO_4	9.97
Fumaric acid	$C_4H_4O_4$	10.94
Aspartic acid	$C_4H_7NO_4$	12.00
Malic acid	$C_4H_6O_5$	12.79
Glutamic acid	$C_5H_9NO_4$	13.34

2 (a) (i) What is the relative formula mass of phosphoric acid?
(Relative atomic masses: H = 1, O = 16, P = 31)

(1 mark)

2 (a) (ii) Using the information above, give **two** pieces of evidence to suggest that phosphoric acid is in the mixture the chemist is analysing.

(2 marks)

2 (b) Aspartic acid is also present in the mixture. The M_r of aspartic acid is 133.
Calculate the percentage mass of carbon in aspartic acid. Carbon has an A_r of 12.

(2 marks)

2 (c) A sample of another compound in the mixture was found to contain 4.8 g of carbon, 1.2 g of hydrogen and 3.2 g of oxygen. Find the empirical formula of this compound.
(Relative atomic masses: H = 1, C = 12, O = 16)

(3 marks)

2 (d) GC-MS is an instrumental method. Give **one** advantage that instrumental methods have over manual methods.

(1 mark)

1. Rate of Reaction

Chemical reactions don't all happen at the same rate — some reactions happen faster than others. There are a number of factors that affect how quickly a reaction goes. Read on to find out more...

Learning Objectives:
- Know that particles have to collide with enough energy in order to react.
- Understand why increasing the temperature increases the rate of a reaction.
- Understand why increasing the concentration (or pressure) increases the rate of a reaction.
- Understand why increasing the surface area of solid reactants increases the rate of reaction.
- Know what is meant by the term activation energy.
- Know that a catalyst is a substance that can speed up a reaction without being changed or used up itself.
- Understand why catalysts are important in industry.
- Be able to weigh up the advantages and disadvantages of using catalysts in industry.

Specification Reference C2.4, C2.4.1

Different reaction rates

Reactions can go at all sorts of different rates. Some reactions happen very quickly, while others happen really slowly.

Examples
- The rusting of iron is a pretty slow reaction — it can take years for a lump of iron to go rusty.
- A moderate speed reaction is a metal (like magnesium) reacting with acid to produce a gentle stream of bubbles.
- A really fast reaction is an explosion, where it's all over in a fraction of a second.

Factors that affect the rate of a reaction

There are four main factors that affect how quickly a reaction goes:

- Temperature — the higher the temperature, the faster the reaction goes.
- Concentration (or pressure for gases) — the more concentrated the reactants (or the higher the pressure), the faster the reaction goes.
- Surface area (size of solid pieces) — the larger the surface area (the smaller the pieces), the faster the reaction goes.
- Catalysts — reactions with a catalyst can go faster than reactions without.

Collision theory

Reaction rates are explained by **collision theory**. Collision theory just says that the rate of a reaction depends on how often and how hard the reacting particles collide with each other.

The basic idea is that particles have to collide in order to react, and they have to collide hard enough (with enough energy). This means there are two ways to increase the rate of reaction:

- Increase the number of collisions, so that the probability of a **successful collision** (a collision that results in a reaction) increases.
- Increase the energy of the collisions, so that more of the collisions are successful collisions.

Increasing the number of collisions

The effects of temperature, concentration (or pressure) and surface area on the rate of reaction can be explained in terms of how often the reacting particles collide.

Temperature

When the temperature is increased the particles all move quicker. If they're moving quicker, they're going to collide more often and more collisions means a faster rate of reaction — see Figure 1.

Tip: Increasing the temperature also increases the energy of the collisions — more on this on the next page.

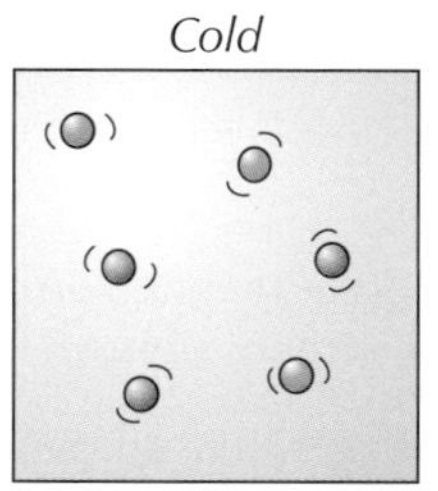

Hot

Particles move quickly.
Lots of collisions.

Figure 1: *A diagram showing why increasing the temperature increases the rate of a reaction.*

Concentration (or pressure)

If a solution is made more concentrated it means there are more particles of reactant knocking about between the water molecules, which makes collisions between the important particles more likely.

Similarly, in a gas, increasing the pressure means the particles are more squashed up together, so there will be more frequent collisions (see Figure 2). More frequent collisions means a faster rate of reaction.

Tip: This makes sense if you think about it — you're much more likely to bump into someone when you're in a crowd of people than when there aren't many people around.

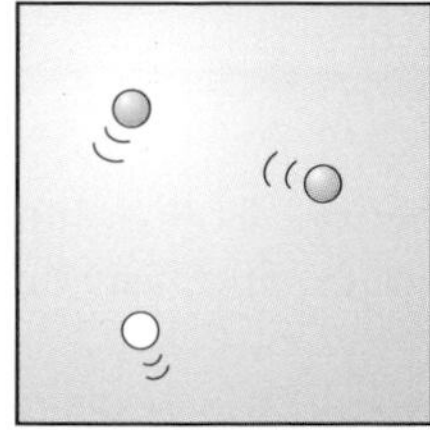

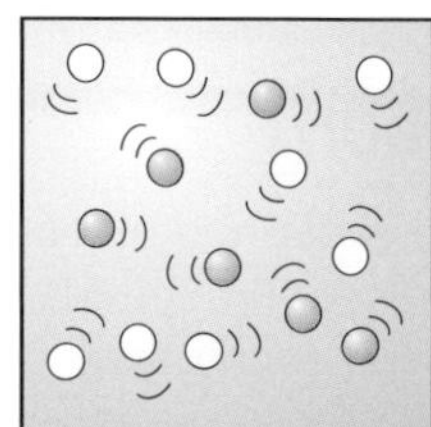

Figure 2: *A diagram showing why increasing the concentration (or pressure) increases the rate of a reaction.*

Surface area

If one of the reactants is a solid then breaking it up into smaller pieces will increase the total surface area. This means the particles around it in the solution will have more area to work on, so there'll be more frequent collisions and the rate of reaction will be faster — see Figure 3.

Small surface area

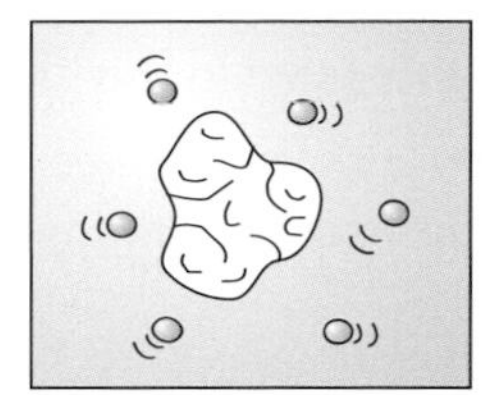

Less area for collisions. Not many collisions.

Large surface area

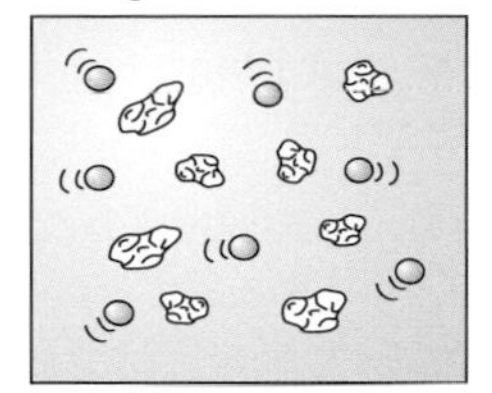

More area for collisions. Lots of collisions.

Figure 3: *A diagram showing why increasing the surface area increases the rate of a reaction.*

Tip: You get the fastest rates of reactions with powders because powders have a very large surface area.

Increasing the energy of collisions

The effect of temperature on reaction rate can also be explained in terms of how much energy the particles have when they collide. A higher temperature doesn't only increase the frequency of collisions — it also increases the energy of the collisions, because it makes all the particles move faster.

Reactions only happen if the particles collide with enough energy. The minimum amount of energy that particles must have in order to react is called the **activation energy**. At a higher temperature there will be more particles colliding with enough energy to make the reaction happen.

Tip: For a collision to be successful, the energy of the particles must be greater than or equal to the activation energy. If the particles don't have enough energy, they will just bounce off each other without reacting.

Catalysts

Many reactions can be speeded up by adding a **catalyst**.

> A catalyst is a substance which can speed up a reaction, without being changed or used up in the reaction.

A solid catalyst works by giving the reacting particles a surface to stick to. This increases the number of successful collisions, speeding the reaction up.

Catalysts in industry

Catalysts are very important for commercial reasons — most industrial reactions use them. Catalysts increase the rate of the reaction, which saves a lot of money simply because the plant doesn't need to operate for as long to produce the same amount of stuff.

Some catalysts also allow the reaction to work at a much lower temperature. That reduces the energy used up in the reaction (the energy cost), which is good for sustainable development (see page 149) and can save a lot of money.

Another advantage is that catalysts never get used up in the reaction, so once you've got them you can use them over and over again.

There are disadvantages to using catalysts, though.

- They can be very expensive to buy, and often need to be removed from the product and cleaned.
- Different reactions use different catalysts, so if you make more than one product at your plant, you'll probably need to buy different catalysts for them.
- Catalysts can be 'poisoned' by impurities, so they stop working.

Example

Sulfur impurities can poison the iron catalyst used in the Haber process (used to make ammonia for fertilisers). That means you have to keep your reaction mixture very clean.

Practice Questions — Fact Recall

Q1 What must happen for a reaction to occur between two particles?

Q2 Explain why increasing the concentration of the reactants increases the rate of a reaction.

Q3 Give two reasons why increasing the temperature increases the rate of a reaction.

Q4 What is the definition of a catalyst?

Q5 a) Give one advantage of using catalysts in industry.

b) Give one disadvantage of using catalysts in industry.

Practice Questions — Application

Q1 The table below contains some rate of reaction data for the reactions of hydrochloric acid with different forms of calcium carbonate:

Form of calcium carbonate	Marble chips	Crushed marble chips	Powdered chalk
Initial rate of reaction (cm^3/min)	0.6	1.4	5.6

Describe and explain these results.

Tip: Don't worry too much about what the units mean in Q1 for now — how to calculate rates of reaction is coming up in the next topic.

Q2 A factory produces ethene by cracking larger hydrocarbons. The owner wants to increase productivity and suggests performing the reaction at a higher temperature.

a) Explain why this would increase productivity.

b) Suggest one other way that the owner could increase productivity.

2. Measuring Rates of Reaction

If you want to measure the rate of a reaction, you're going to need a way to follow what's happening. Here's a guide to measuring rates of reaction...

Learning Objective:
- Know that the rate of a reaction can be calculated by dividing either the amount of reactant used or the amount of product formed by time.

Specification Reference C2.4.1

Calculating rates of reaction

You can find the rate of a reaction either by measuring how quickly the reactants are used up or how quickly the products are formed (although it's usually a lot easier to measure the products forming). Once you've taken these measurements, you can work out the reaction rate using this formula:

$$\text{Rate of reaction} = \frac{\text{Amount of reactant used or product formed}}{\text{Time}}$$

Example

In a reaction, 14.4 cm³ of oxygen gas was produced in the first 8 seconds. Calculate the rate of this reaction.

$$\text{Rate} = \frac{\text{Amount of product formed}}{\text{Time}} = \frac{14.4}{8} = 1.8 \text{ cm}^3\text{/s}$$

Tip: Rate of reaction can have lots of different units. The ones you're most likely to come across are cm^3/s and g/s.

Measuring the formation of product

There are a few different ways that the formation of products during a reaction can be measured.

Tip: A precipitate is basically a solid that is formed in a solution during a chemical reaction.

Precipitation

This is when the product of the reaction is a **precipitate** which clouds the solution. You can observe a mark through the solution and measure how long it takes for the mark to disappear (see Figure 1). The quicker the mark disappears, the quicker the reaction.

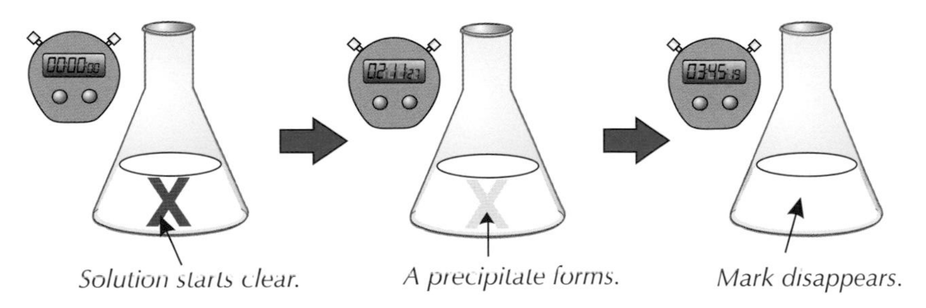

Figure 1: *Measuring the rate of a precipitation reaction.*

This method is simple and easy to do but it only works for reactions where the initial solution is see-through. Also, the result is very subjective — different people might not agree over the exact point when the mark 'disappears'.

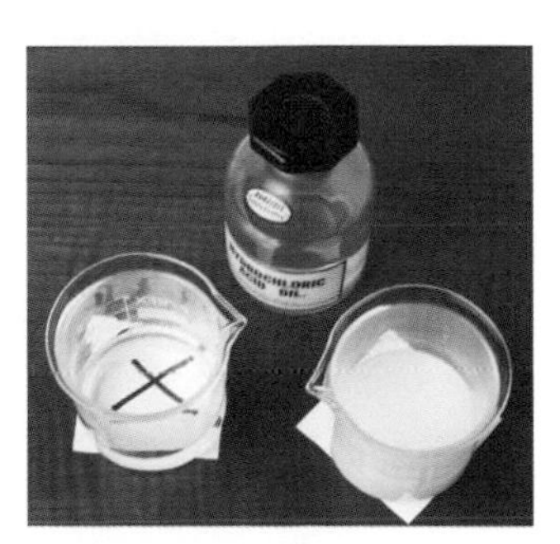

Figure 2: *A reaction that produces a precipitate. When enough precipitate has formed, the cross disappears.*

Change in mass

You can measure the speed of a reaction that produces a gas using a mass balance. You just place the reaction vessel on the balance. As the gas is released the mass disappearing is easily measured — see Figure 3. The quicker the reading on the balance drops, the faster the reaction.

Tip: Gases don't weigh very much so the change in mass can be quite small. The trick is to use a mass balance with a high resolution, so that very small changes in mass can be detected. See page 10 of the How Science Works section for more on resolution.

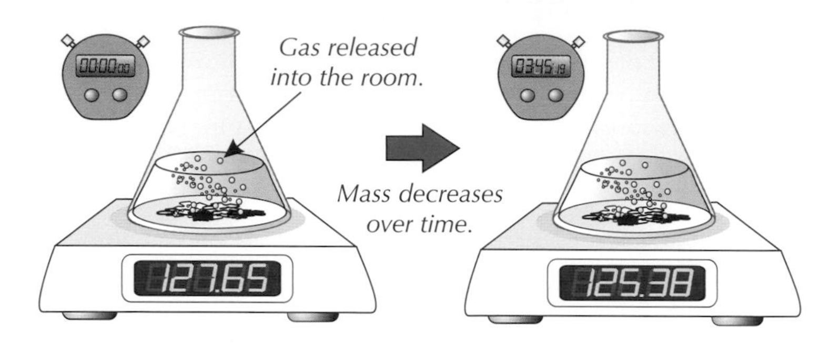

Figure 3: *Measuring the rate of a reaction using a change in mass.*

This is the most accurate of the methods described in this topic because the mass balance is very accurate. But it has the disadvantage of releasing the gas straight into the room, which isn't very good if the gas is dangerous.

Volume of gas given off

You can also measure the rate of a reaction that produces a gas by using a gas syringe to measure the volume of gas given off — see Figure 4. The more gas given off during a given time interval, the faster the reaction.

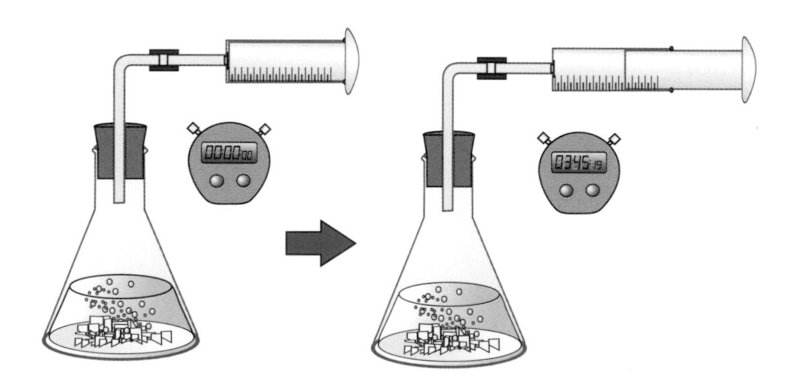

Figure 4: *Measuring the rate of a reaction using the volume of gas produced.*

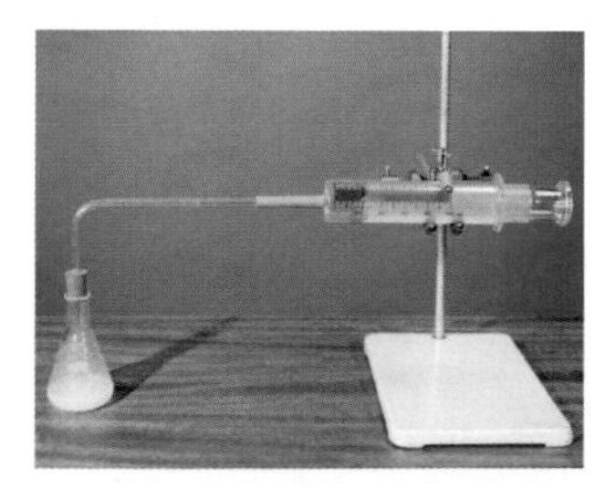

Figure 5: *The volume of gas produced in a reaction being measured.*

Gas syringes usually give volumes to the nearest millilitre, so they're quite precise. Also, the gas isn't released into the room, which is useful if the gas produced is poisonous. You have to be quite careful though — if the reaction is too vigorous, you can easily blow the plunger out of the end of the syringe.

Practice Questions — Fact Recall

Q1 What is the formula for calculating the rate of a reaction?

Q2 Describe how you could measure the rate of a reaction where one of the products was a precipitate.

Q3 A student is measuring the rate of a reaction using a gas syringe.

a) Discuss the advantages and disadvantages of this technique.

b) Suggest another method that the student could use to measure the rate of this reaction.

Tip: The tiny letters in brackets that you find in some equations are called state symbols. They tell you what state each chemical is in:

- (s) means solid,
- (l) means liquid,
- (g) means gas,
- (aq) means dissolved in water.

For more about state symbols, see page 178.

Practice Questions — Application

Q1 The equation below shows the reaction between sulfuric acid and sodium hydrogen carbonate:

$$H_2SO_{4(aq)} + 2NaHCO_{3(s)} \rightarrow Na_2SO_{4(aq)} + 2H_2O_{(l)} + 2CO_{2(g)}$$

Suggest a method for measuring the rate of this reaction.

Q2 The equation below shows the reaction of sodium hydroxide with magnesium chloride:

$$2NaOH_{(aq)} + MgCl_{2(aq)} \rightarrow 2NaCl_{(aq)} + Mg(OH)_{2(s)}$$

Suggest a method for measuring the rate of this reaction. (If you need a clue, have a look at Figure 6.)

Q3 A reaction produced 4.3 cm^3 of carbon dioxide gas in the first 5.0 seconds. Calculate the rate of this reaction in cm^3/s.

Q4 Some potassium metal was added to water and the change in mass was measured on a mass balance. In the first 8.0 seconds, the mass of the reaction decreased from 34.31 g to 32.63 g. Calculate the rate of this reaction in g/s.

Figure 6: *The reaction of sodium hydroxide with magnesium chloride.*

3. Rate of Reaction Graphs

Learning Objective:
- Be able to interpret graphs showing the rates of reactions.

Specification Reference C2.4

Once you've measured the amount of product made or reactant used over time, you can plot your data on a graph.

Graphs showing the rate of a reaction

If you plot the amount of product formed (or the amount of reactant used) in a reaction against time you'll get a graph that looks something like the one in Figure 1. On a graph like this, the rate of the reaction is shown by the gradient (steepness) of the line. The steeper the line, the faster the rate (because it shows that products are being formed, or reactants used up, more quickly).

Graphs of product formed (or reactant used) against time are not straight lines — they're curves that start steep, get shallower and then level off.
This is because reactions start quickly, then slow down and eventually stop.

Exam Tip
In the exam, you could be given a graph that shows the amount of reactant left over time. This will look like an upside down version of the graph in Figure 1:

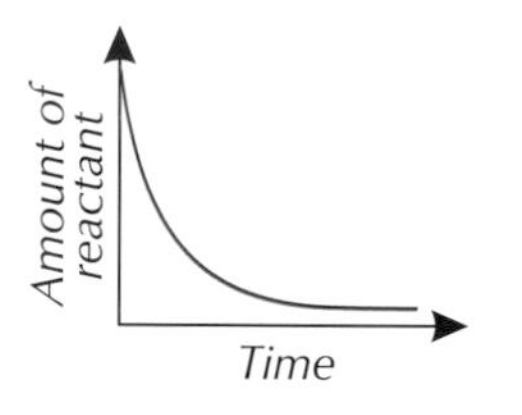

It's still a curve that starts steep and then levels off.

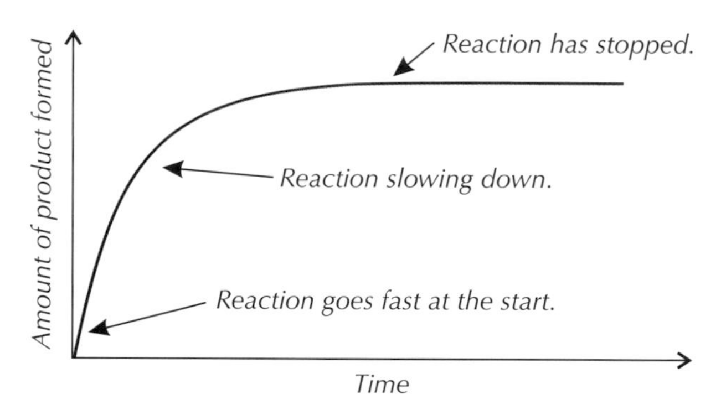

Figure 1: *A graph of amount of product formed against time for a reaction.*

Reactions start quickly because at the beginning of the reaction there are lots of reactant particles around, so collisions between them are very frequent. As the reaction progresses, the reactants get used up so the number of reactant particles decreases. This means collisions between reactant particles get less frequent and the reaction slows down. The reaction stops when all of the reactants are used up.

Tip: See pages 157-160 for more on collision theory and why the concentration of the reactants affects the rate of reaction.

Comparing rates of reaction

You can compare the rate of a reaction performed under different conditions (for example at different temperatures) by plotting a series of lines on one graph. All of the lines will be curves, but the exact shape of each curve will depend on the rate of reaction and the amount of reactant that you started with.

- The fastest reaction will be the line with the steepest slope at the beginning. Also, the faster a reaction goes, the sooner it finishes, which means that the line will become flat earlier.
- Reactions that start off with the same amount of reactants will give lines that finish at the same level on the graph.

Example

A student added some magnesium metal to an excess of hydrochloric acid that had been heated to 30 °C. He recorded the amount of gas formed at regular intervals.

The student repeated the experiment with the acid heated to 40 °C and then to 50 °C. Finally he tried heating the acid to 50 °C and adding double the mass of magnesium. This graph shows all of his results:

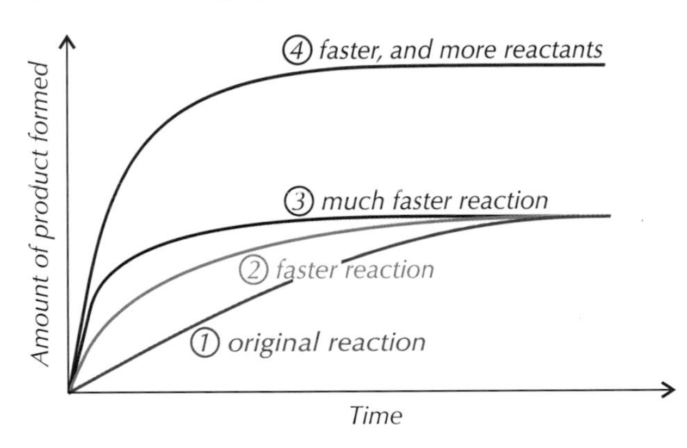

- Line 1 shows the original (fairly slow) reaction at 30 °C. The graph isn't very steep at the start and it takes a long time to level off.
- Lines 2 and 3 show the same reaction taking place and 40 °C and 50 °C. The initial rate of the reaction gets faster as the temperature increases, so the slope of the graphs gets steeper too.
- Lines 1, 2 and 3 all end up at the same level because they produce the same amount of product (though they take different times to get there).
- Line 4 shows the reaction taking place at 50 °C with double the mass of magnesium. It goes faster than the original reaction. It also finishes at a higher level because more reactants were added to begin with.

Exam Tip
You need to be able to interpret graphs like this in your exam so make sure you understand why the shapes of these curves are different.

Tip: There are more examples of rate of reaction graphs coming up on the next few pages.

Practice Questions — Application

Q1 The graph below shows the same reaction performed at three different temperatures. All other conditions were kept the same.

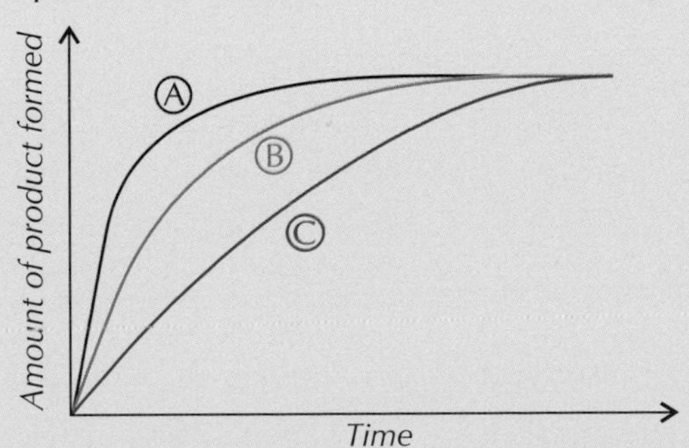

Which of these reactions (A, B or C) was performed at the highest temperature? Explain your answer.

Tip: Remember, you can increase the rate of a reaction by raising the temperature, increasing the reactant concentration (or pressure), adding a catalyst or crushing up a solid reactant (see pages 157-160).

Q2 The graph below shows the same reaction performed with three different concentrations of acid. All other conditions were kept the same.

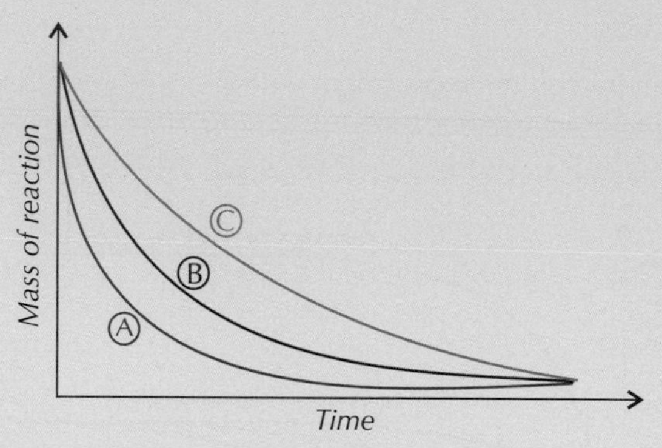

Which of these reactions (A, B or C) was performed with the lowest concentration of acid? Explain your answer.

Q3 The graph below shows the amount of product formed over time in a reaction.

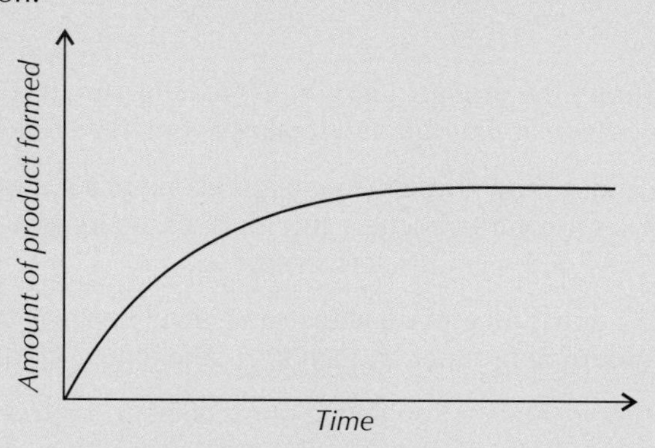

Copy this graph and sketch on the curves that would be produced if the reaction was performed:

a) with double the amount of reactant.

b) with the same amount of reactant but in the presence of a catalyst.

Tip: See page 158 for more on how and why concentration affects the rate of reaction.

Tip: Don't forget — a catalyst is a substance that can speed up the rate of a reaction without being changed or used up in the reaction.

4. Rate of Reaction Experiments

To really understand how rates of reaction can be measured you need to know a few examples of rate of reaction experiments. Luckily there are some coming up right now...

Learning Objectives:
- Know some examples of rate of reaction experiments.
- Be able to interpret graphs showing the rates of reactions.

Specification Reference C2.4

Hydrochloric acid and marble chips

Marble is a form of calcium carbonate ($CaCO_3$). It will react with dilute hydrochloric acid (HCl). The equation for this reaction is shown below:

$$2HCl_{(aq)} + CaCO_{3(s)} \rightarrow CaCl_{2(aq)} + H_2O_{(l)} + CO_{2(g)}$$

Since this reaction produces carbon dioxide gas, you can find the rate by measuring the volume of gas produced — see Figure 1.

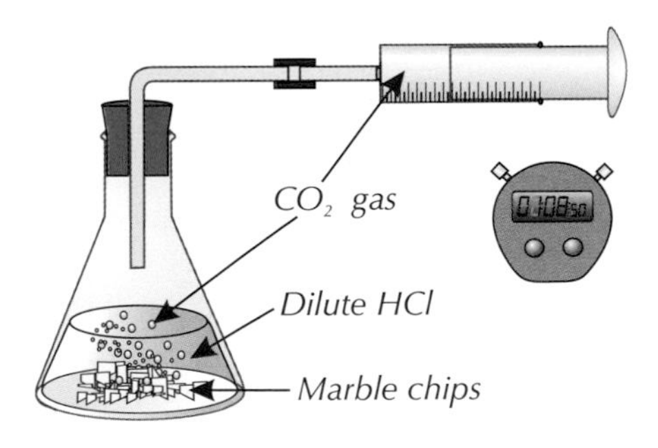

***Figure 1:** Measuring the rate of reaction of HCl with marble chips.*

Tip: Remember, the little letters in brackets in equations like this one tell you what state the chemicals are in. See page 178 for more on state symbols.

Tip: Have a look back at pages 161-162 for lots more on measuring rates of reaction.

This reaction is often used to show the effect of breaking a solid reactant up into smaller bits. Here's what you do:

- Measure the volume of gas evolved with a gas syringe and take readings at regular time intervals.
- Make a table of readings and plot them as a graph. Time goes on the x-axis and volume goes on the y-axis.
- Repeat the experiment with exactly the same volume of acid, and exactly the same mass of marble chips, but with the marble more crunched up.
- Then repeat with the same mass of powdered chalk instead of marble chips. (Chalk is just another form of calcium carbonate)

If you do that, you'll get a graph that looks something like Figure 2.

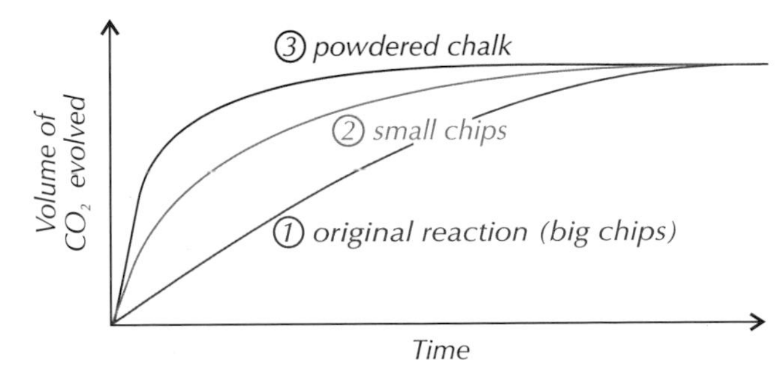

***Figure 2:** Graph showing the reaction of HCl with different forms of $CaCO_3$.*

***Figure 3:** A marble chip (left) and powdered chalk (right) reacting with HCl — the reaction with powdered chalk is much faster.*

The graph in Figure 2 shows that using finer particles results in a faster rate of reaction. This is because using finer particles gives the reactant a larger surface area. And the larger the surface area, the faster the rate of reaction.

Figure 4 shows what happens if you use a greater mass of small marble chips. The extra surface area gives a faster reaction and more gas is evolved overall.

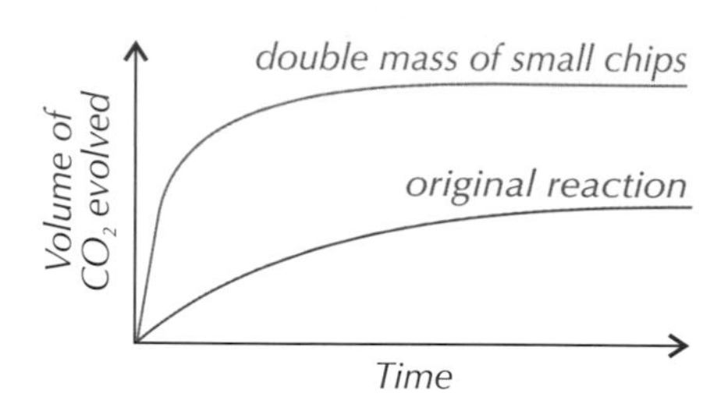

***Figure 4:** Graph showing the reaction of HCl with different amounts and chip sizes of marble.*

Magnesium metal and hydrochloric acid

The reaction of magnesium metal with dilute hydrochloric acid can be used to show the effect of increased reactant concentration on the rate of a reaction. The equation for the reaction is:

$$2HCl_{(aq)} + Mg_{(s)} \rightarrow MgCl_{2(aq)} + H_{2(g)}$$

Tip: You could also measure the amount of hydrogen produced using a gas syringe.

This reaction gives off hydrogen gas, so you can follow the rate of the reaction by measuring the loss in mass using a mass balance. Here's what you do:

- Take readings of mass at regular time intervals.
- Put the results in a table and work out the loss in mass for each reading. Plot a graph.
- Repeat with more concentrated acid solutions, but always with the same amount of magnesium. The volume of acid must always be kept the same too — only the concentration is increased.

This should give you a result like the one shown in Figure 6.

***Figure 5:** Magnesium ribbon reacting with hydrochloric acid — you can see the bubbles of hydrogen gas being produced.*

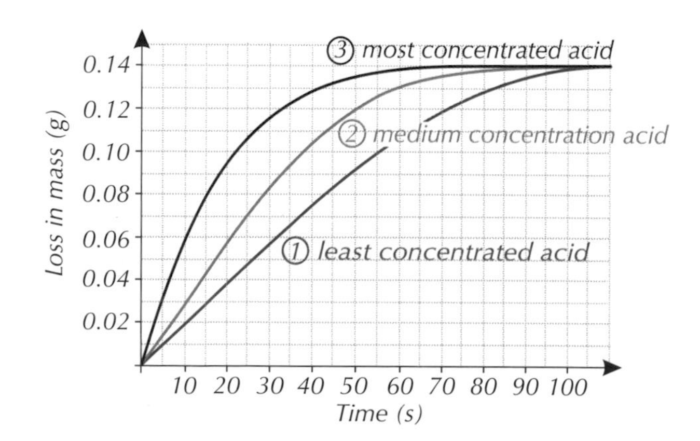

***Figure 6:** Graph showing the reaction of Mg with different concentrations of HCl.*

The graph in Figure 6 shows the expected pattern — a higher concentration gives a steeper graph, with the reaction finishing much quicker.

Sodium thiosulfate and hydrochloric acid

Sodium thiosulfate and hydrochloric acid are both clear solutions. They react together to form a yellow precipitate of sulfur:

$$2HCl_{(aq)} + Na_2S_2O_{3(aq)} \rightarrow 2NaCl_{(aq)} + SO_{2(g)} + S_{(s)} + H_2O_{(l)}$$

The sodium thiosulfate and hydrochloric acid experiment involves watching a black mark disappear through the cloudy sulfur and timing how long it takes to go — see Figure 7.

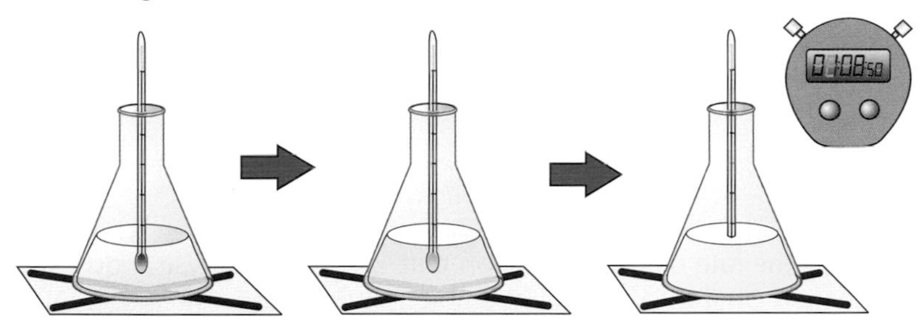

Figure 7: *Measuring the rate of the reaction between sodium thiosulfate and hydrochloric acid.*

This reaction can be repeated for solutions at different temperatures. In practice, it's a bit tricky to do accurately and safely (it's not a good idea to heat an acid directly). The best way to do it is to use a water bath to heat both solutions to the right temperature before you mix them. The volume of liquid and the container used must be kept the same each time, of course.

Tip: This reaction can also be used to test the effects of concentration.

The results will show that the higher the temperature the quicker the reaction and therefore the less time it takes for the mark to disappear. Some typical results are shown in Figure 8.

Temperature (°C)	20	25	30	35	40
Time taken for mark to disappear (s)	193	151	112	87	52

Figure 8: *Results of an experiment comparing the rate of reaction between sodium thiosulfate and hydrochloric acid at different temperatures.*

Tip: Unlike the other experiments in this topic, this one doesn't give you a set of graphs. You just get one lot of readings telling you how long it took for the mark to disappear at each temperature. You could still plot these on a graph though.

Decomposition of hydrogen peroxide

The decomposition of hydrogen peroxide is a good reaction for showing the effect of different catalysts on the rate of reaction. The equation for the decomposition of hydrogen peroxide is:

$$2H_2O_{2(aq)} \rightarrow 2H_2O_{(l)} + O_{2(g)}$$

This is normally quite slow but a sprinkle of manganese(IV) oxide catalyst speeds it up. Other catalysts that work are found in potato peel and blood.

One of the products of this reaction is oxygen gas, which provides an ideal way to measure the rate of reaction using the syringe method — see Figure 10.

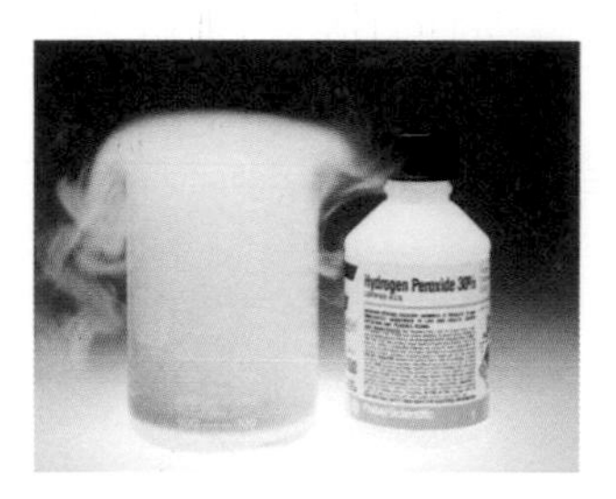

Figure 9: *Decomposition of hydrogen peroxide into water and oxygen gas.*

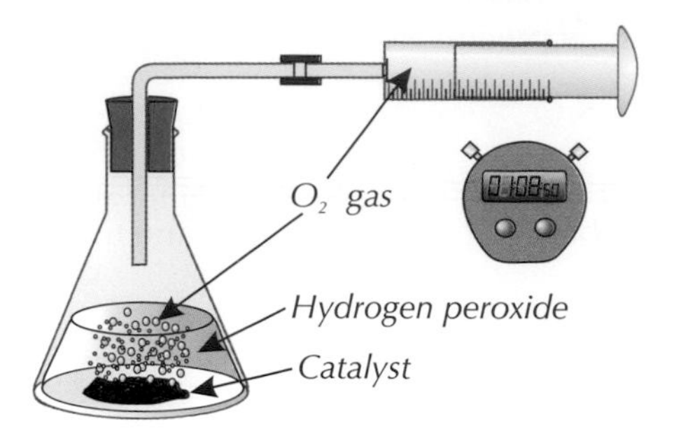

Figure 10: *Measuring the rate of the decomposition of hydrogen peroxide with a catalyst.*

By measuring the rate of gas production with different catalysts, you can work out which catalyst speeds up the reaction the most. The graph in Figure 11 shows the results that you would expect to get.

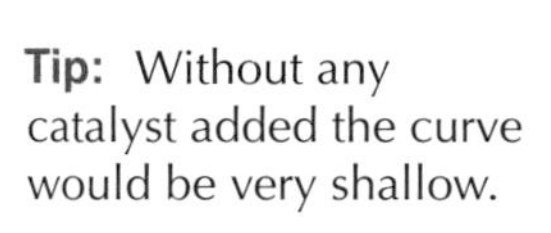

Tip: Without any catalyst added the curve would be very shallow.

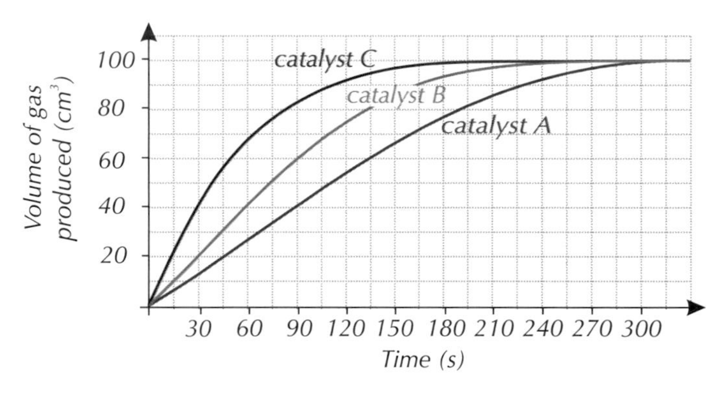

Figure 11: *Graph showing the decomposition of hydrogen peroxide with different catalysts.*

Better catalysts give a quicker reaction, which is shown by a steeper graph that levels off quickly. This reaction can also be used to measure the effects of temperature, or of concentration of the H_2O_2 solution. The graphs will show the same pattern.

Practice Questions — Fact Recall

Q1 Describe an experiment using marble chips that could be used to demonstrate the effect of surface area on the rate of a reaction. What results would you expect?

Q2 Sketch a graph to show the results you would expect if a set mass of magnesium metal was reacted with two different concentrations of hydrochloric acid.

Q3 Describe one way that you could measure the rate of the reaction between sodium thiosulfate and hydrochloric acid.

Tip: Sodium thiosulfate and hydrochloric acid react to form a yellow sulfur precipitate.

Section Checklist — Make sure you know...

Rate of Reaction

- ☐ That in order for a reaction to take place, the reacting particles must collide with sufficient energy.
- ☐ That increasing the temperature, the concentration (or pressure), or the surface area of reactants will increase the rate of reaction, because they increase the number of collisions between particles.
- ☐ That increasing the temperature also increases the rate of reaction because it increases the energy of the reacting particles.
- ☐ That the minimum amount of energy required for a reaction to take place is known as the activation energy.
- ☐ That a catalyst is a substance that can increase the rate of a reaction without be changed or used up.
- ☐ That catalysts are important in industry because they decrease the time taken to produce the same amount of product and reduce the energy used in reactions.
- ☐ That disadvantages to using catalysts in industry include that they are expensive to buy, they only work with one reaction and they can be poisoned.

Measuring Rates of Reaction

- ☐ That a rate of reaction can be calculated by dividing either the amount of reactant used or the amount of product formed by time.
- ☐ That the rate of a reaction that produces a precipitate can be measured by observing a mark through the solution and timing how long it takes for the mark to disappear.
- ☐ That the rate of a reaction that produces a gas can be measured either by monitoring the decrease in mass of the reaction over time (using a mass balance) or by measuring the volume of gas produced (using a gas syringe).

Rate of Reaction Graphs

- ☐ That if you plot a graph showing the amount of product formed (or reactant used) against time, the steepness of the curve will represent the rate of the reaction — the steeper the curve, the faster the rate.
- ☐ That these types of graphs are usually curves because the reaction starts quickly, then slows down and eventually stops as the reactants get used up.
- ☐ That you can compare the rate of a reaction under different conditions by comparing the steepness of the curve at the start of the reaction and the time it takes for the curve to level off.
- ☐ That no matter how quickly the reaction goes, the curve will always finish at the same level, unless you add more reactant.

Rate of Reaction Experiments

- ☐ Some examples of rate of reaction experiments — for example, hydrochloric acid and marble chips, magnesium metal and hydrochloric acid, sodium thiosulfate and hydrochloric acid and the decomposition of hydrogen peroxide.

Learning Objectives:

- Know that energy is transferred to or from the surroundings during a chemical reaction.
- Know that if a reaction transfers energy to the surroundings it is exothermic.
- Know some examples of exothermic reactions and their uses.
- Know that if a reaction absorbs energy from the surroundings it is endothermic.
- Know some examples of endothermic reactions and their uses.
- Know that reversible reactions are endothermic in one direction and exothermic in the other direction.

Specification Reference C2.5.1

1. Energy Transfer in Reactions

When reactions take place, energy is transferred between the reaction and the surroundings. Some reactions give out heat, while others take energy in, making their surroundings colder. Read on to find out more...

Energy transfer

Whenever chemical reactions occur energy is transferred to or from the surroundings. This energy is usually transferred in the form of heat. If energy is transferred to the surroundings, the temperature of the surroundings will increase. If energy is transferred from the surroundings, the temperature of the surroundings will decrease.

Exothermic reactions

An **exothermic reaction** is one which transfers energy to the surroundings. This is shown by a rise in temperature. The best example of an exothermic reaction is burning fuels (combustion). This gives out a lot of heat — it's very exothermic. Neutralisation reactions (between an acid and an alkali) are also exothermic and many **oxidation** reactions are exothermic too.

Examples

- The reaction of potassium hydroxide with hydrochloric acid is a neutralisation reaction. This reaction produces heat — it's exothermic.
- Sodium is oxidised when it reacts with water — when sodium is added to water, it emits heat and moves about on the surface of the water as it is oxidised. The fact that heat is released shows that this is an exothermic reaction.

Uses of exothermic reactions

Exothermic reactions have lots of everyday uses.

Examples

- Some hand warmers use the exothermic oxidation of iron in air (with a salt solution catalyst) to generate heat.
- Self-heating cans of hot chocolate and coffee also rely on exothermic reactions between chemicals in their bases.

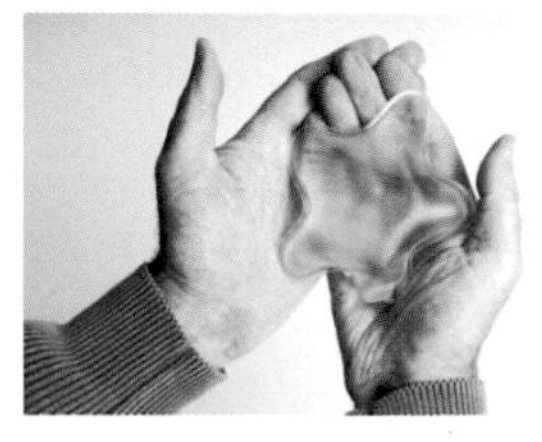

Figure 1: *A chemical hand warmer. It uses an exothermic reaction.*

Endothermic reactions

An **endothermic reaction** is one which takes in energy from the surroundings. This is shown by a fall in temperature. Endothermic reactions are much less common than exothermic reactions, but thermal decomposition reactions are a good example.

Example

The thermal decomposition of calcium carbonate is endothermic. Heat must be supplied to make calcium carbonate decompose into calcium oxide and carbon dioxide. The equation for this reaction is:

$$CaCO_3 \rightarrow CaO + CO_2$$

Uses of endothermic reactions

Endothermic reactions also have everyday uses.

Example

A sports injury pack is a cold pack that can be placed on an injury like a sprain or strain to reduce swelling. Some sports injury packs use endothermic reactions — they take in heat and the pack becomes very cold. This is much more convenient than carrying ice around. Also, this type of cold pack is much more flexible than a block of ice, so it can be wrapped around an injury more easily.

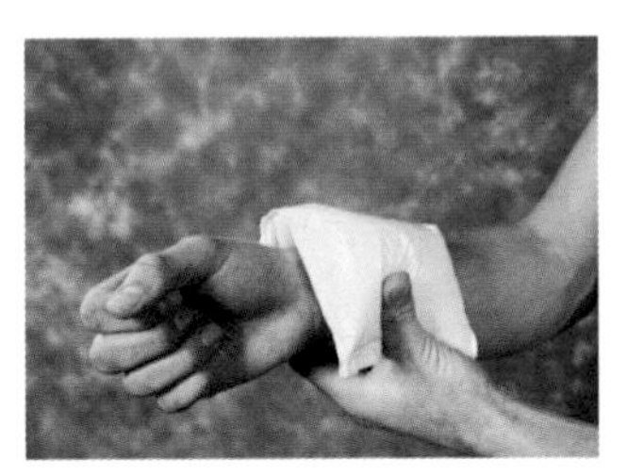

Figure 2: *A cold pack which uses an endothermic reaction being used to treat a sprained wrist.*

Energy transfer in reversible reactions

In reversible reactions, if the reaction is endothermic in one direction, it will be exothermic in the other direction. The energy absorbed by the endothermic reaction is equal to the energy released during the exothermic reaction.

Example

A good example of a reversible reaction is the thermal decomposition of hydrated copper sulfate. The equation for this reaction is:

$$\text{hydrated copper sulfate} \rightleftharpoons \text{anhydrous copper sulfate} + \text{water}$$

- If you heat blue hydrated copper sulfate crystals it drives the water off and leaves white anhydrous copper sulfate powder. This is endothermic.
- If you then add a couple of drops of water to the white powder you get the blue crystals back again and heat is given out. This is exothermic.

The amount of heat that you have to put in to drive all the water out of the anhydrous copper sulfate is the same as the amount of heat that is given out when you add all the water back in to form hydrated copper sulfate.

Tip: "Anhydrous" just means "without water", and "hydrated" means "with water".

Figure 3: *Hydrated copper sulfate (blue) being heated to form anhydrous copper sulfate (white).*

This reaction is shown in Figure 4.

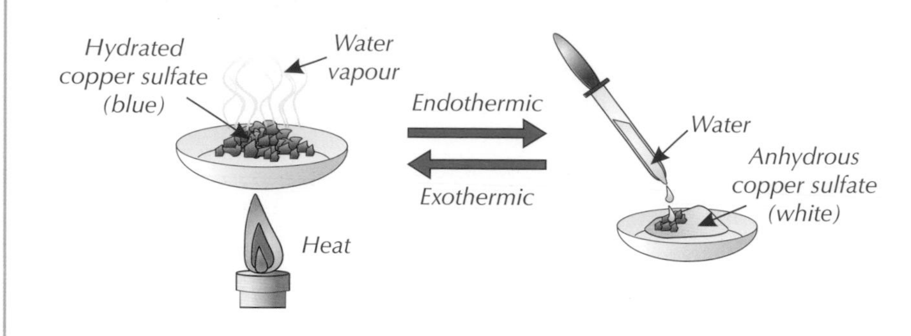

Figure 4: *The reversible reaction between hydrated copper sulfate and anhydrous copper sulfate.*

Practice Questions — Fact Recall

Q1 a) What is an exothermic reaction?

b) Name one type of reaction that is exothermic.

Q2 a) When an endothermic reaction takes place, the temperature around the reaction decreases. Explain why.

b) Give one example of an everyday use of an endothermic reaction.

Q3 If a reaction is exothermic in the forward direction will it give out heat or absorb heat in the reverse direction? Explain your answer.

Section Checklist — Make sure you know...

Energy Transfer in Reactions

- ☐ That during a chemical reaction, energy is either transferred from the reaction to the surroundings, or from the surroundings to the reaction.
- ☐ That exothermic reactions are reactions which transfer energy to the surroundings, resulting in an increase in temperature.
- ☐ That combustion, neutralisation reactions and some oxidation reactions are exothermic.
- ☐ That exothermic reactions are used in hand warmers and self-heating cans.
- ☐ That an endothermic reaction is a reaction which takes energy in from the surroundings, resulting in a decrease in temperature.
- ☐ That thermal decomposition reactions are examples of endothermic reactions.
- ☐ That endothermic reactions are used in sports injury packs.
- ☐ That reversible reactions that are exothermic in the forward direction will be endothermic in the backward direction (and vice versa) and the same amount of energy will be transferred each way.
- ☐ That the thermal decomposition of hydrated copper sulfate is an example of a reversible reaction. It is endothermic in one direction and exothermic in the other.

Exam-style Questions

1 A student is investigating the rate of the reaction between nitric acid and zinc carbonate. The equation for this reaction is shown below:

$$2HNO_{3(aq)} + ZnCO_{3(s)} \rightarrow Zn(NO_3)_{2(aq)} + CO_{2(g)} + H_2O_{(l)}$$

The student used a gas syringe to measure the volume of carbon dioxide produced by this reaction and recorded the volume every 2 minutes for 20 minutes.

1 (a) Suggest another technique that the student could have used to measure the rate of this reaction.

(1 mark)

1 (b) The student's results are shown on this graph.

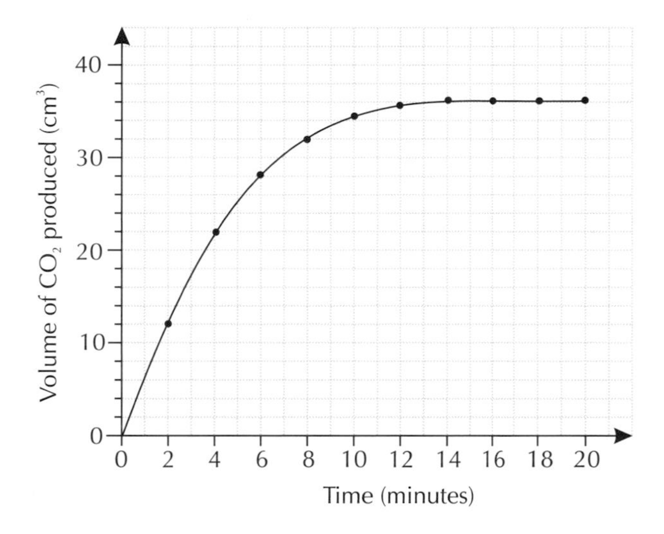

1 (b) (i) Use the graph to estimate how long it took for all of the reactants to be used up in this reaction.

(1 mark)

1 (b) (ii) Calculate the rate of reaction during the first 2 minutes of this reaction. Give your answer in cm^3/min.

(2 marks)

1 (b) (iii) Explain why the rate of this reaction decreased as the reaction progressed.

(2 marks)

1 (c) The student repeated his experiment at a higher temperature.
All other conditions were kept the same.
On the graph above, sketch a curve to show the results he might expect.

(2 marks)

2 In industry, vanadium(v) oxide is used as a catalyst in the following reaction:

$$2SO_{2(g)} + O_{2(g)} \rightleftharpoons 2SO_{3(g)}$$

Sulfur trioxide (SO_3) is used in the synthesis of sulfuric acid.

2 (a) (i) What is a catalyst?

(1 mark)

2 (a) (ii) Discuss the advantages and disadvantages of using catalysts in industrial reactions.

(4 marks)

2 (b) Increasing the pressure changes the rate of this reaction.

2 (b) (i) State the effect that using a higher pressure will have on the rate of this reaction.

(1 mark)

2 (b) (ii) Explain why increasing the pressure has an effect on the rate of this reaction.

(2 marks)

3 A reusable hand warmer contains a solution of sodium acetate trihydrate. When the hand warmer is activated, the sodium acetate trihydrate crystallises and heat is released. The word equation for this reaction is shown below:

sodium acetate trihydrate solution $\rightleftharpoons$ solid sodium acetate trihydrate

3 (a) What type of reaction is this? Circle the correct answer.

neutralisation exothermic combustion endothermic

(1 mark)

3 (b) (i) Using the information above, explain why hand warmers that contain sodium acetate trihydrate are reusable.

(2 marks)

3 (b) (ii) Suggest how the hand warmer could be reset after use, so that it is ready to be used again. Explain your answer.

(2 marks)

1. pH and Neutralisation

The pH of a solution tells you whether it's acidic, alkaline or neutral. This topic is all about pH and how it's measured.

The pH scale

pH is a measure of how acidic or alkaline a solution is. The **pH scale** goes from 0 to 14 (see Figure 1).

- Anything with a pH of less than 7 is an **acid**. The lower the pH, the stronger the acid — the strongest acids have a pH of 0.
- Anything with a pH of greater than 7 is a **base** or an **alkali**. An alkali is a soluble base. The higher the pH, the more alkaline the substance is — the strongest bases and alkalis have a pH of 14.
- Neutral substances are neither acidic nor alkaline and have a pH of exactly 7. Pure water is an example of a neutral substance.

Testing pH

One way to test the pH of a solution is to use an **indicator**. An indicator is a dye that changes colour depending on whether it's above or below a certain pH. A commonly used indicator is **universal indicator**. This indicator is a combination of dyes which gives a different colour at different pH values (see Figure 1) — it's very useful for estimating the pH of a solution.

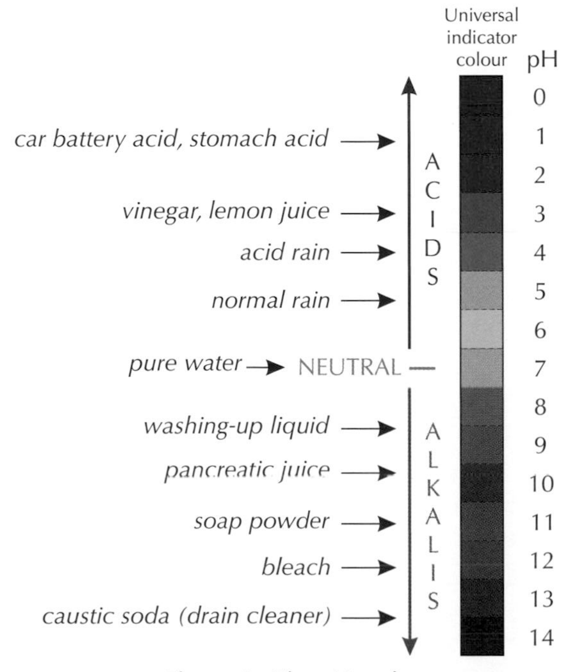

Figure 1: *The pH scale.*

Learning Objectives:

- Know that how acidic or alkaline a solution is can be measured on the pH scale.
- Know that the pH scale runs from 0 to 14 and that a neutral substance has a pH of 7.
- Know that it is hydrogen ions ($H^+_{(aq)}$) that make a solution acidic and hydroxide ions ($OH^-_{(aq)}$) that make a solution alkaline.
- Know the state symbols for solid (s), liquid (l), aqueous (aq) and gas (g).
- Know that in a neutralisation reaction hydrogen ions ($H^+_{(aq)}$) react with hydroxide ions ($OH^-_{(aq)}$) to produce water.

Specification Reference C2.6.1, C2.6.2

Tip: Water from the tap isn't pure so it won't have a pH of exactly 7.

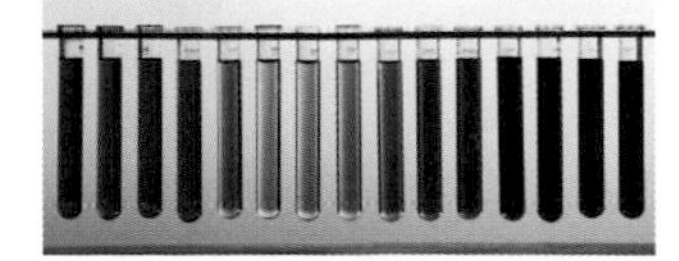

Figure 2: *The colours of universal indicator in solutions with pHs from 0 to 14 (left to right).*

Acids and alkalis

Whether a substance is an acid or an alkali depends on the type of ions that are released when the substance is dissolved in water. Acids form hydrogen ions (H^+) when dissolved in water and alkalis form hydroxide ions (OH^-).

$H^+_{(aq)}$ ions make solutions acidic and $OH^-_{(aq)}$ ions make them alkaline.

State symbols

Tip: Although state symbols aren't only to do with acids and bases it's important you know about them now. It's aqueous H^+ or OH^- ions that make a solution acidic or alkaline, not solid or gaseous ions.

The (aq) after the H^+ and OH^- is an example of a **state symbol**. State symbols show the physical state that a substance is in — (aq) shows that the ions are dissolved in water (aqueous). There are a few other state symbols you need to know about in the box below.

(l) — liquid (g) — gas (s) — solid

Neutralisation reactions

An acid will react with a base to form a salt and water — this is called a **neutralisation** reaction. The general equation for a neutralisation reaction is shown below.

Tip: There are a few examples of neutralisation reactions coming up on the next few pages.

acid + base → salt + water

Neutralisation can also be shown in terms of H^+ and OH^- ions. During neutralisation reactions, hydrogen ions (H^+) from the acid react with hydroxide ions (OH^-) from the base to produce water. The equation for this reaction is:

$$H^+_{(aq)} + OH^-_{(aq)} \rightarrow H_2O_{(l)}$$

When an acid neutralises a base (or vice versa), the products are neutral — they have a pH of 7. An indicator can be used to show that a neutralisation reaction is over.

Example

Universal indicator turns green at the end of a neutralisation reaction — see Figure 3. This shows that the solution has become neutral (and therefore that the reaction has finished).

Figure 3: Universal indicator turning green at the end of a neutralisation reaction.

Practice Questions — Fact Recall

Q1 What is pH a measure of?

Q2 If a solution is neutral, what pH is it?

Q3 a) What range of pHs show that a substance is a base?

b) What is the difference between a base and an alkali?

c) Which type of ion makes solutions acidic and which makes solutions alkaline?

Q4 Which state symbol is used to show that a substance is dissolved in water?

Q5 a) What is the product of the reaction between hydrogen ions (H^+) and hydroxide ions (OH^-)?

b) Write the symbol equation for this reaction, including state symbols.

Practice Questions — Application

Q1 State whether the following solutions are acidic or alkaline.

a) A solution of hydrogen sulfide with a pH of 4.2.

b) A solution of calcium hydroxide with a pH of 12.4.

Q2 a) After adding universal indicator to a solution, the colour changes to yellow. Suggest the pH of this solution.

b) Another solution has a pH of 9. Suggest what colour this solution will go if universal indicator is added to it.

Tip: Have a look back at the pH scale on page 177 to help you work out the answer for Q2.

Q3 What states are the following compounds in?

a) $SO_{2(g)}$ b) $H_2O_{(l)}$

c) $NH_4^+{}_{(aq)}$ d) $AgCl_{(s)}$

Q4 The base calcium carbonate reacts with hydrochloric acid.

a) What type of reaction is this?

b) A salt is formed. What is the other product of this reaction?

2. Making Salts

Salts can be made from metals, metal oxides, metal hydroxides or ammonia. You need to know how this happens and be able to write equations for the reactions that are involved...

Learning Objectives:

- Know that you can make soluble salts by reacting acids with metals.
- Know that not all metals can be used to make salts — some are too reactive and others aren't reactive enough.
- Know that metal oxides and metal hydroxides are bases. Those that are soluble are alkalis.
- Know that you can make soluble salts by reacting acids with bases.
- Understand that the salt formed depends on the metal (or the metal within an oxide or hydroxide) and the acid that has been used to make it.
- Know that when ammonia dissolves in water an alkaline solution is made that can be used to make ammonium salts, which are important fertilisers.

Specification Reference C2.6.1, C2.6.2

Making salts from metals

One way of making soluble salts is by reacting metals with acids.
This reaction produces a salt and hydrogen, as shown in the equation below.

$$\text{acid} + \text{metal} \rightarrow \text{salt} + \text{hydrogen}$$

However, not all metals are suitable to use. Highly reactive metals like sodium are too reactive — many react explosively in the presence of strong acids so it isn't safe to make salts from these metals. Other metals, such as copper, aren't reactive enough — they don't react at all or the reaction is too slow for it to be worthwhile making salts from them.

Reactivity of metals with acids

You can see how reactive different metals are by monitoring the rate of hydrogen production when they react with an acid. The more reactive the metal, the faster the reaction will go. The speed of the reaction is indicated by the rate at which bubbles of hydrogen are given off — a speedy reaction is shown by bubbles being produced rapidly.

The production of hydrogen can be detected using the burning splint test. This involves putting a lit splint at the mouth of the tube containing the metal and the acid. If hydrogen is there you'll hear a 'squeaky pop'. The more reactive the metal, the more hydrogen is produced in a certain amount of time and the louder the 'squeaky pop'.

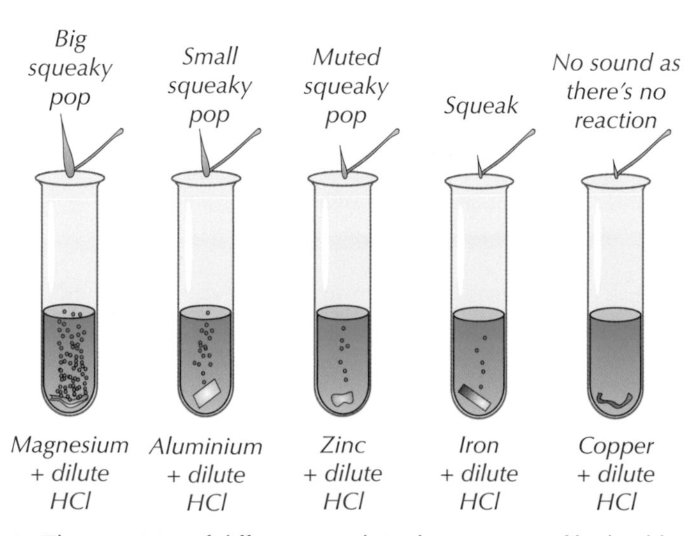

Figure 1: *The reactivity of different metals in the presence of hydrochloric acid.*

Figure 2: *Magnesium reacting with hydrochloric acid.*

Which salt is formed?

The name of the salt produced depends on which metal and acid are used. The first part of the name of the salt come from the metal and the second part of the name comes from the acid that is used.

Example

When you react magnesium with hydrochloric acid you get magnesium chloride:

hydrochloric acid + magnesium → magnesium chloride + hydrogen

Hydrochloric acid always produces chloride salts.

Examples

hydrochloric acid + aluminium → aluminum chloride + hydrogen

$$6HCl_{(aq)} + 2Al_{(s)} \rightarrow 2AlCl_{3(aq)} + 3H_{2(g)}$$

hydrochloric acid + zinc → zinc chloride + hydrogen

$$2HCl_{(aq)} + Zn_{(s)} \rightarrow ZnCl_{2(aq)} + H_{2(g)}$$

Sulfuric acid always produces sulfate salts.

Examples

sulfuric acid + magnesium → magnesium sulfate + hydrogen

$$H_2SO_{4(aq)} + Mg_{(s)} \rightarrow MgSO_{4(aq)} + H_{2(g)}$$

sulfuric acid + aluminium → aluminium sulfate + hydrogen

$$3H_2SO_{4(aq)} + 2Al_{(s)} \rightarrow Al_2(SO_4)_{3(aq)} + 3H_{2(g)}$$

Nitric acid isn't quite so straightforward. It produces nitrate salts when neutralised (this is covered on page 182), but it can produce nitric oxides with metals (rather than nitrate salts) so we won't consider it here.

Tip: The way to remember which acid produces which salt is in the name. Hydrochloric acid produces chloride salts and sulfuric acid produces sulfate salts.

Exam Tip
In the exam you might be asked to work out the salt formed from two reactants or the reactants need to make a particular salt. So it's important that you understand these examples.

Making salts from metal oxides and hydroxides

If for some reason you can't react a metal with an acid to make a soluble salt, another way of making the salt is to react a metal oxide or a metal hydroxide with an acid.

All metal oxides and hydroxides are **bases**. Some of them are **alkalis** because they are soluble in water. Because metal oxides and hydroxides are all bases, they react with acids in a neutralisation reaction. The products of neutralisation reactions are a salt and water. So the general equation for the reaction of metal oxides or metal hydroxides with acids is:

acid + metal oxide or metal hydroxide → salt + water

Tip: Remember, a base is a substance with a pH of more than 7. An alkali is a base that will dissolve in water.

Tip: For more on neutralisation reactions see page 178.

Which salt is formed?

The name of the salt produced depends on the metal in the oxide or hydroxide and the acid that is used. The first part of the name of the salt is the metal in the oxide/hydroxide and the second part of the name comes from the acid that is used.

Example

Reacting hydrochloric acid with copper oxide will give you copper chloride:

hydrochloric acid + copper oxide → copper chloride + water

Reaction with hydrochloric acid gives chlorides, with sulfuric acid gives sulfates and with nitric acid gives nitrates.

Examples

hydrochloric acid + sodium hydroxide → sodium chloride + water

$HCl_{(aq)} + NaOH_{(aq)} \rightarrow NaCl_{(aq)} + H_2O_{(l)}$

sulfuric acid + zinc oxide → zinc sulfate + water

$H_2SO_{4(aq)} + ZnO_{(s)} \rightarrow ZnSO_{4(aq)} + H_2O_{(l)}$

sulfuric acid + calcium hydroxide → calcium sulfate + water

$H_2SO_{4(aq)} + Ca(OH)_{2(s)} \rightarrow CaSO_{4(aq)} + 2H_2O_{(l)}$

nitric acid + magnesium oxide → magnesium nitrate + water

$2HNO_{3(aq)} + MgO_{(s)} \rightarrow Mg(NO_3)_{2(aq)} + H_2O_{(l)}$

nitric acid + potassium hydroxide → potassium nitrate + water

$HNO_{3(aq)} + KOH_{(aq)} \rightarrow KNO_{3(aq)} + H_2O_{(l)}$

Tip: Whether you use an oxide or a hydroxide isn't important — it's the metal in the compound that determines which salt you'll get.

Making salts from ammonia

You can also make salts from ammonia. Ammonia dissolves in water to make an alkaline solution. When this aqueous ammonia reacts with nitric acid it is neutralised and you get a salt — ammonium nitrate:

ammonia + nitric acid → ammonium nitrate

$NH_{3(aq)} + HNO_{3(aq)} \rightarrow NH_4NO_{3(aq)}$

Tip: This is a neutralisation reaction, but it's a bit different from other neutralisation reactions as there's no water produced — just the ammonium salt.

Ammonium salts, such as ammonium nitrate, are used as fertiliser. They supply nitrogen which is an essential nutrient that plants need to make proteins.

Practice Questions — Fact Recall

Q1 Salts can be made when a metal reacts with an acid.

a) Give the general word equation for this reaction.

b) Why are some metals not suitable for reacting with a strong acid to make salts? Give an example.

Q2 Salts can be made when metal hydroxides or metal oxides react with an acid.

a) Are metal hydroxides and metal oxides acids or bases?

b) Give the general word equation for the reaction of an acid with a metal hydroxide.

Q3 Ammonia dissolves in water to produce an alkaline solution.

a) What would you react ammonia with to get ammonium nitrate?

b) Give one use of ammonium nitrate.

Q4 Write a balanced symbol equation for the reaction used to produce ammonium nitrate (NH_4NO_3) from ammonia (NH_3).

Practice Questions — Application

Q1 a) If you react tin (Sn) with sulfuric acid (H_2SO_4), which of the following salts would be produced?

$MgSO_{4(aq)}$ $SnCl_{2(aq)}$ $ZnSO_{4(aq)}$ $SnSO_{4(aq)}$

b) What is the other product of this reaction?

Q2 Write a word equation for the reaction of hydrochloric acid with magnesium hydroxide.

Q3 Name the salt produced in each of the following reactions.

a) Sulfuric acid reacting with iron.

b) Hydrochloric acid reacting with calcium.

Q4 Name the salt produced in each of the following reactions.

a) Nitric acid reacting with copper oxide.

b) Sulfuric acid reacting with potassium hydroxide.

Q5 Write balanced symbol equations for the following reactions and name the salt produced.

a) Hydrochloric acid reacting with magnesium.

b) Nitric acid reacting with sodium hydroxide.

Exam Tip H
If you're a higher tier candidate you could be asked to write a balanced symbol equation for any of the reactions mentioned on the specification, including acid-metal reactions.

3. Methods for Making Salts

There are three experimental techniques you can use to make salts in the lab. Have your conical flasks at the ready and read on to find out more...

Learning Objectives:

- Know that when you make a salt from a metal or insoluble base a filter is used to separate out the excess.
- Know that an indicator can be used to show when a reaction between an acid and an alkali to produce a salt solution is complete.
- Know that solid salts can be made by crystallisation of salt solutions.
- Know that precipitation reactions can be used to make insoluble salts and to remove certain ions from a solution.

Specification Reference C2.6.1

Solubility of salts

If you're making a salt the first thing you need to know is whether it's soluble or not. This is important because it affects which method you need to use. Most chlorides, sulfates and nitrates are soluble — the main exceptions are lead chloride, lead sulfate and silver chloride.

Making soluble salts

When making a soluble salt, the first thing you need to do is choose appropriate reagents to produce that particular salt. This involves picking the right acid and the right metal, insoluble base (a metal oxide or metal hydroxide) or a soluble base (alkali) to react it with. You should be able to work out which are the right reagents to choose from the name of the salt you want to produce (see pages 181-182).

Examples

If you want to make potassium sulfate, you could react sulfuric acid (H_2SO_4) and potassium hydroxide (KOH). The KOH provides the potassium and the H_2SO_4 provides the sulfate, as shown below.

$$H_2SO_{4(aq)} + 2KOH_{(aq)} \rightarrow K_2SO_{4(aq)} + 2H_2O_{(l)}$$

If you want to make copper chloride, you could mix hydrochloric acid and copper oxide (you wouldn't use copper metal as it's not reactive enough to react with hydrochloric acid).

$$2HCl_{(aq)} + CuO_{(s)} \rightarrow CuCl_{2(aq)} + H_2O_{(l)}$$

Tip: Remember, some metals are unreactive and other metals are too reactive to use to make salts (see page 180).

The exact method you use to make the salt depends on whether the reagents you choose are soluble or insoluble.

Making soluble salts from metals or insoluble bases

If you are making a soluble salt by adding an insoluble reagent to an acid, you can add it in excess and separate it out at the end of the reaction using filter paper. Metals are insoluble, as are many metal oxides and metal hydroxides, so this is the method you'd use if you're using any of those. Here's what you do:

1. Put the acid in a beaker. Add the insoluble reactant (the metal, metal oxide or metal hydroxide) and stir — it will dissolve in the acid as it reacts.
2. Keep adding the insoluble reactant until it is in excess. You'll know when this is because there will be some left over that won't react — this shows that all the acid has been neutralised and the reaction has finished.

3. Then you need to filter out the excess insoluble reactant to get the salt solution. This is done using filter paper and a filter funnel (see Figure 1).

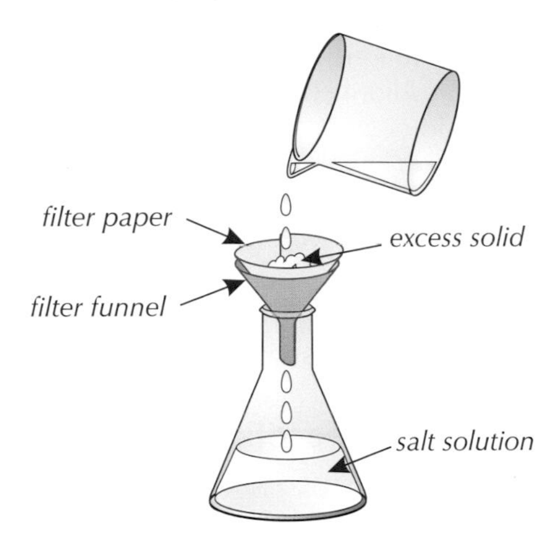

Figure 1: *Filtering out the excess insoluble reactant using filter paper and a filter funnel.*

Figure 2: *Filtering a copper sulfate ($CuSO_4$) solution to remove any excess insoluble reactant.*

Making soluble salts from alkalis

You can't use the method from the previous page with alkalis (soluble bases) like sodium hydroxide, potassium hydroxide or ammonium hydroxides, because you can't tell whether the reaction has finished (as the alkali is soluble in the acid). So you can't just add an excess to the acid and filter out what's left.

To get a pure salt solution you have to add exactly the right amount of alkali to just neutralise the acid — you need to use an **indicator** to show when the reaction has finished. Then you need to repeat it using exactly the same volumes of alkali and acid so the salt isn't contaminated with indicator.

Tip: For more about indicators have a look back at page 177.

Crystallising salts

Whether you're making a soluble salt from an insoluble reactant or an alkali, you'll be left with a salt solution at the end of the reaction. You can convert this into pure, solid crystals of salt using **crystallisation**.

To do this you first need to heat the salt solution to evaporate most of the water and make the solution more concentrated. Then leave the rest of the water to evaporate very slowly at room temperature — this allows the salt to crystallise.

Figure 3: *Copper sulfate ($CuSO_4$) crystals.*

Making insoluble salts

If the salt you want to make is insoluble you can use a **precipitation** reaction to make it. A precipitation reaction is a reaction where one of the products is insoluble and so forms as a solid precipitate in the solution. To make an insoluble salt you just need to pick two aqueous solutions that contain the ions you need and mix them together.

Tip: You couldn't use an insoluble reagent to make an insoluble salt because you wouldn't be able to separate them.

Example

To make lead chloride you need a solution which contains lead ions and one which contains chloride ions. You can mix lead nitrate solution (most nitrates are soluble) with sodium chloride solution (all Group 1 compounds are soluble) as shown below.

$$Pb(NO_3)_{2(aq)} + 2NaCl_{(aq)} \rightarrow PbCl_{2(s)} + 2NaNO_{3(aq)}$$

Tip: The state symbols shows that lead chloride ($PbCl_2$) is a solid, so it will form a precipitate in the solution.

Once the salt has precipitated out (and is lying at the bottom of your flask), you can filter it from the solution, wash it and then dry it on filter paper.

Other uses of precipitation reactions

Precipitation reactions can also be used to remove particular ions from solutions, by making an insoluble salt precipitate that contains the ion. After you separate the precipitate from the solution, you can dispose of it leaving you with a solution that doesn't contain those ions. Precipitation reactions are used to remove ions from lots of things.

Figure 4: *A water treatment works.*

Examples

- To remove poisonous ions, such as lead, from drinking water.
- To remove calcium and magnesium ions from drinking water. These ions make water "hard", which stops soap lathering properly.
- To remove unwanted ions during the treatment of effluent (sewage).

Practice Questions — Fact Recall

Q1 Soluble salts can be made by reacting an alkali with an acid. What is used to determine when the reaction has finished?

Q2 Describe and name the process used to get solid salt crystals from a salt solution.

Q3 a) What type of reaction is used to make insoluble salts?

b) Name another use for this type of reaction.

Practice Questions — Application

Q1 A scientist is making the soluble salt tin chloride ($SnCl_2$) by reacting tin (Sn) with hydrochloric acid (HCl).

a) Write the word equation for this reaction.

b) Describe the experimental method used to make this salt.

Q2 Sam wants to make the insoluble salt magnesium carbonate ($MgCO_3$). To do this he plans to mix magnesium sulfate ($MgSO_4$) with sodium sulfate (Na_2SO_4). Explain why this reaction won't produce magnesium carbonate.

Section Checklist — Make sure you know...

pH and Neutralisation

- ☐ That the pH scale measures how acidic or alkaline a solution is.
- ☐ That solutions with a pH of less than 7 are acidic, solutions with a pH of more than 7 are basic or alkaline and solutions with a pH of exactly 7 are neutral.
- ☐ That an alkali is a base that is soluble in water.
- ☐ That aqueous hydrogen ions ($H^+_{(aq)}$) make a solution acidic and aqueous hydroxide ions ($OH^-_{(aq)}$) make a solution alkaline.
- ☐ That the state symbols in equations are: (s) for solid, (l) for liquid, (aq) for aqueous and (g) for gas.
- ☐ That in a neutralisation reaction, water is produced when hydrogen ions react with hydroxide ions.

Making Salts

- ☐ That soluble salts can be made by reacting hydrochloric acid or sulfuric acid with metals.
- ☐ That the general equation for the reaction of an acid with a metal is: acid + metal → salt + hydrogen.
- ☐ That some metals aren't suitable to use for making salts because they are too reactive (explode in acid) or aren't reactive enough.
- ☐ That metal oxides and metal hydroxides are bases. Those that are soluble in water are alkalis.
- ☐ That you can make soluble salts by reacting acids with metal oxides or metal hydroxides.
- ☐ That the general equation for the reaction of a metal oxide/hydroxide with an acid is: acid + metal oxide/metal hydroxide → salt + water.
- ☐ How the name of salts depends on the metal (or metal within an oxide or hydroxide) and the acid that is used to make it.
- ☐ That when ammonia dissolves in water it forms an alkaline solution. This can react with nitric acid to produce ammonium nitrate, which is commonly used as a fertiliser.

Methods for Making Salts

- ☐ That when making a salt by adding an excess of insoluble base or metal to an acid, the excess base or metal is filtered out at the end of the reaction.
- ☐ That when making a salt from an alkali, an indicator is used to show when the reaction has finished.
- ☐ That soluble salts are converted into solid salts by crystallisation of the salt solutions.
- ☐ That precipitation reactions are used to make insoluble salts.
- ☐ That precipitation reactions can also be used as a way of extracting undesired ions from solutions.

Exam-style Questions

1 The pH of a substance determines whether it is an acid, a base or neutral.

1 (a) Complete the sentences using the words in the box below.

an acid	a base	neutral

1 (a) (i) Toothpaste has a pH of 8.2 so it is ____________ .

(1 mark)

1 (a) (ii) Ethanol has a pH of 7.0 so it is ____________ .

(1 mark)

1 (a) (iii) Fresh milk has a pH of 6.5 so it is ____________ .

(1 mark)

1 (b) Niall has a substance with a pH of 4.

1 (b) (i) What type of ions are released when this substance dissolves in water?

(1 mark)

1 (b) (ii) Which of the following could Niall add to his solution to neutralise it?

Potassium hydroxide (pH 13) Pure water (pH 7) Sulfuric acid (pH 1)

(1 mark)

1 (b) (iii) Describe how Niall could determine when the neutralisation reaction has finished.

(2 marks)

1 (b) (iv) Write an equation, including state symbols, to show what happens during a neutralisation reaction in terms of the ions involved.

(2 marks)

2 There are a number of different ways to make soluble salts.

2 (a) One way of making soluble salts involves reacting acids with metal oxides.

2 (a) (i) Copy and complete the general equation for this reaction shown below:

acid + metal oxide → ________ + ________

(2 marks)

2 (a) (ii) What type of reaction is the reaction between a metal oxide and an acid?

(1 mark)

2 (b) Ryan is making a soluble salt by mixing magnesium oxide (MgO) with hydrochloric acid (HCl).

2 (b) (i) Name the salt produced when magnesium oxide reacts with hydrochloric acid.

(1 mark)

2 (b) (ii) Given that magnesium oxide is insoluble, explain how Ryan will know that the reaction between magnesium oxide and hydrochloric acid has finished.

(2 marks)

2 (b) (iii) Describe how Ryan could get from the finished reaction mixture to pure solid salt crystals.

(3 marks)

3 Barium is a very reactive metal that can be used to make a variety of useful salts, including the soluble salt barium chloride ($BaCl_2$) and the insoluble salt barium sulfate ($BaSO_4$).

3 (a) Barium chloride is made by reacting barium hydroxide ($Ba(OH)_2$) with hydrochloric acid (HCl).

3 (a) (i) Write a balanced symbol equation for the reaction between barium hydroxide and hydrochloric acid.

(2 marks)

3 (a) (ii) Barium hydroxide is an alkali. What is an alkali?

(2 marks)

3 (a) (iii) Suggest why barium chloride isn't made by reacting barium directly with hydrochloric acid.

(1 mark)

3 (b) Barium sulfate can be made from barium chloride using a precipitation reaction.

3 (b) (i) Which acid would you react with barium chloride to make barium sulfate?

(1 mark)

3 (b) (ii) In the context of making barium sulfate, why is it important that barium chloride is soluble?

(1 mark)

3 (b) (iii) Precipitation reactions are used in industrial settings, as well as in the production of salts. Give **two** other uses for precipitation reactions.

(2 marks)

1. Electrolysis — The Basics

Learning Objectives:
- Know that when an electric current is passed through a molten or dissolved ionic compound it is broken down into the elements it's made of, and that this is called electrolysis.
- Know what an electrolyte is.
- Know that dissolved or molten ionic substances contain free ions.
- Be able to describe electrolysis in terms of the movement of positive and negative ions towards electrodes.
- Be able to describe oxidation and reduction in terms of the loss and gain of electrons.
- Know that oxidation takes places at the positive electrode and reduction takes place at the negative electrode.
- H Be able to write half equations for the reactions at the electrodes during electrolysis.
- Know that the products of electrolysis are determined by how reactive the elements involved are.

Specification Reference C2.7, C2.7.1

You've met electrolysis briefly before — it's used to extract metals from rocks. You need to know a bit more about it now though — how it works, how to predict the products of electrolysis, and (if you're doing higher tier) how to represent the different reactions that take place using equations. Here we go...

What is electrolysis?

If you pass an electric current through an ionic substance that's molten (has been melted) or in solution, it breaks down into the elements it's made of. This is called **electrolysis**. For example, the electrolysis of aluminium oxide breaks aluminium oxide down into aluminium and oxygen.

Electrolytes

Electrolysis requires a liquid to conduct the electricity, called the **electrolyte**. Electrolytes contain free ions — they're usually the molten or dissolved ionic substance (see Figure 1). In either case it's the free ions which conduct the electricity and allow the whole thing to work.

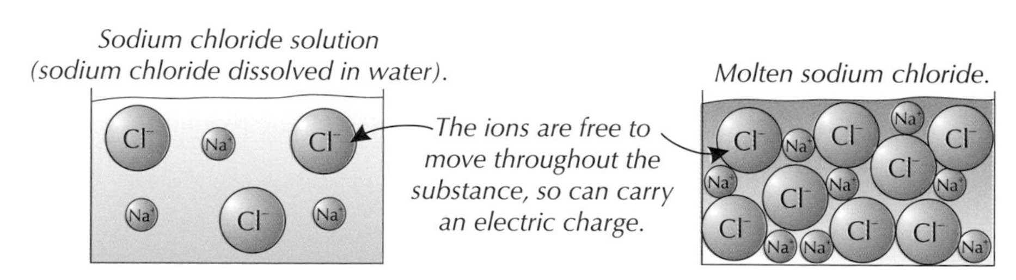

Figure 1: *Free ions in melted and dissolved sodium chloride.*

How electrolysis works

Electrolysis is based on an electrical circuit that includes an electrolyte and two electrodes. In electrolysis, the electrodes are placed into the electrolyte and ions move from one electrode to the other — this allows the conduction of electricity through the circuit. Electrons are taken away from ions at the positive electrode and given to other ions at the negative electrode. As ions gain or lose electrons they become atoms or molecules and are released. These atoms or molecules are the products of electrolysis.

Example

Lead bromide ($PbBr_2$) is an ionic compound, so when it is molten it will conduct electricity. Electrolysis of lead bromide breaks it down into lead (Pb) and bromine (Br_2). So, the electrolyte is lead bromide and the products of electrolysis are lead and bromine. Here's how it works...

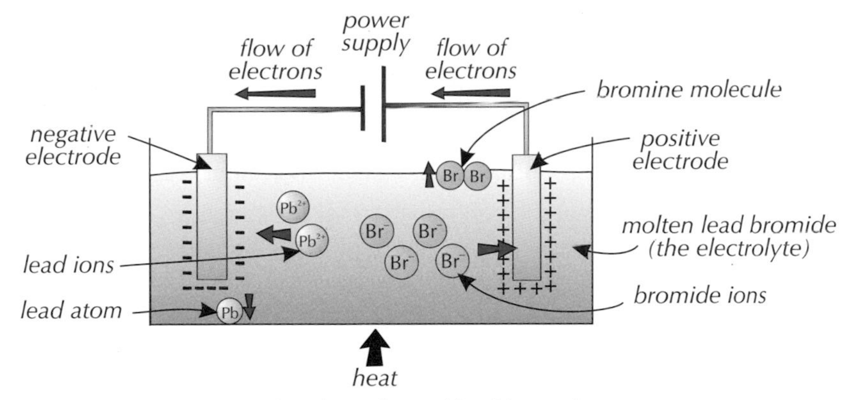

Figure 2: *The electrolysis of lead bromide.*

Molten lead bromide contains positively charged lead ions and negatively charged bromide ions.

- The positive ions are attracted towards the negative electrode. Here, each lead ion gains two electrons and becomes a lead atom.
- The negative ions are attracted towards the positive electrode. Here, bromide ions lose one electron each and form bromine molecules (Br_2).

Tip: How many electrons each ion needs to gain or lose to become an atom or molecule depends on the charge on the ion. Have a look back at pages 112 for more on this.

Oxidation and reduction

Electrolysis always involves an **oxidation** reaction and a **reduction** reaction.

- Oxidation is a loss of electrons.
- Reduction is a gain of electrons.

So, in electrolysis, reduction happens at the negative electrode (where ions gain electrons) and oxidation occurs at the positive electrode (where ions lose electrons).

Example continued...

- In the electrolysis of lead bromide the lead ions gain electrons. This is a reduction reaction, and the lead ions are said to be reduced.
- The bromide ions lose electrons. This is an oxidation reaction and the bromide ions are said to be oxidised.

Exam Tip
You can remember what oxidation and reduction are using the mnemonic OILRIG, which stands for: Oxidation Is Loss, Reduction Is Gain.

Tip: You can talk about reduction and oxidation in terms of the loss or gain of oxygen, but when you're dealing with electrolysis you need to describe them in terms of electrons.

Half equations Higher

Half equations show the reactions at the electrodes. Here's how to write a half equation for the reaction that takes place at the negative electrode:

Step 1: Write the symbol for the positive ion in the electrolyte on the left-hand side of the equation.

Step 2: Write the symbol for the neutral atoms or molecules produced on the right-hand side of the equation.

Step 3: Balance the number of atoms in the equation.

Step 4: Balance the charges by adding electrons (shown as e^-).

You can do the same to get the half equation for the reaction at the positive electrode, starting with the negative ion on the left-hand side of the equation.

Tip: H For the half equation to show the reaction at the positive electrode you can balance the charges by adding or subtracting electrons. For the half equation for the negative electrode you can only add electrons.

Tip: H These equations are called half equations because each one only shows half of the overall reaction that takes place during electrolysis.

Exam Tip H
You can check your half equations are correct by making sure that the charges balance and the atoms balance. If they don't, you've gone wrong somewhere.

Example **Higher**

These are the half equations for the electrolysis of lead bromide:

Negative electrode:

Step 1: Pb^{2+}

Step 2: $Pb^{2+} \rightarrow Pb$

Step 3: There's one lead ion on the left and one lead atom on the right, so the number of atoms is balanced.

Step 4: A charge of 2+ on the left hand side needs to be balanced out by two electrons, so that the overall charge of both sides is the same (0). So the half equation for the reaction at the negative electrode is:

$$Pb^{2+} + 2e^- \rightarrow Pb$$

Positive electrode:

Step 1: Br^-

Step 2: $Br^- \rightarrow Br_2$

Step 3: There are two bromine atoms on the right so there need to be two bromide ions on the left to balance the equation.

$$2Br^- \rightarrow Br_2$$

Step 4: A charge of 2– on the left hand side needs to be balanced out by two electrons on the right hand side, so that the overall charge on both sides is equal (2–). So the half equation for the reaction at the negative electrode is:

$$2Br^- \rightarrow Br_2 + 2e^-$$

Or, you could subtract two electrons from the left-hand side to give both sides a charge of zero. This would give you this half equation:

$$2Br^- - 2e^- \rightarrow Br_2$$

The charges in this half equation are still balanced because (–2) – (–2) = 0

Predicting the products of electrolysis

Sometimes there are more than two types of free ions in the electrolyte. For example, if a salt is dissolved in water there will be some H^+ and OH^- ions as well as the ions from the salt in the solution. In this situation, the products of electrolysis depend on how reactive the elements involved are.

At the negative electrode, if metal ions and H^+ ions are present, the metal ions will stay in solution if the metal is more reactive than hydrogen. This is because the more reactive an element, the keener it is to stay as ions. So, hydrogen will be produced unless the metal is less reactive than it.

At the positive electrode, if OH^- and halide ions (Cl^-, Br^-, I^-) are present then molecules of chlorine, bromine or iodine will be formed. If no halide is present, then oxygen will be formed.

Tip: The electrolysis of sodium chloride solution is a classic example of electrolysis with more than two types of ions present. There's more on this on page 194.

Exam Tip
You'll be given a reactivity series (like the one in Figure 3) in your exam, so you'll be able to look up whether a metal is more or less reactive than hydrogen.

Practice Questions — Fact Recall

Q1 a) What happens to a molten ionic substance when an electric current is passed through it?

b) What is this process called?

Q2 Why are dissolved ionic substances able to conduct electricity?

Q3 Describe what happens at the positive electrode during electrolysis in terms of electrons.

Q4 What type of ions are attracted towards the negative electrode?

Q5 What is reduction?

Q6 At which electrode does reduction happen?

Q7 Bromide ions and hydroxide ions are in an electrolyte during electrolysis. What substance will form at the positive electrode?

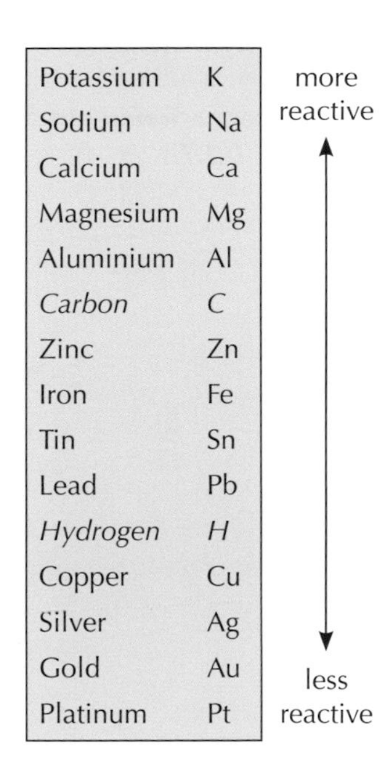

Potassium	K
Sodium	Na
Calcium	Ca
Magnesium	Mg
Aluminium	Al
Carbon	*C*
Zinc	Zn
Iron	Fe
Tin	Sn
Lead	Pb
Hydrogen	*H*
Copper	Cu
Silver	Ag
Gold	Au
Platinum	Pt

***Figure 3:** The reactivity series of metals (plus carbon and hydrogen).*

Practice Questions — Application

Q1 Molten zinc chloride can undergo electrolysis. The ions in the electrolyte are Zn^{2+} and Cl^-. The electrodes are made of graphite.

a) Give the name of the electrolyte.

b) Which electrode do the chloride ions move towards?

c) Describe what happens to the chloride ions at this electrode.

d) Are the zinc ions oxidised or reduced during electrolysis?

Q2 The products of the electrolysis of potassium bromide solution are hydrogen and bromine. Explain why potassium is not produced.

Tip: You can use the reactivity series in Figure 3 to help you answer Q2.

Q3 Complete the half equations below to show the reactions that happen during the electrolysis of two different solutions:

a) $Br^- \rightarrow Br_2$ and $H^+ \rightarrow H_2$

b) $Cu^{2+} \rightarrow Cu$ and $O^{2-} \rightarrow O_2$

2. Electrolysis of Sodium Chloride

Now you've got the basics covered, it's time to have a look at an example of electrolysis in more detail — the electrolysis of sodium chloride solution...

Learning Objectives:

- Know that the products of the electrolysis of sodium chloride solution are hydrogen, chlorine and sodium hydroxide.
- Know the uses of chlorine and sodium hydroxide in industry.
- Be able to describe the electrolysis of sodium chloride solution in terms of ions, electrons, electrodes, oxidation and reduction.
- H Be able to write half equations for the electrolysis of sodium chloride solution.

Specification Reference C2.7.1

The products of sodium chloride electrolysis

When common salt (sodium chloride, NaCl) is dissolved in water and electrolysed, it produces three useful products — hydrogen (H_2), chlorine (Cl_2) and sodium hydroxide (NaOH). These products are pretty useful in industry. Chlorine has many uses, for example, in the production of bleach and plastics. Sodium hydroxide is a very strong alkali and is used widely in the chemical industry, for example, to make soap.

The process of sodium chloride electrolysis

Sodium chloride solution contains sodium ions (Na^+), chloride ions (Cl^-), hydrogen ions (H^+) and hydroxide ions (OH^-). The hydrogen ions and hydroxide ions come from the water. The electrolysis of sodium chloride is shown in Figure 1.

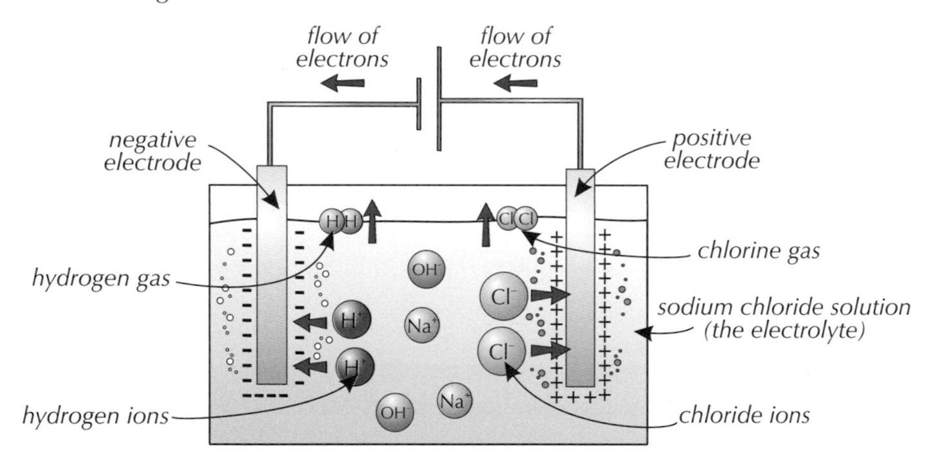

Figure 1: *The electrolysis of sodium chloride.*

At the negative electrode

The positive hydrogen ions are attracted to the negative electrode. Here, they gain one electron each and combine to form hydrogen molecules (H_2). This is a **reduction** reaction and causes hydrogen to be released at the negative electrode.

At the positive electrode

The negative chloride ions are attracted to the positive electrode. Here, they lose one electron each and combine to form chlorine molecules (Cl_2). This is an **oxidation** reaction, and causes chlorine to be released at the positive electrode.

Ions remaining in solution

The sodium ions stay in solution because they're more reactive than hydrogen. Hydroxide ions from water are also left behind. This means that sodium hydroxide (NaOH) is left in the solution.

Tip: See page 193 for more on how to work out whether the metal ions or hydrogen ions stay in solution.

Half equations Higher

To write the half equations for the electrolysis of sodium chloride, follow the steps on page 192.

Negative electrode:

Step 1: H^+

Step 2: $H^+ \rightarrow H_2$

Step 3: There are two hydrogen atoms on the right, so there need to be two ions on the left to balance the equation.

$2H^+ \rightarrow H_2$

Step 4: Balance out the charge of 2+ on the left hand side by adding two electrons, so that the overall charge of both sides is zero.

$2H^+ + 2e^- \rightarrow H_2$

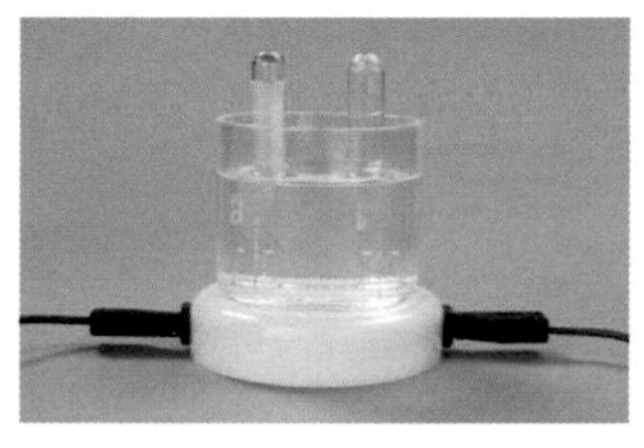

Figure 2: The electrolysis of sodium chloride. Hydrogen and chlorine gas are collected in the test tubes.

Positive electrode:

Step 1: Cl^-

Step 2: $Cl^- \rightarrow Cl_2$

Step 3: There are two chlorine atoms on the right, so there need to be two chloride ions on the left to balance the equation.

$2Cl^- \rightarrow Cl_2$

Step 4: Balance out the charge of 2– on the left by adding two electrons on the right, so that the overall charge of both sides is 2–.

$2Cl^- \rightarrow Cl_2 + 2e^-$

Or, you could subtract two electrons from the left, to give both sides a charge of zero. This half equation would be:

$2Cl^- - 2e^- \rightarrow Cl_2$

Exam Tip H
For the half equation at the positive electrode it doesn't matter whether you add electrons to the right-hand side of the equation or take them away from the left-hand side. Just use the method that you're happiest with.

Practice Questions — Fact Recall

Q1 Sodium hydroxide is one product of the electrolysis of sodium chloride solution. What are the other two products?

Q2 Give one industrial use of sodium hydroxide.

Q3 Which product is formed at the negative electrode?

Q4 Which product is formed as the result of a reduction reaction?

Q5 Explain why sodium hydroxide is produced during the electrolysis of sodium chloride solution.

3. Electrolysis of Aluminium Ore

Learning Objectives:
- Know that aluminium is extracted from aluminium oxide by electrolysis.
- Know why aluminium oxide is dissolved in molten cryolite before being electrolysed.
- Know that aluminium and oxygen are products of the electrolysis of aluminium oxide, and which electrodes they are formed at.
- Know why carbon dioxide is produced during electrolysis of aluminium oxide.
- H Be able to write half equations for the electrolysis of aluminium oxide.

Specification Reference C2.7.1

Next up, the electrolysis of aluminium oxide to get pure aluminium. The basics of electrolysis are all the same here, but there are a few twists to learn...

Aluminium

Aluminium's a very abundant metal, but it is always found naturally in compounds. Its main ore is bauxite, and after mining and purifying, a white powder is left. This is pure aluminium oxide, Al_2O_3. The aluminium has to be extracted from this using electrolysis.

Extracting aluminium by electrolysis

Aluminium oxide (Al_2O_3) has a very high melting point of over 2000 °C — so melting it would be very expensive. Instead the aluminium oxide is dissolved in molten cryolite (a less common ore of aluminium). This brings the melting temperature down to about 900 °C, which saves energy, making the process cheaper and easier. The electrolysis of aluminium oxide is shown in Figure 1.

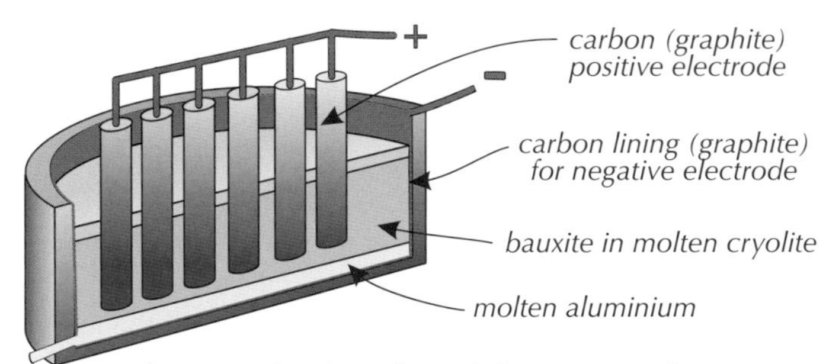

Figure 1: *The electrolysis of aluminium oxide.*

Tip: The normal rules of electrolysis apply here — the positive ions are attracted to the negative electrode where they're reduced, and the negative ions are attracted to the positive electrode where they're oxidised.

The electrodes are made of carbon (graphite), a good conductor of electricity. Aluminium forms at the negative electrode and oxygen forms at the positive electrode. The oxygen then reacts with the carbon in the electrode to produce carbon dioxide. This means that the positive electrodes gradually get 'eaten away' and have to be replaced every now and again.

Half equations Higher

The half equations for these reactions are:

Negative electrode: $Al^{3+} + 3e^- \rightarrow Al$

Positive electrode: $2O^{2-} \rightarrow O_2 + 4e^-$

Exam Tip H
Make sure you're happy with how to work out these half equations. (Have a look at page 192 for the steps.)
In the exam, you'll be given a data sheet with the formulae of some ions. So if you don't know the charges on the ions you can look them up.

Practice Questions — Fact Recall

Q1 Why is aluminium oxide dissolved in molten cryolite before it undergoes electrolysis?

Q2 a) Give the name of the product formed at the positive electrode.

b) Give the name of the product formed at the negative electrode.

Q3 Why is carbon dioxide produced in this electrolysis reaction?

4. Electroplating

And finally, a clever use of electrolysis — electroplating.

Learning Objectives:
- Know that using electrolysis to coat an object in another material is called electroplating.
- Know that electroplating can be used to coat objects with silver or copper.

Specification Reference C2.7, C2.7.1

What is electroplating?

Electroplating is a process that uses electrolysis to coat the surface of one metal with another metal. For example, you might want to electroplate silver onto a brass cup to make it look nice.

The negative electrode is the metal object you want to plate and the positive electrode is the pure metal you want it to be plated with. You also need the electrolyte to contain ions of the plating metal. The ions that plate the metal object come from the solution. These ions are replaced in the solution by more positive ions from the positive electrode.

Example

To electroplate silver onto a brass cup, you make the brass cup the negative electrode (to attract the positive silver ions), and a lump of pure silver the positive electrode. Then you dip them both in a solution of silver ions (for example, silver nitrate). The silver ions in the solution are attracted towards the brass cup, where they gain electrons, turn into silver atoms and stick to it. The positive electrode releases more silver ions into the solution.

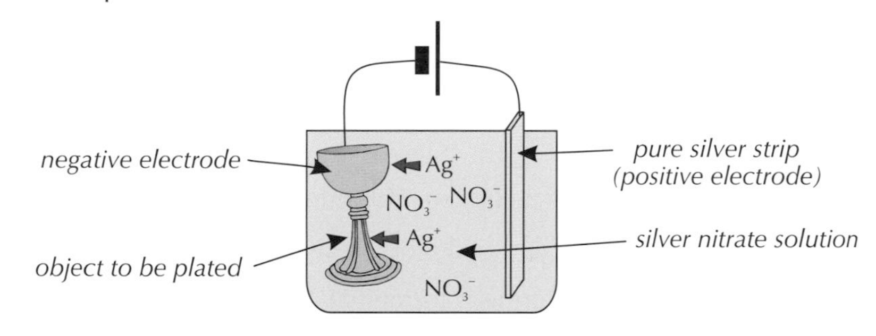

Figure 1: *Electroplating silver onto a brass cup.*

Figure 2: *Objects above an electroplating tank. The objects are lowered into the tank to electroplate them.*

Uses of electroplating

There are lots of different uses for electroplating. For example:

Decoration

Silver is attractive, but very expensive. It's much cheaper to plate a boring brass cup with silver, than it is to make the cup out of solid silver — but it looks just as pretty.

Conduction

Metals like copper conduct electricity well — because of this they're often used to plate metals for electronic circuits and computers.

Tip: Silver and copper are just two examples of metals that can be used for electroplating — lots of different metals can be used.

Practice Questions — Fact Recall

Q1 What is electroplating?

Q2 Name two metals that might be used to plate another material.

Q3 Give two uses of electroplating.

Section Checklist — Make sure you know...

Electrolysis — The Basics

- ❑ That dissolved and molten ionic substances contain free ions, so they can conduct electricity.
- ❑ That passing an electric current through a molten or dissolved ionic substance will break it down into its elements, and that this process is called electrolysis.
- ❑ That the liquid that conducts the electricity and is broken down is called the electrolyte.
- ❑ That positive ions are attracted to the negative electrode, where they gain electrons and form neutral atoms or molecules. This is called a reduction reaction.
- ❑ That negative ions are attracted to the positive electrode, where they lose electrons and form neutral atoms or molecules. This is called an oxidation reaction.
- ❑ H How to write half equations to show the reactions that take place at the electrodes.
- ❑ That if there are more than two types of free ions in solution during electrolysis, the products formed depend on how reactive the elements involved are.

Electrolysis of Sodium Chloride

- ❑ That the electrolysis of sodium chloride solution produces hydrogen, chlorine and sodium hydroxide.
- ❑ That chlorine is used to make bleach and plastics and sodium hydroxide is used to make soap.
- ❑ Why hydrogen is formed at the negative electrode and chlorine is formed at the positive electrode.
- ❑ That sodium ions and hydroxide ions (from water) are left in solution, forming sodium hydroxide.

Electrolysis of Aluminium Ore

- ❑ That electrolysis is used to extract aluminium from its ore (aluminium oxide).
- ❑ That aluminium oxide is dissolved in molten cryolite before electrolysis takes place, as this reduces the temperature at which it can be melted, and so reduces the cost.
- ❑ Why aluminium is formed at the negative electrode and oxygen is formed at the positive electrode.
- ❑ That the oxygen produced reacts with the carbon in the electrode to form carbon dioxide.

Electroplating

- ❑ That electroplating is when electrolysis is used to coat the surface of one metal with another.
- ❑ That objects can be electroplated with silver or copper, for decorative or practical purposes.

Exam-style Questions

You may use the reactivity series from Figure 3 on page 193 to help you answer Q1.

1 Copper chloride is an ionic compound. When dissolved in water it forms copper chloride solution. Copper chloride solution can undergo electrolysis.

1 (a) Give the name of the electrolyte used in this electrolysis.

(1 mark)

1 (b) The ions present in the copper chloride solution are Cu^{2+}, Cl^-, H^+ and OH^-.

1 (b) (i) Where do the H^+ and OH^- ions come from?

(1 mark)

1 (b) (ii) Copper ions move towards the negative electrode.
Describe what happens to the copper ions at the negative electrode.

(2 marks)

1 (b) (iii) Explain why copper metal is produced at the negative electrode, rather than hydrogen gas.

(2 marks)

1 (c) Chlorine gas is produced at the positive electrode.

1 (c) (i) Give **one** industrial use of chlorine.

(1 mark)

1 (c) (ii) Complete the half equation for the reaction that occurs at the positive electrode.

$$\ldots\ldots Cl^- \rightarrow Cl_2 + \ldots\ldots$$

(2 marks)

2 Electrolysis can be used to coat a material with a layer of a metal.
The equipment used to coat a ring with silver is shown below.

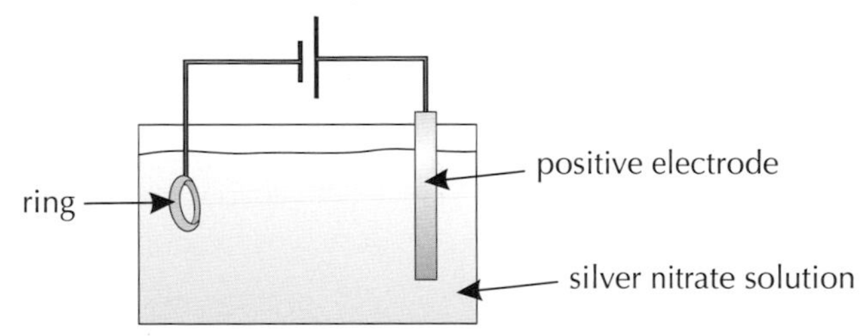

2 (a) What name is given to the process of coating a material with metal using electrolysis?

(1 mark)

2 (b) What is the negative electrode in the process shown above?

(1 mark)

2 (c) What substance is broken down during the process shown above?

(1 mark)

2 (d) Oxidation occurs at the positive electrode. What is oxidation?

(1 mark)

Learning Objectives:

- Know that the gradient of an object's distance-time graph gives the speed of the object.
- Be able to interpret an object's motion from its distance-time graph.
- Be able to draw a distance-time graph for an object that's stationary or moving in a straight line at a steady speed.
- H Be able to calculate the speed of an object at a given point in time using the gradient of its distance-time graph.

Specification Reference P2.1.2

1. Distance-Time Graphs

Distance-time graphs show how far an object travels in a given time. They're useful in physics because they help you keep track of an object's motion.

What are distance-time graphs?

Distance-time graphs are a good way of describing something travelling through time and space. They have time on the horizontal axis and the distance travelled by an object on the vertical axis.

Speed = distance ÷ time, so the gradient (slope) of a distance-time graph tells you how fast your object is travelling. This is because the gradient is the change in the distance (vertical axis) divided by the change in time (horizontal axis).

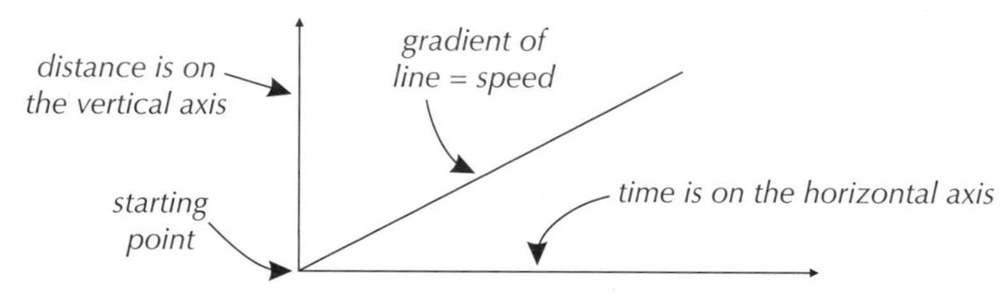

Figure 1: *A basic distance-time graph.*

Drawing and interpreting distance-time graphs

Distance-time graphs can come in two forms. The first just shows the total distance travelled, regardless of direction. You'd get one of these if you plotted the reading on a car's mileage counter against time. The second shows the distance travelled from the starting point in a straight line. In this case, the distance can decrease (if the object is travelling back towards its starting point).

You need to be able to draw and interpret distance-time graphs in the exam. Here are some important points to remember for an object's distance-time graph:

1. Gradient = speed.
2. Flat sections are where it's stationary — it's stopped.
3. Straight uphill or downhill sections mean it is travelling at a steady speed.
4. The steeper the graph, the faster it's going.
5. Downhill sections mean it's going back toward its starting point.
6. Curves represent acceleration (speeding up) or deceleration (slowing down) (page 204).
7. A steepening curve means it's accelerating/speeding up — the gradient is increasing.
8. A levelling off curve means it's decelerating/slowing down — the gradient is decreasing.

Figure 2: *The mileage counter in a car. This one is just ticking over to 19 797.*

Example 1

This distance-time graph shows an object that moves off from its starting point at a steady speed for 20 seconds then stops for 20 seconds. It then accelerates for 25 seconds and decelerates for 25 seconds before resuming a steady speed for 30 more seconds.

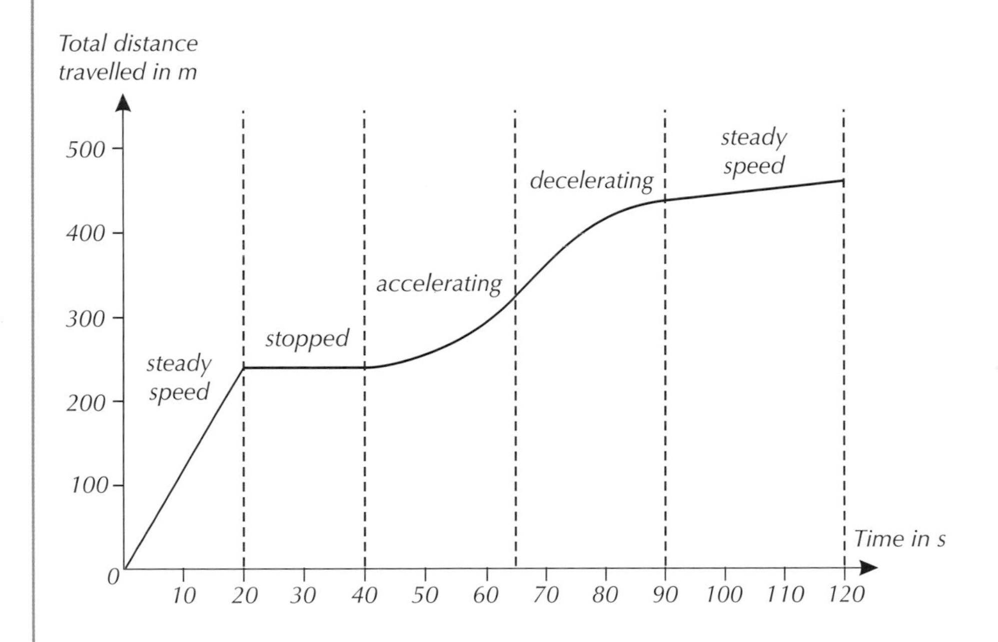

Tip: This graph shows the total distance travelled — this can't go down, so the gradient can't be negative.

Example 2

Draw a distance-time graph for an object that travels 10 m at a steady speed in 20 seconds, stops for 5 seconds, then returns back to its starting point at a steady speed, taking 5 seconds to do so.

- The object starts at a steady speed for 10 m and 20 s, so mark a point on the graph at 10 m and 20 s. Then draw a straight line between the origin and that point.
- When it's stopped, the graph will be horizontal, so draw a horizontal line from this point that lasts 5 seconds.
- It returns to its starting point in 5 seconds at a steady speed, so draw another straight line linking the graph back to 0 m in 5 s.

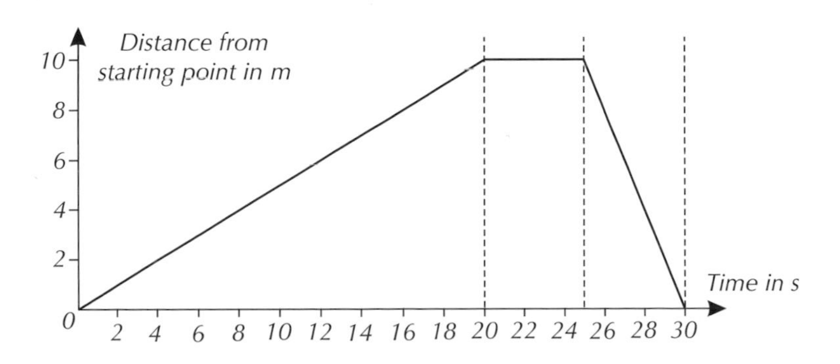

Exam Tip
You only need to know how to draw distance-time graphs for an object that's stationary or moving at a steady speed in a straight line.

Tip: If you have a negative gradient, the size of the gradient shows the speed. The fact that it's negative tells you it's travelling in the opposite direction (back to its starting point).

Calculating speed from distance-time graphs Higher

To calculate the speed shown by a given (straight) section of a distance-time graph, you just need to calculate the gradient, i.e.:

Exam Tip H
The equations sheet won't tell you how to calculate the gradient — so you need to learn how to do this.

$$\text{speed} = \text{gradient} = \frac{\text{change in vertical}}{\text{change in horizontal}}$$

Make sure you check the scales on the axes of the graph — don't just measure the changes in vertical and horizontal with a ruler. It's also important to check the units — the distance might be in kilometres, miles, etc. and the time might be in minutes, hours, etc.

Example Higher

Using the graph from example 2 on the previous page, find the speed of the object during the first 20 s.

Look at the first 20 s of the graph:

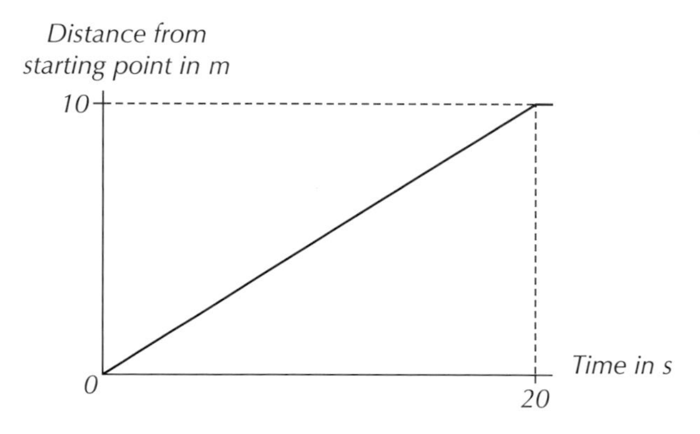

To find the speed you need to find the change on the vertical axis and the change on the horizontal axis.

Change in vertical = 10 – 0 = 10 m
Change in horizontal = 20 – 0 = 20 s

Then just divide the change in vertical by the change in horizontal to find the speed of the object:

$$\begin{aligned}\text{speed} &= \text{gradient} \\ &= \frac{\text{change in vertical}}{\text{change in horizontal}} \\ &= \frac{10}{20} = 0.5 \text{ m/s}\end{aligned}$$

Practice Questions — Fact Recall

Q1 What does the gradient of a distance-time graph represent?

Q2 For this distance-time graph, say what's happening to the speed of the object in each of the sections labelled *A*, *B*, *C* and *D*.

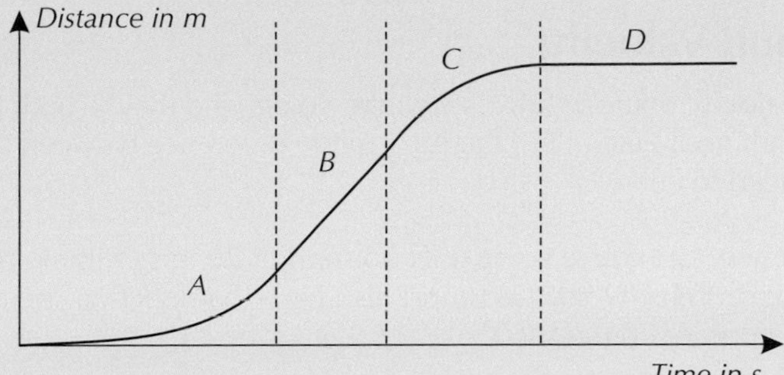

Q3 How would you calculate the speed of an object during a given time period from its distance-time graph (assuming the speed is constant).

Practice Questions — Application

Q1 An object moving in a straight line accelerates for 10 seconds and then moves at a steady speed for 5 seconds. Describe the distance-time graph for the object during this time.

Q2 Look at this table showing the distance (in a straight line) of a toy car from its starting position over a period of time.

Time (s)	0	2	4	6	8	10	12	14	16
Distance (m)	0	10	20	20	20	15	10	5	0

a) Draw a distance-time graph to represent the car's motion. Join the plotted points using straight lines.

b) According to the graph, during which time period is the car not moving?

Q3 Look at this distance-time graph for a moving object.

a) Describe the motion of the object between 2 and 11 seconds.

b) Calculate the speed of the object between 11 and 13 seconds.

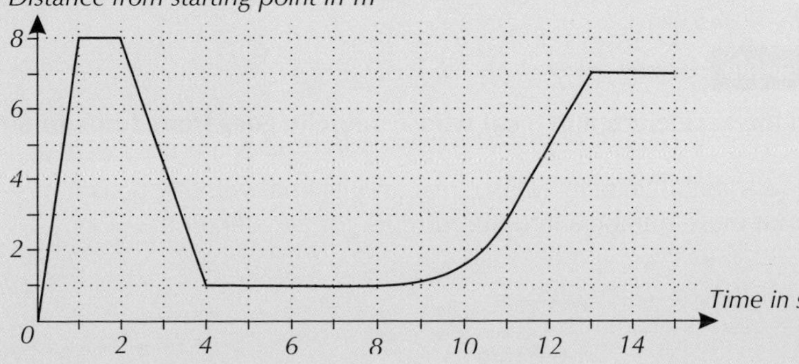

2. Velocity-Time Graphs

Velocity, like distance, can also be plotted against time to help you find out about an object's motion. Just make sure you don't get it confused with speed.

Learning Objectives:
- Know that a speed in a given direction is called velocity.
- Know that acceleration is how quickly the velocity is changing.
- Be able to calculate the acceleration of an object over a given time from its initial and final velocity.
- Be able to interpret an object's motion from its velocity-time graph.
- Know that the gradient of a velocity-time graph represents the acceleration of the object.
- H Be able to calculate the acceleration of an object from its velocity-time graph.
- H Be able to calculate the distance travelled by an object in a given time from its velocity-time graph.

Specification Reference P2.1.2

Speed and velocity

Speed and **velocity** both say how fast you're going, and they're both measured in m/s (or km/h, mph, etc.). But there's a subtle difference between them which you need to know.

Speed is just how fast you're going (e.g. 30 mph or 20 m/s) with no regard to the direction. Velocity however must also have the direction specified, e.g. 30 mph north or 20 m/s, 060°.

Velocity is speed in a given direction.

Acceleration

Acceleration is definitely not the same as velocity or speed:

- Acceleration is how quickly the velocity is changing.
- This change in velocity can be a change in speed or a change in direction or both.

You can calculate the acceleration of an object using this formula:

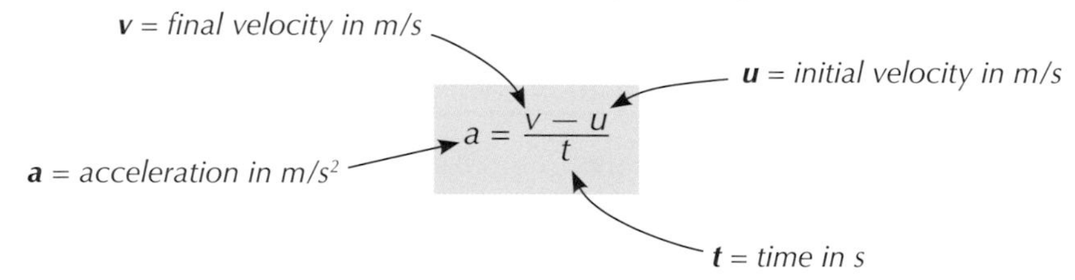

$$a = \frac{v - u}{t}$$

The '$v - u$' represents a change in velocity, i.e. the difference between the final velocity of an object and its initial velocity.

You don't have to worry about the change in direction part for calculations in this section — the object will always be travelling in a straight line. The units of acceleration are m/s^2 — don't get them confused with the units for speed and velocity, m/s.

Tip: If the acceleration isn't constant, this formula gives you the average acceleration.

Tip: Acceleration can have a positive or a negative value. If it's negative, it's a deceleration (i.e. the object is slowing down).

Tip: If you struggle to remember which velocity is which, think of it this way — *u* comes before *v* in the alphabet, so *u* is initial velocity and *v* is final velocity.

Example

Find the acceleration of a cat whose velocity goes from 2 m/s to 6 m/s in 5 s.

The cat's initial velocity (u) is 2 m/s and its final velocity (v) is 6 m/s. Just put these numbers into the formula for acceleration:

$$a = \frac{v - u}{t} = \frac{6 - 2}{5}$$
$$= 0.8 \text{ m/s}^2$$

Example Higher

A car starts from rest and accelerates at a rate of 2 m/s² for 8.2 seconds. Find its velocity after this time.

- Start by rearranging the formula for acceleration to make final velocity the subject:

$$a = \frac{v - u}{t} \Rightarrow v = (a \times t) + u$$

- Then just put the numbers in:

$$v = (a \times t) + u$$
$$= (2 \times 8.2) + 0$$
$$= 16.4 \text{ m/s}$$

Exam Tip H
In the exam you might get a mark for substituting the right numbers in for the right terms. If you find it easier, you could try substituting the numbers in and then rearranging.

Velocity-time graphs

You can plot a **velocity-time graph** to show an object's motion — it's quite similar to drawing a distance-time graph (page 200). Time goes on the horizontal axis and velocity goes on the vertical axis.

Acceleration is the change in an object's velocity over time, or velocity ÷ time. So the gradient of a velocity-time graph tells you the acceleration of your object. This is because the gradient is the change in the velocity (vertical axis) divided by the change in time (horizontal axis).

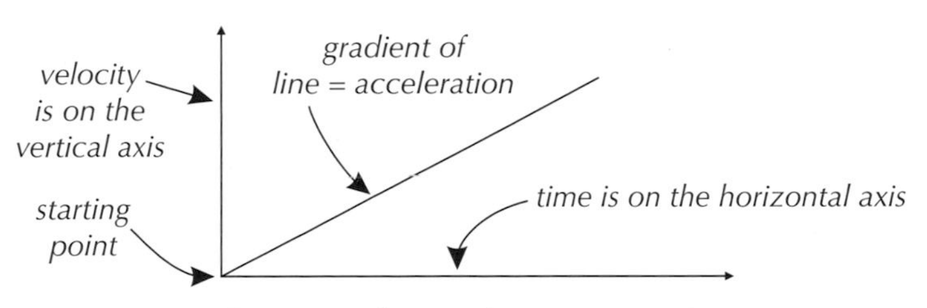

Figure 1: *A basic velocity-time graph.*

Here are some important things you need to remember about velocity-time graphs:

1. The gradient of a velocity-time graph gives the object's acceleration.
2. Flat sections represent steady speed.
3. The steeper the graph, the greater the acceleration or deceleration.
4. Uphill sections are acceleration.
5. Downhill sections are deceleration.
6. A curve means changing acceleration.

Exam Tip
Assume the object is travelling in a straight line, unless you're told otherwise.

Example

This velocity-time graph shows an object that accelerates from rest to 30 m/s in 20 seconds then travels at a steady velocity for 20 seconds. It then accelerates at an increasing rate for 30 seconds, travels at a steady 50 m/s for a further 30 seconds and finally decelerates back to rest in 20 seconds.

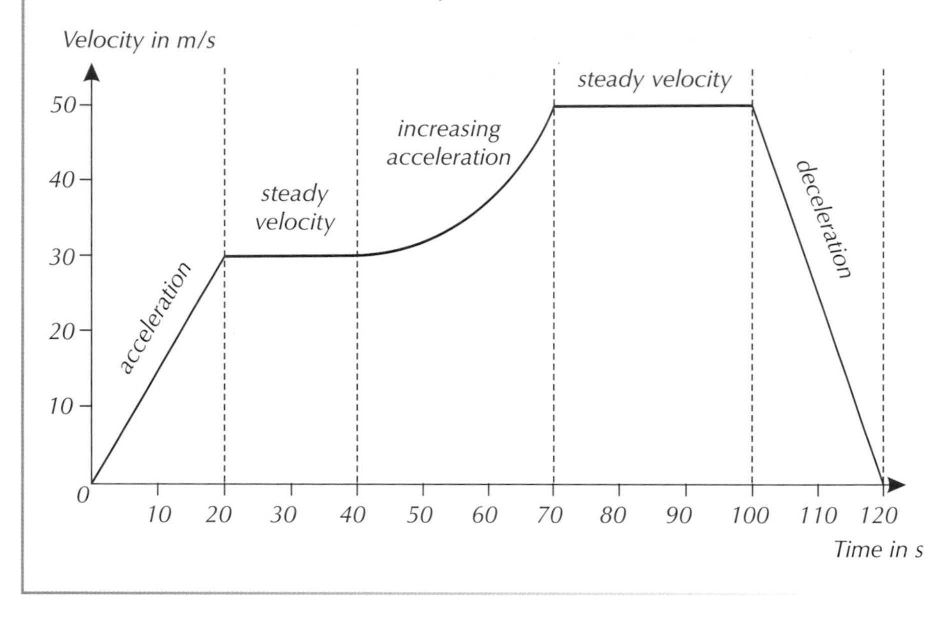

Calculating acceleration from a velocity-time graph Higher

The acceleration of an object can be found by calculating the gradient of its velocity-time graph.

Tip: This is the same method as finding the speed from a distance-time graph (see page 202).

$$\text{acceleration} = \text{gradient} = \frac{\text{change in vertical}}{\text{change in horizontal}}$$

Example **Higher**

This is a velocity-time graph for a race car accelerating from 0 to 50 m/s. Calculate the acceleration of the car between 3 and 6 seconds.

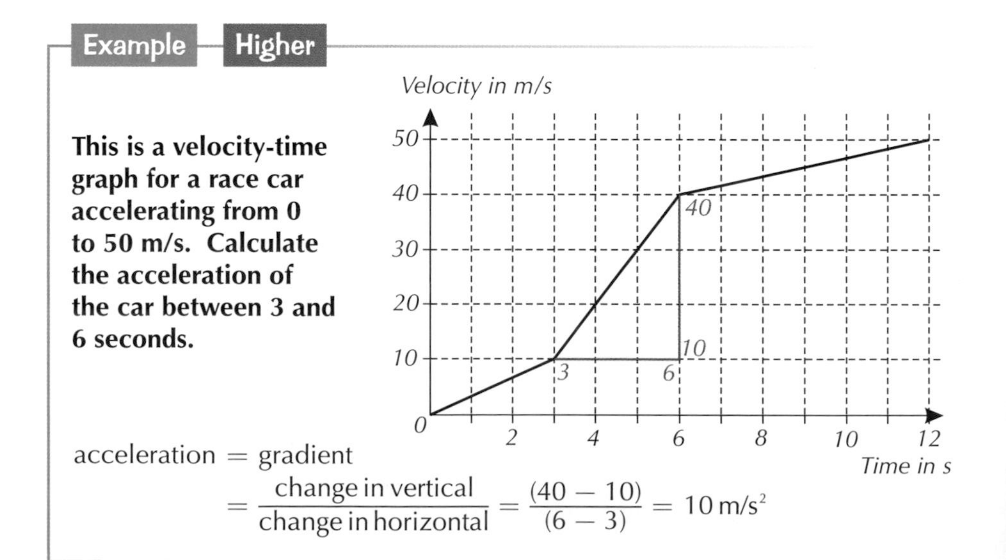

$$\text{acceleration} = \text{gradient}$$
$$= \frac{\text{change in vertical}}{\text{change in horizontal}} = \frac{(40 - 10)}{(6 - 3)} = 10\ \text{m/s}^2$$

Calculating distance travelled from a velocity-time graph Higher

The distance travelled in any time interval is equal to the area under the velocity-time graph in that interval.

Example Higher

For the same car as in the previous example, calculate the distance travelled between 3 and 6 seconds.

- The distance travelled is equal to the area under the graph, so look at the graph between 3 and 6 seconds. It might seem difficult to work out the area of this part of the graph, but you can make it easier by splitting the area into a triangle (***A***) and a rectangle (***B***).

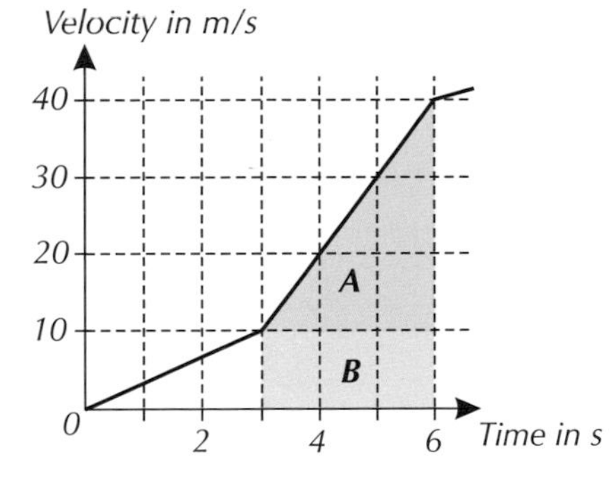

- You can then calculate the area of each shape individually:

$$\text{Area}_A = \frac{1}{2} \times \text{base} \times \text{height} = \frac{1}{2} \times 3 \times 30 = 45$$

$$\text{Area}_B = \text{base} \times \text{height} = 3 \times 10 = 30$$

- Then just find the total area by adding Area_A and Area_B together:

distance travelled = total area under graph
= 45 + 30 = 75 m

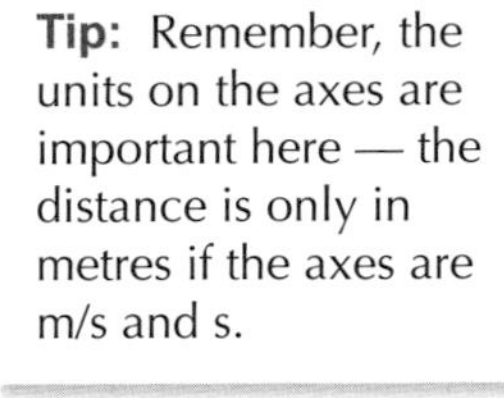

Tip: Remember, the units on the axes are important here — the distance is only in metres if the axes are m/s and s.

Tip: The area of a triangle is given by ½ × base × height.

Practice Questions — Fact Recall

Q1 What's the difference between the speed of an object and the velocity of an object?

Q2 What is acceleration?

Q3 Write down the formula for working out the acceleration of an object, and say what each term represents and what units it's measured in.

Q4 What does the gradient of a velocity-time graph represent?

Q5 What does the area under a velocity-time graph represent?

Practice Questions — Application

Q1 Say whether the following quantities are a speed or a velocity.

a) 47.2 mph	b) 12.1 m/s

c) 10 km/h west	d) 91.2 mph

Q2 A car is travelling forwards at 25 m/s and the driver applies the brakes. The car's velocity drops steadily for 5 seconds until it becomes 10 m/s. Find its acceleration during this time.

Tip: Remember, acceleration can have a negative value (in which case it can be called deceleration).

Q3 Below is a velocity-time graph for a cyclist during a race.

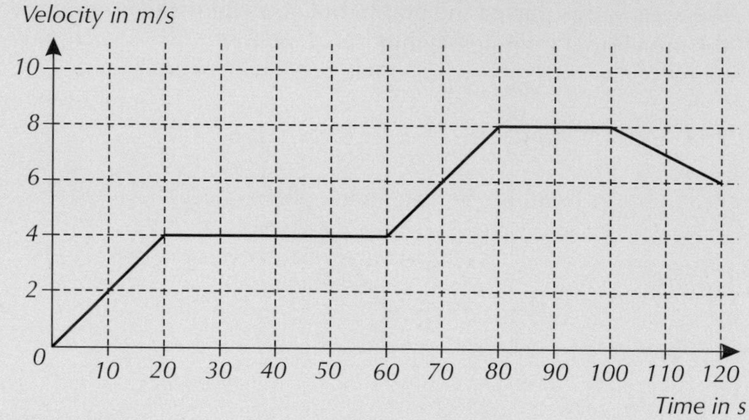

a) What's the cyclist's velocity at 40 seconds?

b) During which part(s) of the race is the cyclist decelerating?

c) What's the cyclist's acceleration between 60 and 80 seconds?

d) How far does the cyclist travel in the first 60 seconds of the race?

Q4 A runner is running at a steady velocity. When she sees the finish line she accelerates at a constant rate of 0.3 m/s^2 until she crosses the finish line 5 seconds later. If her velocity at the finish line is 7.1 m/s, what was her velocity before she started accelerating?

3. Resultant Forces

Resultant forces are a clever little concept that make it easier to work out what's going on in a complicated situation with lots of forces involved.

Learning Objectives:
- Know that all the forces acting at a point can be replaced by a single force called the resultant force.
- Know that the resultant force has the same effect as all of the individual forces it represents.
- Understand that if a resultant force acts on an object, the object's velocity will change.
- Be able to calculate the resultant of multiple forces acting in the same or opposite directions along a straight line.

Specification Reference P2.1.1

What is a resultant force?

The notion of a **resultant force** is a really important one for you to get your head round. In most real situations there are at least two forces acting on an object along any direction.

If you have a number of forces acting at a single point, you can replace them with a single force (so long as the single force has the same effect on the motion as the original forces acting all together). The overall force you get is called the resultant force.

The resultant force will decide the motion of the object — whether it will accelerate, decelerate or stay at a steady speed. If there is a non-zero resultant force acting on an object, then the object will change its state of rest or motion. In other words:

> A non-zero resultant force acting on an object causes a change in its velocity. This means the object will accelerate.

Tip: Remember a deceleration is just a negative acceleration.

Force diagrams

A force diagram shows all of the forces acting on an object, the direction in which the forces acting and their relative size. Each force is represented by an arrow, and the larger the force the larger the arrow.

Example

This force diagram shows the forces acting on a person who's running. Air resistance and friction act in the opposite direction to the forwards thrust. Gravity acts downwards and the reaction force of the ground acts upwards.

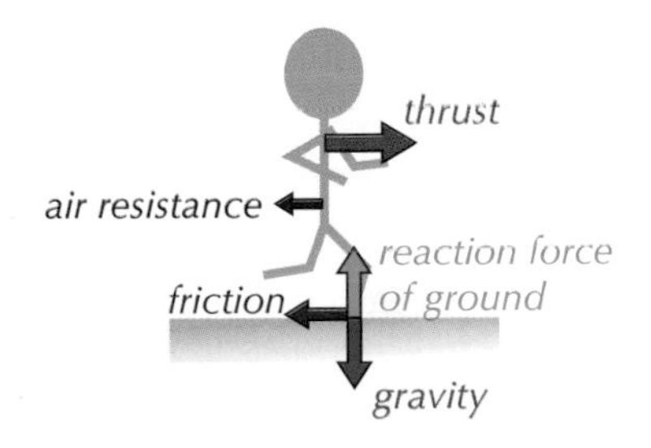

Tip: There's more about air resistance on page 218. There's more about gravity and reaction forces on page 216.

Force diagrams make it easier to see the direction and (relative) size of the resultant force acting on an object.

Determining the resultant force

If the forces on an object all act along the same line (they're all parallel and act in the same or the opposite direction), the resultant force is found by finding the sum of all the forces.

To do this, set a direction as the positive. Then add all the forces acting in that direction and subtract all the forces acting in the opposite direction.

Tip: Assume the driving force and air resistance are the only two forces acting on the car.

Example

A vintage sports car is driving along with a driving force of 1000 N. Air resistance of 600 N is acting in the opposite direction. What is the resultant force on the car and how does it affect the car's velocity?

Set the forwards (right) direction as the positive, then add any forces in this direction and subtract any forces in the opposite direction.
So the resultant force = 1000 – 600 = 400 N (to the right).

There's a resultant force so the car will accelerate.

Practice Questions — Fact Recall

Q1 What's a resultant force?

Q2 What happens if a non-zero resultant force acts on an object?

Practice Question — Application

Q1 The diagram shows the horizontal forces acting on a boat.

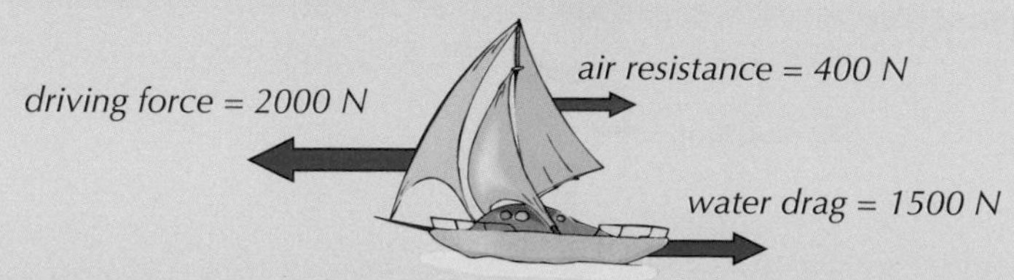

a) Find the resultant horizontal force acting on the boat.

b) Is the boat accelerating? Explain your answer.

4. Forces and Acceleration

Resultant forces are often described as being 'non-zero' (i.e. there is one) or 'zero' (i.e. there isn't one) — and you need to know their effects.

Learning Objectives:
- Know the effect of no resultant force acting on a stationary object.
- Know the effect of a resultant force acting on a stationary object.
- Know the effect of no resultant force acting on a moving object.
- Know the effect of a resultant force acting on a moving object.
- Be able to calculate the acceleration of an object from its mass and the resultant force acting on it.
- Be able to calculate the force acting on an object from its mass and acceleration.

Specification Reference
P2.1.1, P2.1.2

Resultant forces in different situations

The effect of a resultant force acting on an object depends on whether or not the object is moving. On a similar note, an object with zero resultant force acting on it will behave in a way that depends on its current motion. There are four different situations you need to know about:

- Zero resultant force acting on a stationary object.
- Non-zero resultant force acting on a stationary object.
- Zero resultant force acting on a moving object.
- Non-zero resultant force acting on a moving object.

Resultant forces and stationary objects

Objects don't just start moving on their own — if there's no resultant force acting on a stationary object, there's no acceleration and it will just stay put.

If the resultant force on a stationary object is zero, the object will remain stationary.

Example

A ball is being held stationary by two taut strings. The force to the left (F_1) is the same as the force to the right (F_2). So, even though forces are acting on it in both directions, the resultant force on it is zero. Consequently, it remains stationary.

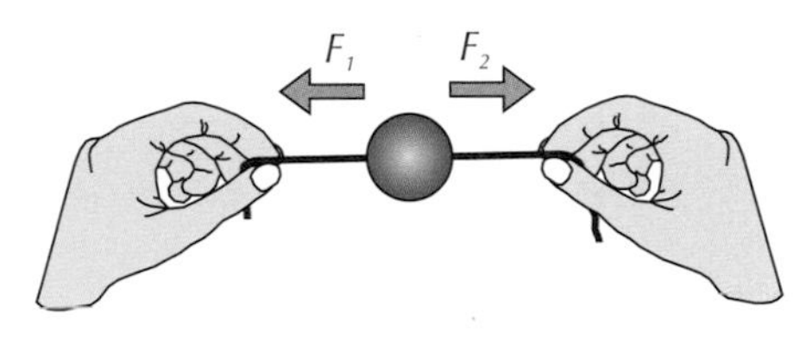

A non-zero resultant force will always produce acceleration (or deceleration). So, if an object is stationary, its velocity will change and it will start moving.

If the resultant force on a stationary object is non-zero, the object will accelerate in the direction of the resultant force.

Example

One of the hands lets go of the string that's keeping the ball stationary. Now the ball experiences a resultant force of F_2 to the right, and accelerates in that direction.

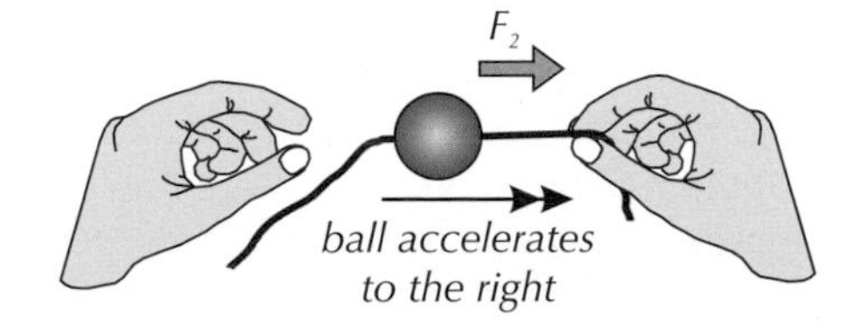

Resultant forces and moving objects

If there's no resultant force acting on an object, it won't change velocity. That means if it's already moving, it will just keep moving at the same velocity.

> If there is no resultant force on a moving object it'll just carry on moving at the same velocity.

If any object (be it a train, a car, a horse, or anything else really) is moving at a constant velocity then the forces on it must all be balanced. Never let yourself stray down the path of thinking that things need a constant resultant force to keep them moving — this is a common misconception.

To keep going at a steady speed, there must be zero resultant force. This doesn't mean there must be no driving force, it means the driving force is balanced by other forces, like friction and air resistance.

Example

A van travelling at a steady velocity has zero resultant force acting on it. This is because the driving force from the engine is balanced by friction forces.

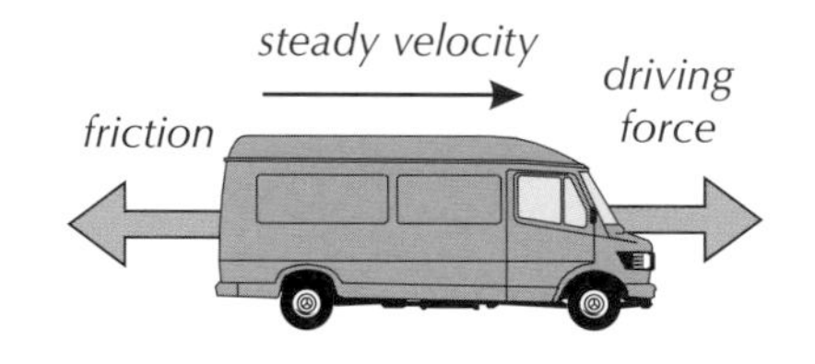

On the other hand:

> If there is a non-zero resultant force on a moving object it will accelerate in the direction of the force.

Resultant forces and acceleration

When a resultant force acts on an object, the acceleration it experiences can take five different forms:

- starting
- stopping
- changing direction
- speeding up
- slowing down

On a force diagram (see page 209), the total size of the arrows in one direction will be different to the total size of the arrows in the opposite direction. This is because there's an imbalance of forces causing the non-zero resultant force.

Example

A van is driving (forwards) at a steady velocity and the driver applies the brakes. This increases the friction and gives a resultant force in the opposite direction to the van's velocity, so it experiences a deceleration.

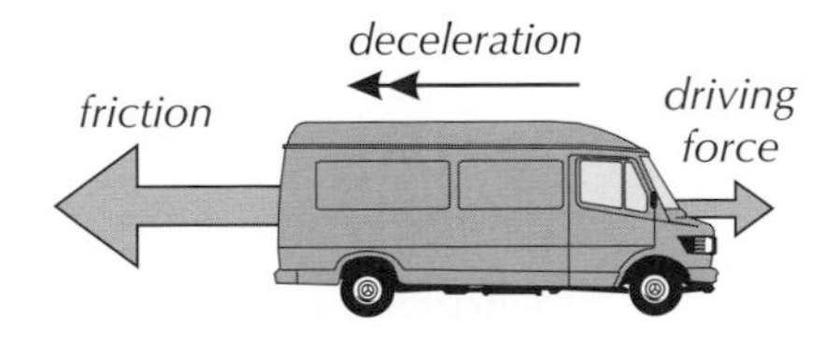

To calculate the acceleration produced by a resultant force, or the size of the resultant force producing an acceleration, use these formulas:

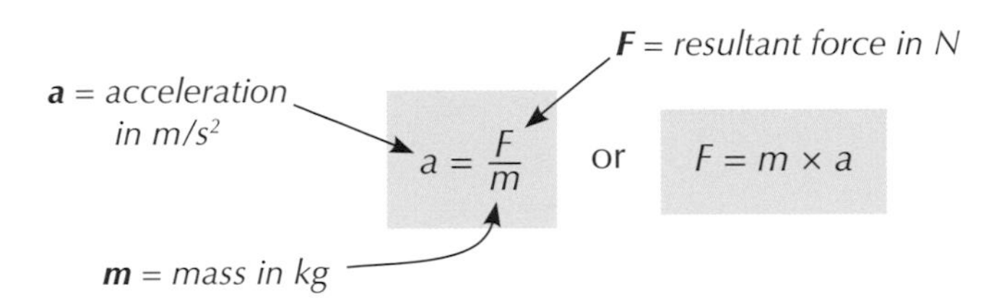

Example 1

A car with a mass of 1300 kg has an engine that provides a driving force of 5200 N. At 70 mph the drag force acting on the car is 5100 N. Find its acceleration at 70 mph.

- First draw a force diagram to represent the situation:

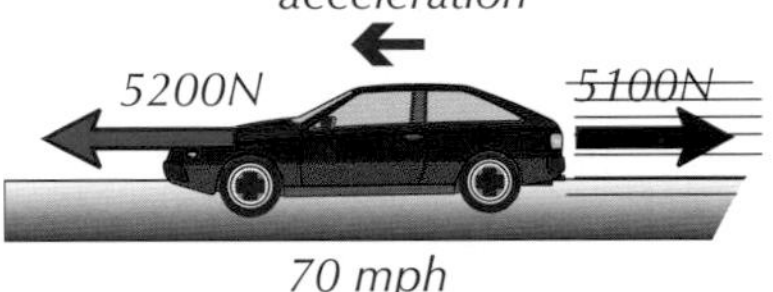

- Then work out the resultant force and acceleration of the car:

Resultant force = 5200 – 5100 = 100 N

$$a = \frac{F}{m} = \frac{100}{1300} = 0.077 \text{ m/s}^2 \text{ (to 2 s.f.)}$$

Tip: There's more about drag forces on page 218.

Tip: See page 350 for more on significant figures in answers.

Example 2

A car with a mass of 900 kg accelerates from rest with an acceleration of 2.5 m/s². Calculate the driving force provided by the car's engine.

The car is starting from rest, so you don't need to worry about any drag forces acting on it — the resultant force is just the driving force.

$$F = m \times a = 900 \times 2.5$$
$$= 2250 \text{ N}$$

Practice Questions — Fact Recall

Q1 Say what will happen to the object in each of the following cases:

a) No resultant force acting on a stationary object.

b) A resultant force acting on a stationary object.

c) No resultant force acting on a moving object.

d) A resultant force acting on a moving object in the same direction as its motion.

e) A resultant force acting on a moving object in the opposite direction to its motion.

Q2 Write down the formula used for calculating the resultant force acting on an object from its mass and its acceleration. Say what each term represents and the units it's measured in.

Practice Questions — Application

Q1 If a rocket is moving through space at a steady velocity, what can you say about the resultant force acting on the rocket?

Q2 Two identical remote-control cars take part in a straight race across flat ground. One of the cars is loaded with a large rock. Which of the two will win the race? Explain your answer.

Q3 When a catapult is released, it applies 305 N of force to a rock with a mass of 1.5 kg in a time of 0.4 s. Find the acceleration of the rock during this time.

Q4 Two cars are starting from rest at full power. Which engine is providing a larger driving force?

acceleration = 2.3 m/s^2

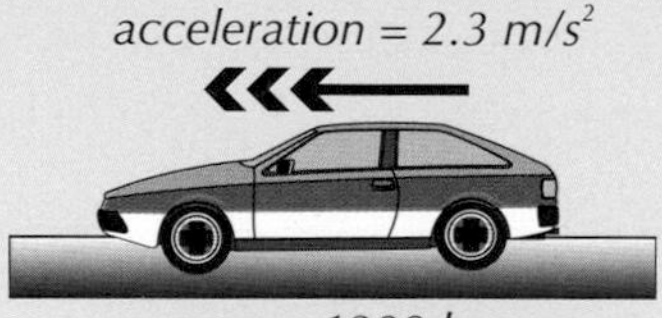

mass = 1200 kg

acceleration = 3.1 m/s^2

mass = 820 kg

5. Weight and Reaction Forces

You might not have thought about it, but your chair is currently pushing up against you (assuming you're sat down, that is). It's all to do with your weight and the reaction force that results from it — read on and all will become clear.

Learning Objectives:

- Be able to calculate the weight of an object using its mass and the gravitational field strength, g.
- Know that when two objects interact, they exert forces on each other that are equal but opposite.

Specification Reference
P2.1.1, P2.1.4

Gravitational force

Gravity is the force that causes all masses to attract each other, but you only notice it when one or more of the masses are really big, e.g. a planet. Anything near a planet or star is attracted to it very strongly.

This has two important effects:

1. On the surface of a planet, it makes all things accelerate (see page 204) towards the ground.
2. It gives everything a weight (see below).

Weight, mass and gravity

Weight and mass are not the same — mass is just the amount of 'stuff' in an object. For any given object this will have the same value anywhere in the universe.

Weight is caused by the pull of the gravitational force. In most exam questions the weight of an object is just the force of gravity pulling it towards the centre of the Earth.

An object has the same mass whether it's on Earth or on the Moon — but its weight will be different. A 1 kg mass will weigh less on the Moon (about 1.6 N) than it does on Earth (about 10 N), simply because the gravitational force pulling on it is less.

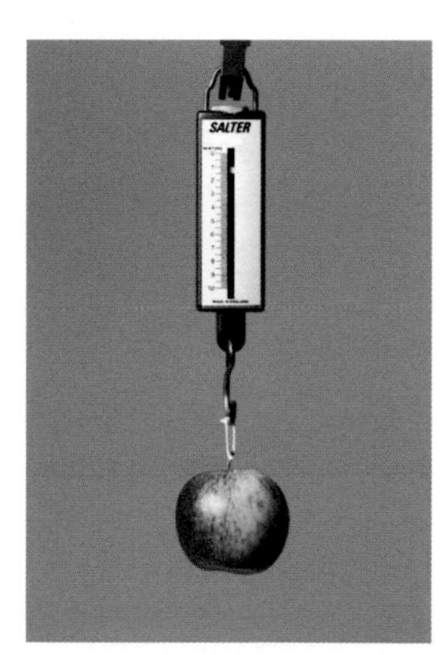

Figure 1: *Measuring the weight of an apple using a newton meter.*

Weight is a force measured in newtons. It's measured using a spring balance or newton meter. Mass is not a force. It's measured in kilograms with a mass balance (an old-fashioned pair of balancing scales).

There's an important formula you need to know relating mass, weight and gravity:

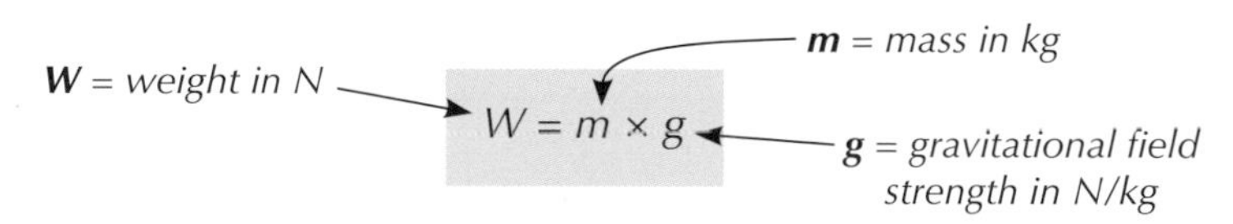

The letter 'g' represents the strength of gravity and its value is different for different planets. On Earth, g is around 10 N/kg. On the Moon, where gravity is much weaker, g is only about 1.6 N/kg.

Example

What is the weight, in newtons, of a 5 kg mass, both on Earth (g = 10 N/kg) and on the Moon (g = 1.6 N/kg)?

Just use the formula $W = m \times g$ in each case:

On Earth:

$$W = m \times g = 5 \times 10 = 50 \text{ N}$$

On the Moon:

$$W = m \times g = 5 \times 1.6 = 8 \text{ N}$$

Example **Higher**

The value of g on Mars is 3.71 N/kg. What's the mass of a buggy on Mars if its weight on Mars is 4552 N?

Just rearrange the formula to make mass the subject, then plug in the correct numbers:

$$W = m \times g \Rightarrow m = \frac{W}{g} = \frac{4452}{3.71} = 1200 \text{ kg}$$

Reaction forces

Reaction forces are forces that result from one object applying a force to another object. They always act in the opposite direction to the original, 'action' force. You've probably heard the law in physics that "every action has an equal and opposite reaction" — what this really means is:

Figure 2: British physicist Sir Isaac Newton. The idea of equal and opposite forces is the basis Newton's third law of motion.

> When two objects interact, the forces they exert on each other are equal but opposite.

Example

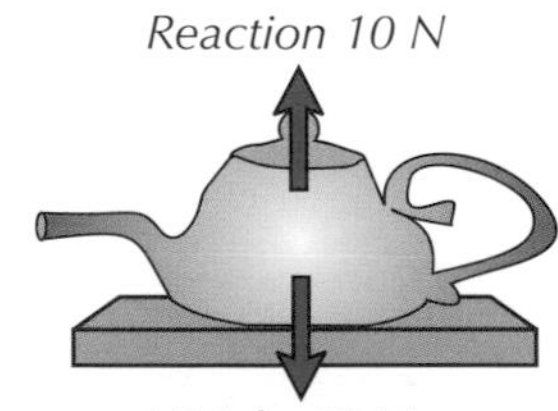

- A teapot resting on a table isn't moving, and so the resultant force on it must be zero (see page 211). That doesn't mean no forces are acting on it.
- The force of gravity (or weight) is acting downwards.
- This causes a reaction force from the surface pushing up on the object.
- This is the only way it can be in balance — without a reaction force, it would accelerate downwards due to the pull of gravity.
- The resultant force on the teapot is zero: 10 N – 10 N = 0 N.

The slightly tricky thing to get your head round is this — if the forces are always equal, how does anything ever go anywhere? The important thing to remember is that the two forces are acting on different objects.

Example

Think about a pair of ice skaters.

When skater A pushes on skater B (the 'action' force), she feels an equal and opposite force from skater B's hand (the 'reaction' force). Both skaters feel the same sized force, in opposite directions, and so accelerate away from each other.

Skater A will be accelerated more than skater B, though, because she has a smaller mass — $a = F/m$ (see page 213). It's the same sort of thing when you go swimming. You push back against the water with your arms and legs, and the water pushes you forwards with an equal-sized force in the opposite direction.

Practice Questions — Fact Recall

Q1 What's the difference between mass and weight?

Q2 Give the formula for calculating the weight of an object, and say what each symbol represents and the units it's measured in.

Q3 Finish this statement:
When two objects interact, they exert forces on each other that are...

Practice Questions — Application

Q1 Which has a larger weight? A 6.3 kg dog on Earth (g = 10 N/kg) or a 21 kg dog on the Moon (g = 1.6 N/kg)?

Q2 A tennis racquet with a mass of 300 g hits a ball with a mass of 60 g. Which of the two objects will experience a greater acceleration, and why?

Learning Objectives:

- Know that if a vehicle is travelling at a steady speed, the driving force (provided by the engine) balances the resistive forces acting on the vehicle.
- Know that the frictional forces that oppose the motion of an object moving through a fluid increase with the object's speed.
- Understand how a vehicle's shape and engine power can affect its top speed.
- Know that an object falling through a fluid initially accelerates until the frictional forces on it balance the object's weight and it reaches its terminal velocity.
- Be able to draw and interpret velocity-time graphs for falling objects reaching terminal velocity.
- Understand how the use of a parachute can affect an object's terminal velocity.

Specification Reference
P2.1.3, P2.1.4

6. Friction and Terminal Velocity

In an ideal world, things would just move freely without needing any external driving force, but realistically friction is there to stop that. It's not all bad though — without friction we'd never be able to stop and take a break.

Friction

If an object has no force propelling it along it will always slow down and stop because of **friction** (unless you're in space where there's nothing to rub against).

Friction always acts in the opposite direction to movement. To travel at a steady speed, the driving force needs to balance the frictional forces.

Example

If a car is travelling at a steady speed, the force provided by the engine is exactly the same as the resistive forces acting on the car.

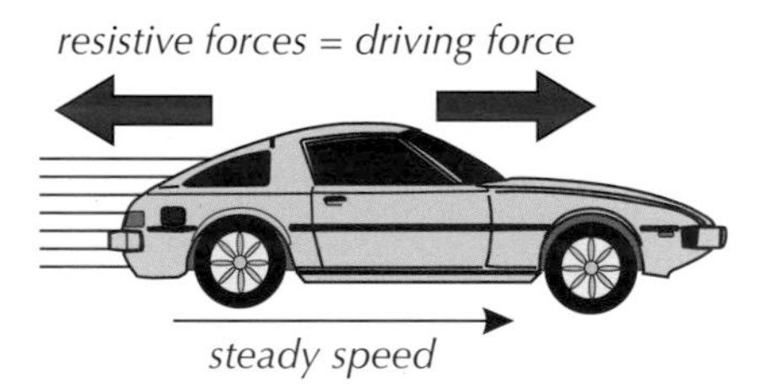

You get friction between two surfaces in contact or when an object passes through a fluid — in which case it's usually called drag. A fluid is just a gas or a liquid — e.g. air, water, oil, etc.

Drag

Most of the resistive forces are caused by **air resistance** or "**drag**". The most important factor by far in reducing drag in fluids is keeping the shape of the object streamlined. A streamlined object is one that allows fluids to flow over it easily, so that they don't slow down the object much as it passes through them.

The opposite extreme is a parachute which is about as high drag as you can get — which is, of course, the whole idea.

Example

A sports car is designed to allow fluids to flow over it easily, reducing drag and letting it move through air without much effort. Vans aren't designed to go particularly fast and so their design is much less streamlined. This means they have to use a greater driving force to move at the same speed as a sports car.

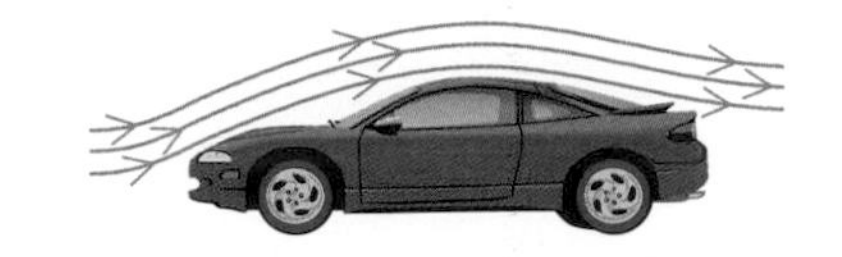

Frictional forces from fluids always increase with speed. A car has much more friction to work against when travelling at 70 mph compared to 30 mph. So at 70 mph the engine has to work much harder just to maintain a steady speed.

Figure 1: *Force diagrams of a car moving at 30 mph and 70 mph. As the speed of a car increases, the frictional forces acting on it increase so the engine works harder to maintain a steady speed.*

Ways of increasing the top speed of a vehicle

There are two ways of changing a vehicle to increase its top speed:

1. Reducing drag.
   This can be done by altering the shape of the vehicle to make it more streamlined.
2. Increasing the power of the vehicle's engine.
   This way, the driving force becomes larger and so the drag force on the vehicle will equal the driving force at a higher speed.

Figure 2: *Racing cars have incredibly powerful engines as well as a low, streamlined body. This is what helps them shoot round the track at break-neck speeds.*

Terminal velocity

Generally when an object falls through a very large distance, it won't just keep accelerating at the same rate until it hits the ground. Its acceleration will decrease until it reaches a steady velocity, called **terminal velocity**.

When a falling object first sets off, the force of gravity is much more than the frictional force slowing it down, so it accelerates. As the object moves faster, the frictional forces that act on it become greater.

This gradually reduces the acceleration until eventually the frictional force is equal to the accelerating force and then it won't accelerate any more. It will have reached its maximum speed or terminal velocity and will fall at a steady speed.

The velocity-time graph for a falling object starts with a steep gradient (i.e. a large acceleration), which gradually decreases until the object reaches terminal velocity. From this point, the graph becomes flat — the forces are balanced and the object is no longer accelerating, so the gradient is zero.

Tip: If you'd like a refresher on velocity-time graphs, head to page 204.

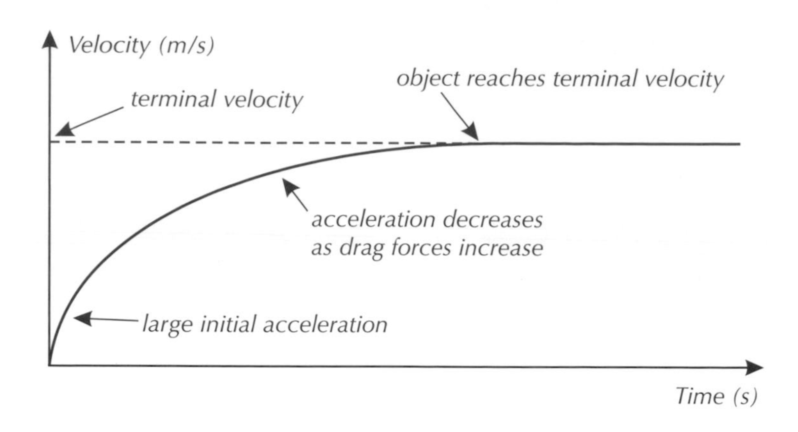

Figure 3: *The velocity-time graph for a falling object.*

Factors affecting terminal velocity

The terminal velocity of falling objects depends on their shape and area. The accelerating force acting on all falling objects is gravity and it would make them all fall at the same rate, if it wasn't for air resistance. This means that on the Moon, where there's no air, rocks and feathers dropped simultaneously will hit the ground together.

Example

Calculate the acceleration due to gravity of a rock and a feather on the moon. The value of *g* on the moon is 1.6 N/kg.

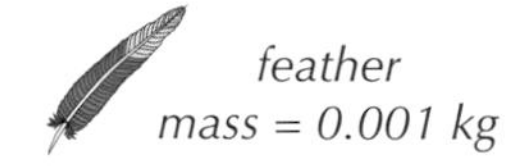

First calculate the weight of each object (see page 215):

$$W = m \times g = 5 \times 1.6 = 8 \text{ N}$$

$$W = m \times g = 0.001 \times 1.6 = 0.0016 \text{ N}$$

Then calculate the acceleration due to gravity:

$$a = \frac{F}{m} = \frac{W}{m} = \frac{8}{5} = 1.6 \text{ m/s}^2$$

$$a = \frac{F}{m} = \frac{W}{m} = \frac{0.0016}{0.001} = 1.6 \text{ m/s}^2$$

Figure 4: *Apollo 15 astronaut David Scott demonstrating that a hammer and a feather fall to the ground at the same speed on the moon.*

However, on Earth, air resistance causes things to fall at different speeds, and the terminal velocity of any object is determined by its drag in comparison to its weight. The frictional force depends on its shape and area.

Example

The most important example is the human skydiver. Without his parachute open he has quite a small area and a force of "$W = mg$" pulling him down. He reaches a terminal velocity of about 120 mph.

But with the parachute open, there's much more air resistance (at any given speed) and still only the same force "$W = mg$" pulling him down. This means his terminal velocity comes right down to about 15 mph, which is a safe speed to hit the ground at.

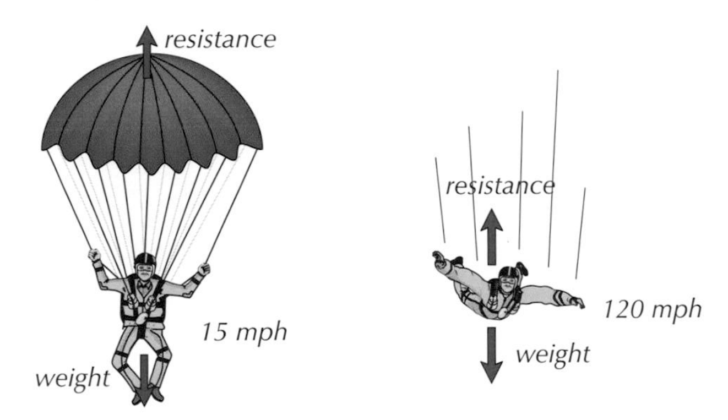

Figure 6: A skydiver at terminal velocity with and without parachute. Resistance has become equal to weight in both cases — the difference is the speed at which this has happened.

Figure 5: A base jumper using a parachute to slow down his free fall so that he can land safely.

Practice Questions — Fact Recall

Q1 What must the resistive forces acting on a car be equal to if the car is travelling at a steady speed over flat ground?

Q2 What's drag?

Q3 What's the relationship between an object's speed and the drag it experiences?

Q4 Explain what two features of a car can be changed to increase its top speed.

Q5 Sketch a velocity-time graph for an object that reaches terminal velocity falling through a fluid.

Practice Questions — Application

Q1 Why does a feather fall slower than a rock on Earth but not on the Moon?

Q2 Explain, in terms of forces, why using a parachute reduces a skydiver's terminal velocity.

7. Stopping Distances

Stopping distances are important — awareness of them can make the difference between crashing and not. It's easy to get stopping, braking and thinking distances confused, so make sure you learn what each one means.

Learning Objectives:

- Know that the stopping distance of a vehicle is the sum of the thinking distance and the braking distance.
- Know that the faster a vehicle's moving, the bigger braking force it will need to stop within a given distance.
- Know that for a given braking force, the faster a vehicle is moving the greater its stopping distance.
- Know the factors that can affect thinking distance and reaction time.
- Know the factors that can affect a vehicle's braking distance.
- Know what happens to the kinetic energy of a car when its brakes are applied

Specification Reference P2.1.3

Stopping distance

The total **stopping distance** of a vehicle is the distance covered in the time between the driver first spotting a hazard and the vehicle coming to a complete stop.

The total stopping distance is the sum of the thinking distance and the braking distance.

- The **thinking distance** is the distance the vehicle travels during the driver's reaction time.
- The **braking distance** is the distance the vehicle travels after the brakes are applied until it comes to a complete stop.

Example

A man is driving along and sees a hazard on the road, applying the brakes for an emergency stop. His thinking distance is 11 m and his braking distance is 32 m. What's his stopping distance?

Stopping distance = thinking distance + braking distance

= 11 + 32

= 43 m

Figure 1 shows typical stopping distances taken from the Highway Code. The actual stopping distance will depend on the vehicle and the driver, but if the hazard is closer than the distances shown then it's likely there will be a collision.

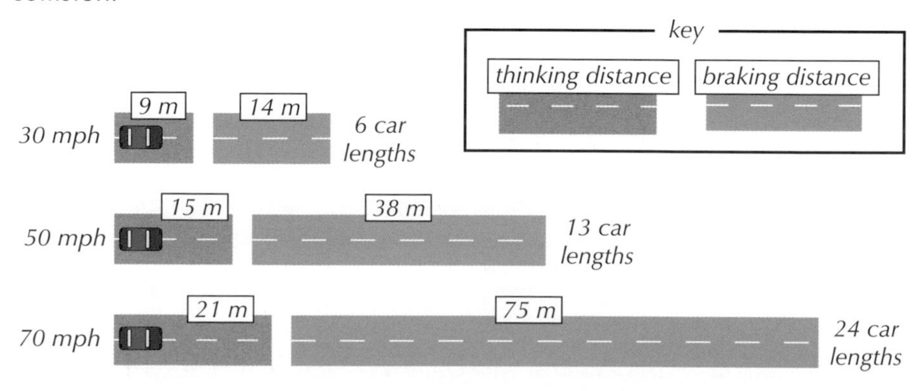

Figure 1: *Typical stopping distances taken from the Highway Code.*

Many factors affect your total stopping distance. Looking at things simply:

- If you need to stop in a given distance, then the faster a vehicle's going, the bigger braking force it'll need.
- Likewise, for any given braking force, the faster you're going, the greater your stopping distance.

But in real life it's not quite that simple — if your maximum braking force isn't enough, you'll go further before you stop.

Thinking distance

Thinking distance is affected by two main factors:

1. How fast you're going — whatever your reaction time, the faster you're going, the further you'll go in that time.
2. How quick to respond you are — this can be affected by tiredness, drugs, alcohol and a lack of concentration.

Bad visibility and distractions can also be a major factor in accidents — lashing rain, messing about with the radio, bright oncoming lights, etc. might mean that a driver doesn't notice a hazard until they're quite close to it. It doesn't affect your thinking distance, but you start thinking about stopping nearer to the hazard, and so you're more likely to crash.

Braking distance

Braking distance is affected by four main factors:

1. How fast you're going — the faster you're going, the further it takes to stop.
2. How good your brakes are — all brakes must be checked and maintained regularly. Worn or faulty brakes will let you down catastrophically just when you need them the most, i.e. in an emergency.
3. How good the tyres are — tyres should have a minimum tread depth of 1.6 mm in order to be able to get rid of the water in wet conditions.
4. How good the grip is — as well as the condition of the tyres, this also depends on the weather conditions and the road surface. Water, ice, leaves, diesel spills, muck on the road etc. can greatly increase the braking distance, and cause the car to skid — often you only discover this when you try to brake hard. You don't have as much grip, so you travel further before stopping.

Figure 2: *Petrol spills on roads can reduce grip and cause tyres to skid, increasing the braking distance.*

Braking and kinetic energy transfer

A moving car can have a lot of kinetic energy. To slow down a car the kinetic energy needs to be converted into other types of energy (using the law of conservation of energy).

When the brakes of a car are applied, the friction between the wheels and the brake pads converts kinetic energy to heat energy, causing the temperature of the brakes to increase.

In other words, work is done by the braking force to convert the kinetic energy of the car into thermal energy and a little sound energy. See page 233 for more on doing work.

Practice Questions — Fact Recall

Q1 a) What's the stopping distance of a vehicle?

b) What's the thinking distance of a vehicle?

c) What's the braking distance of a vehicle?

Q2 Name three factors that can affect a driver's reaction time.

Q3 Other than a vehicle's speed, name three factors that can affect its braking distance.

Q4 Say whether each of the following would affect the thinking distance or the braking distance of a vehicle.

a) Ice on the road

b) Alcohol intake

c) Tiredness

d) Petrol spills

e) Fog

Q5 Explain what happens to the kinetic energy of a vehicle when it uses its brakes to come to a stop.

Practice Questions — Application

Q1 A vehicle has a thinking distance of 15 m and a braking distance of 38 m. What's the stopping distance of the vehicle?

Q2 Explain why it's a good idea to leave more distance than usual between your car and the car in front when driving in heavy rain.

8. Forces and Elasticity

Applying a force to an object doesn't always cause it to accelerate. If it's attached to something, it might just change shape instead. Some objects will keep their new shape, while others will spring right back to where they started.

Learning Objectives:
- Know that applying a force to an object may cause it to stretch or change in shape.
- Know that an object that can change shape under an applied force and return to its original shape is known as an elastic object.
- Know that when a force does work to change the shape of an elastic object, the object stretches and stores elastic potential energy.
- Be able to calculate the force applied to an elastic object, given its extension and its spring constant k.
- Know that the extension of an elastic object is directly proportional to the force applied up to a point called the limit of proportionality.

Specification Reference P2.1.5

Elastic objects

When you apply a force to an object you may cause it to stretch or change in shape. An **elastic object** will return to its original shape after the force has been removed. Many objects behave as elastic objects when only a small force is applied.

Examples

A metal spring, the band in a slingshot and a plastic ruler held over the edge of a table can all return to their original shape after an applied force has been removed.

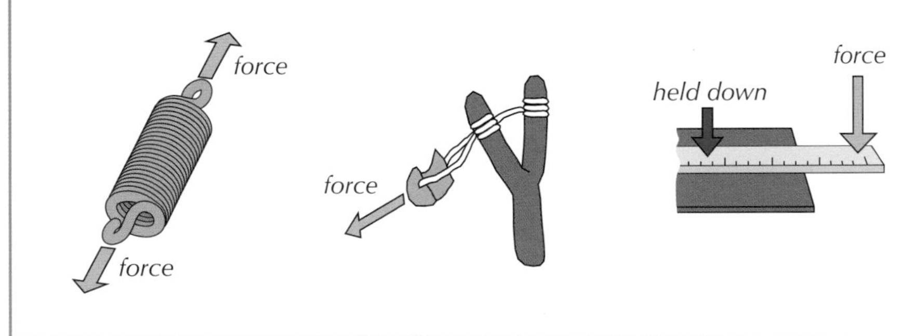

Elastic potential energy

Work is done to an elastic object to change its shape. This energy is not lost but is stored by the object as **elastic potential energy**. The elastic potential energy is then converted to kinetic energy when the force is removed and the object returns to its original shape, e.g. when a spring or an elastic band bounces back.

For a non-elastic object, energy will be lost through permanently changing its shape, breaking it, heating it up, etc. The important thing to remember is that for elastic objects, all of the energy is stored as elastic potential energy.

The extension of elastic objects

If a spring is supported at the top and then a weight attached to the bottom, it stretches. The extension, e, of a stretched spring (or other elastic object) is directly proportional to the load or force applied, F.

Tip: This is known as Hooke's law.

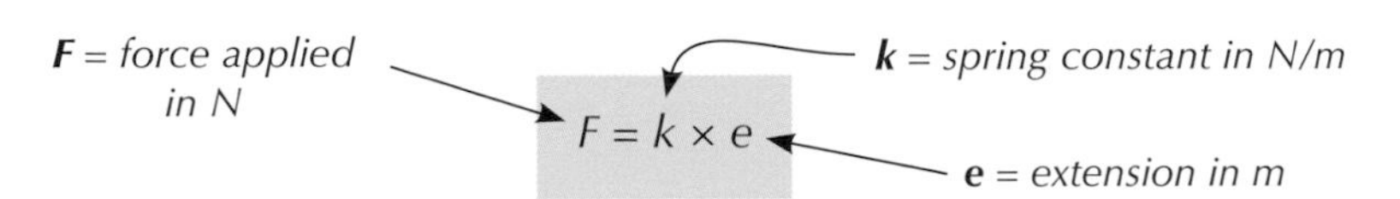

k is the spring constant. Its value depends on the material that you are stretching and it's measured in newtons per metre (N/m).

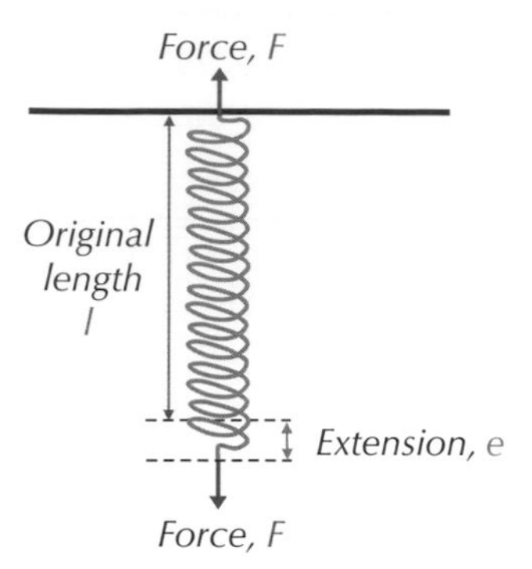

***Figure 1:** The extension, e, of a stretched spring is the difference between its stretched length and its original length (i.e. with no force applied).*

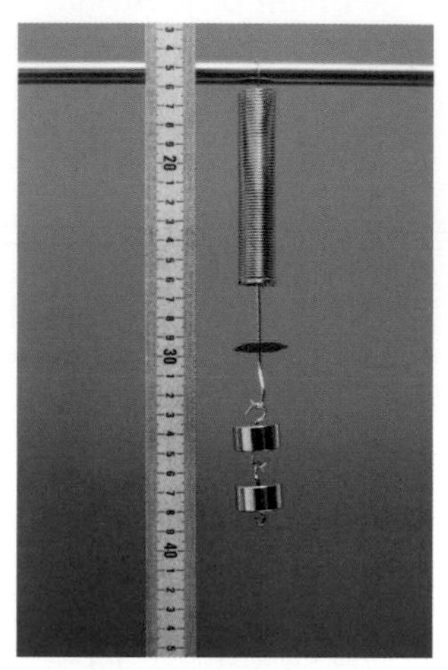

***Figure 2:** An experiment investigating the extension of a spring when weights are applied to it.*

Example

When no force is applied, a spring has a length of 23.2 cm. When a lead ball is suspended from it, the spring extends to a length of 25.1 cm. If the spring constant k = 60 N/m, calculate the weight of the lead ball.

Start by finding the extension of the spring after the lead ball is attached:

$$e = 25.1 - 23.2$$
$$= 1.9 \text{ cm}$$

Be careful with units here — the formula uses extension in metres, so make sure you convert any numbers first:

$$1.9 \text{ cm} = \frac{1.9}{100} \text{ m} = 0.019 \text{ m}$$

Then put the numbers into the equation for force:

$$F = k \times e$$
$$= 60 \times 0.019$$
$$= 1.14 \text{ N}$$

Example **Higher**

A 12 N weight is suspended from a spring with a spring constant of 96 N/kg. Calculate the extension of the spring.

Rearrange the formula to make e the subject:

$$F = k \times e \Rightarrow e = \frac{F}{k}$$

Then put the right numbers in:

$$e = \frac{12}{96} = 0.125 \text{ m}$$

Exam Tip H
You might find rearranging equations easier if you use a formula triangle:

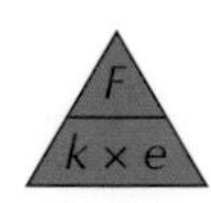

The limit of proportionality

There's a limit to the amount of force you can apply to an object for the extension to keep on increasing proportionally. Figure 3 shows force against extension for an object.

For small forces, force and extension are directly proportional. So the first part of the graph shows a straight-line relationship between force and extension and the object acts as an elastic object.

There is a point at which the object will no longer extend proportionally with an applied force. This is known as the **limit of proportionality**.

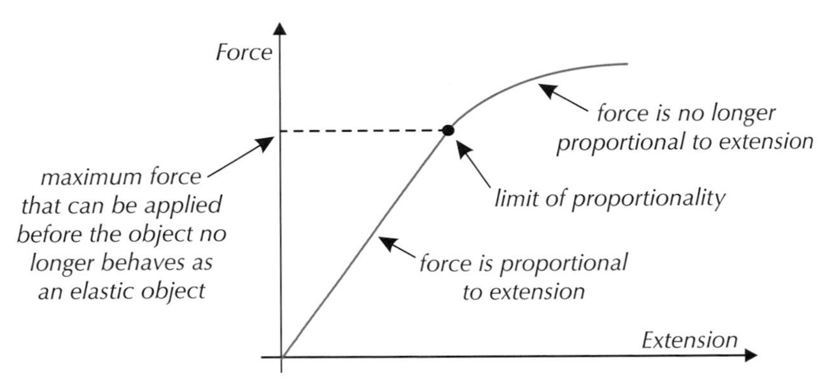

Figure 3: *A graph showing the force applied to an object against its extension. The force is proportional to extension up to the limit of proportionality.*

Tip: See page 14 for more on the relationships shown by graphs.

Practice Questions — Fact Recall

Q1 What's the missing word? "Applying a .... to an object can cause it to stretch or change in shape."

Q2 What name is given to an object that can return to its original shape after being stretched?

Q3 In what form is energy stored when work is done to stretch a spring elastically?

Q4 Write down the formula for calculating the force applied to a spring from its extension and its spring constant. Say what each term represents and the units it's measured in.

Q5 What's the limit of proportionality?

Practice Question — Application

Q1 An old-fashioned set of weighing scales consists of a bowl suspended from a spring with spring constant k = 69 N/m. Some flour is placed in the bowl, causing the spring to extend by 2.7 cm. How much does the flour weigh?

Section Checklist — Make sure you know...

Distance-Time Graphs

- ❑ That the speed of an object is given by the gradient of its distance-time graph.
- ❑ What the distance-time graph for an object looks like when it's stationary, moving at a steady speed, accelerating or decelerating.
- ❑ How to draw a distance-time graph for an object that's stationary or moving at a steady speed in a straight line.
- ❑ **H** How to calculate the gradient of an object's distance-time graph to find the object's speed.

Velocity-Time Graphs

- ❑ That speed tells you how fast something's going and velocity is the speed in a given direction.
- ❑ That acceleration tells you how much velocity changes in a given time.
- ❑ How to calculate the acceleration of an object from its initial and final velocity and time elapsed.
- ❑ What a velocity-time graph for an object looks like when it's moving at a steady speed, accelerating and decelerating.
- ❑ That the gradient of an object's velocity-time graph represents the object's acceleration at that point.
- ❑ **H** How to calculate the gradient of an object's velocity-time graph to find the object's acceleration.
- ❑ **H** How to find the distance an object travels in a given time period by calculating the area under the object's velocity-time graph for that time period.

Resultant Forces

- ❑ That all the individual forces acting at a point can be combined to produce a resultant force which has the same effect as the individual forces.
- ❑ That a non-zero resultant force acting on an object will cause a change in its rest state or motion, i.e. cause it to accelerate or decelerate in the direction of the force.
- ❑ How to calculate the resultant of two or more forces acting along a straight line.

Forces and Acceleration

- ❑ That if the resultant force on a stationary object is zero, it will remain stationary.
- ❑ That if the resultant force on a stationary object is not zero, it will accelerate (start moving) in the direction of the resultant force.
- ❑ That if the resultant force on a moving object is zero, it will keep moving at the same velocity.
- ❑ That if the resultant force on a moving object is not zero, it will accelerate in the direction of the resultant force.
- ❑ How to calculate the acceleration of an object using the formula $a = F \div m$.
- ❑ How to calculate the resultant force acting on an object using the formula $F = m \times a$.

cont...

Weight and Reaction Forces

- ☐ How to calculate the weight of an object given its mass and the local value of gravitational field strength (g) using the formula $W = m \times g$.
- ☐ That when two objects interact, they exert forces on each other that are equal but opposite.

Friction and Terminal Velocity

- ☐ That if a vehicle is travelling at a steady speed, the driving force must be balanced by the resistive forces acting on the vehicle.
- ☐ That when an object moves through a fluid, frictional forces opposing its motion increase with speed.
- ☐ That most of the resistive forces that oppose (a vehicle's) motion are caused by air resistance.
- ☐ That a vehicle's top speed can be increased by making it more streamlined or making its engine more powerful.
- ☐ That an object falling through a fluid will initially accelerate due to gravity, but resistive forces acting on it increase until the resultant force acting on it becomes zero and it reaches terminal velocity.
- ☐ How to draw and interpret velocity-time graphs for objects falling through a fluid and reaching terminal velocity.
- ☐ That the gradient of a falling object's velocity-time graph decreases because the resistive forces acting on it increase with velocity.
- ☐ That changing the shape of an object can change the resistive forces acting on it, and hence why using a parachute reduces a skydiver's terminal velocity.

Stopping Distances

- ☐ That the sum of the thinking distance and braking distance gives the stopping distance of a vehicle.
- ☐ That the braking force needed to stop a vehicle within a certain distance increases with the vehicle's speed. Similarly, for a given braking force the braking distance will increase with the vehicle's speed.
- ☐ The factors that can affect thinking distance, such as tiredness, drugs, alcohol and distractions.
- ☐ The factors that affect a vehicle's braking distance, such as speed, road conditions, condition of brakes and condition of tyres.
- ☐ That when a vehicle's brakes are applied, work is done by friction between the brakes and the tyres to convert kinetic energy into other forms of energy, including heat.

Forces and Elasticity

- ☐ That a force acting on an object may cause it to stretch or change in shape.
- ☐ That an elastic object is one that can return to its original shape after being stretched by a force.
- ☐ That when an elastic object stretches, a force does work to store elastic potential energy inside it.
- ☐ How to calculate the force acting on an elastic object given its extension and its spring constant, k.
- ☐ That the limit of proportionality is the point at which no more force can be applied to an elastic object before its extension is no longer proportional to the applied force.

Exam-style Questions

1 This is a velocity-time graph for a car during a journey to the local shops.

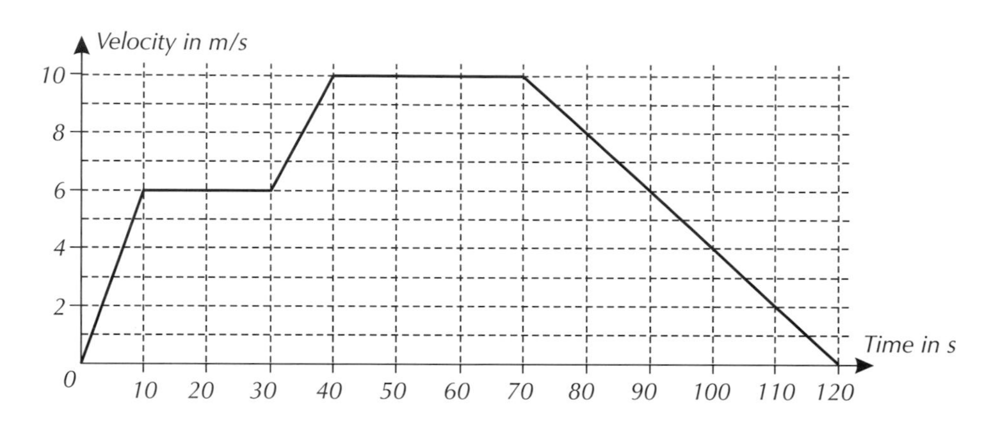

1 (a) During which time period(s) does the graph show a negative acceleration?

(1 mark)

1 (b) (i) Calculate the acceleration of the car between 30 and 40 seconds.

Show clearly how you work out your answer. Give your answer in m/s^2.

(3 marks)

1 (b) (ii) If the car has a mass of 980 kg, calculate the resultant force acting on the car between 30 and 40 seconds.

Use the correct equation from the equations listed on page 402.
Show clearly how you work out your answer. Give your answer in N.

(2 marks)

1 (c) Use the graph to calculate how far the car travels between 30 and 40 seconds.

Show clearly how you work out your answer. Give your answer in m.

(3 marks)

1 (d) The car is driving in heavy rain. Suggest and explain **two** ways in which this could affect the stopping distance of the car.

(2 marks)

1 (e) Before arriving at the shops, the driver applies the brakes. Explain, in terms of energy transfer, how the brakes cause the car to slow down and come to a stop.

(3 marks)

2 A truck is travelling along a straight, flat road at its top speed of 65 mph.

2 (a) (i) What is the resultant force acting on the truck?

(1 mark)

2 (a) (ii) Suggest the cause of most of the frictional forces acting on the truck.

(1 mark)

2 (b) On a clear, dry day, the truck's stopping distance with this driver is 74 m.
The stopping distance is the sum of the thinking distance and the braking distance.

Explain what is meant by thinking distance and braking distance.

(2 marks)

2 (c) Modifications can be made to the truck to increase its top speed.

Explain how each of the following modifications would achieve this effect.

2 (c) (i) Replacing the engine with one that provides a greater driving force.

(2 marks)

2 (c) (ii) Changing the body of the truck to make it more streamlined.

(2 marks)

3 A skydiver jumps from a plane and reaches terminal velocity after 15 seconds.

3 (a) Draw a ring around the correct answer in the box to complete the sentence.

Before reaching terminal velocity,

the force due to gravity is	greater than the resistive force due to air resistance. smaller than the resistive force due to air resistance. the same as the resistive force due to air resistance.

(1 mark)

3 (b) Draw a ring around the correct answer in the box to complete the sentence.

After reaching terminal velocity,

the force due to gravity is	greater than the resistive force due to air resistance. smaller than the resistive force due to air resistance. the same as the resistive force due to air resistance.

(1 mark)

3 (c) Sketch a velocity-time graph for the skydiver during the first 40 seconds of his dive.

(4 marks)

3 (d) After 40 seconds the skydiver opens a parachute.

3 (d) (i) What effect will opening a parachute have on the skydiver's terminal velocity?

(1 mark)

3 (d) (ii) What effect will opening a parachute have on the resistive forces acting on the skydiver at a given speed?

(1 mark)

4 An astronaut is on a space walk where gravitational forces and air resistance acting on the astronaut are assumed to be 0. He pushes against a rock with a force F, as shown.

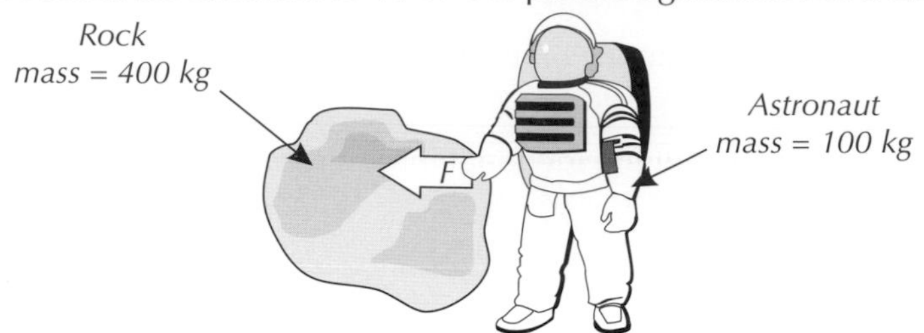

4 (a) The astronaut experiences a reaction force from the rock.
State the size and direction, relative to F, of this reaction force.

(1 mark)

4 (b) The astronaut pushes against the rock for 1.2 seconds and he accelerates during this time. After this point the astronaut moves away from the rock at a velocity of 3 m/s.

4 (b) (i) Calculate the acceleration of the astronaut while he's in contact with the rock.
Use the correct equation from the equations listed on page 402.
Show clearly how you work out your answer. Give your answer in m/s^2.

(3 marks)

4 (b) (ii) Calculate the size of force F.
Use the correct equation from the equations listed on page 402.
Show clearly how you work out your answer.

(3 marks)

5 The diagram shows a mass suspended from a spring, attached to a solid workbench.

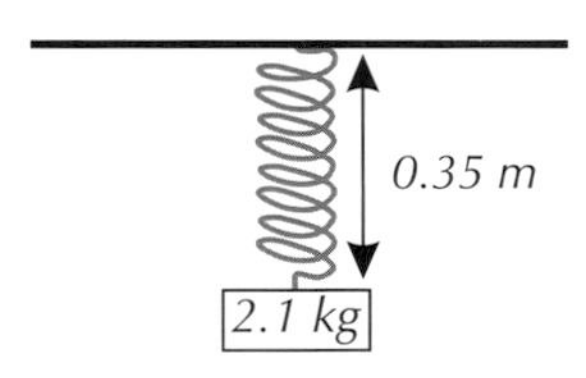

5 (a) Calculate the weight of the suspended mass. Use g = 10 N/kg.
Use the correct equation from the equations listed on page 402.
Show clearly how you work out your answer. Give your answer in N.

(2 marks)

5 (b) Explain why the spring gains elastic potential energy when the mass is suspended.

(2 marks)

5 (c) The spring has a natural length of 0.29 m. Calculate the spring constant of the spring.
Use the correct equation from the equations listed on page 402.
Show clearly how you work out your answer.

(4 marks)

1. Work and Potential Energy

Potential energy sounds exciting — like anything could happen. What's most likely to happen, though, is that work will be done.

Learning Objectives:
- Know that when a force moves an object through a distance, work is done.
- Know that when work is done, energy is transferred from one form to another.
- Be able to use the formula $W = F \times d$.
- Know what gravitational potential energy is and be able to use the formula $E_p = m \times g \times h$.

Specification Reference P2.2.1

Work done

In Physics '**work done**' has a specific meaning, and you need to know what that is.

When a force moves an object through a distance, energy is transferred and work is done.

Luckily, that statement sounds far more complicated than it needs to.

Try this:

1. Whenever something moves, something else is providing some sort of 'effort' to move it (see Figure 1).
2. The thing putting the effort in needs a supply of energy (like fuel or food or electricity etc.).
3. It then does 'work' by moving the object — and one way or another it transfers the energy it receives (as fuel) into other forms.
4. Whether this energy is transferred 'usefully' (e.g. by lifting a load) or is 'wasted' (e.g. lost as heat through friction), you can still say that 'work is done'.

Remember, 'work done' and 'energy transferred' are one and the same. (And they're both given in joules.)

Figure 1: *A diagram showing how work is done when a person supplies energy to a broom and sweeps.*

You can work out how much work is done using the following formula:

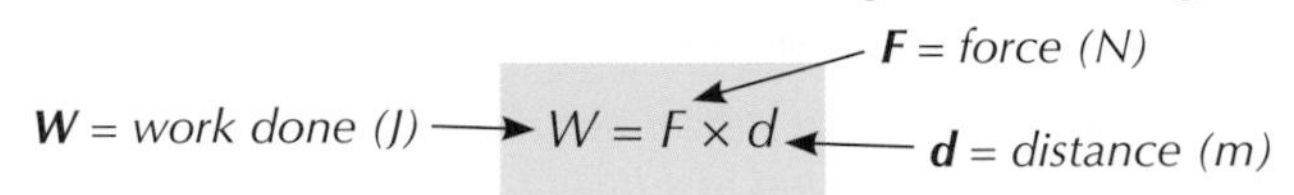

Tip: The distance is the distance in the direction of the force.

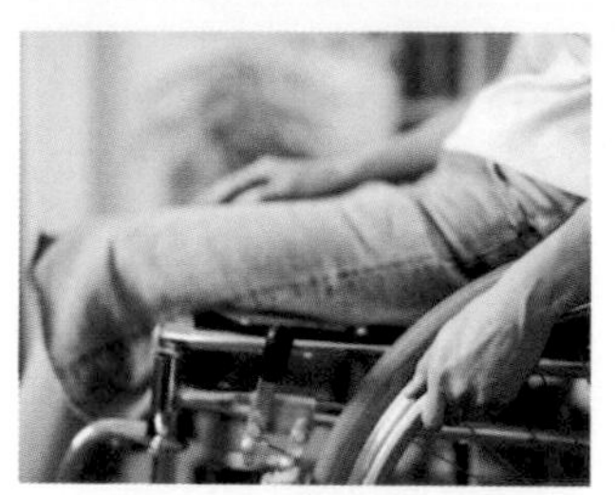

Figure 2: A wheelchair user pushing the wheels of her chair. She does work against friction by transferring chemical energy (from food) to kinetic energy when the chair moves.

Whether the force is friction or weight or tension in a rope, it's always the same. To find how much energy has been transferred (in joules), you just multiply the force in N by the distance moved in m.

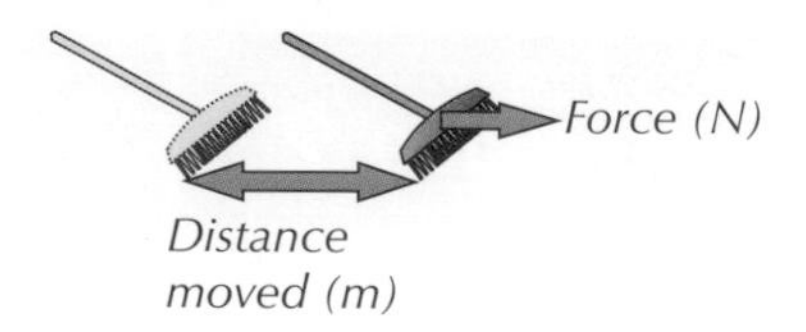

Example

Some kids drag a tractor tyre 5 m over rough ground. They pull with a total force of 340 N in the direction of the motion. Find the energy transferred.

Force = 340 N
Distance = 5 m

Then put the numbers into the formula for work done:

$W = F \times d = 340 \times 5 = 1700$ J.

So, the energy transferred is 1700 J.

Tip: H This formula triangle will help if you need to rearrange the formula:

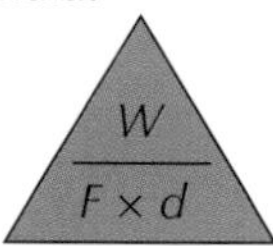

Turn to page 352 if you need help with formula triangles.

Example **Higher**

248 J of work is done when a rock is pushed 35 cm. How much force was it pushed with in the direction of motion?

Work done = 248 J
Distance = 35 cm = 0.35 m

Rearranging $W = F \times d$, $F = \frac{W}{d} = \frac{248}{0.35} = 710\,\text{N}$ (to 2 s.f.)

Tip: H The actual answer you get here is 708.5714286. But it's sensible to round your answer to 2 significant figures (s.f.) — turn to page 350 for more on s.f..

Gravitational potential energy

Gravitational potential energy, measured in joules, is the energy that an object has by virtue of (because of) its vertical position in a gravitational field.

When an object is raised vertically, work is done against the force of gravity (it takes effort to lift it up) and the object gains gravitational potential energy.

$$E_p = m \times g \times h$$

E_p = *gravitational potential energy (J)*
h = *height (m)*
m = *mass (kg)*
g = *gravitational field strength (N/kg)*

On Earth the gravitational field strength (g) is approximately 10 N/kg.

No height above ground, so no potential energy

Potential energy at this height = m × g × h

m

m

h

Figure 3: A diagram showing how the gravitational potential energy of a mass (m) increases when it is lifted to a height (h) in a gravitational field.

Tip: If an object falls from a height, its gravitational potential energy is converted to kinetic energy as it falls.

Example

A 47 kg mass is slowly raised through 6.3 m.
Find the gain in potential energy.

Just plug the numbers into the formula:

$$E_p = m \times g \times h = 47 \times 10 \times 6.3 = 2961 \text{ J}$$

Example **Higher**

A flea of mass 0.5×10^{-3} g jumps vertically from the ground. At the top of the jump the flea has 1.25×10^{-6} J of gravitational potential energy.

How high does the flea jump?

$E_p = 1.25 \times 10^{-6}$ J
$m = 0.5 \times 10^{-3}$ g $= 0.5 \times 10^{-6}$ kg
$g = 10$ N/kg

Rearranging $E_p = m \times g \times h$, $h = \frac{E_p}{m \times g} = \frac{1.25 \times 10^{-6}}{(0.5 \times 10^{-6}) \times 10} = 0.25\,\text{m}$

Exam Tip H
Take a look at page 352 if you need help with rearranging formulas. This formula triangle might help:

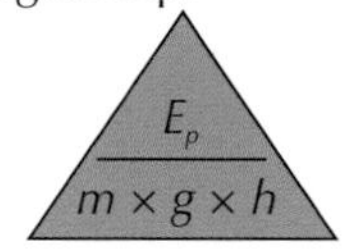

Make sure you practise before you get into the exam hall.

Practice Questions — Fact Recall

Q1 What is 'work done'?

Q2 Give the formula for work done. Say what each of the terms represents and what units they should be in.

Q3 What is gravitational potential energy?

Q4 What is the formula for working out gravitational potential energy? What does each term represent and what units should they be in?

Exam Tip
Although you'll get a formula sheet in the exam, you still need to understand what the terms mean and how to use them.

Practice Questions — Application

Q1 A bike is pushed 20 m using a steady force of 250 N in the direction of motion. How much energy is transferred?

Q2 A 43 000 kg plane is flying 10 600 m above the ground. How much gravitational potential energy does it have? (Assume that the gravitational field strength (*g*) is 10 N/kg.)

Q3 An 80 kg man climbs 1 m up a rope with a steady force of 1000 N.

a) How much work does he do?

b) How much gravitational potential energy does he gain?

Q4 A toy car is pushed with 25 N of force and 375 J of work is done. How far is the car pushed in the direction of the force?

Q5 A cat is sitting on a tree branch that's 2.3 m from the ground. The cat has 86.4 J of gravitational potential energy.

What is the mass of the cat?

2. Kinetic Energy

More energy — this time it's kinetic. Kinetic energy is the energy of movement and, as always, it can be transferred to other types of energy.

Learning Objectives:
- Know what kinetic energy is, and that it depends on an object's mass and speed.
- Be able to use the formula: $E_k = \frac{1}{2} \times m \times v^2$
- Know that when work is done against frictional forces kinetic energy is transferred into heat energy (and some sound).
- Know that the work done by brakes to stop a moving object is equal to its original kinetic energy.
- Be able to describe how kinetic energy is transferred in certain situations e.g. objects falling or objects entering the Earth's atmosphere.

Specification Reference P2.2.1

What is kinetic energy?

Anything that's moving has **kinetic energy**.

There's a slightly tricky formula for it, so you have to concentrate a little bit harder for this one.

$$E_k = \frac{1}{2} \times m \times v^2$$

E_k *= kinetic energy (J)*
v *= speed (m/s)*
m *= mass (kg)*

Remember, the kinetic energy of something depends both on mass and speed. The greater the mass and the faster it's going, the bigger its kinetic energy.

Figure 1: *A diagram to show how the kinetic energy of a moving object depends on its mass (m) and velocity (v).*

Example

A van of mass 2450 kg is travelling at 40 m/s. Calculate its kinetic energy.

You just plug the numbers into the formula — but watch the 'v^2'.

$$\text{K.E.} = \frac{1}{2} \times m \times v^2 = \frac{1}{2} \times 2450 \times 40^2 = 1\ 960\ 000\ \text{J}$$

Tip: Kinetic energy can be represented by K.E. or E_k. It doesn't matter which one you use — just make sure you know how to use the formula.

Example **Higher**

A moped with 1.17×10^4 J of kinetic energy travels at 12 m/s. What is the mass of the moped?

$E_k = 1.17 \times 10^4$ J
$v = 12$ m/s

Rearranging $E_k = \frac{1}{2} \times m \times v^2$,

$$m = \frac{2 \times E_k}{v^2} = \frac{2 \times (1.17 \times 10^4)}{12^2} = 162.5\ \text{kg}$$

Tip: H This formula triangle might help if you need to rearrange the kinetic energy formula:

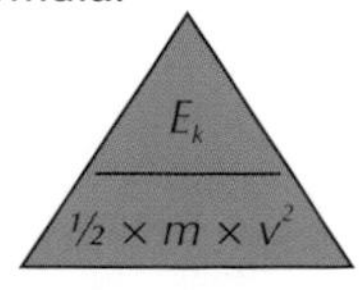

Transferring kinetic energy

Braking

As you've seen on page 224, when a car brakes its kinetic energy is transferred into heat energy by friction between the brake pads and the wheels, and work is done. So, the work done by the brakes will be equal to the amount of kinetic energy that's transferred to heat energy:

kinetic energy transferred = work done by brakes

$$\tfrac{1}{2} \times m \times v^2 = F \times d$$

m = *mass of car and passengers (kg)*
v = *speed of car (m/s)*
F = *braking force (N)*
d = *braking distance (m)*

Tip: Remember, the principle of conservation of energy states that energy can never be created or destroyed — only converted into different forms.

Tip: Stopping distance increases a lot with speed (see page 223) and this is why — the braking distance is proportional to the speed of the car squared.

Example

A van with a mass of 2700 kg is travelling at 10 m/s. The van brakes and comes to a complete stop.

How much work is done by the brakes?

$$\begin{aligned}\text{work done} &= \text{kinetic energy transferred} \\ &= \tfrac{1}{2} \times m \times v^2 \\ &= \tfrac{1}{2} \times 2700 \times 10^2 \\ &= 135\,000\ \text{J}\end{aligned}$$

Tip: Remember, work done is measured in joules because it's energy.

Example Higher

A 1300 kg car is travelling at 15 m/s. The driver brakes and brings the car to a stop over 46 m.

What is the average braking force needed to stop the car?

kinetic energy transferred = work done by brakes
Rearranging, $\tfrac{1}{2} \times m \times v^2 = F \times d$:

$$\begin{aligned}F &= \frac{\tfrac{1}{2} \times m \times v^2}{d} \\ &= \frac{\tfrac{1}{2} \times 1300 \times 15^2}{46} \\ &= 3200\ \text{N (to 2 s.f.)}\end{aligned}$$

Exam Tip
Although you'll be given a formula sheet in the exam, it won't tell you what units they're in. So, make sure you learn the units for each quantity before you go into the exam.

Falling objects

When something falls, its potential energy (see page 234) is converted into kinetic energy. So the further it falls, the faster it goes — see Figure 2.

Potential energy at this height = $m \times g \times h$

Potential energy lost = kinetic energy gained

More potential energy lost = more kinetic energy gained

Figure 2: A diagram showing how the gravitational potential energy of a falling object is converted to kinetic energy. The higher the object is to begin with, the more kinetic energy it'll have when it hits the ground.

Tip: At first glance this may look tricky, but it just combines two formulas you already know.

potential energy lost = kinetic energy gained

$$m \times g \times h = \frac{1}{2} \times m \times v^2$$

g = gravitational field strength (N/kg)
h = height object falls from (m)
m = mass of falling object (kg)
v = maximum speed of object (m/s)

When an object falls, some of the kinetic energy it gains is transferred into heat and sound.

Tip: This is why a falling object makes a noise when it hits the ground. The further and faster it falls, the more kinetic energy it has — so the louder the bang.

Examples

When meteors and space shuttles enter the atmosphere, they have a very high kinetic energy. Friction due to collisions with particles in the atmosphere transfers some of their kinetic energy to heat energy and work is done.

The temperatures can become so extreme that most meteors burn up completely and never hit the Earth. Only the biggest meteors make it through to the Earth's surface, becoming meteorites.

Space shuttles have heat shields made from special materials which lose heat quickly, allowing the shuttle to re-enter the atmosphere without burning up.

Figure 3: A meteor burning up as it enters the Earth's atmosphere.

Practice Questions — Fact Recall

Q1 What is kinetic energy?

Q2 Which of these has the most kinetic energy: a small dog walking slowly or a large dog running fast? Explain why.

Q3 What is the formula for calculating kinetic energy? What does each term represent and what units are they in?

Practice Questions — Application

Q1 How much kinetic energy does each of the following have?

a) A 2 kg rabbit running at 2.1 m/s.

b) A 20 g ball rolling at 0.5 m/s.

c) A man on a bike (total mass 120 kg) moving at 4 m/s.

d) A 50 g object moving at 100 cm/s.

Q2 A 240 kg spaceship is travelling at 1500 m/s. The pilot brakes and the spaceship comes to a complete stop. How much work is done by the brakes?

Q3 How much energy is transferred when a 24 g carrot sliding at 3.5 m/s is brought to a stop?

Q4 A 100 g object falls from a 2 m high shelf. Assuming no energy is lost as heat or sound, how much kinetic energy does it have when it hits the ground?

Q5 Which of these has more kinetic energy?
A 240 g frog moving at 1.5 m/s or a 215 g rat moving at 1.6 m/s.

Q6 An ice skater is moving across the ice at 0.25 m/s. She has 2.1 J of kinetic energy. What is her mass?

Q7 A 12.5 g ball with 40 J of kinetic energy is flying through the air. How fast is it moving?

Q8 A 1 kg potato with 450 J of gravitational potential energy falls to the ground. What is the maximum speed of the potato?

Exam Tip
Watch out for data given in the 'wrong' units in the exam. Double-check the numbers are in the 'right' units before you stick them into the formula.

Tip: Take gravitational field strength (*g*) to be 10 N/kg.

Tip: H Make sure you practise rearranging the kinetic energy formula — the v^2 makes it a bit tricky.

Learning Objectives:

- Know what power is.
- Be able to use the formula: $P = \frac{E}{t}$

Specification Reference P2.2.1

3. Power

Power — this might be familiar from learning about energy, electricity and cars. It's a really important concept that pops up all over the place because power is all about how quickly energy is transferred.

What is power?

Power is not the same thing as force, nor energy.

Power is the "rate of doing work" — i.e. how much per second.

A powerful machine is not necessarily one which can exert a strong force (though it usually ends up that way). A powerful machine is one which transfers a lot of energy in a short space of time.

Figure 1: *A grasshopper's legs transfer a small amount of energy, but in a very short time — this makes them very powerful.*

This is the very easy formula for power:

$$P = \frac{E}{t}$$

P *= power (watts)*

E *= work done or energy transferred (J)*

t *= time taken (s)*

Watts and joules per second

The proper unit of power is the watt. One watt = 1 joule of energy transferred per second. Don't ever say "watts per second" — it's nonsense.

Example

A motor transfers 4.8 kJ of useful energy in 2 minutes. Find its power output.

Energy transferred = 4.8 kJ = 4800 J
Time taken = 2 minutes = 2 × 60 s = 120 s

$$P = \frac{E}{t} = \frac{4800}{120} = 40 \text{ W (or 40 J/s)}$$

Example **Higher**

How long does it take for a 550 W motor to transfer 110 J of energy?

Rearranging $P = E \div t$,

$t = E \div P$
$= 110 \div 550$
$= 0.2$ s

Tip: H This formula triangle might help with rearranging the formula for power:

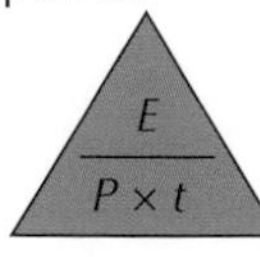

Calculating your power output

Human beings don't come with a power rating, but that doesn't mean you can't work out your own power output. There are a few different ways to measure the power output of a person...

Example 1 — the timed run upstairs

Imagine a 62 kg person running up some stairs. If it takes them 14 s, you can work out how much energy is transferred in that time — the energy transferred is equal to the gravitational potential energy gained.

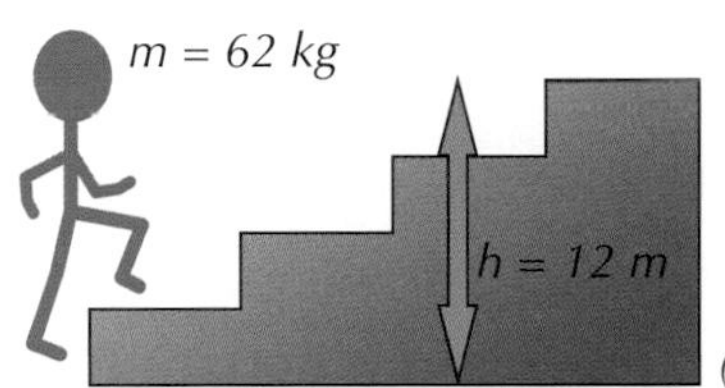

(Nowhere near to scale.)

$E_p = m \times g \times h$, so in this case (taking g = 10 N/kg):

$$\text{power ouput} = \frac{\text{energy transferred}}{\text{time taken}} = \frac{m \times g \times h}{t} = \frac{62 \times 10 \times 12}{14} = 530\ \text{W}$$

Tip: Can't remember much about gravitational potential energy? Flick back to page 234 for a reminder.

Tip: The real answer is actually 531.4285714 which rounds down to 530 (to 2 s.f.). See page 350 if you need a reminder about significant figures.

Example 2 — the timed acceleration

Now the 62 kg person starts running from a standing start. It takes them 4 s to reach a top speed of 8 m/s.

This time, the energy transferred is equal to the kinetic energy gained.

m = 62 kg

t = 4 s

0 → 8 m/s

$E_k = \frac{1}{2} \times m \times v^2$, so:

$$\text{power} = \frac{\text{energy transferred}}{\text{time taken}} = \frac{\frac{1}{2} \times m \times v^2}{t} = \frac{\frac{1}{2} \times 62 \times 8^2}{4} = 496\ \text{W}$$

Tip: If kinetic energy is puzzling you, take a look at page 236.

Tip: HOW SCIENCE WORKS — To get accurate results from these experiments, you should do them several times and find an average. There's more about accurate results on page 10.

Practice Questions — Fact Recall

Q1 What is meant by the term 'power'?

Q2 The formula for power is $P = \frac{E}{t}$. What does each term represent and what units are they measured in?

Practice Questions — Application

Q1 Find the power output of the following motors:

a) One that transfers 150 J of energy in 37.5 s.

b) One that transfers 79.8 kJ of energy in 42 s.

c) One that transfers 7215 kJ of energy in 9.5 minutes.

Q2 Sarah runs up a 45 m high hill in 50 s. What is her power output if her mass is 58 kg?

Q3 Bo runs a 100 m race. His mass is 82 kg. From a standing start it takes him 20.5 s to accelerate to 8.0 m/s. What is his power output?

Q4 How long does each of the following take?

a) A 525 W motor to transfer 1344 J of energy.

b) A 2.86 kW toaster to transfer 1430 J of energy.

Q5 How much energy do the following transfer?

a) A machine running for 35 s with a power output of 1240 W.

b) A 1500 W heater switched on for 17 minutes.

4. Momentum and Collisions

If something is moving along, it'll have some momentum. How much depends on its mass and velocity. If it collides with something, it'll 'share' its momentum with it...

Learning Objectives:
- Understand what momentum is.
- Be able to use the formula $p = m \times v$.
- Know that the total momentum before a collision is equal to the total momentum after it, in a closed system.

Specification Reference
P2.2.2

Momentum

Momentum (p) is a property of moving objects. The greater the mass of an object and the greater its velocity (see p.204) the more momentum the object has.

Momentum is a vector quantity — it has size and direction (like velocity, but not speed).

$$p = m \times v$$

p = *momentum (kg m/s)*
m = *mass (kg)*
v = *velocity (m/s)*

Example

A 1800 kg rhino is running north at 9.5 m/s. How much momentum does it have?

$p = m \times v = 1800 \times 9.5 = 17\,100$ kg m/s to the north

Example **Higher**

A 40.0 kg rock that is falling off a cliff has 484 kg m/s momentum. What is the rock's velocity?

Rearranging $p = m \times v$,

$$v = \frac{p}{m} = \frac{484}{40.0} = 12.1 \text{ m/s downwards}$$

Tip: H Use this formula triangle to help you rearrange the formula:

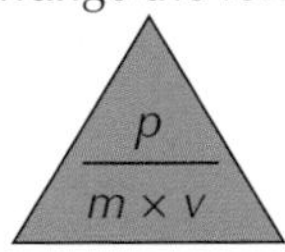

Have a look at page 352 for more on formula triangles.

Collisions and explosions

In a closed system, the total momentum before an event (e.g. a collision or an explosion) is the same as after the event. This is called **conservation of momentum**.

Tip: A closed system is just a fancy way of saying that no external forces act.

In some collisions the objects bump into one another and stay stuck (for example, if you throw a lump of clay at a wall). In other collisions, the objects bounce off each other (e.g. when snooker balls hit each other — see Fig. 1).

Figure 1: *When the white snooker ball collides with the red one, momentum will be conserved.*

In both types of collision, the momentum is always conserved (if it's a closed system).

In the exam you might have to do calculations involving the momentum of two different objects.

Figure 2: *Ice skaters rely on momentum to keep themselves moving across the ice.*

Tip: Sue's velocity has a minus sign in front of it because it's to the left.

Example 1

Two skaters approach each other, collide and move off together as shown. What is their combined momentum before the collision?

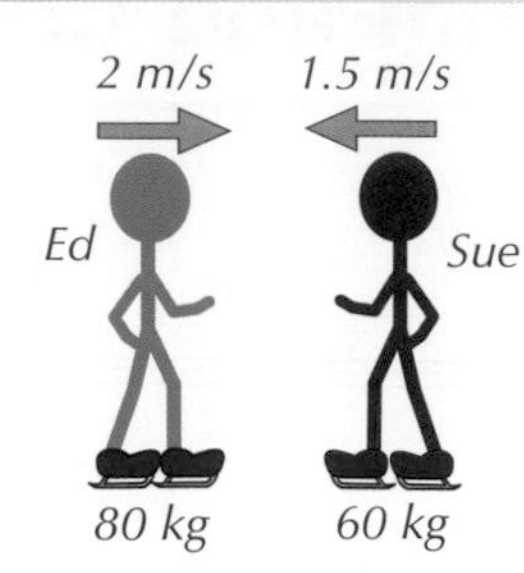

Before collision

After collision

- Choose which direction is positive.

  I'll say "positive" means "to the right".

- Next, work out the total momentum before the collision:

  Total momentum = momentum of Ed + momentum of Sue
  $= [m_{Ed} \times v_{Ed}] + [m_{Sue} \times v_{Sue}]$
  $= [80 \times 2] + [60 \times (-1.5)] = 70$ kg m/s to the right

Example 1 — continued | Higher

At what velocity do Ed and Sue move after the collision?

After collision

- Work out what the total momentum after the collision is:

  Total momentum = momentum of Ed and Sue together
  $= m_{Ed+Sue} \times v_{Ed+Sue}$
  $= (80 + 60) \times v$
  $= 140v$

- Finally, find out what v is:

  Momentum before collision = momentum after collision
  $70 = 140v$
  $$v = \frac{70}{140} = 0.5 \text{ m/s to the right}$$

Tip: The final velocity is positive, so it's to the right.

The momentum of a stationary system before an explosion is zero, so, due to conservation of momentum, the total momentum after the explosion is zero too.

Tip: Conservation of momentum is why a gun recoils as it is fired.

Example 2

A gun fires a bullet as shown. At what speed does the gun move backwards?

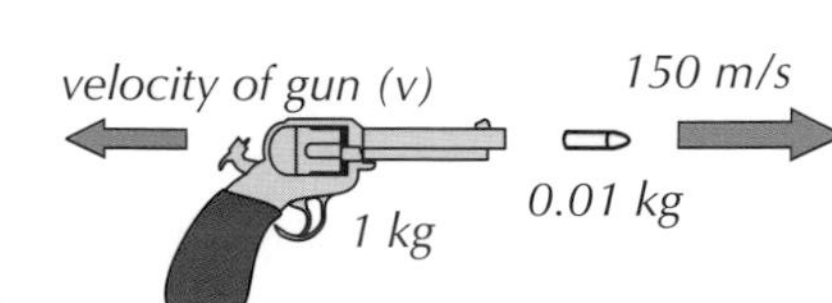

After bullet is fired

- Say "positive" means "to the right".
- Total momentum before firing = 0 kg m/s
- Total momentum after = momentum of bullet + momentum of gun
  $= (0.01 \times 150) + (1 \times v) = 1.5 + v$
- So, $1.5 + v = 0$, i.e. $v = -1.5$ m/s
  The gun moves backwards at 1.5 m/s.

Tip: To get $v = -1.5$, all I've done is take 1.5 from each side of the equation.

Practice Questions — Fact Recall

Q1 What does the momentum of an object depend on?

Q2 What is the formula for calculating the momentum of an object? Say what each term represents and what its units are.

Q3 What is the principle of conservation of momentum?

Practice Questions — Application

Q1 Work out the momentum of the following:

a) A 100 g magnet moving north at 0.6 m/s.

b) A 0.8 g bug travelling to the left at 12 m/s.

c) A 5.2 kg rock falling vertically downwards 8 m/s.

Q2 Two skaters (A and B) collide and move off together.
Skater A, with a mass of 98 kg, was moving right at 1.75 m/s.
Skater B, with a mass of 53 kg, was moving left at 2.31 m/s.
What is their combined momentum after the collision?

Q3 A stationary gas canister explodes. What is the momentum of the system before and after the explosion? Explain how you know.

Q4 What is the velocity of the following?

a) A 0.95 kg turtle swimming south with 3.04 kg m/s momentum.

b) A 57 g tennis ball moving with 1.71 kg m/s momentum towards the net.

c) A 2000 kg car travelling east with 45 000 kg m/s of momentum.

Q5 What is the mass of the following?

a) A child skiing down a slope at 0.75 m/s with 31.5 kg m/s momentum.

b) A dog running at 7.5 m/s with 210 kg m/s of momentum.

Q6 A bullet is fired from a stationary gun. Afterwards the 1 kg gun moves backwards at 2 m/s and the bullet moves forwards at 200 m/s. What is the mass of the bullet?

Q7 Two skiers (C and D) crash into each other and move off together to the left at 1.5 m/s after the collision.
Skier C has a mass of 56 kg and was moving right at 1.3 m/s before the collision. Skier D has a mass of 70 kg.

What was the velocity of skier D before the collision?

5. Car Design and Safety

Learning Objectives:
- Be able to compare different braking systems, including regenerative brakes.
- Understand the effects of crumple zones, side impact bars, seat belts and air bags on energy and momentum changes in cars.

Specification Reference P2.2

Anything fast-moving and heavy can be dangerous — and that includes cars. It's why so much thought is put into making cars safe as well as pretty.

Car design and changes in momentum

When a force acts on an object, it causes a change in momentum. A larger force acting for the same length of time means a faster change of momentum (and so a greater acceleration).

Likewise, if someone's momentum changes very quickly (like in a car crash), the forces on the body will be very large, and more likely to cause injury.

This is why cars are designed with safety features that slow people down over a longer time when they have a crash — the longer it takes for a change in momentum, the smaller the force.

Figure 1: *A brake disc on a car. When the brakes are applied, the brake pads(on the left of the disc) rub against the brake discs (silver disc) and work is done to slow down the car using friction.*

Car brakes

When you apply the brakes to slow down a car, work is done (see Figure 1 and p.237). The brakes reduce the kinetic energy of the car by transferring it into heat (and sound) energy (see p.224). Figure 2 shows the heat generated during braking.

Figure 2: *A thermogram showing the heat generated around a car wheel during braking. White is hottest (where the brake discs are) and blue is coolest.*

Regenerative brakes

In traditional braking systems that would be the end of the story, but new regenerative braking systems used in some electric or hybrid cars make use of the energy, instead of converting it all into heat during braking.

- Regenerative brakes use the system that drives the vehicle to do the majority of the braking.
- Rather than converting the kinetic energy of the vehicle into heat energy, the brakes put the vehicle's motor into reverse. With the motor running backwards, the wheels are slowed.
- At the same time, the motor acts as an electric generator, converting kinetic energy into electrical energy that is stored as chemical energy in the vehicle's battery. This is the advantage of regenerative brakes — they store the energy of braking rather than wasting it. It's a nifty chain of energy transfer.

Tip: Regenerative braking systems can work in other ways too — the kinetic energy can be transferred to a flywheel or stored as electrical energy in a bank of capacitors.

Car crashes and energy transfer

If a car crashes it will slow down very quickly — this means that a lot of kinetic energy is converted into other forms of energy in a short amount of time, which can be dangerous for the people inside. In a crash, there'll be a big change in momentum (see p.243) over a very short time, so the people inside the car experience huge forces that could be fatal.

Cars are designed to convert the kinetic energy of the car and its passengers in a way that is safest for the car's occupants. They often do this by increasing the time over which momentum changes happen, which lessens the forces on the passengers.

Crumple zones

Crumple zones at the front and back of the car crumple up on impact. The car's kinetic energy is converted into other forms of energy by the car body as it changes shape. Crumple zones increase the impact time, decreasing the force produced by the change in momentum.

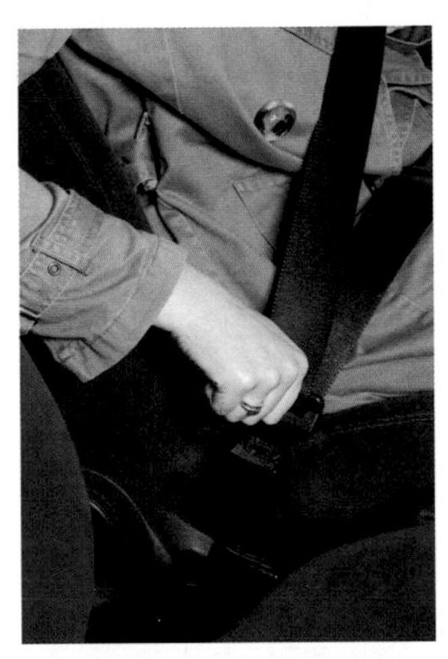

Figure 3: *A seat belt. They decrease the rate of change of momentum of a passenger in a crash.*

Side impact bars

Side impact bars are strong metal tubes fitted into car door panels. They help direct the kinetic energy of the crash away from the passengers to other areas of the car, such as the crumple zones.

Seat belts

Seat belts stop the wearer from hitting hard surfaces in the car or being thrown out through the windscreen. They also stretch slightly, increasing the time taken for the wearer to stop, which reduces the forces acting on the chest. Some of the kinetic energy of the wearer is absorbed by the seat belt stretching.

Figure 4: *An inflated air bag in a car. In a crash, the air bag inflates to act as a 'cushion'.*

Air bags

Air bags also slow you down more gradually and prevent you from hitting hard surfaces inside the car.

Practice Questions — Fact Recall

Q1 What are regenerative brakes?

Q2 Name four different safety features found in cars and explain how they reduce the risk of injury for passengers.

Section Checklist — Make sure you know...

Work and Potential Energy

- ☐ That work is done (and energy is transferred) when a force moves an object through a distance.
- ☐ How to use the formula $W = F \times d$.
- ☐ That an object has gravitational potential energy due to its vertical position in a gravitational field.
- ☐ How to use the formula $E_p = m \times g \times h$.

Kinetic Energy

- ☐ That a moving object has kinetic energy and you can calculate how much it has using the formula $E_k = ½ \times m \times v^2$.
- ☐ That when work is done by friction to slow down an object, kinetic energy is transferred into heat (and sound) energy and that the work done to stop an object is equal to its initial kinetic energy.
- ☐ That gravitational potential energy is transferred to kinetic energy when an object falls.
- ☐ How to interpret the transfer of kinetic energy in given situations e.g. objects entering the atmosphere.

Power

- ☐ That power is the rate of doing work and can be calculated using the formula $P = \frac{E}{t}$.
- ☐ That power is measured in watts, where 1 watt = 1 J/s.

Momentum and Collisions

- ☐ That moving objects have momentum that depends on their mass and velocity.
- ☐ How to calculate the momentum of an object, including its direction, using the formula $p = m \times v$.
- ☐ That the principle of conservation of momentum states that in a closed system, the total momentum before an event is the same as after the event.

Car Design and Safety

- ☐ That normal brakes reduce kinetic energy by transferring it to heat.
- ☐ That regenerative brakes reduce kinetic energy by transferring it to electrical energy that's stored in the vehicle's battery as chemical energy.
- ☐ That crumple zones in a vehicle are designed to crumple on impact, decreasing the force caused by the change in momentum.
- ☐ That side impact bars direct kinetic energy away from car passengers in a crash, reducing the force on them.
- ☐ That seat belts reduce forces on the wearers in a crash by increasing the time taken for them to stop, as well as preventing them from hitting hard surfaces in the car or being thrown out through the windscreen.
- ☐ That air bags inflate during a crash to act as a cushion, increasing the time a passenger takes to stop.

Exam-style Questions

1 A 1540 kg car is travelling at 10 m/s.

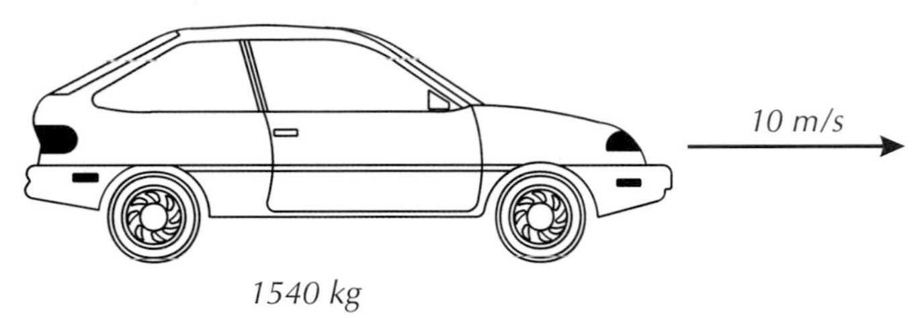

1 (a) The car has a driving force of 3000 N.
How much work is done by the car when it travels 500 m?
Use the correct equation from the equations listed on page 402.
Clearly show how you work out your answer. Give your answer in joules.

(2 marks)

1 (b) Calculate the momentum of the car.
Use the correct equation from the equations listed on page 402.
Clearly show how you work out your answer.

(3 marks)

1 (c) A pedestrian steps into the path of the car.
The driver applies the brakes to bring the car to a sudden stop.

1 (c) (i) How does the kinetic energy of the car change when the brakes are applied?

(1 mark)

1 (c) (ii) The car's brakes heat up as the car slows down.
Explain why this happens.

(1 mark)

1 (c) (iii) How much work is done by the brakes in bringing the car to a stop?
Use the correct equation from the equations listed on page 402.
Clearly show how you work out your answer.

(3 marks)

1 (d) The car has several safety features, including seat belts.

Seat belts prevent the wearer from hitting hard surfaces or being thrown out of the car. Explain how else the car's seat belts reduce the risk of injury to the driver and passengers when the car comes to a sudden stop.

(4 marks)

2 Zaf has a mass of 85 kg. He runs up some stairs carrying a 10 kg box.

2 (a) The staircase is 12 m high and it takes Zaf 18 s to reach the top.

2 (a) (i) How much gravitational potential energy have Zaf and the box gained when he reaches the top of the stairs?

Use the correct equation from the equations listed on page 402.

Clearly show how you work out your answer. Give your answer in joules.

(2 marks)

2 (a) (ii) What is Zaf's power output when he runs up the stairs?

Use the correct equation from the equations listed on page 402.

Clearly show how you work out your answer.

Give your answer in watts to an appropriate number of significant figures.

(3 marks)

2 (b) At the top of the stairs Zaf walks along the corridor, still carrying the box.

Calculate Zaf's velocity if he has 153.9 J of kinetic energy.

Use the correct equation from the equations listed on page 402.

Clearly show how you work out your answer. Give your answer in m/s.

(2 marks)

3 A white snooker ball collides with a stationary blue snooker ball. Both balls have a mass of 0.16 kg. Before the collision, the white ball moves to the right at 0.5 m/s.

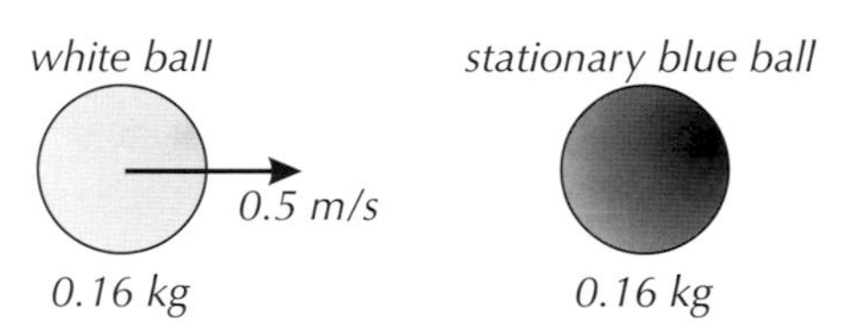

After the collision, the white ball moves right at 0.1 m/s.

3 (a) What is meant by the conservation of momentum?

(1 mark)

3 (b) Calculate the total momentum of the system before the collision.

Use the correct equation from the equations listed on page 402.

Clearly show how you work out your answer. Give your answer in kg m/s.

(3 marks)

3 (c) What is the velocity of the blue ball after the collision?

Use the correct equation from the equations listed on page 402.

Clearly show how you work out your answer. Give your answer in m/s.

(4 marks)

1. Static Electricity

This section is all about electric circuits (yawn) — but don't get your pillow out just yet. Static electricity is the cause of all sorts of fun and games and you get the pleasure of learning all about it — joy.

Learning Objectives:

- Know that some substances are conductors, which electrical charges can move easily through, e.g. metals.
- Know that rubbing together certain insulating materials can cause negatively charged electrons to be transferred from one material to the other. The material that loses electrons will become positively charged. The material that gains the electrons will have an equal but negative charge.
- Know that two electrically charged materials will exert a force on each other when brought close together.
- Know that objects with opposite charges attract and objects with the same type of charge will repel each other.

Specification Reference P2.3.1

Insulators and conductors

Electrical charges can move easily through some materials, and less easily through others.

- If electrical charges can easily move through a material, it is called an electrical **conductor**. Metals are known to be good conductors.
- If electrical charges cannot easily move through a material, it is called an electrical **insulator**. Plastics and rubbers are usually good insulators.

Example

Electrical wires and cables are usually made up of both electrical insulators and conductors.

- They have a core made out of an electrical conductor so that electric charge can flow through it easily.
- They also have a casing made of an electrical insulator to stop you getting an electric shock by touching the wire or cable.

Figure 1: *An electrical cable. The core is made from copper (left) and the casing is made from two types of rubber (right).*

Static charge

A **static charge** is an electric charge which cannot move. They're often (but not always) found in electrical insulators where charge cannot flow freely. They can be positive (+ve) or negative (–ve).

When certain insulating materials are rubbed together, negatively charged electrons will be scraped off one and dumped on the other.

This will leave a positive static charge on the one that loses electrons and a negative static charge on the one that gains electrons. Which way the electrons are transferred depends on the two materials involved — see the example on the next page.

Tip: A static charge can build up in a conductor if it's isolated, i.e. if there's nowhere for the charge to flow to.

Tip: +ve means positive and –ve means negative — you might see these abbreviations used sometimes.

Both positive and negative static charges are only ever produced by the movement of electrons. The positive charges definitely do not move.

A positive static charge is always caused by electrons moving away elsewhere. The material that loses the electrons loses some negative charge, and is left with an equal positive charge.

Tip: Polythene and acetate are types of plastic. They're electrical insulators.

Examples

The classic examples of static build up are polythene and acetate rods being rubbed with a cloth duster.

- With the polythene rod, electrons move from the duster to the rod. The rod becomes negatively charged and the cloth has an equal positive charge.

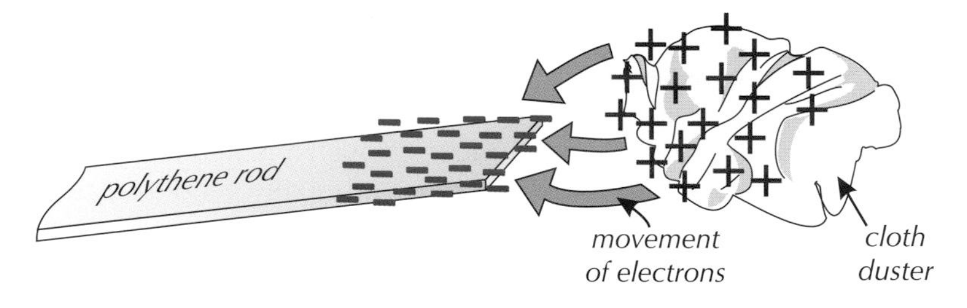

Figure 2: *A polythene rod being rubbed with a cloth duster to create static charge.*

- With the acetate rod, electrons move from the rod to the duster. The rod becomes positively charged and the cloth has an equal negative charge.

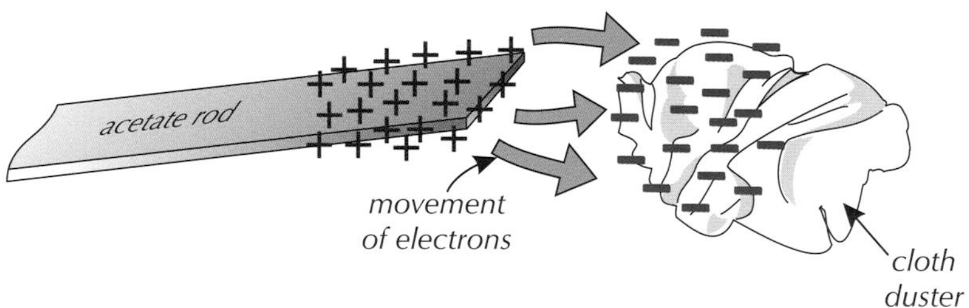

Figure 3: *An acetate rod being rubbed with a cloth duster to create static charge.*

When two electrically charged objects are brought close together they exert a force on one another (see Figure 4 on the next page). These forces get weaker the further apart the two things are.

- Two things with opposite electric charges are attracted to each other.
- Two things with the same electric charge will repel each other.

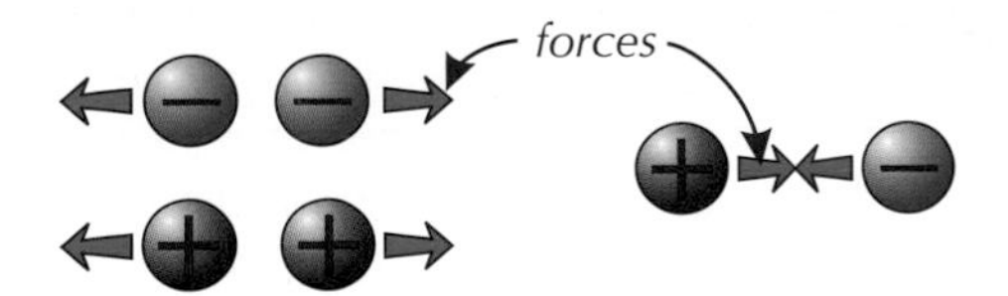

Figure 4: *A diagram showing the forces that different electric charges exert on one another.*

Practice Questions — Fact Recall

Q1 What is an electrical conductor? Give an example of one.

Q2 What causes some insulators to become positively charged when they are rubbed against another insulator?

Q3 Say whether the following objects will attract, repel, or feel no force when brought close together:

a) Two positively charged objects.

b) Two negatively charged objects.

c) A negatively charged object and a positively charged object.

Practice Question — Application

Q1 A woman uses a plastic hair brush to brush her hair. Both the hair brush and her hair become electrically charged.

a) When the woman looks in the mirror, her hairs are standing on end. Explain why.

b) The hairbrush has a charge of –0.5 nC. What is the total charge on the woman's hair?

Tip: Plastic and hair are both electrical insulators.

Tip: 1 nC = 1×10^{-9} C (it's short for nano-coulomb).

2. Circuit Basics

Now on to circuits. You've probably seen circuit symbols before, but there are quite a few that you need to know. So first things first, let's have a bit of circuit training...

Learning Objectives:

- Know the standard circuit symbols for the following components: cell, battery, switch (open and closed), lamp, ammeter, voltmeter, resistor, variable resistor, fuse, thermistor, diode, light-emitting diode (LED), light-dependant resistor (LDR).
- Be able to interpret and draw circuit diagrams.

Specification Reference P2.3.2

Circuit symbols

You need to know (and be able to draw) each of the following circuit symbols. You'll learn a bit more about some of them later in this section and the next.

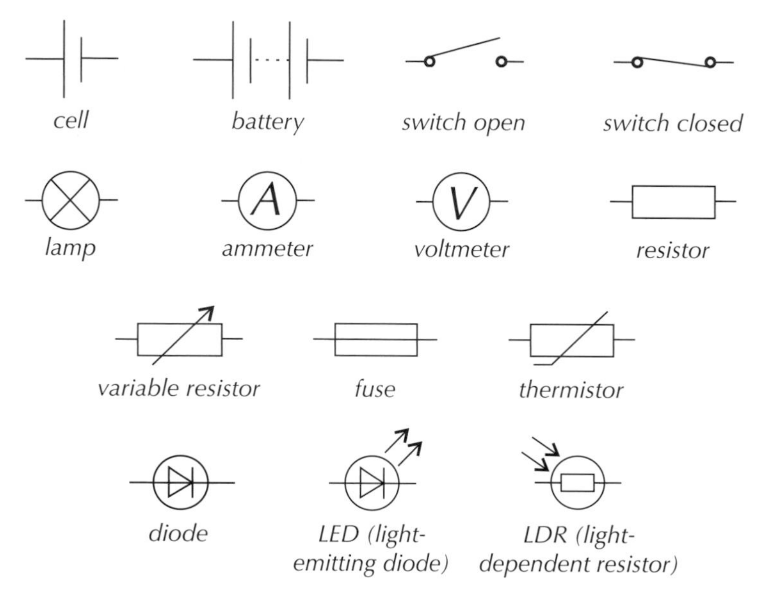

Figure 1: *Circuit symbols for a variety of circuit components.*

Tip: You might see cells or batteries drawn with the shorter line a bit 'fatter' than the longer one, like this: ⊣⊢

They both mean the same thing though.

Tip: Wires are just represented by straight lines.

Circuit diagrams

You might be asked to draw a circuit, or to find a problem with one.

One thing to make sure of is that your circuit is complete. If component isn't connected in a circuit properly, it won't work.

A circuit is complete if you can follow a wire from one end of the battery (or other power supply), through any components to the other end of the battery — see Figure 2.

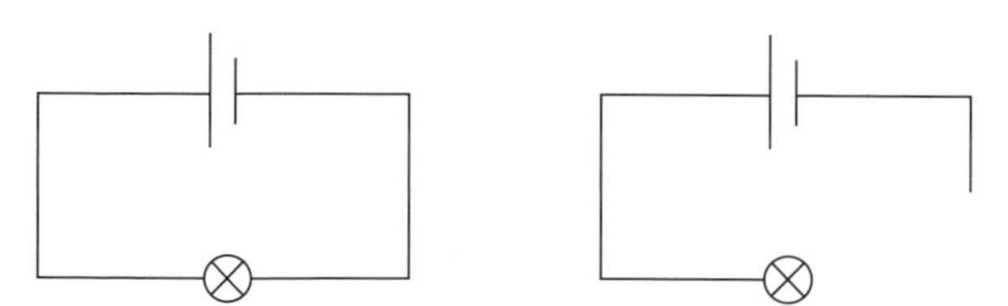

Figure 2: *(Left) A complete circuit. All the wires are joined to something at both ends and the lamp will light. (Right) An incomplete circuit. The lamp won't light.*

Tip: You can make a circuit incomplete on purpose by turning a switch to the off position. Switches allow you to turn circuits (and so components) on and off.

Voltmeters and ammeters

Voltmeters and ammeters always have to be connected in a circuit in a certain way, otherwise they won't do what they are meant to.

- A voltmeter is always connected 'across' a component — this is known as 'in parallel'.
- An ammeter is always connected 'in line' with a component — this is known as 'in series'.

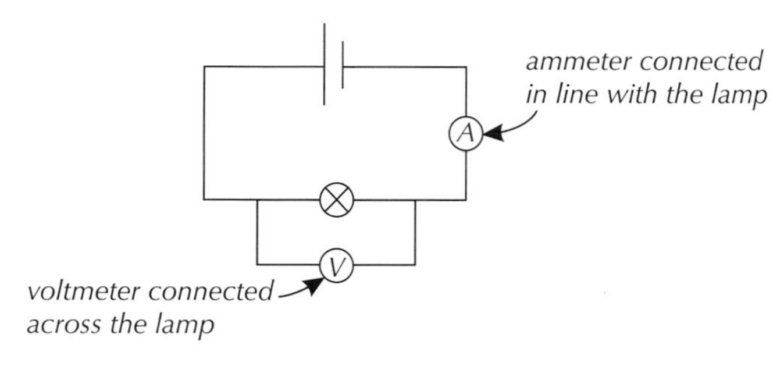

Figure 3: *A circuit with a voltmeter and an ammeter connected correctly.*

Tip: A voltmeter measures the voltage (potential difference) across a components and an ammeter measures the current through a component.

Tip: Head to pages 267-275 if you want to learn more about what 'in series' and 'in parallel' mean.

Practice Questions — Fact Recall

Q1 Draw the circuit symbol for a:

a) battery b) resistor c) fuse d) lamp e) diode

Q2 What is an incomplete circuit?

Practice Questions — Application

Q1 Draw a complete circuit containing a cell, a lamp, and an open switch which can be used to turn the lamp on and off.

Q2 Draw a complete circuit containing a battery, a resistor and a voltmeter measuring the voltage across the resistor.

Q3 Draw a circuit containing a cell, a thermistor and an ammeter.

Q4 In which of these circuits will the lamp be lit up?

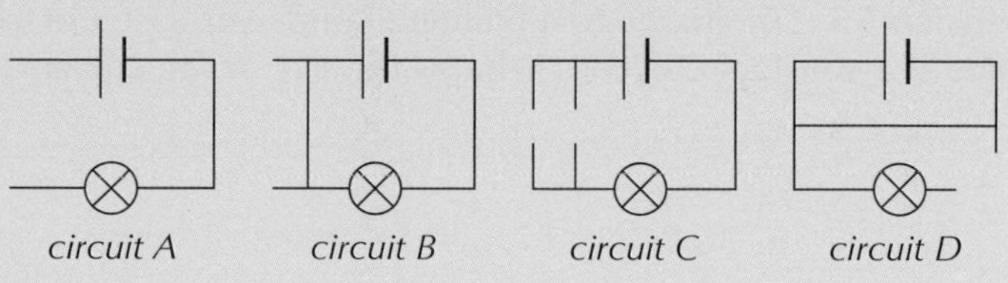

3. Current and Potential Difference

Current is just a flow of electrical charge in a circuit and potential difference is the thing that pushes it round. There are formulas for both which you'll need to practise using.

Learning Objectives:

- Know that the flow of electric charge is called electric current.
- Know that the rate of flow of electric charge is the size of an electric current.
- Know how to calculate electric current using the equation $I = Q \div t$.
- Know that potential difference (voltage) is the work done per coulomb of charge that passes between two points in an electric circuit.
- Know how to calculate potential difference using $V = W \div Q$.

Specification Reference P2.3.2

Current

An electric **current** is a flow of electric charge. Cells (and other power supplies) always have a positive terminal (the longer line), and a negative terminal (the shorter line). Current flows from positive to negative around a circuit.

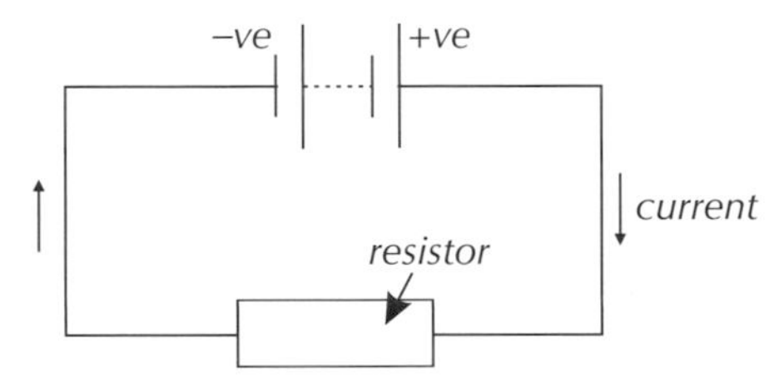

Figure 1: *Current flowing from positive to negative in an electric circuit.*

Tip: Confusingly, the electrons in a circuit actually flow from negative to positive. But when scientists realised this they never bothered to change the way that current was defined, so we still say it flows from positive to negative.

The size of the current is the rate of flow of charge. It's measured in amperes, A. When current flows past a point in a circuit for a length of time then the charge that has passed is given by this formula:

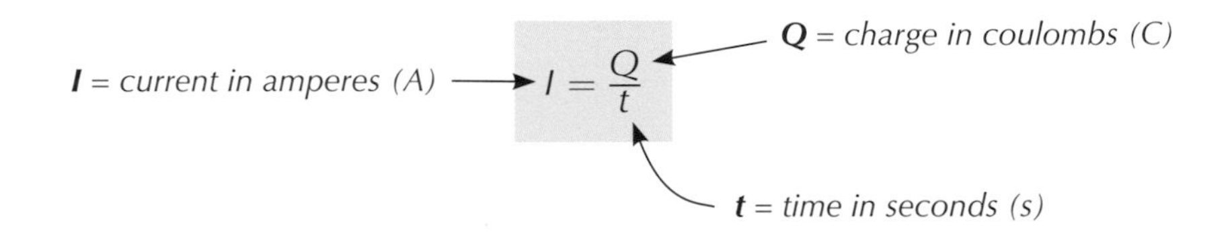

More charge passes around the circuit when a bigger current flows.

Figure 2: *The circuit symbol for an ammeter. An ammeter is used to measured the size of the current flowing in a circuit.* *See page 260 for more.*

Example

A cell transfers 75 C of charge to a filament lamp over a period of 60 seconds at a constant current. What is the size of the current?

$I = Q \div t$
$= 75 \div 60$
$= 1.25$ A

Example — Higher

A battery charger passes a current of 2.5 A through a cell over a period of 4 hours. How much charge does the charger transfer to the cell altogether?

You've got $I = 2.5$ A and $t = 4 \times 60 \times 60$ s $= 14\,400$ s. Rearrange the current formula ($I = Q \div t$) for Q and plug in the numbers.

$Q = I \times t = 2.5 \times 14\,400 = 36\,000$ C

Tip: H You can use a formula triangle to rearrange the equation for current. See page 352 for how to use formula triangles.

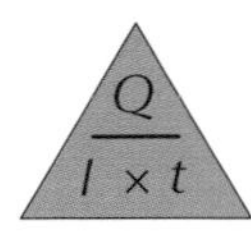

Potential difference

Current will only flow through a component if there is a **potential difference (p.d.)** across that component.

Potential difference (or **voltage**) is like the driving force that pushes the current round. It's the work done (the energy transferred, measured in joules, J) per coulomb of charge that passes between two points in an electrical circuit.

Potential difference is measured in volts, V, and is given by this formula:

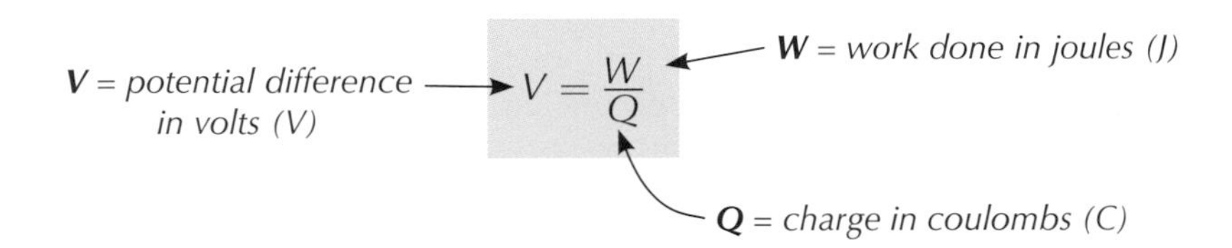

So, the potential difference across an electrical component is the amount of energy that is transferred by that electrical component (e.g. to light and heat energy by a lamp) per unit of charge supplied.

Tip: Voltage and potential difference (p.d.) mean the same thing. You can use either in your exam and scoop up the marks (so long as you use it correctly).

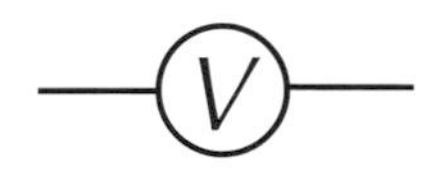

Figure 3: *The circuit symbol for a voltmeter. A voltmeter is used to measure the potential difference between two points in a circuit — that's why it's placed across a component. See page 260 for more.*

Example

It takes 720 kJ of energy to move a charge of 50 000 C through an electric motor. Calculate the potential difference across the motor.

$Q = 50\,000$ C and $W = 720$ kJ $= 720\,000$ J

So $V = W \div Q = 720\,000 \div 50\,000 = 14.4$ V

Tip: 1 kJ = 1000 J.

Tip: H You can use a formula triangle to rearrange the equation for potential difference.

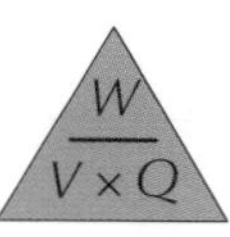

Exam Tip
If you're given a lot of data and you're not sure where to start, write down all the quantities you've got and what you want to find. Then have a look on the formula sheet for equations that link the quantities you've been given.

Example **Higher**

The potential difference across a lamp in a circuit is 2.3 V. The current in the circuit is 0.5 A. How much energy is transferred by the lamp if it is lit for 2 minutes?

Energy transferred is the same thing as work done — so you need W. Rearrange the equation for potential difference to get $W = V \times Q$.

But you've not been given the charge, Q — you need to work it out using the equation on page 256.

$Q = I \times t = 0.5 \times (2 \times 60) = 60$ C

Put this into the equation for work done (energy transferred):

$W = Q \times V = 60 \times 2.3 = 138$ J

Practice Questions — Fact Recall

Q1 What is electric current?

Q2 In what direction does current flow in a circuit?

Q3 What is the formula linking charge, current and time? Write down the units each quantity is measured in.

Q4 What is potential difference?

Q5 What is the formula linking potential difference, work done and charge? Write down the units each quantity is measured in.

Practice Questions — Application

Q1 A cell has a charge of 102 C passing through it every minute. Calculate the current flowing through the cell.

Q2 In a circuit, it takes 1440 J to transfer 60 C of charge through a component over 2 minutes.

a) What is the current through the component?

b) What is the potential difference across the component?

Q3 A small torch bulb is powered by a 6.00 V cell. The bulb transfers 315 J of electrical energy in 37.0 seconds. Calculate the current through the bulb.

4. Resistance

Resistance is just how much a component in a circuit slows down the flow of current. It's different for each component, and it's related to the size of the current and the potential difference.

Learning Objectives:

- Know that the current through a component depends on its resistance.
- Understand and be able to use the equation: $V = I \times R$.
- Know how a circuit can be used to find the resistance of a component by measuring the current through it and the p.d. across it.
- Know that *I-V* graphs show how the current through a component varies with the p.d.
- Know that for a resistor at a constant temperature, the current through it is proportional to the p.d. across it and it produces a straight-line *I-V* graph.
- Know that the resistance of a filament lamp increases as the temperature of the filament increases.
- Know the shape of an *I-V* graph for a filament lamp.
- **H** Be able to explain the varying resistance of a filament lamp in terms of ions and electrons.

Specification Reference P2.3.2

Resistance

Resistance is anything in the circuit which reduces the flow of current. It is measured in ohms, Ω. The greater the resistance of a component, the smaller the current that flows (for a given potential difference across the component).

The resistance of a component is linked to potential difference across it and current through it by the following formula (Ohm's law):

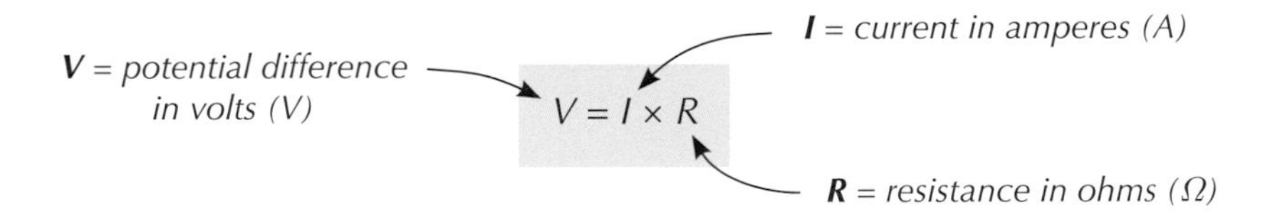

Example

The ammeter in the circuit shown reads 3.4 A and the resistance of the resistor is 5.6 Ω. What is the p.d. across the resistor?

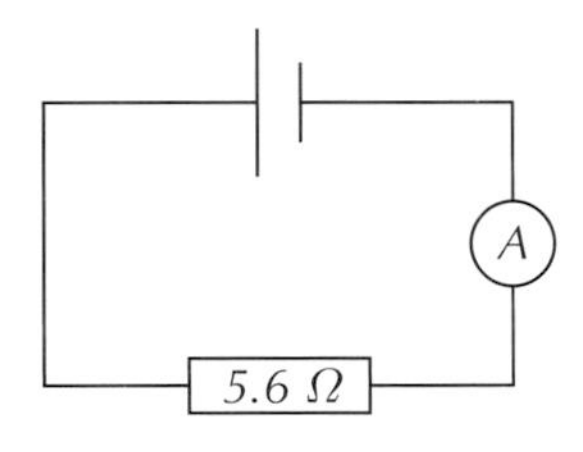

$V = I \times R = 3.4 \times 5.6 = 19$ V (to 2 s.f.)

Example **Higher**

Voltmeter *V* reads 6 V and resistor *R* is 4 Ω. What is the current through ammeter *A*?

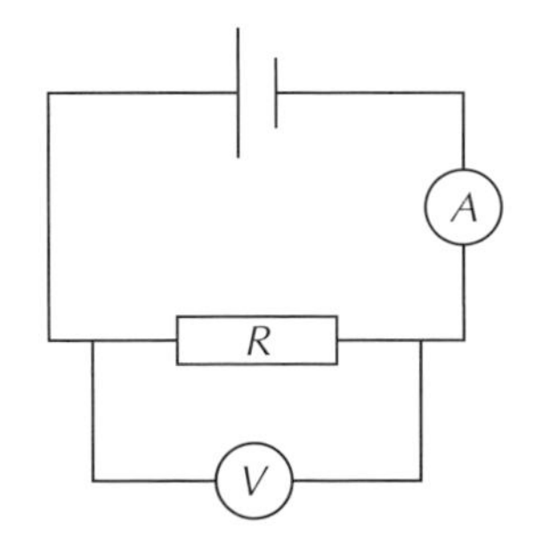

Use the formula triangle for $V = I \times R$.
We need to find *I*, so the version we need is $I = V \div R$.

$I = V \div R = 6 \div 4 = 1.5$ A

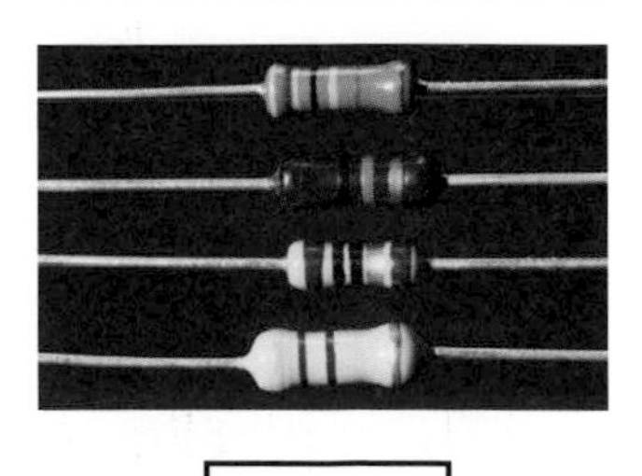

Figure 1: *Different sized resistors (top) and the resistor circuit symbol (bottom).*

Investigating resistance

This is the circuit you use if you want to know the resistance of a component. You find the resistance by measuring the current through and the potential difference across the component.

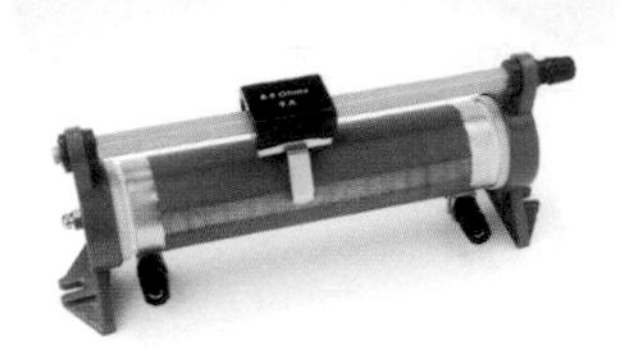

Figure 2: A type of variable resistor. They can be used to control the amount of current flowing through a circuit.

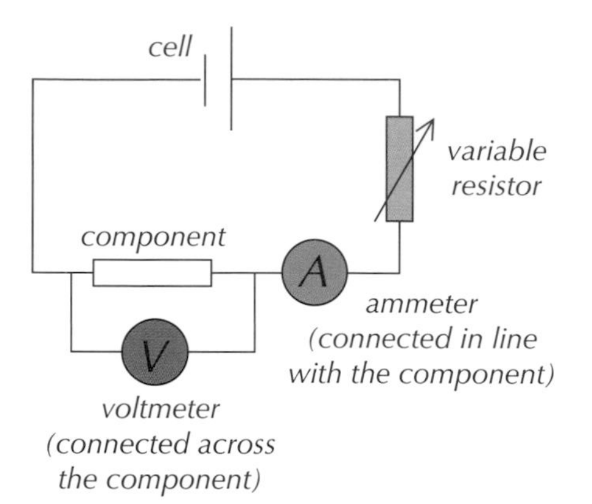

Figure 3: A circuit diagram for the standard test circuit, used to find out the resistance of a component.

Tip: You'll learn more about the different ways components can be connected in circuits on pages 267-275.

The component, the ammeter and the variable resistor are all connected in series (in a line) and they can be put in any order in the main circuit. The voltmeter must be placed in parallel with (across) the component under test — see Figure 3. Anywhere else is a definite no-no.

Tip: You should take a sensible number of measurements — enough so you can plot a graph (see below) and be able to spot a pattern.

As you vary the resistance of the variable resistor it alters the current flowing through the circuit. This allows you to take several pairs of readings from the ammeter and voltmeter. You can then plot these values for current and potential difference on a graph and find the resistance — see below.

To get readings for negative values of potential difference, you should switch the way the wires are connected to the power source and repeat. The current will flow in the opposite direction through the component, giving negative values of potential difference and current.

Current-potential difference graphs

Current-potential difference (I-V) graphs show how the current varies as you change the potential difference. The inverse of the gradient (p.202) of the graph at a certain point gives the resistance of the component.

Tip: H The gradient of an I-V graph is $I \div V$. If you rearrange $V = I \times R$ you see that $R = V \div I$ $= 1 \div$ gradient.

This means resistance = 1 ÷ gradient. In other words, the steeper the graph the lower the resistance. For a straight-line graph, the gradient of the line is constant, so the resistance of the component is steady. If the graph curves, it means the resistance is changing.

If you're calculating the resistance at a point from an I-V graph you don't actually need to calculate the gradient. Just pick any point on the graph — the potential difference divided by the current at that point gives you the resistance. If it's a straight-line graph, every point will give you the same value for resistance.

You need to know the I-V graphs for a resistor and a lamp as well as a diode (given on page 263).

Different resistors

The current through a resistor (at constant temperature) is directly proportional to potential difference. Different resistors have different resistances, and hence slopes of different gradients — see Figure 5.

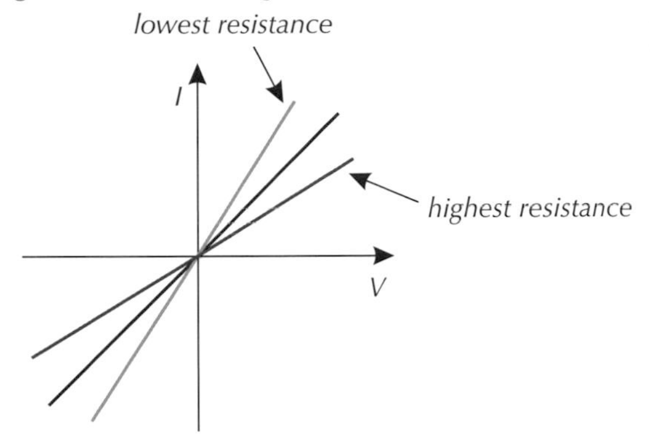

Figure 5: I-V graphs for resistors with different resistances. The resistance is 1 ÷ gradient for each I-V graph.

Figure 4: A circuit board containing resistors. Resistors are used in almost all circuits to control the flow of current and prevent things from overheating.

Tip: Remember, the steeper the gradient, the lower the resistance.

Filament lamp

A filament lamp contains a filament, which is designed to get hot and glow. As more current flows through the lamp, the temperature of the filament increases which causes the resistance to increase, hence the curve.

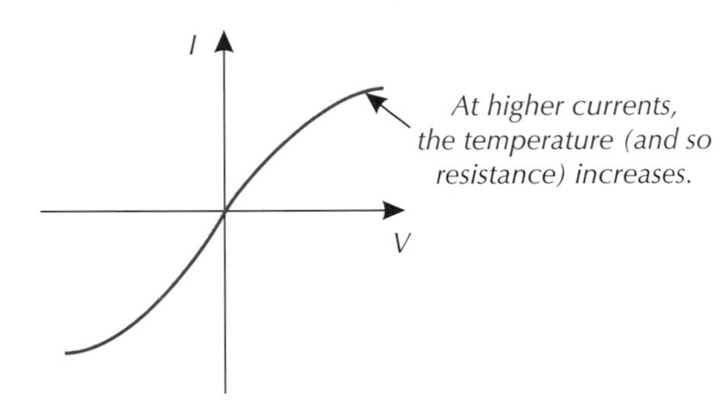

Figure 6: An I-V graph for a filament lamp. It's curved because the resistance is changing.

Temperature effects on resistance Higher

When an electrical charge flows through a component with resistance, some of the electrical energy is transferred to heat energy and the component gets hot.

This heat energy causes the ions in the conductor to vibrate more. With the ions jiggling around it's more difficult for the charge-carrying electrons to get through the component — the current can't flow as easily and the resistance increases.

For most components there is a limit to the amount of current that can flow. More current means an increase in temperature, which means an increase in resistance, which means the current decreases again.

This is why the graph for the filament lamp levels off at high currents (see Figure 6).

Practice Questions — Fact Recall

Q1 What is resistance? What unit is resistance measured in?

Q2 Write down the equation linking resistance, potential difference and current.

Q3 Draw a circuit diagram of a circuit you could use to test the resistance of a component.

Q4 How do you find the resistance of a resistor at a constant temperature from its *I*-*V* graph?

Q5 Sketch an *I*-*V* graph for:

a) a resistor at a constant temperature b) a filament lamp

Q6 Explain, in terms of ions and electrons, why the resistance of a filament lamp increases as the temperature of the filament increases.

Practice Questions — Application

Q1 A current of 0.015 A is flowing through a 2.0 Ω resistor. What is the potential difference across the resistor?

Q2 A current of 0.6 A flows through an electric motor. The potential difference across the motor is 14.4 V. Calculate the resistance of the motor.

Q3 The graph below shows the *I*-*V* graph of a resistor at a constant temperature. Calculate its resistance.

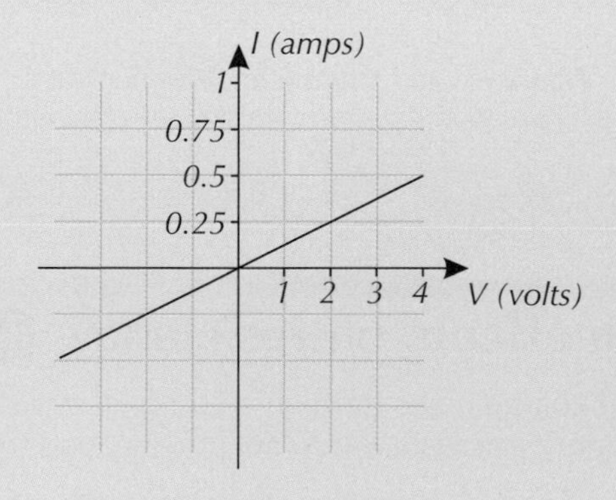

5. Diodes and LEDs

Diodes and LEDs work differently depending on the direction in which you connect them in the circuit. This can be very useful in electronics.

Learning Objectives:

- Know that current only flows in the forward direction through a diode.
- Know that the resistance of a diode in the reverse direction is very high.
- Know the shape of the *I-V* graph for a diode.
- Know that a light-emitting diode (LED) is a type of diode that emits light when a current flows through it in the forward direction.
- Understand the reasons behind LEDs being used increasingly as a form of lighting, including their energy and cost efficiency.

Specification Reference P2.3.2

Diodes

A diode lets current flow freely through it in one direction (the forward direction), but not in the other (the reverse direction). This is because it has a very high resistance in the reverse direction.

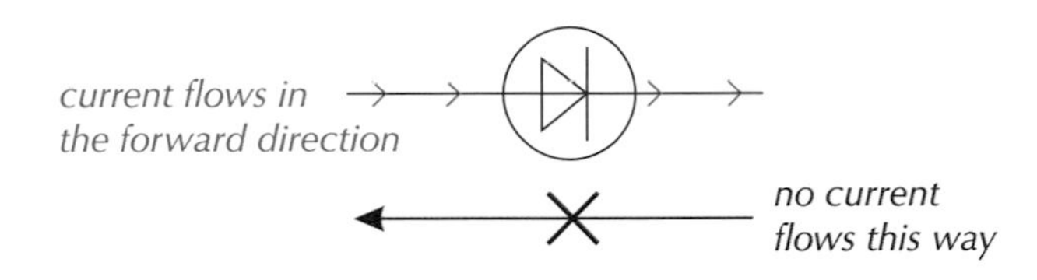

Figure 1: *A diagram illustrating which way current is able to flow in a diode.*

You need to know the *I-V* graph (p.260) for a diode — it looks like this:

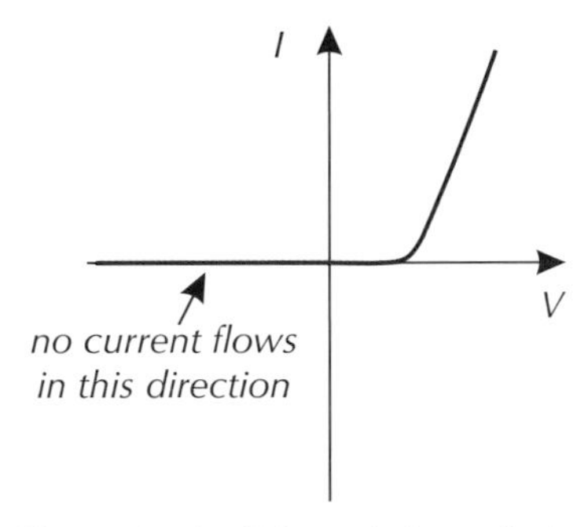

Figure 2: *An I-V graph for a diode. Current only flows in one direction.*

Tip: The ⊳| part of the circuit symbol for a diode is like an arrow pointing in the forward direction. Current can only flow in the direction of the arrow.

Light-emitting diodes (LEDs)

A light-emitting diode (LED) emits light when a current flows through it in the forward direction. LEDs indicate the presence of current in a circuit.

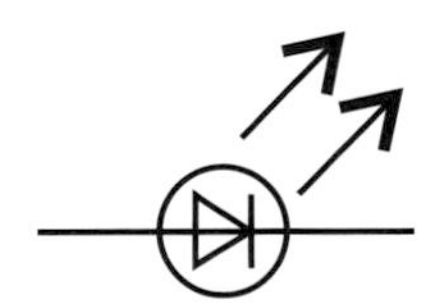

Figure 3: *The circuit symbol for an LED.*

LEDs are being used more and more for lighting, as they have several advantages over filament bulbs.

- LEDs have a much longer lifetime than filament bulbs (there's no filament to burn out).
- LEDs are more energy efficient that filament bulbs — this means that they waste less energy as heat, so more energy is transferred to useful (light) energy.
- LEDs use a much smaller current to operate (and waste less energy), so they are cheaper to run and more cost effective.

Figure 4: *LED light bulbs.*

However, there are still some disadvantages:

- They are more expensive to buy than filament bulbs.
- You often need multiple LEDs to provide the same amount of light as a filament bulb.

LEDs have many other uses in all sorts of technology:

Figure 5: *A pill camera illuminated by LEDs. The camera can be swallowed and the LEDs illuminate inside the body.*

Examples

- In appliances (e.g. TVs), LEDs are used to show that they are switched on.
- In remote controls, an LED will light up when you press a button.
- In medicine, LEDs are used for illumination in a pill camera (a camera that you swallow — see Figure 5).
- In LED TVs as a backlight to the picture on the screen.
- And many more, including traffic lights, car brake lights and digital clocks.

Practice Questions — Fact Recall

Q1 Describe how the resistance of a diode changes as the current through it increases in:

a) the forwards direction. b) the backwards direction.

Q2 Sketch an *I-V* graph for a diode.

Q3 What does a light-emitting diode (LED) do when current flows through it in the forward direction?

Q4 Give one application of an LED.

Practice Questions — Application

Tip: Head back to page 256 if you need a reminder of the direction in which current travels in a circuit.

Q1 Will the LED light up in the circuit shown? Explain your answer.

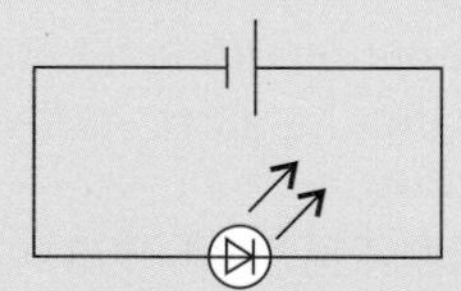

Q2 A student tests component A using a standard test circuit and plots this graph of his data. What would you expect component A to be?

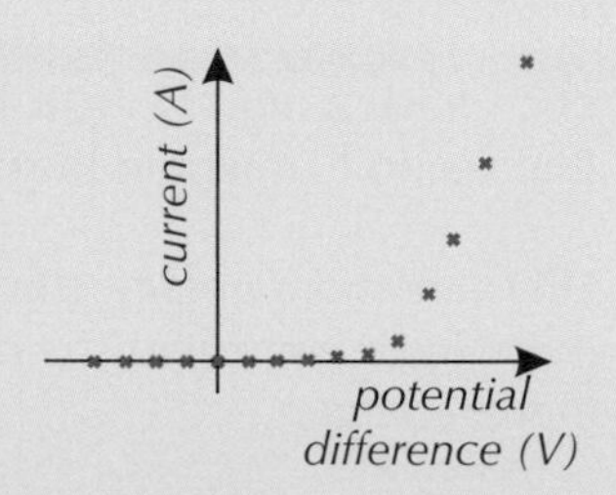

Q3 Evaluate whether it is better to use an LED or a filament bulb for the standby light of a digital radio.

6. LDRs and Thermistors

You've just got two more circuit devices to learn about in this section — LDRs and thermistors...

Learning Objectives:
- Know that for a light-dependent resistor (LDR), the resistance decreases as the light intensity increases.
- Know that LDRs can be used to switch on lights when it gets dark.
- Know that for a thermistor, the resistance decreases as the temperature increases.
- Know that thermistors can be used in thermostats.

Specification Reference P2.3.2

Light-dependent resistors (LDRs)

An LDR is a resistor that is dependent on the intensity of light. Simple really.

- In bright light, the resistance falls (see Figure 1).
- In darkness, the resistance is highest.

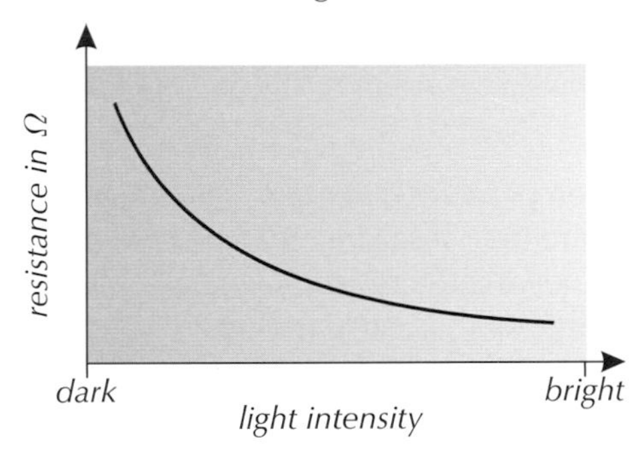

Figure 1: *A graph of resistance against light intensity for a light-dependent resistor (LDR).*

LDRs can be used where a function depends on light levels, e.g. when you want a component to only work in the dark.

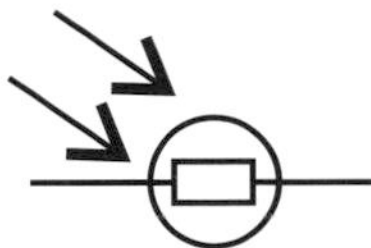

Figure 2: *An LDR (top) and its circuit symbol (bottom).*

Examples

- Automatic night lights and outdoor lighting such as street lights use LDRs. When the light level falls, the resistance of the LDR increases to a level that triggers the light to turn on.
- Some burglar detectors use LDRs too. A light beam is shone at an LDR. If someone walks in front of it and breaks the light beam, the resistance of the LDR shoots up and an alarm is triggered.

Figure 3: *Automatic street lighting on a motorway.*

Thermistors

Thermistors are another type of resistor — their resistance depends on their temperature. You only need to know about NTC (Negative Temperature Coefficient) thermistors. An NTC thermistor's resistance decreases as the temperature increases.

Tip: You'll mostly see NTC thermistors just called 'thermistors' because you don't need to know about any other types.

- In hot conditions, the resistance drops (see Figure 5).
- In cool conditions, the resistance goes up.

Figure 4: *The circuit symbol for a thermistor.*

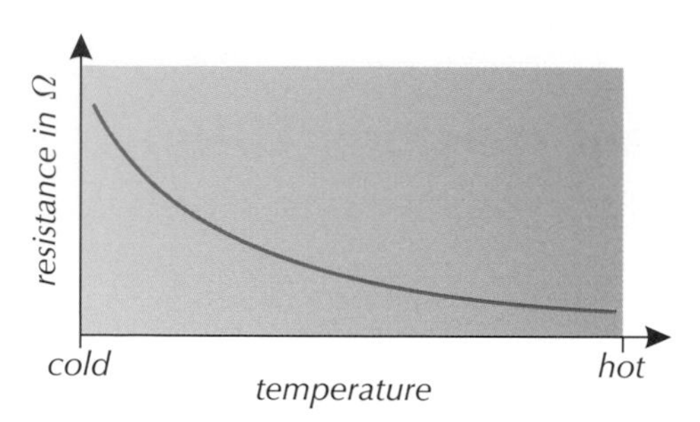

Figure 5: *A graph of resistance against temperature for an NTC thermistor.*

Thermistors are useful in temperature detectors called thermostats. They are connected in a circuit where their resistance can be measured. As resistance varies with temperature, knowing the resistance means you can detect the temperature of the thermistor (and its surroundings).

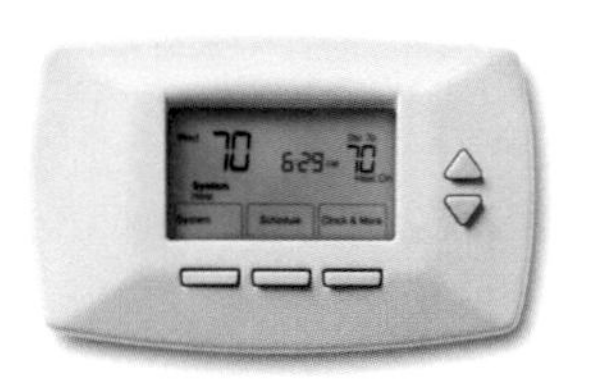

Figure 6: *A digital thermostat from a heating system. You might have a thermostat in your house somewhere to control your heating system.*

Example

Thermostats can be used in car engine temperature sensors to make sure the engine isn't overheating.

Practice Questions — Fact Recall

Q1 Sketch a graph of resistance against light intensity for an LDR.

Q2 How can you lower the resistance of a thermistor?

Q3 Give one application of:

a) LDRs b) thermistors

Practice Question — Application

Q1 The circuit shown forms part of a burglar alarm. The ohmmeter measures the resistance of the component it is connected to. The circuit is connected to another circuit containing an alarm — if the resistance rises above a certain level, the alarm is sounded.

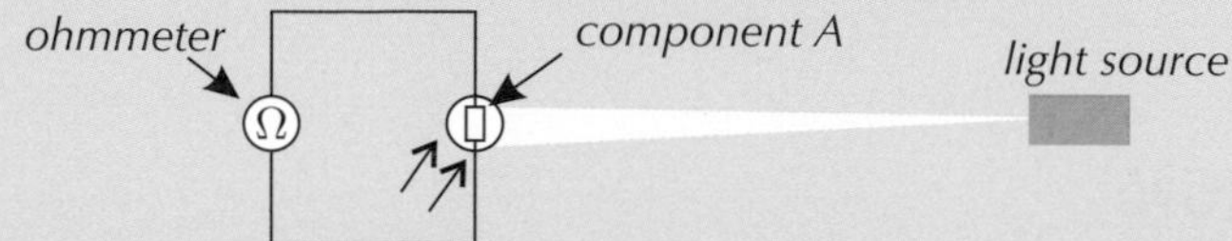

a) What is component A?

b) A cat passes through the beam of light. Explain why this causes the alarm to sound.

7. Series Circuits

So you're a circuit components whizz... know everything there is to know... but how are you going connect them? Components can either be connected in series or parallel. First up, series circuits — they're basically just big loops.

Learning Objectives:

- Know that the potential difference of multiple cells connected in series and in the same direction is the sum of the potential differences of each cell.
- Know that the potential difference of a power supply is shared across all of the components connected in series with it.
- Know that the same current flows through all components connected in series.
- Know that the total resistance in a series circuit is the sum of the resistances of all the components in it.

Specification Reference P2.3.2

Components in series

In **series circuits**, the different components are connected in a line, end to end, between the positive and negative ends of the power supply (except for voltmeters, which are always connected across a component — see page 255).

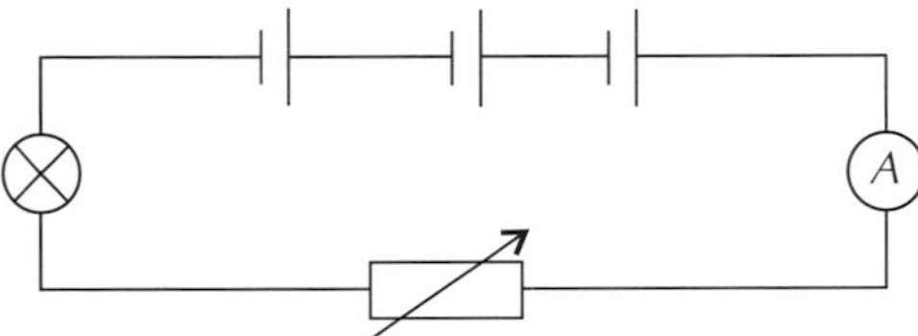

Figure 1: *A circuit in which each component is connected in series — you can draw a single line that travels along the wires and passes through every component once before returning to your starting point.*

If you remove or disconnect one component, the circuit is broken and they all stop. This is generally not very handy, and in practice very few things are connected in series — but you need to know all the details anyway.

Potential difference in series circuits

There is a bigger potential difference (p.d.) when more cells are connected in series, provided the cells are all connected the same way.

You just add up all the individual cell p.d.s to find the total power source p.d.

Tip: Ammeters are always connected in series with the components that they are measuring the current through — even if the circuit is not a series circuit (p.255).

Example

One 12 V cell will provide a circuit potential difference of 12 V, but two 12 V cells connected in series (in the same direction) will provide a potential difference of 24 V across the circuit.

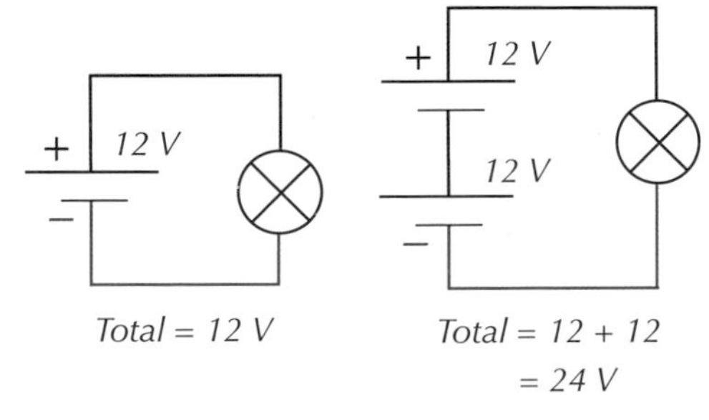

Figure 2: *A diagram showing the total circuit potential difference in a series circuit with one 12 V cell (left) and a series circuit with two 12 V cells connected in the same direction (right).*

> **Tip:** Remember, potential difference and voltage are the same thing.

In series circuits the total potential difference of the supply is shared between the various components. So the potential differences round a series circuit always add up to equal the source potential difference. If two or more components are the same, the p.d. across them will also be the same.

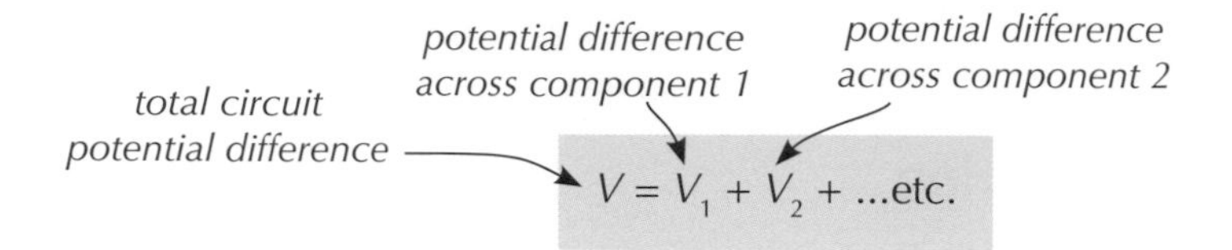

Example 1

In the diagram, two cells and two lamps are connected in series. The total potential difference across the circuit is the sum of the p.d.s of the two batteries, so:

$$V = 1.5\ \text{V} + 1.5\ \text{V} = 3.0\ \text{V}$$

The potential differences, V_1 and V_2, of the two lamps add up to 3.0 V:

$$V = V_1 + V_2 = 3.0\ \text{V}$$

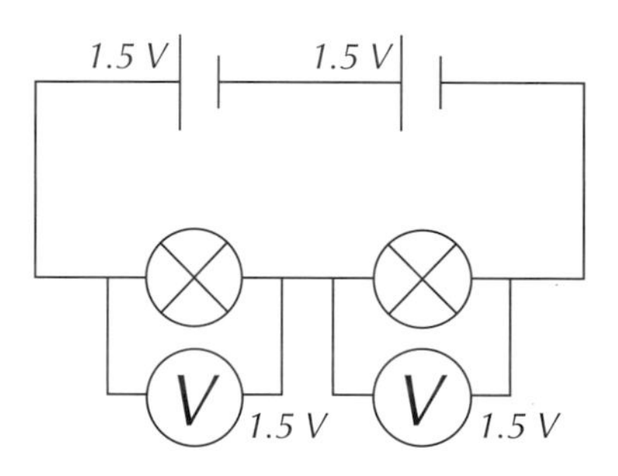

Figure 3: *A circuit diagram containing two cells and two identical lamps connected in series. The potential difference from the cells is split evenly across the lamps.*

> **Tip:** Remember, voltmeters are always connected across the component they are measuring.

Example 2

Christmas fairy lights are about the only real-life example of things that are sometimes connected in series, and we all know what a pain they are when the whole lot go out just because one of the bulbs is faulty.

The only advantage is that the bulbs can be very small because the total 230 V (from the mains) is shared out between them, so each bulb only has a small potential difference across it (roughly 12 V for a set of 20 bulbs).

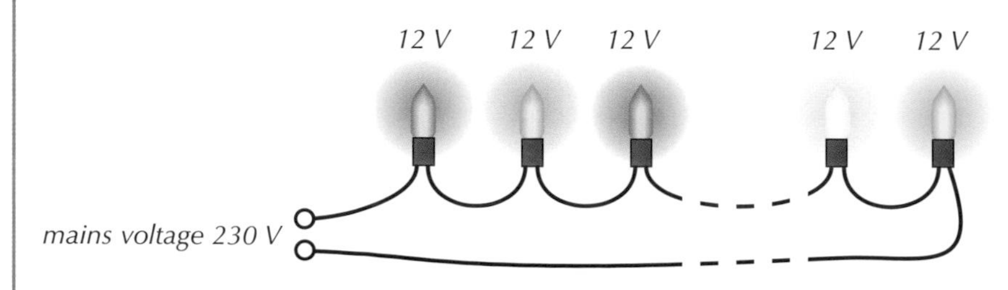

Figure 4: *Fairy lights connected in series. The lights form part of a set of 20 lights, so the potential difference across each one is only about 12 V, i.e. $\frac{1}{20}$ of the mains voltage (230 V).*

> **Tip:** A lot of fairy lights are actually part of a parallel circuit (page 272) these days — they have an adapter that brings the voltage down, so the lights can still be diddy but it doesn't matter if one of them blows.

Current in series circuits

In series circuits the same current flows through all parts of the circuit:

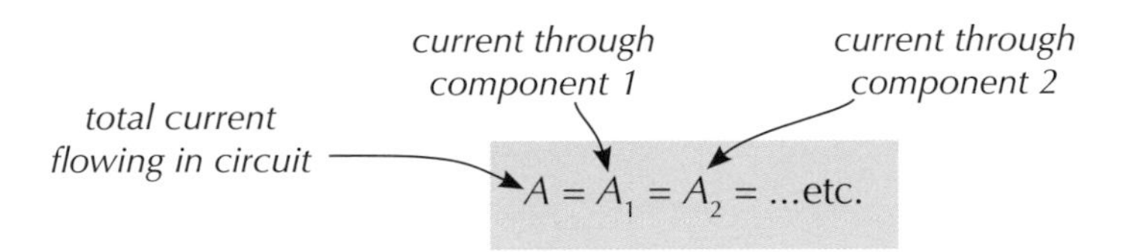

The size of the current is determined by the total potential difference of the cells and the total resistance of the circuit, using the equation $V = I \times R$ (from page 259).

Tip: This is why ammeters must be connected in series — so that the same current flows through the ammeter and the component that you want to measure the current through.

Example

In the diagram, two lamps are connected in series. The current through each lamp (and in fact the whole circuit) is exactly the same.

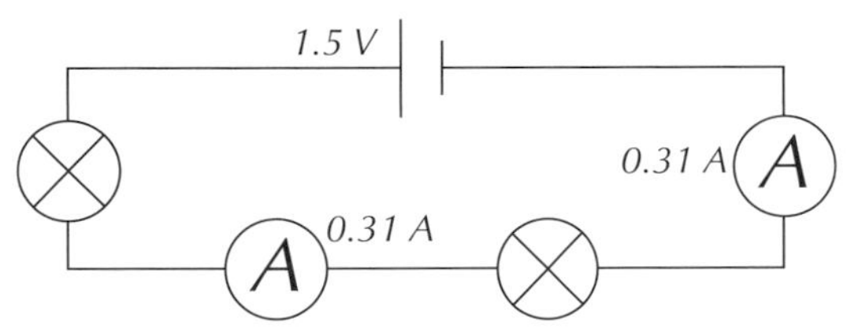

Figure 5: *A series circuit containing two lamps and two ammeters, showing that the current is the same throughout the circuit.*

Resistance in series circuits

In series circuits the total resistance is just the sum of all the resistances:

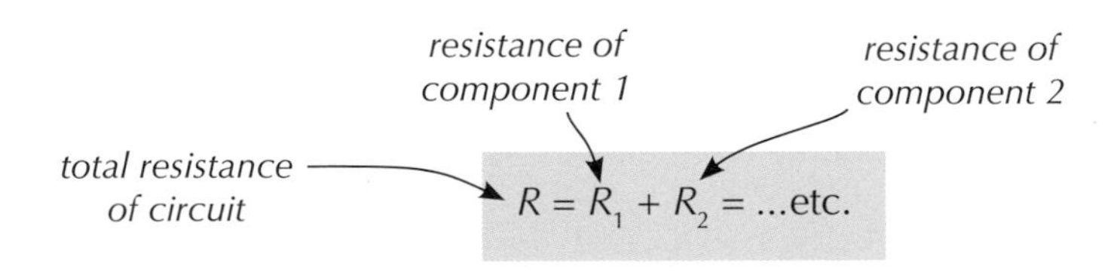

The bigger the resistance of a component, the bigger its share of the total potential difference.

Example 1

Find the total resistance of this circuit.

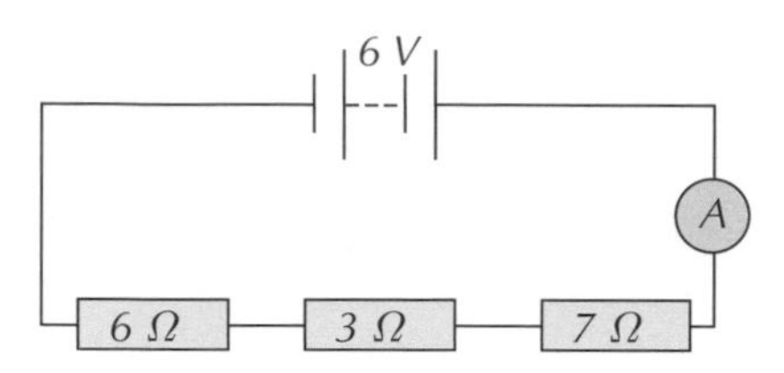

Tip: The resistance of the ammeter and wires is so small that you don't need to worry about it.

The total resistance of a series circuit is the sum of the resistances of each component:

$$R = 6\ \Omega + 3\ \Omega + 7\ \Omega = 16\ \Omega$$

The ammeter in the circuit diagram reads 0.375 A.
Find the potential difference across the 7 Ω resistor.

- The current is the same everywhere in the circuit, so the current through the 7 Ω resistor is $I = 0.375$ A.
- The resistance of the resistor is clearly (I hope...) $R = 7\ \Omega$.
- Use the equation from page 259:

$$V = I \times R = 0.375 \times 7 = 2.625\ \text{V}$$

Example 2 Higher

Find the current flowing in the circuit shown.

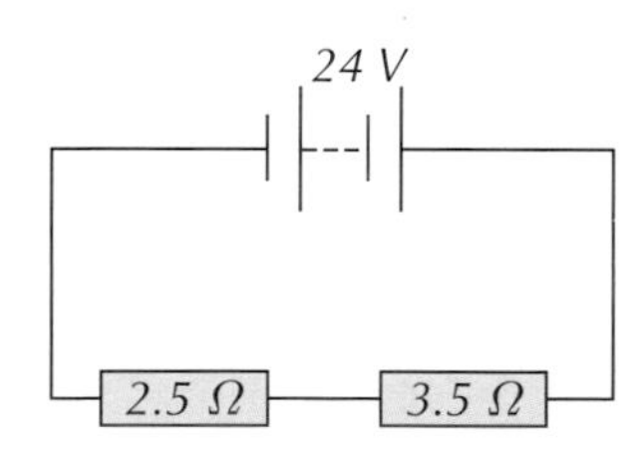

- The total resistance of the circuit is:

$$R = 2.5\ \Omega + 3.5\ \Omega = 6\ \Omega$$

- The total potential difference in the circuit is equal to the battery potential difference: $V = 24$ V.
- Rearrange the equation $V = I \times R$ and plug in the numbers for V and R to find the total current. So the total current in the circuit is:

$$I = V \div R = 24 \div 6 = 4\ \text{A}$$

Tip: H Use this formula triangle to rearrange $V = I \times R$:

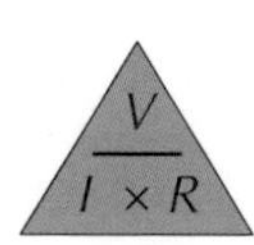

Summary of series circuits

There are four simple rules to remember for series circuits:

- The p.d. of the cells adds up to the source p.d.
- The source p.d. is split across the components.
- The current is the same through all the components.
- The total resistance of the circuit is the sum of all the resistances of the separate components.

You'll need to be able to use these rules in all sorts of circuit examples in the exam, so make sure you know them.

Practice Questions — Fact Recall

Q1 What does 'connected in series' mean?

Q2 What type of circuit component must always be connected in series?

Q3 How should you connect extra cells in a circuit in order to increase the total potential difference across the circuit?

Q4 True or false? Every component connected in series has the same potential difference across it.

Q5 What can you say about the current through each component connected in series?

Q6 How do you calculate the total resistance of a series circuit?

Practice Questions — Application

Q1 The circuit shown has a 7 Ω resistor and a filament lamp in series. Ammeter A reads a constant value of 1.5 A.

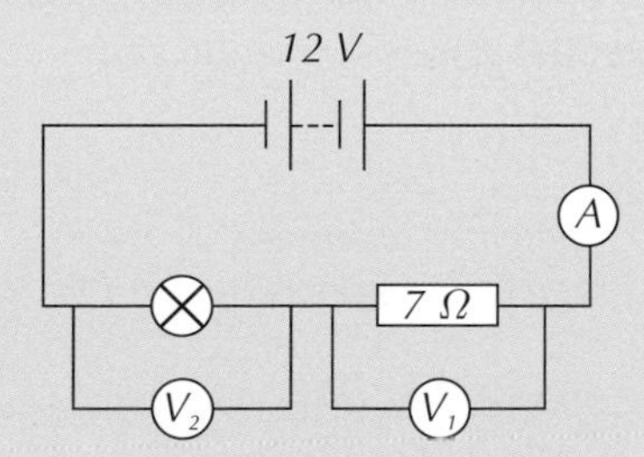

a) What is the current through the filament lamp?

b) What potential difference will voltmeter V_1 measure?

c) What potential difference will voltmeter V_2 measure?

Q2 Find the resistance of the filament lamp in Q1.

Tip: Remember the total V in the circuit will be equal to $V_1 + V_2$.

8. Parallel Circuits

Learning Objectives:

- Know that all components connected in parallel will have the same potential difference across them.
- Know that the total current in a parallel circuit is the sum of the currents through each of the branches of the parallel circuit.

Specification Reference P2.3.2

In parallel circuits, components or groups of components are on their own separate loop or branch. They're much more useful than series circuits because you can turn off each loop separately, without turning off the rest.

Components in parallel

Components connected in **parallel** each have their own branch in a circuit connected to the positive and negative of the supply (except ammeters). If you remove or disconnect one of them, it will hardly affect the others at all. This is because current can still flow in a complete loop (p.254) from one end of the power supply to the other through the branches that are still connected.

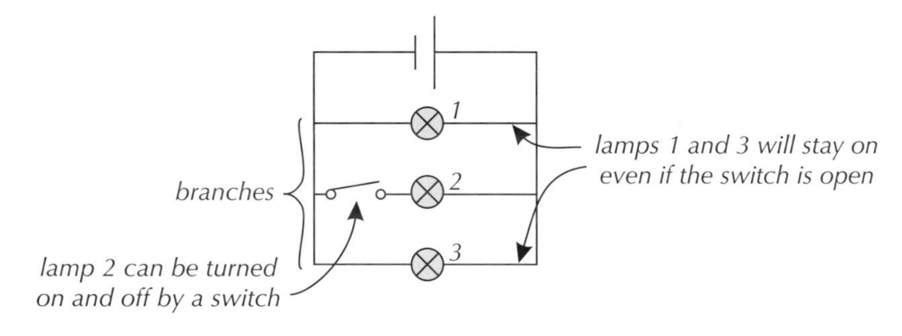

Figure 1: *A circuit diagram with three lamps connected in parallel, one of which can be switched on and off by a switch.*

Figure 2: *All the light switches in your house are just switches on a big parallel circuit. Each set of lights is on its own branch.*

This is obviously how most things must be connected, for example in cars and in household electrics. You have to be able to switch everything on and off separately.

Potential difference in parallel circuits

Each branch in a parallel circuit has the same potential difference as the power supply, so the potential difference is the same across all components connected in parallel:

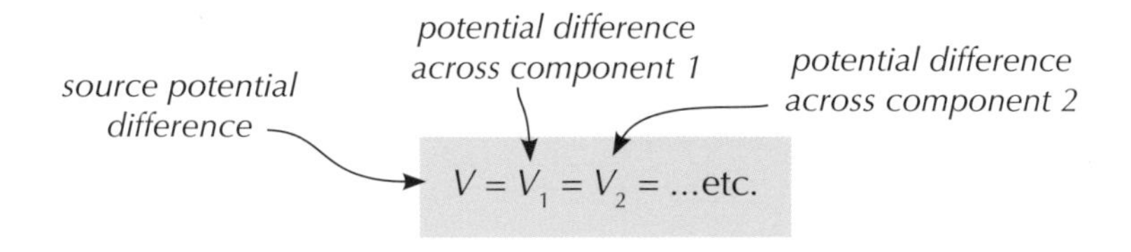

$$V = V_1 = V_2 = \text{...etc.}$$

This means that identical lamps connected in parallel will all be at the same brightness.

Tip: Voltmeters must be connected in parallel with the component that they're measuring because that's the only way they'll have the same p.d. across them as the component.

Example 1

Two lamps connected in parallel with a 1.5 V cell will both have 1.5 V of potential difference across them.

$V_{cell} = V_{lamp\ 1} = V_{lamp\ 2}$

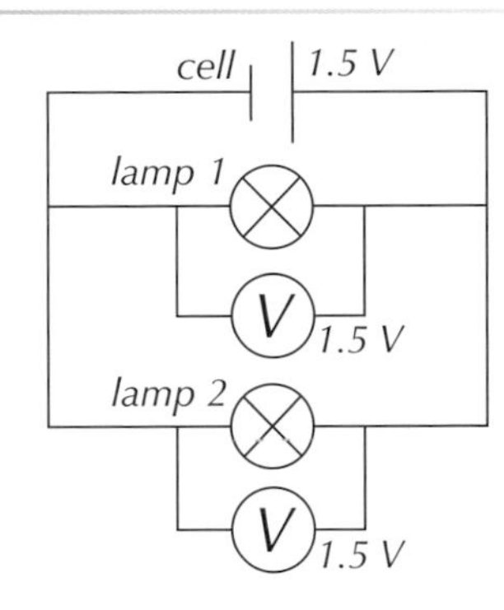

Figure 3: Two lamps connected in parallel with a cell — both lamps have the same potential difference across them as the cell.

Example 2

Everything electrical in a car is connected in parallel. Parallel connection is essential in a car to give these two features:

- Everything can be turned on and off separately.
- Everything always has the full p.d. of the battery across it. This is useful because it means that you can listen to the radio on full blast without it having much effect on the brightness of your lights.
- The only slight effect is that when you turn lots of things on the lights may briefly go a bit dim because the battery can't provide full potential difference under heavy load. This is normally a very slight effect. You can spot the same thing at home when you turn a kettle on, if you watch very carefully.

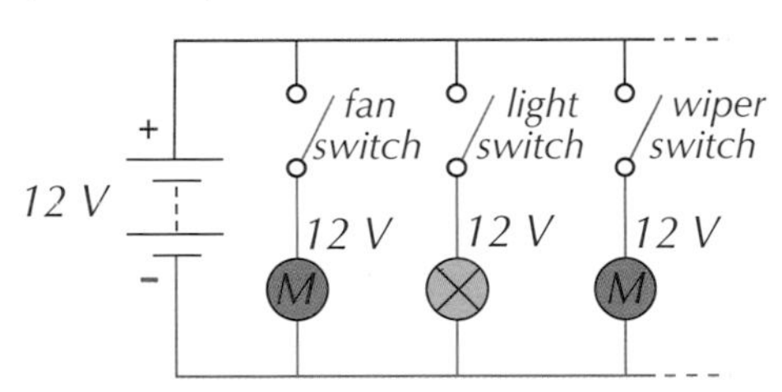

Figure 5: A circuit diagram to give an idea of how the electronic components in a car are connected in a parallel circuit.

Figure 4: A car dashboard. Everything that you can turn on and off from your dashboard will be on its own parallel circuit branch connected to the car battery.

Tip: (M) is the symbol for a motor.

Current in parallel circuits

In parallel circuits the total current flowing around the circuit is equal to the total of all the currents through the separate branches.

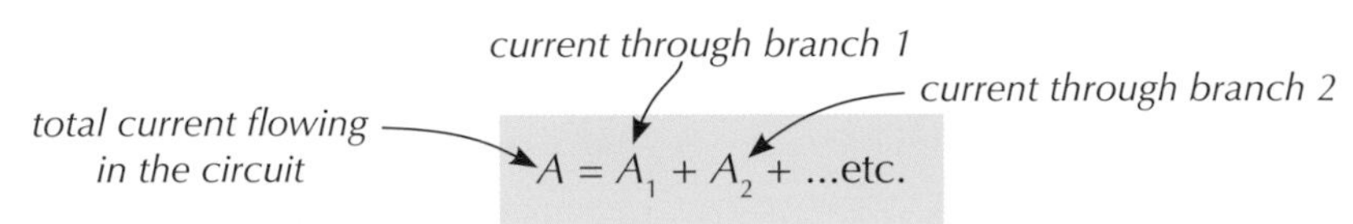

This means that unlike voltage, the current going through each branch is less that the total current in the circuit. Whenever the circuit splits into one or more branches, a certain amount of the current flows through each branch. The current through each component inside a branch is the same — it's like a mini series circuit. The same amount of current that entered the branch must then leave the branch when it rejoins the rest of the circuit.

If two identical components are connected in parallel then the same current will flow through each component.

Example

Two lamps connected in parallel will share the total current in the circuit. In Figure 6:

$$A_1 = A_2 + A_3$$

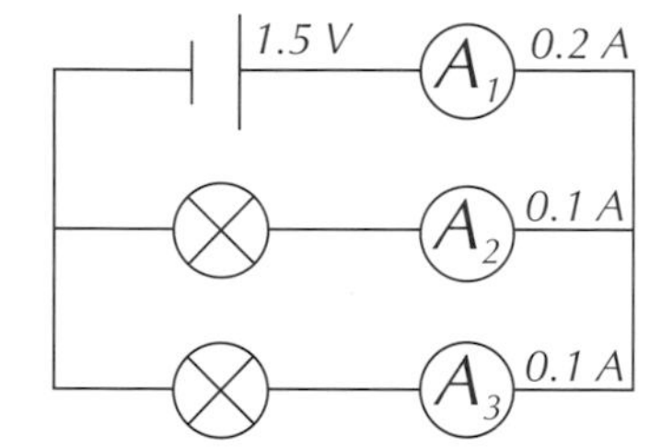

Figure 6: *A circuit diagram showing identical lamps connected in parallel.*

Summary of parallel circuits

There are only two rules for parallel circuits, know them well:

- The p.d. across each branch is the same as the source p.d.
- The current is split across the branches, and the total current is the sum of the current of each branch.

Tip: Remember for parallel circuits:
$A = A_1 + A_2 + ...$etc. and
$V = V_1 = V_2 + ...$etc.

Example

Find the potential difference across, and the current through resistor Y in the circuit shown.

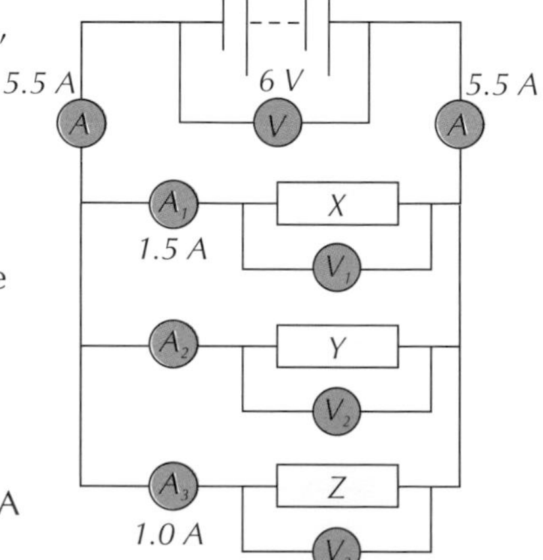

The resistors are all connected in parallel, so the p.d. across each resistor in the circuit is the same as the supply p.d. So the p.d. across resistor Y is 6 V.

The total current through the circuit is the same as the sum of the currents in the branches:

$$5.5 \text{ A} = 1.5 \text{ A} + A_2 + 1.0 \text{ A}$$

Rearranging to find A_2:

$$A_2 = 5.5 \text{ A} - 1.5 \text{ A} - 1.0 \text{ A} = 3.0 \text{ A}$$

Mixed series and parallel circuits

You can have a circuit that contains components connected in series and components connected in parallel — see Figure 7. Just make sure you apply the right rules to the right bits.

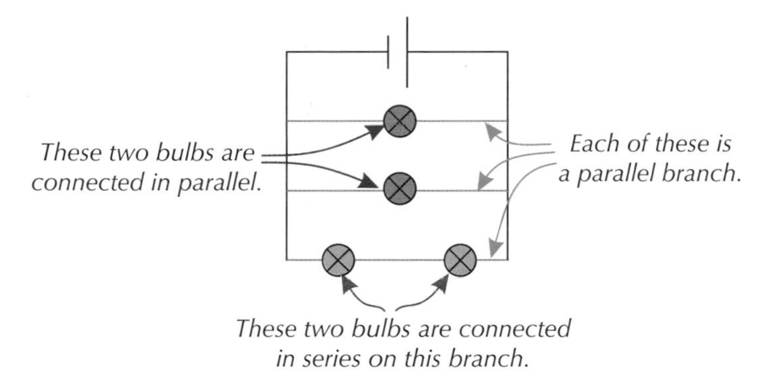

Figure 7: *A circuit with components connected in series and parallel with each other.*

Exam Tip
You might have to deal with simple circuits that are a mixture of parallel and series like this in the exam, so make sure you understand what's going on at each component.

Example

In the circuit shown in Figure 8, the potential difference across each branch would be 1.5 V.

On the branch with two lamps connected in series, the p.d. is then split between the two lamps (page 267).

$$1.5\text{ V} = V_1 + V_2 = V_3$$

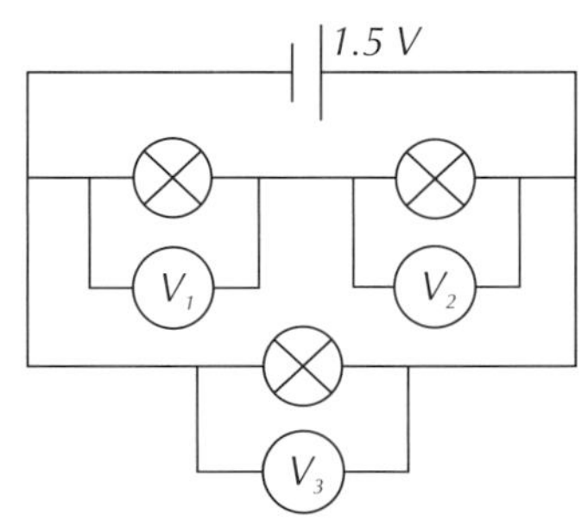

Figure 8: *A circuit diagram showing lamps connected in parallel and in series.*

Practice Questions — Fact Recall

Q1 What does 'connected in parallel' mean?

Q2 Why are parallel circuits more useful than series circuits in household electrics?

Q3 What can you say about the potential difference across all the components connected in parallel with a power supply? Assume each component is on a branch with no other components.

Q4 If you know the current in every branch of a parallel circuit, how can you work out the total current in the circuit?

Practice Questions — Application

Q1 A parallel circuit is shown.

When the switch is closed, ammeter A reads 0.75 A. Calculate:

(a) The p.d. across voltmeter V.

(b) The total current in the circuit is 2 A. Calculate the resistance of the lamp.

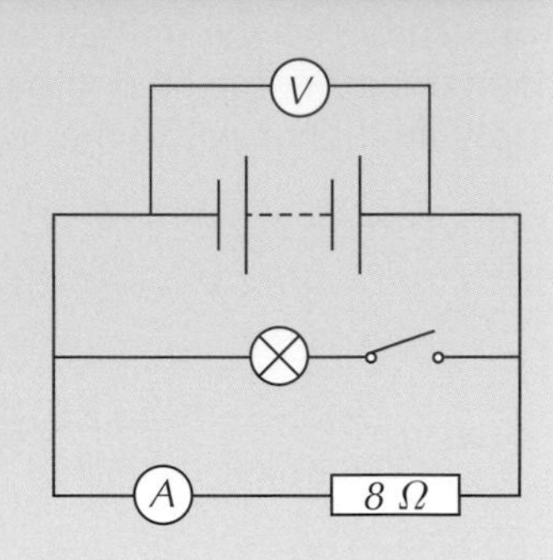

Q2 Look at this circuit.

a) If switch S is open, ammeter A reads 0.7 A. Find the potential difference across the battery.

b) If switch S is closed, ammeter A reads 0.5 A:

(i) Find the potential difference across lamp B.

(ii) Find the potential difference across resistor R_2.

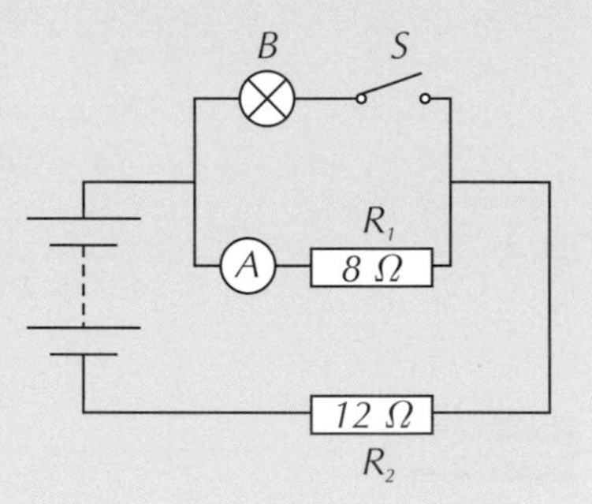

Tip: Look back at page 271 for series circuit rules.

Section Checklist — Make sure you know...

Static Electricity

- ☐ That electrical conductors (e.g. metals) are materials that electrical charge can move through easily.
- ☐ That a static charge is a charge which cannot move.
- ☐ That rubbing two insulating materials together can cause negatively charged electrons to move from one to the other, giving both materials an equal (but opposite) charge.
- ☐ That a material which loses electrons is left with a positive charge and a material that gains electrons is left with a negative charge.
- ☐ That electrically charged objects exert a force on one another — objects with the same charge repel each other and objects with opposite charges attract.

Circuit Basics

- ☐ How to draw the standard circuit symbols for a cell, a battery, a switch (open and closed), a lamp, an ammeter, a voltmeter, a resistor, a variable resistor, a fuse, a thermistor, a diode, a light-emitting diode (LED) and a light-dependent resistor (LDR).
- ☐ How to draw and interpret a circuit diagram.

Current and Potential Difference

- ☐ That an electric current is a flow of charge and that the size of the current is the rate of flow of the electric charge.
- ☐ That the size of an electric current (I) can be calculated using $I = Q \div t$, where Q is charge in C and t is time in s.
- ☐ That the potential difference across part of a circuit is the work done (or energy transferred in joules, J) per coulomb of charge that passes across that part of the circuit.
- ☐ That potential difference (V) can be calculated using $V = W \div Q$ where W is work done in J.

Resistance

- ☐ That the greater the resistance (R) of a component, the smaller the size of the current flowing through it for a given potential difference.
- ☐ That potential difference, resistance and current can be calculated using $V = I \times R$.
- ☐ That by measuring the potential difference across and current through a component, you can work out a component's resistance.
- ☐ That the inverse of the gradient of a current-potential difference (I-V) graph for a component gives you the resistance of the component.
- ☐ The I-V graphs for different resistors at a fixed temperature and a filament lamp, and how resistance changes for each component.
- ☐ That current is directly proportional to potential difference for a resistor at a fixed temperature.
- ☐ **H** Why the resistance of a filament bulb increases as the temperature of the filament increases in terms of the ions and electrons in the filament.

cont...

Diodes and LEDs

- ❑ That a diode is a component which only allows electric current to flow through it in one direction — it has a very high resistance in the other direction.
- ❑ The *I-V* graph for a diode.
- ❑ That light-emitting diodes (LEDs) emit light when current flows through them in one direction only.
- ❑ That LEDs are being used more and more for lighting because they are more energy and cost efficient than other forms of lighting (e.g. filament bulbs).
- ❑ That LEDs have many applications, e.g. in electrical appliances and medicine.

LDRs and Thermistors

- ❑ That light-dependent resistors (LDRs) are resistors whose resistance depends on light intensity — the resistance is lowest in the brightest light.
- ❑ That LDRs can be used in automatic lighting and security devices.
- ❑ That thermistors are resistors whose resistance depends on temperature — their resistance decreases as the temperature increases.
- ❑ That thermistors can be used in thermostats.

Series Circuits

- ❑ That components are connected in series if they are all connected in a line, end to end.
- ❑ That the total potential difference across cells connected in series and in the same direction is the sum of the individual potential differences of the cells.
- ❑ That the potential difference of the power supply in a series circuit is split across the components.
- ❑ That the current in a series circuit is the same everywhere.
- ❑ That the total resistance of a series circuit can be found by calculating the sum of the resistances of the components.

Parallel Circuits

- ❑ That a component is connected in parallel if it is connected separately to the positive and negative ends of the battery, on its own branch.
- ❑ That the potential difference across components connected in parallel with a power supply is the same as the potential difference across the power supply.
- ❑ That the total current in a parallel circuit is the sum of the currents in the branches.

Exam-style Questions

1 Electrostatic spray-painting is a method used to paint car bodies using electrostatic charges. The car body is given a negative charge, and a paint gun gives each paint droplet a positive charge, as shown in the diagram.

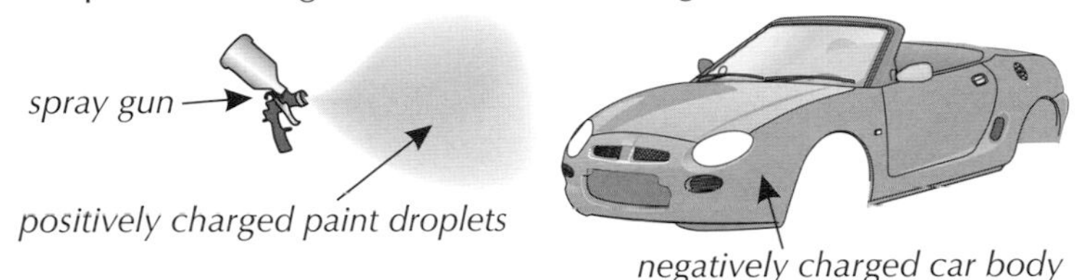

1 (a) Explain how the paint droplets become positively charged.

(1 mark)

1 (b) Complete the sentence by drawing a circle around the correct answer from the box.

The force felt between one paint droplet and another is

attractive.
repulsive.

(1 mark)

1 (c) Suggest why giving the paint droplets and the car opposite charges reduces the amount of paint wasted when a car is spray-painted.

(2 marks)

2 An electric motor and a filament lamp are both connected in parallel to a battery. The total size of the electric current in the circuit is 1.2 A. It takes 210 J of energy to move 15 C of charge through the motor in 30 seconds.

2 (a) What is the size of the electric current in a circuit a measure of?

(1 mark)

2 (b) Calculate the potential difference across the battery.
Use the correct equation from the equations listed on page 402.
Clearly show how you work out your answer. Give your answer in volts.

(2 marks)

2 (c) (i) Calculate the current passing through the filament lamp.
Use the correct equation from the equations listed on page 402.
Clearly show how you work out your answer. Give your answer in amps.

(3 marks)

2 (c) (ii) Calculate the resistance of the filament lamp.
Use the correct equation from the equations listed on page 402.
Clearly show how you work out your answer. Give your answer in ohms.

(2 marks)

3 The circuit diagram shown is for a basic electric fan that can run in two modes, automatic or continuous, by flicking a switch to position 1 or position 2.

In continuous mode, the fan will run continuously and be supplied with a constant current. In automatic mode, the current through the fan will increase as the temperature in the room increases.

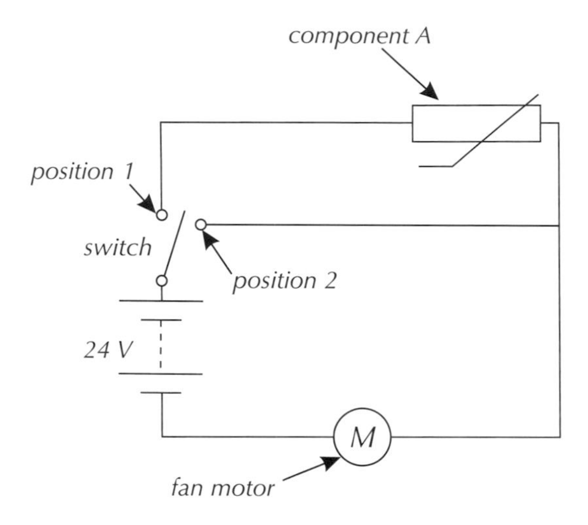

3 (a) What is component A?

(1 mark)

3 (b) The company that produces this fan decides to add a red LED to the circuit to indicate the fan is operating (in either mode), and a green LED to indicate that the fan running in automatic mode.
Sketch a possible circuit diagram of the deluxe model, labelling the coloured LEDs.

(3 marks)

3 (c) Explain how an increase in temperature will lead to an increase in current through the fan when it's in automatic mode.

(2 marks)

4 The circuit shown was used to record values of the current through and the potential difference across component X at a constant temperature.

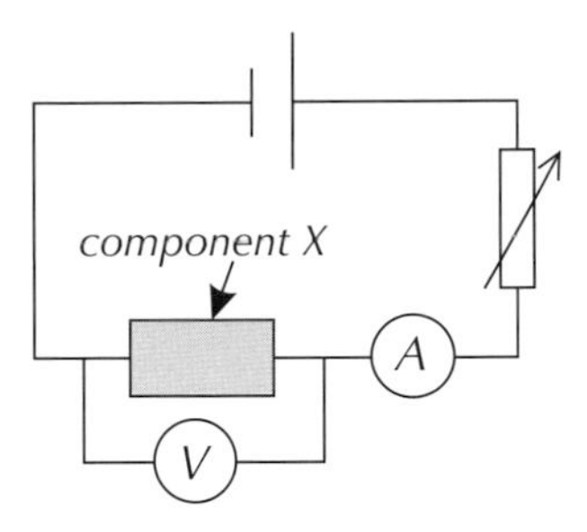

4 (a) Explain how the variable resistor is used to change the current in a circuit.

(1 mark)

The data collected for component X using this circuit is displayed on the graph.

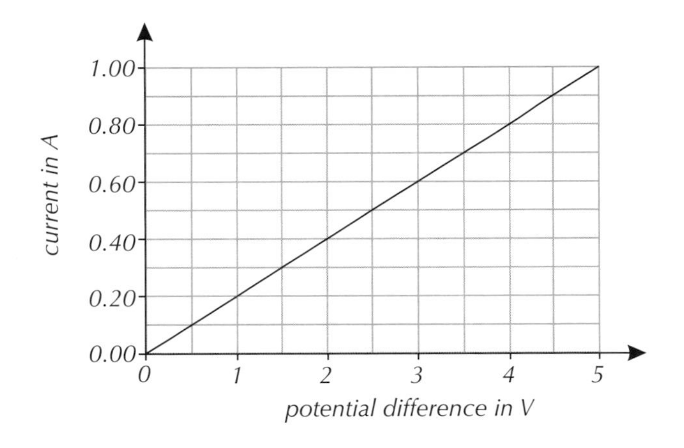

4 (b) What is component X?

(1 mark)

4 (c) Calculate the resistance of component X.

Clearly show how you work out your answer. Give your answer in ohms.

(2 marks)

4 (d) Component Y is the same type of component as component X but has a higher resistance at the same temperature. Which of the three graphs below shows the *I-V* graphs of component X and component Y? Explain your answer.

(2 marks)

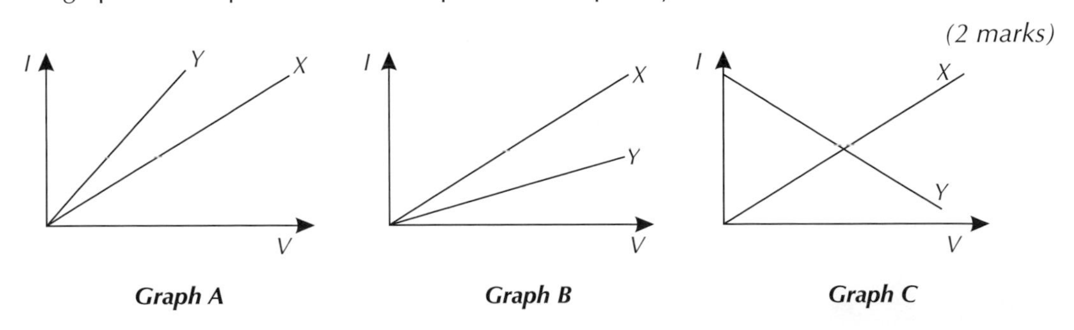

Learning Objectives:

- Know that direct current (d.c.) is the current supplied by cells and batteries and that it always passes in the same direction.
- Know that alternating current (a.c.) is current that constantly changes direction.
- Know that mains electricity is a.c. with a frequency of 50 Hz and a voltage of around 230 V in the UK.
- Be able to interpret and compare oscilloscope traces showing d.c. and a.c.
- H Be able to calculate the time period and frequency of an a.c. supply from an oscilloscope trace.

Specification Reference P2.4.1

Tip: d.c. and a.c. can also be written as DC and AC.

Tip: Remember, voltage is also known as potential difference (p.d.).

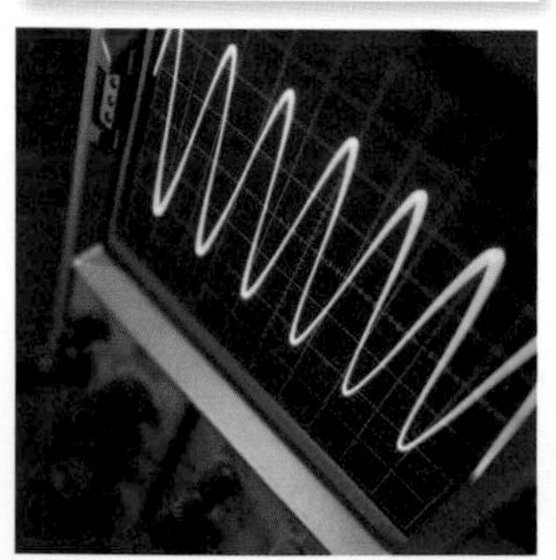

Figure 2: A real cathode ray oscilloscope.

1. Mains Electricity

We use mains electricity all the time without really thinking about it, but actually there is lots to think about. For a start, it's not the same as the electricity from batteries, which always flows in the same direction — mains electricity changes direction constantly.

Direct current and alternating current

Electric current is the movement of charge carriers (see p.256). To transfer energy, it doesn't matter which way the charge carriers are going.

Cells and batteries supply **direct current** (d.c.). This just means that the current always keeps flowing in the same direction.

However, the UK mains supply (the electricity you access when you plug something into a wall socket) is an **alternating current** (a.c.) supply — the current is constantly changing direction. The frequency of the a.c. mains supply is 50 cycles per second or 50 Hz (hertz) and the voltage is approximately 230 volts.

Cathode ray oscilloscopes

A cathode ray oscilloscope (CRO) is basically a snazzy voltmeter. You can use one to 'see' how the voltage of an electricity supply changes over time. Figure 1 shows a CRO and how it can be used.

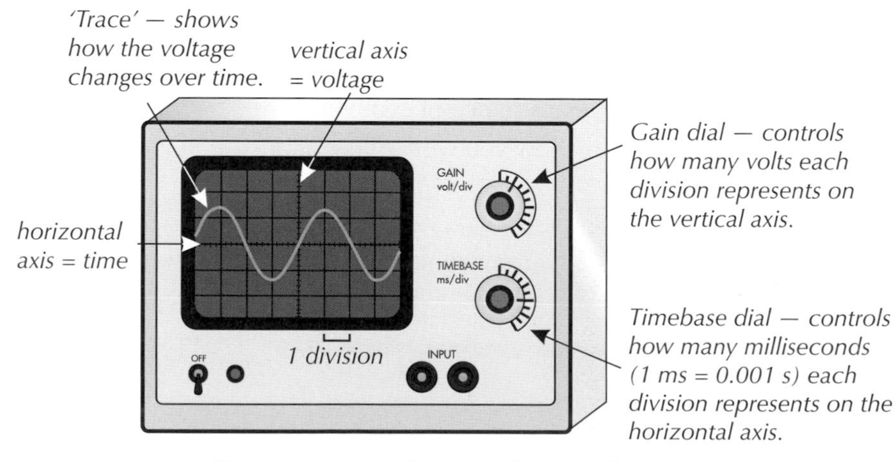

***Figure 1:** A cathode ray oscilloscope showing a trace.*

Each main division (or square) on the screen is usually divided into five smaller divisions so it can be read more precisely. So, each minor division is 0.2 of a major division.

Reading an oscilloscope trace

d.c. supply

If you plug in a d.c. supply, the trace you get is just a straight line. The voltage of the supply is just the distance from the straight line trace to the centre line.

Tip: For a d.c. supply, it doesn't matter what the timebase (horizontal axis) is set to.

Example

This is a CRO trace for a d.c. supply. The gain dial is set to 1 V/div (vertical axis).

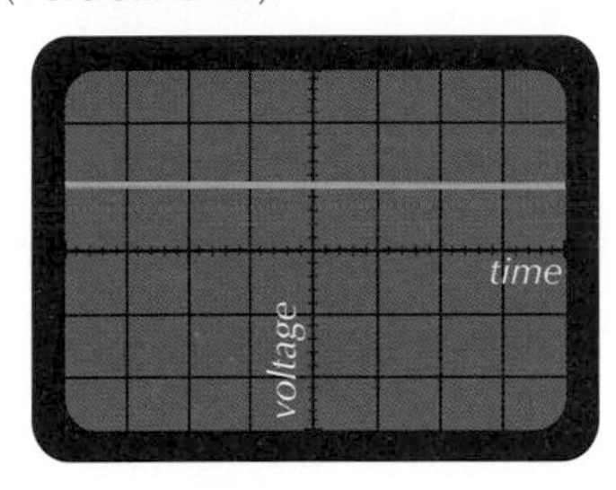

- Distance from trace to centre line = 1 division.
- Gain dial set to 1 V/div, so potential difference = 1 V.

Exam Tip
If you have to work out p.d. from an oscilloscope trace in the exam, always double check what each division represents — you can't just assume that 1 division = 1 V.

a.c. supply

If you plug an a.c. supply into an oscilloscope, the trace goes up and down in a regular pattern — some of the time it's positive and some of the time it's negative.

The vertical height of the a.c. trace at any point shows the voltage at that point. By measuring the maximum height of the trace from the centre line you can find the peak potential difference of the a.c. supply.

Example

This is a CRO trace for an a.c. supply. The gain dial is set to 20 V/div (vertical axis) and the timebase is set to 5 ms/div (horizontal axis).

The peak p.d. is one major division and two minor divisions from the centre line — so it's 1.4 divisions in total.

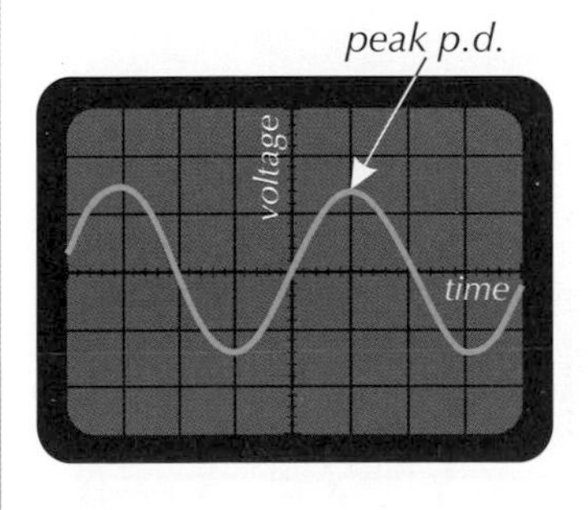

- Distance from peak p.d. to centre line = 1.4 divisions.
- Gain dial set to 20 V/div, so peak p.d. = 1.4 × 20 = 28 V.

Tip: Remember, each minor division is 0.2 of a major division.

Time period and frequency Higher

You can use the CRO trace to work out the time period and frequency of an a.c. supply. The **time period** is the time taken to complete one cycle, e.g. from crest to crest.

Exam Tip
Watch out — the time period is measured in seconds. If you have data in any other units (e.g. milliseconds), you'll need to convert them to seconds.

You can then work out the frequency of the supply using this formula:

$$\text{frequency (Hz)} = \frac{1}{\text{time period (s)}}$$

Example **Higher**

This trace comes from an oscilloscope with the timebase set to 6 ms/div. Find the time period and the frequency of the a.c. supply.

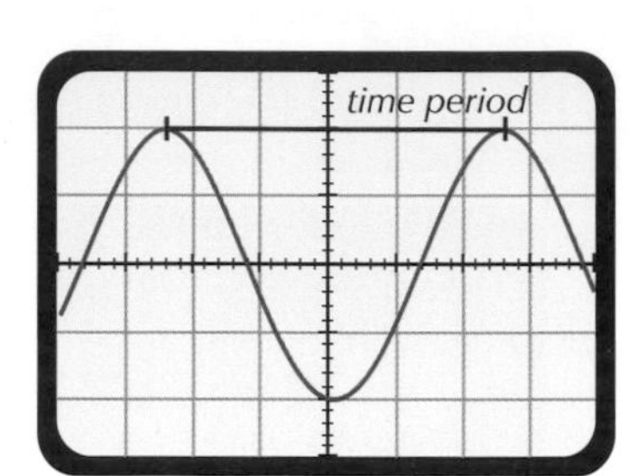

To find the time period, measure the horizontal distance between two peaks.

The time period of the signal is 5 divisions.
Multiply this by the timebase:
Time period = 5 × 6 = 30 ms = 0.03 s

To find the frequency, use the formula:

$$\text{frequency} = \frac{1}{\text{time period}} = \frac{1}{0.03} = 30\text{ Hz (to 1 s.f.)}$$

Tip: Remember, 1 ms = 0.001 s, so to convert from milliseconds to seconds you need to divide by 1000.

Practice Questions — Fact Recall

Q1 What is direct current (d.c.)? Give two sources of d.c.

Q2 What does a.c. stand for? How is it different from d.c.?

Q3 What is the frequency and voltage of the mains supply in the UK?

Q4 On a cathode ray oscilloscope screen, what do the vertical and horizontal axes represent?

Q5 If you know the time period of a supply, how do you work out its frequency?

Practice Questions — Application

Q1 Look at the oscilloscope traces below. For both traces, gain is set at 5 V/div. Find the p.d. for **A** and the peak p.d. for **B**.

A

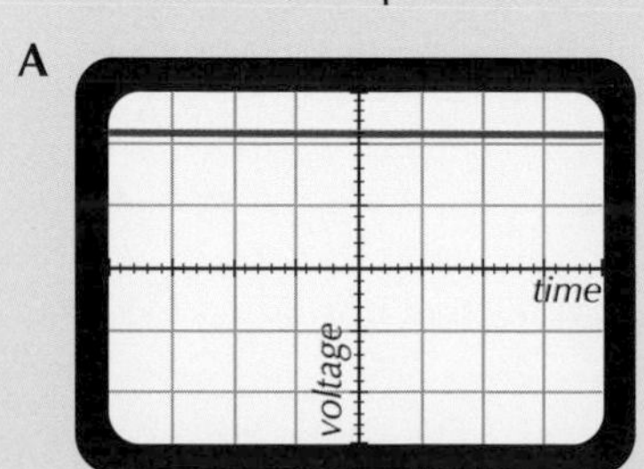

B

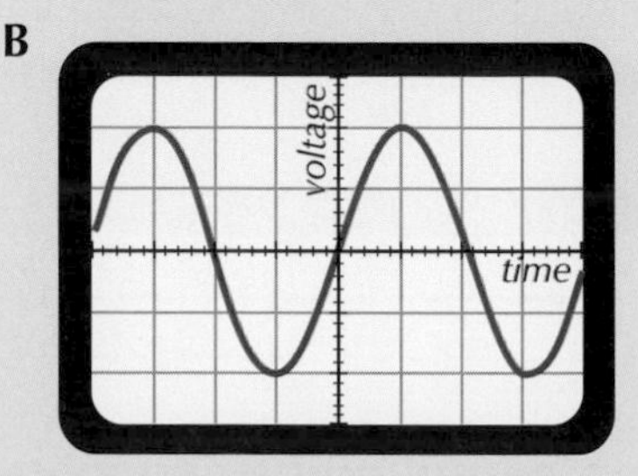

Q2 Work out the frequency of an a.c. supply with a time period of 0.05 s.

2. Electricity in the Home

Electricity's really dangerous stuff — and there are hazards all over the place. So, make sure you watch out for anything that can cause stray sparks...

Learning Objectives:
- Be able to identify electrical hazards in the home.
- Know the structure of three-core and two-core electrical cables.
- Know that in the UK, most electrical appliances that use the mains electricity power supply have a cable and a three pin plug.
- Know the structure of a three-pin plug and how to wire one.

Specification Reference P2.4.1

Electrical hazards

A likely exam question will show you a picture of domestic bliss but with various electrical hazards in the picture such as kids shoving their fingers into sockets and stuff like that, and they'll ask you to list all the hazards. This should be mostly common sense, but it won't half help if you already know some of the likely hazards, so learn these 9 examples:

1. Long cables — can trip you up or overheat and cause a fire if they're bundled up.
2. Frayed cables — exposed wires could give you an electric shock.
3. Too many plugs in one socket — the socket could overheat and cause a fire.
4. Cables in contact with something hot — could overheat and cause a fire.
5. Water near sockets or cables — water conducts electricity so this could give you an electric shock, or even cause electrocution.
6. Shoving things into sockets — this could also give you an electric shock or cause electrocution.
7. Damaged plugs — exposed live parts could give you an electric shock.
8. Empty light bulb sockets — touching the socket could give you an electric shock.
9. Appliances without their covers on — exposed live parts could give you an electric shock.

Figure 1: *Extension cords can be handy, but take care. They can overheat and cause a fire if you don't uncoil them completely.*

Tip: Live parts are parts with electricity flowing through them.

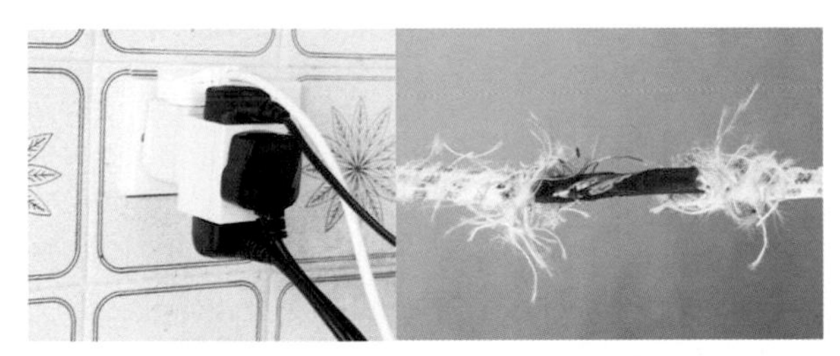

Figure 2: *Two electrical hazards to watch out for in the home — overloaded plug sockets (left) and frayed cables (right).*

Electrical cables

There are two different kinds of electrical cables that you need to know about — three-core and two-core cables.

Three-core cables

Most electrical appliances are connected to the mains supply by **three-core cables**. This means that they have three wires inside them, each with a core of copper and a coloured plastic coating, shown in Figures 3 and 4.

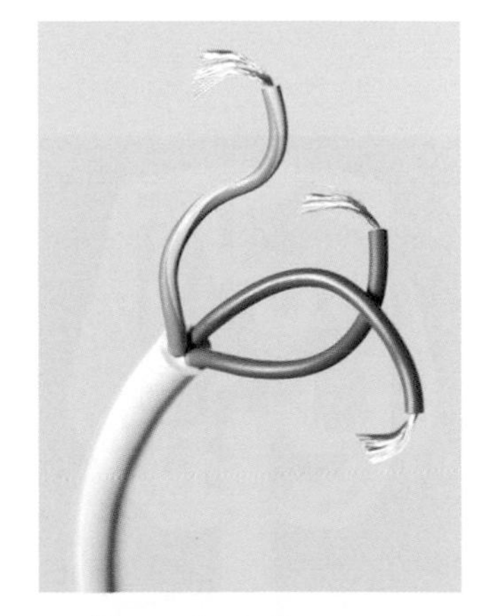

Figure 3: *A three-core electrical cable with a live wire (brown), a neutral wire (blue) and an earth wire (yellow/green).*

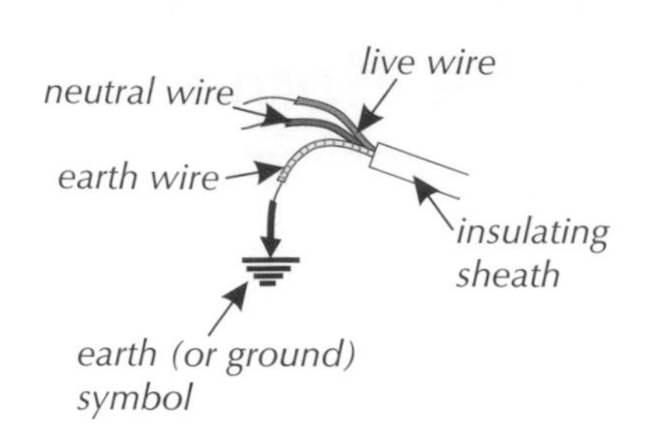

Figure 4: *A three-core electrical cable showing the live, neutral and earth wires.*

The brown **live wire** in a mains supply alternates between a high positive and negative voltage.

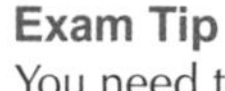

Exam Tip
You need to know the colour coding of the wires — so make sure you learn it.

The blue **neutral wire** is always at 0 V. Electricity normally flows in and out through the live and neutral wires only.

The green and yellow **earth wire** is for protecting the wiring, and for safety — it works together with a **fuse** (see page 288) to prevent fire and shocks. It is attached to the metal casing of the appliance and carries the electricity to earth (and away from you) should something go wrong and the live or neutral wires touch the metal case.

Two-core cables

Two-core cables are the same as three-core cables, except that they don't have an earth wire. They're used for electrical appliances that have a casing that won't conduct electricity — there's more about them on page 291.

Three-pin plugs and cables

Most appliances are connected to the UK mains supply using a three-pin plug and a three-core cable. Each pin is connected to a specific wire so that they can all do their jobs.

In the exam, you might be asked about the materials and safety features of three-pin plugs and cables.

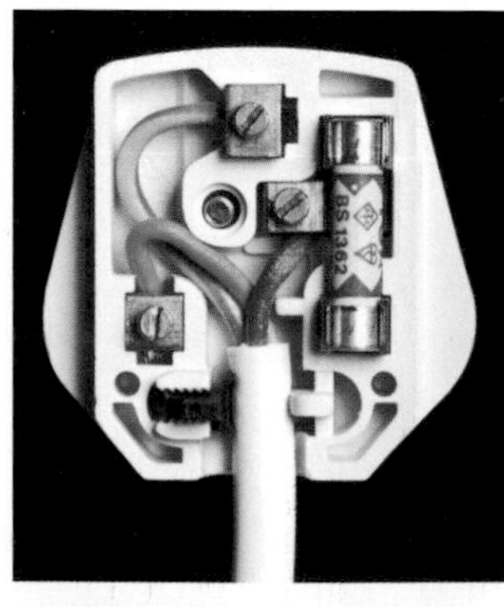

Figure 5: *A three-pin plug with the live, neutral and earth wires correctly wired in.*

Wiring

To be safe, it's really important that the wiring of a plug is right. Have a look at Figures 5 and 6 — here are the things to look out for:

- That the right coloured wire is connected to each pin and is firmly screwed in.
- No bare wires showing inside the plug.
- Cable grip tightly fastened over the cable outer layer.

The cable that's wired into the plug is also important. Different appliances need different amounts of electrical energy. Thicker cables have less resistance, so they carry more current (see page 290).

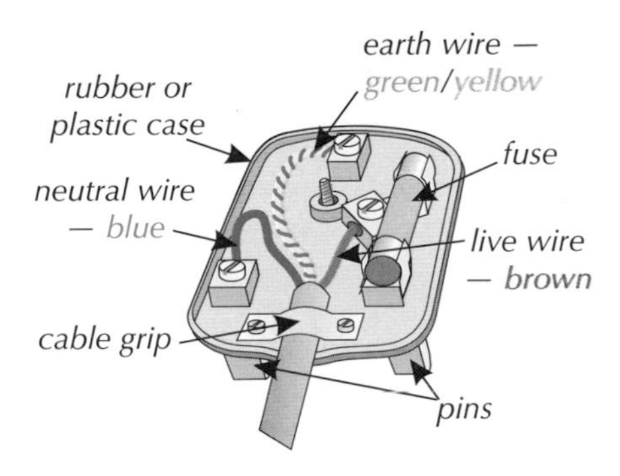

Figure 6: *A diagram showing the correct wiring of a three-pin plug. The right coloured wire is attached to each pin, there are no bare wires and the cable grip is firmly in place.*

Tip: If a two-core cable is used, there will be no earth wire connected — but this can be unsafe it the appliance isn't double insulated (see page 291).

Materials

The materials used to make a plug are chosen so that the plug works well and is safe.

- The metal parts of a plug are often made of copper or brass because they are very good conductors.
- The case, cable grip and cable insulation are made of rubber or plastic because they're really good insulators, and flexible too.

This all keeps the electricity flowing where it should.

Exam Tip
In this case, we're talking about electrical insulators and conductors. If you start writing about thermal (heat) conductors and insulators in plugs you'll lose marks.

Practice Questions — Fact Recall

Q1 Give six examples of common electrical hazards in the home.

Q2 What is the colour coding of the wires in a three-core cable?

Q3 a) Describe the p.d. in the live and neutral wires in a three-core cable.

b) What is the role of the earth wire in a three-core cable?

Q4 What's the difference between a three-core and a two-core cable?

Q5 Draw a correctly wired three-pin plug.

Q6 What materials are used to make a three-pin plug? Explain why they're chosen.

Practice Question — Application

Q1 Describe and explain the electrical hazards that can be seen in this picture of appliances in a home.

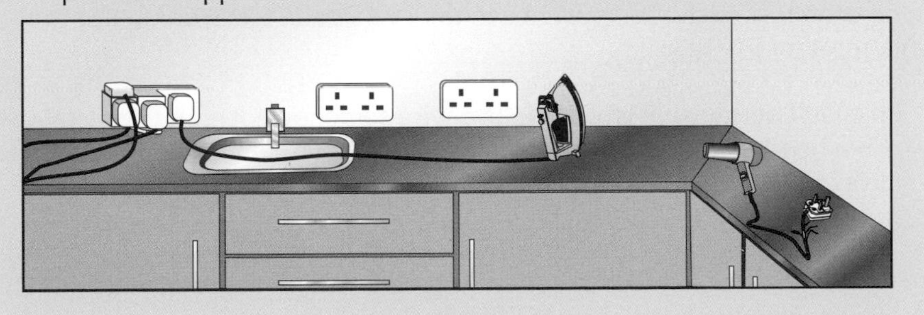

3. Safety Devices in Circuits

Learning Objectives:

- Understand how a fuse or circuit breaker, together with an earth wire, breaks a circuit in the event of an electrical fault.
- Be able to compare the uses of circuit breakers and fuses.
- Know that the larger the current, the thicker a cable needs to be to carry it. This causes a link between cable thickness and fuse rating.
- Know what Residual Current Circuit Breakers (RCCBs) are and how they protect circuits.
- Understand why appliances with metal casings are earthed, whereas double insulated appliances are not.

Specification Reference P2.4.1

Circuits in the home are designed to cut out if too much current flows, if a fault develops or if someone touches a live part of an appliance. There are a few clever ways that they do this.

Fuses, circuit breakers and earthing

Fuses, circuit breakers and earthing are used in electrical appliances to protect the user and the circuit.

A fuse or a circuit breaker can prevent damage during a current surge (where too much current flows in the circuit) or if someone touches part of an appliance that's live. An earth wire works with a fuse or a circuit breaker if there's an electrical fault in an appliance.

Fuses

An electrical fuse consists of a tube containing a short length of wire (see Figure 1). In a three-pin plug (see pages 286-287), the current flows through a fuse to the live wire. If the current is too high, the fuse wire will melt and break the circuit.

Figure 1: *Electrical fuses.*

Circuit breakers

Circuit breakers are an electrical safety device used in some circuits. Like fuses, they protect the circuit from damage if too much current flows.

When circuit breakers detect a surge in current in a circuit, they break the circuit by opening a switch in the live wire. They operate much faster than fuses — they break the circuit as soon as there is a current surge — no time is wasted waiting for the current to melt a fuse. This makes them safer.

A circuit breaker (and the circuit they're in) can easily be reset by flicking a switch on the device (see Figure 2). This makes them more convenient than fuses — which have to be replaced once they've melted.

They are, however, a lot more expensive to buy than fuses.

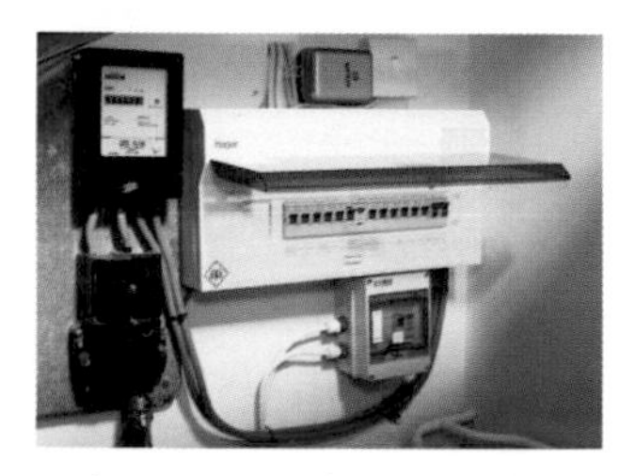

Figure 2: *A domestic fuse box (the white box on the right) has a circuit breaker linked to a black switch for each circuit in a home. If there's a surge in current in a circuit, its switch will flick down and the electricity will be cut off.*

Earthing

The earth wire works together with a fuse or circuit breaker to prevent damage being done to a circuit or appliance in the event of an electrical fault. They work together like this:

1. If a fault develops in which the live wire somehow touches the metal case, then because the case is earthed, too great a current flows in through the live wire, through the case and out down the earth wire.
2. This surge in current melts the fuse (or trips the circuit breaker in the live wire) when the amount of current is greater than the fuse rating. This cuts off the live supply and breaks the circuit.

3. This isolates the whole appliance, making it impossible to get an electric shock from the case. It also prevents the risk of fire caused by the heating effect of a large current.

Example

If a fault develops in a toaster with a metal casing, the earth wire and the fuse in its plug work together to stop the flow of current. This prevents someone being hurt if they touch the casing. Here's how it works:

- A fault allows the live wire to touch the metal casing of the toaster. As a result, there's a surge of current out through the earth wire.

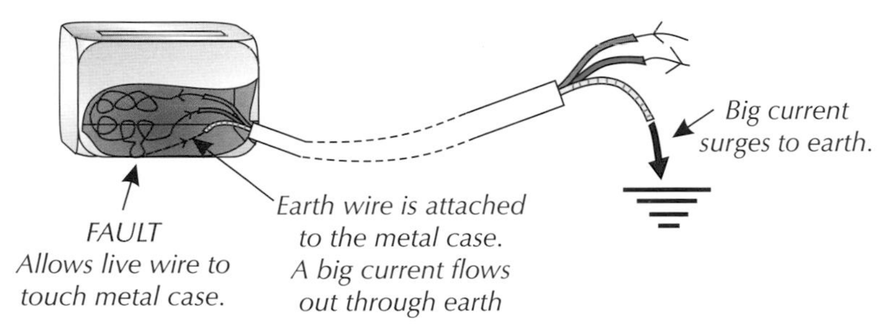

Figure 3: *A diagram showing the current surge to earth when an appliance develops a fault that causes a current to flow through its casing.*

- The big current flows through the fuse — when the surge exceeds the fuse rating, the fuse will melt.

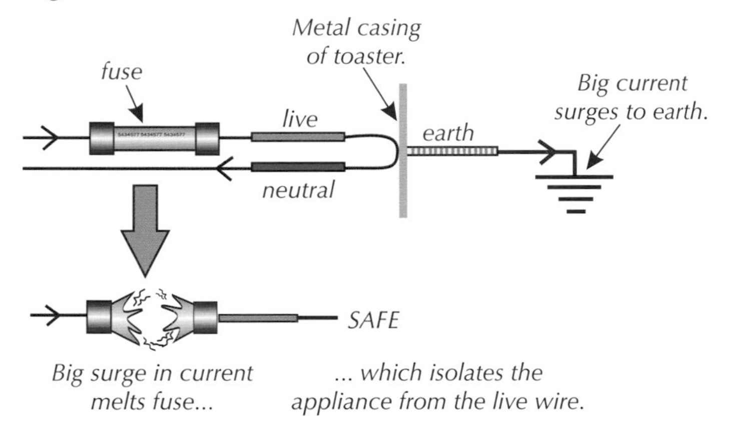

Figure 4: *A diagram showing how the fuse breaks the circuit when the appliance casing becomes live.*

Exam Tip
A fuse breaks a circuit by melting. In the exam, you won't get a mark if you say it snaps or breaks.

Fuse ratings

Fuses should be rated as near as possible but just higher than the normal operating current of the appliance they're in. In the UK, plugs usually have 3 A or 13 A fuses in them. Big appliances with high power ratings (see page 294) usually use a 13 A fuse. Smaller, less powerful appliances usually use a 3 A fuse.

Tip: Fuses in domestic appliances are usually rated 3 A or 13 A, but some older appliances use 5 A fuses.

Tip: There's more about working out what fuse is needed for an appliance on page 295.

Examples

A 1200 W dishwasher will use a 13 A fuse, whereas an 85 W CD player will use a 3 A fuse.

Cable thickness

The larger the current, the thicker the cable you need to carry it safely. More powerful appliances draw more current from the mains supply (see page 294), so they should be connected with a thicker cable. Figure 5 shows how the maximum safe current for a typical cable increases with cable thickness.

Tip: This table just shows some examples — you can get much thicker cables than this, for example with a cross-sectional area of 10 mm^2 or 16 mm^2.

Cross-sectional area of cable / mm^2	*Maximum safe current / A*
1.0	*10*
1.25	*13*
1.5	*15*
2.5	*20*
4.0	*25*

Figure 5: *A table to show how thicker electrical cables can carry larger currents safely.*

This is why the fuse rating needed for appliances usually increases with the thickness of the appliance cable.

Examples

A general lighting circuit might use a 1 mm^2 cable and a 5 A fuse, whereas a cooker would need to use a 6 mm^2 cable and a circuit breaker with a 40 A rating.

Residual Current Circuit Breakers

Figure 6: *An RCCB detects a difference in current between the live and neutral wires in an appliance and cuts off the power. This one can be reset by pressing the blue button.*

One type of circuit breaker used to protect users from electrocution instead of a fuse (or a standard circuit breaker) and an earth wire is a **Residual Current Circuit Breaker (RCCB)**.

Normally exactly the same current flows through the live and neutral wires. If somebody touches the live wire, a small but deadly current will flow through them to the earth. This means the neutral wire carries less current than the live wire. The RCCB detects this difference in current and quickly cuts off the power by opening a switch.

RCCBs even work for small current changes that might not be large enough to melt a fuse. Since even small current changes could be fatal, this means RCCBs are more effective at protecting against electrocution. They're also much faster than fuses at cutting off the electricity supply.

Double insulated appliances

As you've seen, all appliances with metal cases are usually "earthed" to reduce the danger of electric shock. "Earthing" just means the case must be attached to an earth wire. An earthed conductor can never become live.

If the appliance has a plastic (or another insulator) casing and no metal parts showing then it's said to be **double insulated**. Anything with double insulation like that doesn't need an earth wire — just a live and neutral. Cables that only carry the live and neutral wires are known as two-core cables.

Tip: A double insulated appliance still needs a fuse or circuit breaker to protect against current surges.

Figure 7: *A double insulated hair dryer. Its casing is plastic so can never become live, which means it doesn't need an earth wire.*

Practice Questions — Fact Recall

Q1 A live wire has a fuse connected to it.

a) What is a fuse?

b) What should happen to the fuse if there's a current surge?

Q2 Give one advantage and one disadvantage of using a circuit breaker to protect against damage in a current surge compared to a fuse.

Q3 How is the fuse for an appliance plug chosen?

Q4 Explain why a high-powered appliance needs a different electrical cable to a very low-powered appliance.

Q5 What is an RCCB and what does it do?

Q6 What does it mean if an appliance is double insulated?

Learning Objectives:

- Know that resistors get hot when current flows through them.
- Understand that appliances such as lamps waste energy as heat, but that choosing more efficient appliances, e.g. CFL lamps, can reduce this.
- Understand that efficiency should be taken into account when choosing appliances.

Specification Reference P2.4.2

4. Energy and Efficiency in Circuits

Efficiency is one of the things to keep an eye out for when you're choosing new appliances. It's not just about looks when it comes to electrics.

Electricity and energy transfer

Electrical energy is just another form of energy — which means that it is always conserved. Energy can be transferred from one form to another, stored or dissipated — but it can never be created or destroyed.

So anything that supplies electricity is also supplying energy. Cells, batteries, generators, etc. all transfer energy to components in a circuit.

Example

Electrical energy can be transferred to different types of energy by different appliances.

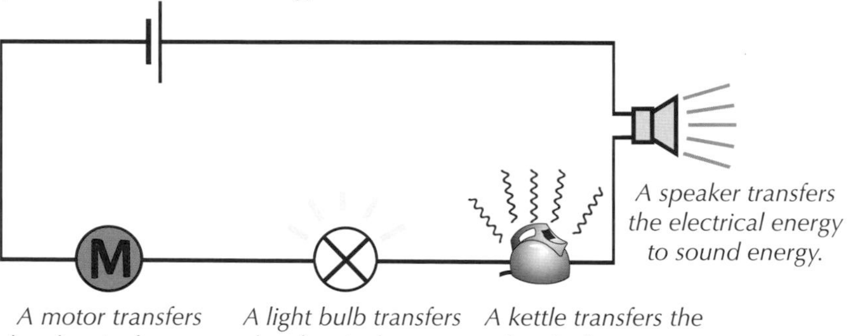

Figure 1: *A circuit containing various appliances that transfer electrical energy into other forms of energy.*

Resistors and heat

Whenever a current flows through anything with electrical resistance (which is pretty much everything) then electrical energy is converted into heat energy.

- The more current that flows, the more heat is produced.
- A bigger voltage means more heating because it pushes more current through.

Example

Filament bulbs work by passing a current through a very thin wire, heating it up so much that it glows. Rather obviously, they waste a lot of energy as heat.

Figure 2: *A filament bulb. Current causes the filament to heat up so much that it glows.*

Energy-efficient appliances

All this energy wasted as heat can get a little depressing — but there is a solution.

When you buy electrical appliances you can choose to buy ones that are more energy efficient. These appliances transfer more of their total electrical energy input to useful energy.

Example

Less energy is wasted as heat in energy-saving bulbs such as compact fluorescent lamps (CFLs) and light-emitting diodes (p.263) than in ordinary filament bulbs.

Unfortunately, they can cost more to buy, but over time the money you save on your electricity bills pays you back for the initial investment.

Figure 3: *Two types of CFLs — also known as energy-saving light bulbs. They're much more efficient than filament bulbs because they waste a lot less heat energy.*

Efficiency is just one of the many things you should consider when choosing an electrical appliance. Power of the appliance is another one (see p.294).

Practice Questions — Fact Recall

Q1 a) Give two examples of appliances that transfer electrical energy.

b) For each appliance given in part a), give one form of energy that the electrical energy is transferred to.

Q2 How is energy wasted when electric charge flows through a circuit component with electrical resistance?

Q3 Why is it important to choose efficient electrical appliances?

Q4 What are CFLs? Why are they now often used in preference to traditional filament bulbs?

5. Power and Energy Transfer

Learning Objectives:

- Know how power, energy transferred and time are related and be able to use the formula $P = \frac{E}{t}$.
- Know that power should be considered when choosing an appliance.
- Know how power, potential difference and current are related and be able to use the formula $P = I \times V$.
- Be able to calculate the fuse needed for an appliance from its power and the potential difference of the electricity supply.

Specification Reference P2.4.2

Here's a topic that brings lots of electricity stuff together — power, fuses, current, potential difference and energy transfer. No loose ends around here.

Power and energy transfer

The total energy transferred by an appliance depends on how long the appliance is on and the power at which it's operating.

The **power** of an appliance is the energy that it transfers per second.

$$P = \frac{E}{t}$$

P = *power (W)*
E = *energy transferred (J)*
t = *time (s)*

Power is another thing to consider when choosing an electrical appliance — a more powerful appliance will transfer more energy in the same amount of time.

Example

To work out the power of an appliance that transfers 1200 J of energy in 150 s, you just put the numbers into the formula:

$$P = \frac{E}{t} = \frac{1200}{150} = 8\text{ W}$$

Example **Higher**

If a 2.5 kW kettle is on for 5 minutes, how much energy is transferred by the kettle?

First make sure the numbers are in the right units:

power = 2.5 kW = 2500 W
time = 5 minutes = 300 s

Then rearrange the formula:

$E = P \times t = 2500 \times 300 = 750\ 000\text{ J} = 750\text{ kJ}$

Tip: H If you're doing the higher paper, you might need to rearrange the power equation. Using a formula triangle like this one can really help.

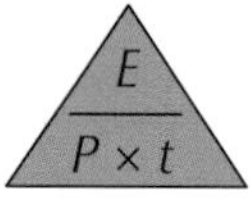

See page 352 for more on how to use formula triangles.

Electrical power and potential difference

You've met potential difference before — it's just voltage (page 257). If you know the potential difference across an appliance and the current flowing through it you can work out its power using this formula:

$$P = I \times V$$

P = *power (W)*
V = *potential difference (V)*
I = *current (A)*

Example

What's the power input of a light bulb that draws 0.2 A of current from a 230 V supply?

Just put the numbers into the equation:

$$P = I \times V = 0.2 \times 230$$
$$= 46 \text{ W}$$

Example **Higher**

A toy car supplied by a 13 V battery has a power output of 42 W. Find the current it draws from the battery.

First rearrange the equation for power to make current the subject:

$$P = I \times V \Rightarrow I = \frac{P}{V}$$

Then put the numbers in:

$$I = \frac{P}{V} = \frac{42}{13} = 3.2 \text{ A (to 2 s.f.)}$$

Tip: H Remember trusty formula triangles can help you rearrange this formula. Have a peek at p.352 for more on them.

Fuse ratings

Most electrical goods show their power rating and voltage rating. To work out the size of fuse needed for an appliance, you need to work out the current that the appliance will use if it's operating at its power and voltage ratings.

The power rating gives the maximum power at which you can safely use the appliance at the voltage given. For most appliances in the UK the power and voltage ratings are the power and voltage at which they operate when they're plugged into a 230 V mains supply.

Figure 1: *A label showing the voltage and power rating of an electric appliance.*

You can work out the size of the fuse needed using the same formula, but rearranged:

$$I = \frac{P}{V}$$

I = *current*, ***P*** = *power*, ***V*** = *potential difference*

Exam Tip
If you're sitting the foundation paper you won't need to rearrange $P = I \times V$ to get this equation, but you could be asked to use this equation to find a fuse rating.

Normally, the fuse you choose should be rated just a little higher than the normal current.

Example

A hair dryer is rated at 230 V, 1 kW. Should a 3 A, 5 A or 13 A fuse be used?

1 kW = 1000 W, so $I = \frac{P}{V} = \frac{1000}{230} = 4.3$ A

A 5 A fuse is ideal for the hair dryer — it's just a bit higher than 4.3 A.

Exam Tip
Fuses normally come in set sizes. You'll probably be given a list of available options in the exam.

Exam Tip
You'll be given the formulas for power on the equations sheet in the exam, but you still need to know how to use them and what units are needed.

Practice Questions — Fact Recall

Q1 What is the formula for working out the power of an appliance in terms of the energy it transfers? What does each term represent and what are their units?

Q2 a) What is the formula that relates power, current and potential difference?

b) What units are each of them measured in?

c) How would you use this formula to work out what fuse an appliance needs?

Practice Questions — Application

Q1 A homeowner is choosing a cooker. Cooker A is rated at 9800 W and cooker B is rated at 10200 W. Which cooker will use the most energy in 20 minutes?

Q2 An appliance transfers 2400 J of energy in 1300 s. What is its power output?

Q3 An appliance draws 3 A of current from the mains supply (230 V). What's the power of the appliance?

Q4 It takes an appliance 8 minutes to transfer 3.6 kJ of energy. What is the power of the appliance?

Q5 A toaster is rated at 230 V and 0.9 kW. Should a 3 A, 5 A or 13 A fuse be fitted in the toaster?

Q6 How long does it take a 15 W bulb to transfer 300 J of energy?

Q7 A 2.1 kW heater is on for 30 minutes. How much energy does it transfer?

Q8 Microwave A is rated at 900 W and takes 4 minutes to cook a ready meal. Microwave B is rated at 650 W and takes 6 minutes to cook a ready meal. Assuming both microwaves are working at maximum power, which transfers the most energy in cooking the meal?

6. Energy Transfer and Charges Higher

If you're sitting the higher tier exams there's a tiny bit more you need to know on energy transfers in circuits, then you can skip on to the section summary and exam questions. Read on...

Learning Objectives:

- H Be able to calculate how much energy something transfers using the formula $E = V \times Q$.

Specification Reference
P2.4.2

Energy transferred in a circuit Higher

When an electrical charge (Q) goes through a change in potential difference (V), then energy (E) is transferred. Energy is supplied to the charge at the power source to 'raise' it through a potential. The charge gives up this energy when it 'falls' through any potential drop in components elsewhere in the circuit, as shown in Figure 1.

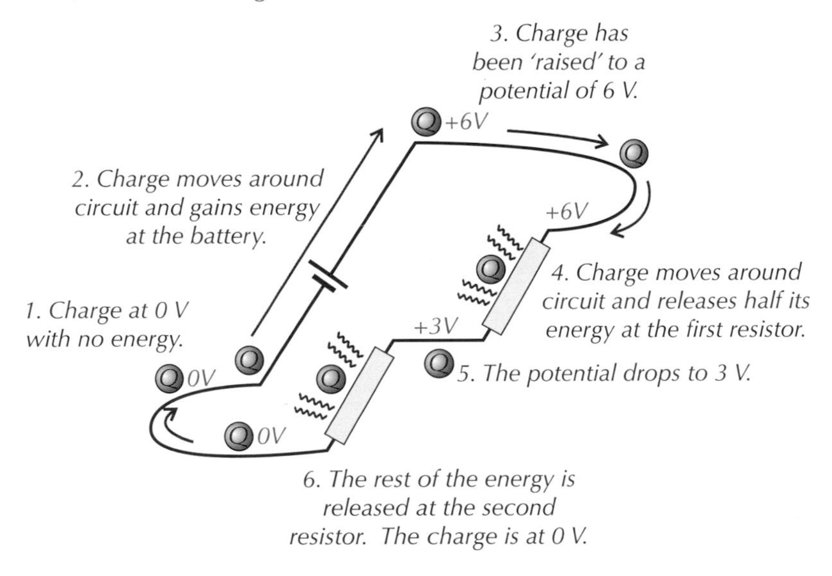

***Figure 1:** An electrical charge passing round a circuit and transferring electrical energy through circuit components. As it does this, its potential changes.*

The potential difference between two points is the energy transferred per unit charge passing between the two points and you can calculate it using this formula:

$$E = V \times Q$$

E *= energy transferred (J)*
Q *= charge (C)*
V *= potential difference (V)*

Tip: Sometimes we say energy is 'transformed'. It means the same as transferred.

The bigger the change in p.d. (or voltage), the more energy is transferred for a given amount of charge passing through the circuit.

That means that a battery with a bigger voltage will supply more energy to the circuit for every coulomb of charge which flows round it, because the charge is raised up "higher" at the start (see Figure 1) — and more energy will be transferred in the circuit too.

Example Higher

The motor in an electric toothbrush is attached to a 3 V battery. The total charge that passes a point in the motor circuit over 3 minutes is 144 C. Calculate the energy transformed by the motor. Explain why the kinetic energy output of the motor will be less than the energy you calculated.

To calculate the energy transformed you need to use the formula $E = V \times Q$.

charge = 144 C, potential difference = 3 V

$E = V \times Q = 3 \times 144 = 432$ J

The kinetic energy output of the motor will be less than 432 J because the motor won't be 100% efficient. Not all the of the energy will be transformed to kinetic energy — some of it will be transformed into sound and heat.

Tip: There's more about efficiency on page 293.

Practice Question — Fact Recall

Q1 Give the formula that links energy transferred, potential difference and charge, and state what units are used for each term.

Practice Questions — Application

Tip: If you need help rearranging equations, take a look at page 352.

Q1 240 C of charge passes through an appliance connected to a 5 V battery. How much energy does the appliance transfer?

Q2 Calculate the potential difference a 4 C charge passes through when it transfers 22 J of energy.

Section Checklist — Make sure you know...

Mains Electricity

- [ ] That cells and batteries supply direct current (d.c.), which always passes in the same direction.
- [ ] That alternating current (a.c.) changes direction constantly.
- [ ] That in the UK, the mains electricity is alternating current at 50 Hz and approximately 230 V.
- [ ] How to interpret an oscilloscope trace.
- [ ] How to calculate the potential difference of a d.c. supply, or the peak potential difference of an a.c. supply from an oscilloscope trace.
- [ ] H How to use an oscilloscope trace to work out the time period and frequency of a.c.

cont...

Electricity in the Home

- ☐ How to identify some common hazards in the use of mains electricity.
- ☐ The structure of two-core and three-core cables.
- ☐ That most electrical appliances connect to the mains by a cable and three-pin plug.
- ☐ That a live wire is brown, a neutral wire is blue and an earth wire is yellow/green.
- ☐ The structure and wiring of a three-pin plug.
- ☐ What materials are used for three-pin plugs and why they're chosen.

Safety Devices in Circuits

- ☐ How a circuit is broken by a fuse or circuit breaker if there's an electrical fault.
- ☐ How the use of a fuse compares with the use of a circuit breaker.
- ☐ How earth wires and fuses protect circuits and people if the case of an appliance becomes live.
- ☐ That cable thickness is related to the fuse rating of an appliance.
- ☐ What a Residual Current Circuit Breaker is and what it does.
- ☐ What double insulated appliances are and why they don't need to be earthed.

Energy and Efficiency in Circuits

- ☐ That electrical charge flowing through a resistor causes it to get hot.
- ☐ That electrical appliances such as filament bulbs waste a lot of energy as heat, but that there are more efficient appliances available such as CFLs.
- ☐ That the efficiency of an electrical appliance should be considered when choosing which appliance to buy and use.

Power and Energy Transfer

- ☐ How to use the formula $P = \frac{E}{t}$ to work out the power of an appliance, and that you should consider power when choosing an appliance.
- ☐ How to work out the power of an appliance using the formula $P = I \times V$, and so how to determine the size of fuse needed for an appliance by considering its power and voltage ratings.

Energy Transfer and Charges

- ☐ **H** How to calculate the energy transferred by an appliance using the formula $F = V \times Q$.

Exam-style Questions

1 A kettle with a metal casing is linked to the mains electricity using a three-core cable and a three-pin plug.

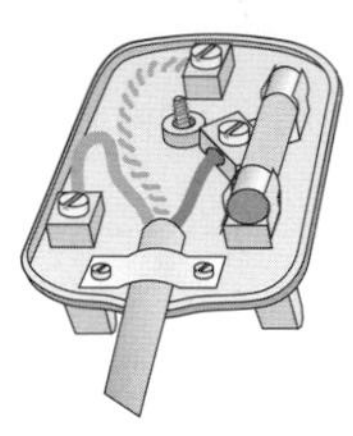

1 (a) The three-core cable has a live wire, an earth wire and a neutral wire inside it.

1 (a) (i) Complete the sentence by drawing a circle around the correct answer.

The live wire has a [brown / blue / green/yellow] coating.

(1 mark)

1 (a) (ii) State what sort of appliance can safely use a two-core cable. Explain why.

(2 marks)

1 (b) The kettle is rated at 230 V and 0.6 kW. Calculate the size of fuse that should be used in the plug from these available options: 3 A, 5 A or 13 A.

Use the correct equation from the equations listed on page 402.

Clearly show how you work out your answer.

(4 marks)

1 (c) A fault in the kettle causes a current to flow in the kettle's metal casing. The casing is connected to an earth wire. Describe the process that leads to the electricity supply being cut off.

(3 marks)

2 An electrician installs a 10.2 kW oven and a 1.2 kW dishwasher.

2 (a) Explain why the electrician should use a thicker cable to connect the oven to the mains than to connect the dishwasher.

(3 marks)

2 (b) The dishwasher is connected to an RCCB instead of being fitted with a fuse. Give one advantage of using a RCCB instead of a fuse to help protect the dishwasher user from getting a fatal electric shock.

(1 mark)

2 (c) The oven is connected to a UK mains supply and transfers 7 038 000 J of electrical energy in the time it takes to cook a meal.

2 (c) (i) Calculate how long it takes to cook the meal.

Use the correct equation from the equations listed on page 402.

Clearly show how you work out your answer.

Give your answer in seconds.

(2 marks)

2 (c) (ii) Calculate the total amount of charge that passes through the oven.

Use the correct equation from the equations listed on page 402.

Clearly show how you work out your answer.

Give your answer in coulombs.

(3 marks)

3 Look at the oscilloscope trace below. The timebase is set at 3 ms/div and the gain is set at 5 V/div.

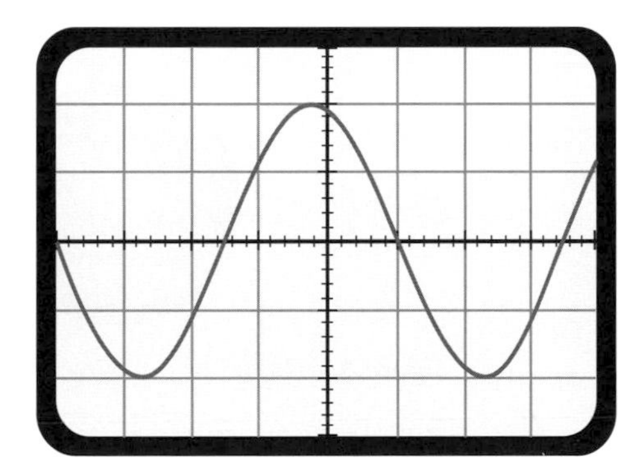

3 (a) (i) State what type of current is shown by the trace.

Give a reason for your answer.

(2 marks)

3 (a) (ii) Explain why this trace cannot be caused by connecting the oscilloscope to a battery.

(1 mark)

3 (b) Calculate the peak potential difference shown by the trace.

(2 marks)

3 (c) Calculate the frequency of the current.

Clearly show how you work out your answer.

Give your answer in Hz.

(4 marks)

Learning Objectives:
- Know what the plum pudding model of the atom is.
- Know how the results of scattering experiments by Rutherford and Marsden resulted in the plum pudding model of the atom being replaced by the current nuclear model.
- Know that according to the nuclear model, the atom is mostly empty space.

Specification Reference P2.5

1. Rutherford Scattering

You'll be learning about the 'nuclear model' of the atom shortly. But first it's time for a trip back in time to see how scientists came up with it. And it's got a bit to do with plum puddings.

The plum pudding model

The Greeks were the first to think about **atoms**. A man called Democritus in the 5th Century BC thought that all matter was made up of identical lumps called "atomos". But that's about as far as the theory got until the 1800s...

In 1804 John Dalton agreed with Democritus that matter was made up of tiny spheres ("atoms") that couldn't be broken up, but he reckoned that each element was made up of a different type of "atom".

Nearly 100 years later, J J Thomson discovered that **electrons** could be removed from atoms. So Dalton's theory wasn't quite right (atoms could be broken up). Thomson suggested that atoms were spheres of positive charge with tiny negative electrons stuck in them like plums in a plum pudding.

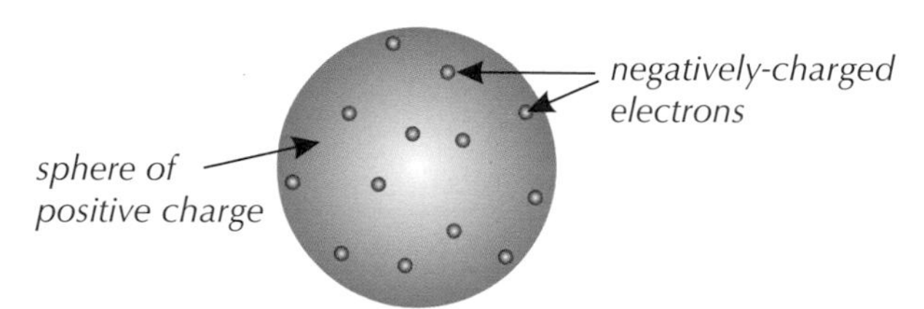

Figure 1: *The plum pudding model of the atom.*

That "plum pudding" theory didn't last very long though...

The Rutherford scattering experiment

In 1909 Rutherford and Marsden tried firing a beam of **alpha particles** (see p.307) at thin gold foil — see Figure 2. A circular detector screen surrounding the gold foil and the alpha source was used to detect alpha particles deflected by any angle.

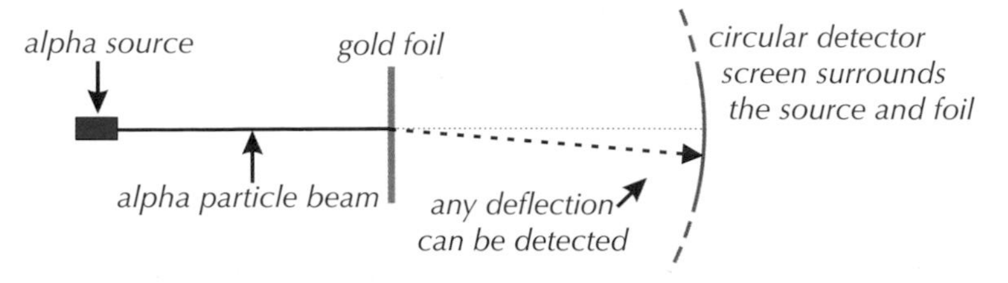

Figure 2: *The experimental set-up for detecting whether alpha particles have been scattered by gold foil.*

They expected that the positively-charged alpha particles would be deflected by the electrons by a very small amount if the plum pudding model was true.

In fact, most of the alpha particles just went straight through the foil, but the odd one came straight back at them. This was frankly a bit of a shocker for Rutherford and Marsden. The results of Rutherford scattering showed that atoms must have a small, positively-charged **nuclei** at the centre (see Figure 3).

Tip: Nuclei is the plural of nucleus.

Here's why:

- Most of the atom must be empty space because most of the alpha particles passed straight through the foil.
- The nucleus must have a large positive charge as some positively-charged alpha particles were repelled and deflected by a big angle.
- The nucleus must be small as very few alpha particles were deflected back.

Tip: Remember, like charges repel each other (page 253).

Tip: These results provided new evidence, causing the accepted model of the atom to be changed — see page 2 for more on how new theories are accepted with new evidence. HOW SCIENCE WORKS

some alpha particle are deflected by a large angle due to the large positive charge of the nucleus

a small number of alpha particles are deflected back

beam of alpha particles

nucleus

most alpha particles are not deflected

Figure 3: *A diagram showing some positively-charged alpha particles passing straight through a gold atom, and some being deflected by the atom's nucleus.*

This led Rutherford and Marsden to come up with the **nuclear model** of the atom that we still use today (see page 304).

Figure 4: *The New Zealand physicist Ernest Rutherford.*

Practice Questions — Fact Recall

Q1 Describe the plum pudding model of the atom.

Q2 What results were expected from the Rutherford scattering experiment?

Q3 What results were seen in the Rutherford scattering experiment? How did they show that the atom has a small, positively-charged nucleus and is mostly empty space?

Learning Objectives:

- Know the basic structure of the atom, according to the nuclear model.
- Understand that the nucleus is extremely small compared to the size of the atom.
- Know the relative electric charges and the relative masses of all three particles in the atom.
- Know that the atom has no charge, and that the number of protons and electrons in an atom are equal.
- Know that if an atom loses or gains an electron, it becomes a charged particle called an ion.
- Know what the atomic number and the mass number of an atom are.
- Know that all atoms of an element have the same atomic number.
- Know that atoms of an element with different mass numbers are called isotopes.

Specification Reference P2.5.1

2. Atoms and Isotopes

So now you know where the nuclear model of the atom comes from, it's time to learn all about it.

The atom

According to the nuclear model, the atom contains three types of particles:

- **electrons** (which are negatively charged),
- **protons** (which are positively charged) and
- **neutrons** (which are neutral — they have no charge).

The nucleus is at the centre of the atom. It contains protons and neutrons — which gives it an overall positive charge. It is tiny but it makes up most of the mass of the atom.

The rest of the atom is mostly empty space. The negative electrons whizz round the outside of the nucleus really fast. They give the atom its overall size — the radius of the atom's nucleus is about 10 000 times smaller than the radius of the atom. Crikey.

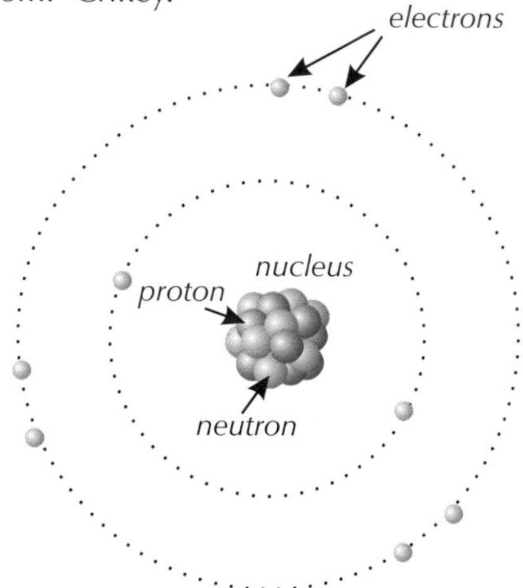

Figure 1: *The atom (not to scale).*

Tip: Particles that are smaller than an atom are called 'subatomic particles'.

Each particle has a relative mass and a relative charge. Relative just means in relation to the other particles — it's so you can compare their masses and charges. Make sure you learn the relative charge and mass of each particle:

particle	mass	charge
proton	1	+1
neutron	1	0
electron	$\frac{1}{2000}$	−1

Figure 2: *The relative masses and charges of the particles in the atom.*

Atoms have no charge overall. The charge on an electron is the same size as the charge on a proton — but opposite (see Figure 2). This means the number of protons always equals the number of electrons in a neutral atom.

Ions

Atoms are neutral, but if some electrons are added or removed, the atom becomes a charged particle called an **ion**. Different ions of the same element still have the same number of protons and neutrons, but a different number of electrons.

Tip: Atoms and ions of the same element have the same number of protons in their nuclei. An element is defined by the number of protons in the nuclei of its ions or atoms, e.g. an ion or atom with eight protons in its nucleus is the element oxygen.

Example

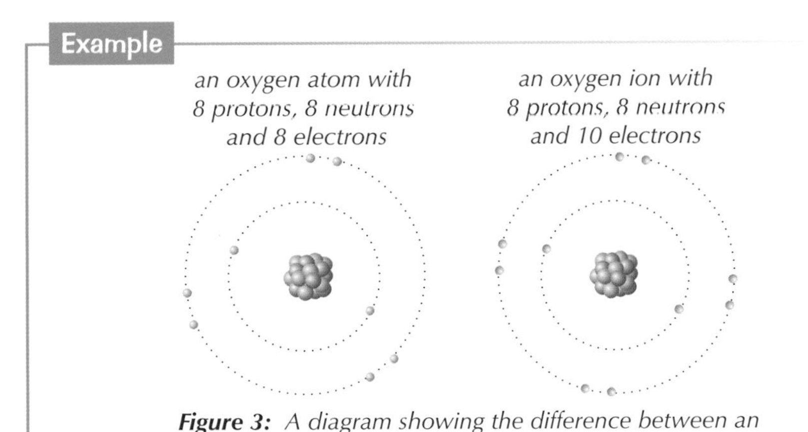

Figure 3: *A diagram showing the difference between an uncharged oxygen atom (left) and an oxygen ion (right).*

Atomic number and mass number

You need to know how to describe the number of protons and neutrons in a nucleus:

- The number of protons in the nucleus of an atom is called the **atomic number**.
- The number of protons plus the number of neutrons in the nucleus of an atom is called the **mass number**.

An element can be described using the mass number and atomic number of its atoms. The notation looks like this:

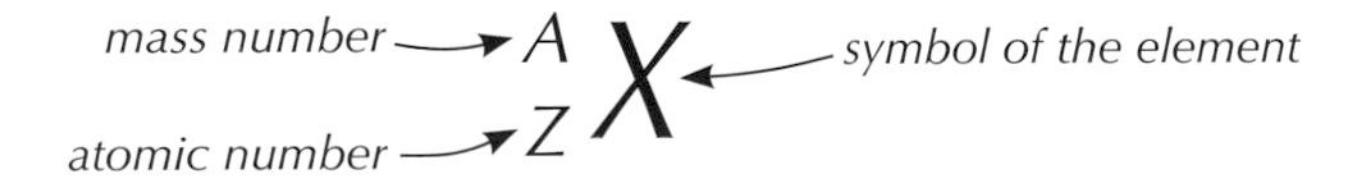

Tip: The symbol of the element is just a letter (or sometimes two letters) that tell you what element it is. For example, O is used for oxygen.

Atoms of an element always have the same atomic number, but they can have different mass numbers (see next page).

Examples

- An atom of carbon with 6 protons and 6 neutrons would be ${}^{12}_{6}C$.
- An atom of oxygen with 8 protons and 9 neutrons would be ${}^{17}_{8}O$.

Isotopes

Isotopes are different forms of the same element. Isotopes are atoms with the same number of protons but a different number of neutrons.

This means they have the same atomic number, but different mass numbers.

Example

Carbon-12 and carbon-14 are good examples of isotopes:

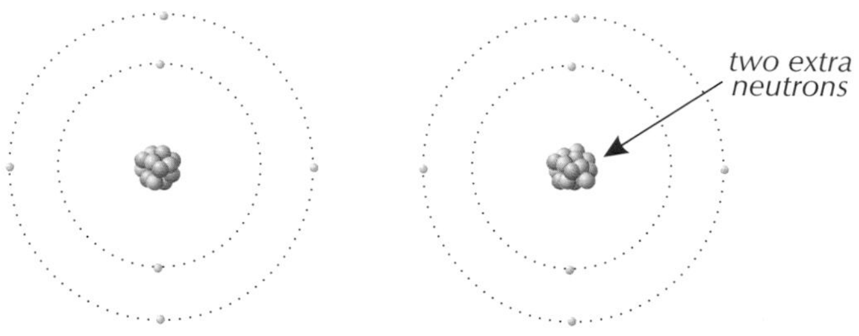

carbon-12, $^{12}_{6}C$ carbon-14, $^{14}_{6}C$

two extra neutrons

6 neutrons
6 protons

8 neutrons
6 protons

Figure 4: *Two isotopes of carbon — carbon-12 (left) and carbon-14 (right).*

Most elements have different isotopes, but there's usually only one or two stable ones. The other isotopes tend to be radioactive, which means they decay into other elements and give out radiation (see next page).

Practice Questions — Fact Recall

Q1 What three types of particle make up an atom?

Q2 Which subatomic particle is not found in the nucleus?

Q3 What is the relative mass and charge of a neutron?

Q4 What can you say about the number of protons and electrons in a neutral atom? Why?

Q5 What is meant by atomic number and mass number?

Q6 What can you say about the atomic number of two atoms of the same element?

Q7 What is an isotope of an element?

Practice Question — Application

Q1 Particle A has 17 protons, 18 neutrons and 18 electrons.
Particle B has 17 protons and 20 neutrons and 17 electrons.

a) What is the overall charge of particle A?

b) Explain how you know that particle A is an ion.

c) Explain how you know that particles A and B are isotopes of the same element.

Tip: You can work out the overall charge on a particle by adding up the relative charges of all its subatomic particles.

3. Radioactivity

Radioactivity is all to do with things randomly giving out radiation. Some radiation is ionising, which means it can knock electrons off atoms to create ions. You need to know about three types of ionising radiation.

Learning Objectives:

- Know that radioactive decay is the process of radioactive substances giving out radiation from the nuclei of their atoms.
- Know that radioactive decay is completely random and will happen all the time, no matter what is done to a radioactive substance.
- Know what alpha, beta and gamma radiation are made of.
- Be able to compare the ionising powers and penetrations through air and materials of alpha, beta and gamma radiation.
- H Be able to balance nuclear equations for alpha and beta decay.
- Know that alpha and beta radiation are deflected by magnetic and electric fields, but gamma isn't.
- H Be able to explain the behaviour of alpha, beta and gamma radiation in a magnetic and electric field in terms of their relative mass and charge.

Specification Reference P2.5.2

Radioactive decay

Radioactive substances give out radiation from the nuclei of their atoms all the time — no matter what is done to them. This process is called **radioactive decay**.

This process is entirely random. This means that if you have 1000 unstable nuclei, you can't say when any one of them is going to decay, and neither can you do anything at all to make a decay happen. It's completely unaffected by physical conditions like temperature or by any sort of chemical bonding etc.

Unstable isotopes of elements will decay into stable ones by radioactive decay.

Radioactive substances give out one or more of these three types of radiation as they decay — **alpha**, **beta** or **gamma**.

Alpha decay

An alpha particle, α, is two neutrons and two protons — the same as a helium nucleus. When an atom decays by emitting an alpha particle, two protons and two neutrons are lost from the nucleus.

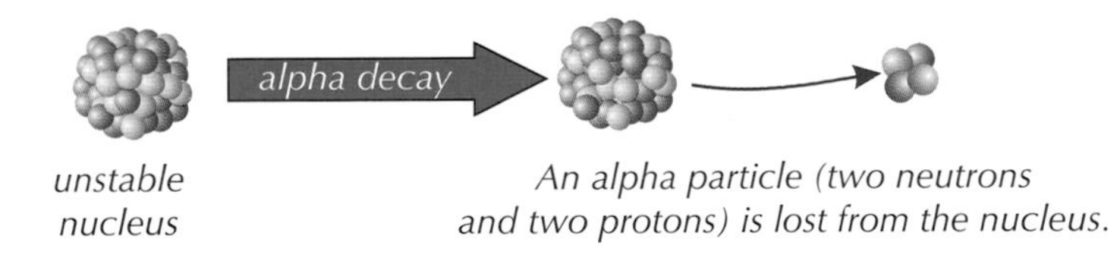

Figure 1: *An unstable nucleus decaying by emitting an alpha particle.*

Alpha particles are relatively big, heavy and slow moving. This means they don't penetrate very far into materials and are stopped quickly, even when travelling through air.

Because of their size they are strongly ionising, which just means they bash into a lot of atoms and knock electrons off them before they slow down, which creates lots of ions — hence the term "ionising" (see Figure 3).

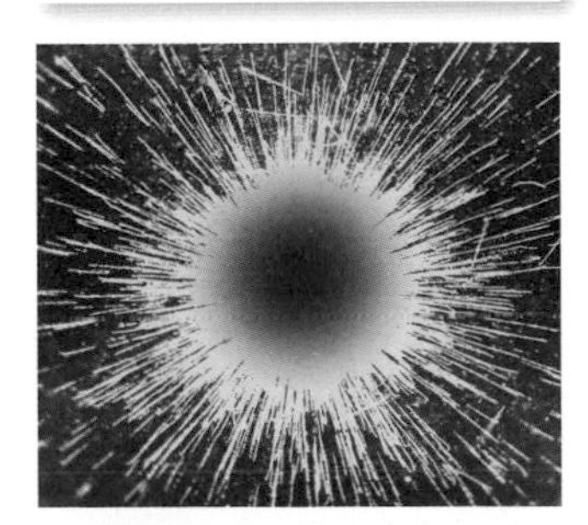

Figure 2: *Yellow tracks showing the paths of alpha particles emitted from a radioactive substance.*

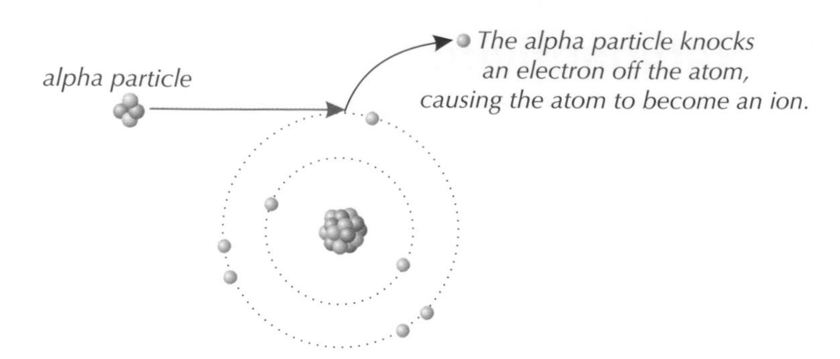

Figure 3: *An alpha particle ionising an atom.*

Beta decay

A **beta particle**, β, is just an electron so it has virtually no mass and a relative charge of –1 (see page 304).

When a nucleus decays by beta decay, a neutron turns into a proton in the nucleus, which releases a β-particle.

Tip: You don't need to know why a neutron turning into a proton releases a beta particle, just make sure you know that it comes from the nucleus. It's not just one of the electrons that are whizzing around outside the nucleus jumping off.

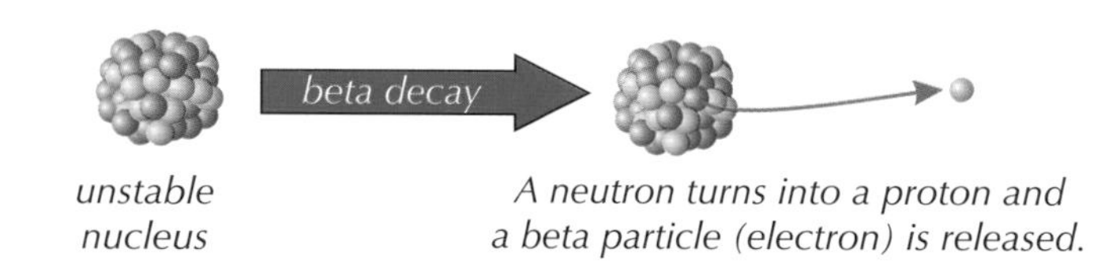

Figure 4: *An unstable nucleus decaying by emitting a beta particle.*

Beta particles move quite fast and they are quite small. They penetrate moderately into materials before colliding, have a long range in air, and are moderately ionising too.

Tip: Beta particles are in between alpha and gamma in terms of their properties.

Gamma decay

Gamma rays, γ, are very short wavelength electromagnetic (EM) waves. Gamma rays have no mass and no charge.

They penetrate far into materials without being stopped and pass straight through air. This means they are weakly ionising because they tend to pass through rather than collide with atoms. Eventually they hit something and do damage.

Tip: Gamma radiation is slightly different to alpha and beta radiation because it's an EM wave instead of a particle.

Nuclear equations Higher

You can write alpha and beta decays as nuclear equations. They are just equations that show what atoms you started with, what radiation was emitted and what atoms you're left with. The mass and atomic numbers have to balance up on both sides of the equation (before and after decay).

You'll need to be familiar with the notation on page 305, and how alpha and beta particles can be written in this notation.

- Alpha particles are helium nuclei (symbol: He or α) with 2 protons and 2 neutrons, so they are written $^{4}_{2}He$.

- Beta particles are electrons (symbol: e or β) so they have no protons or neutrons, and the mass number is 0. The number of protons is also 0, but we write –1 where the atomic number goes because a beta particle has a charge of –1. This helps us balance the charges on each side. So a beta particle is written $^{0}_{-1}e$.

Tip: **H** Gamma rays (symbol: γ) have no protons or neutrons and no charge so we just write them as $^{0}_{0}\gamma$.

Example **Higher**

Uranium-238 can decay into thorium-234 by emitting an alpha particle. Uranium has 92 protons and thorium has 90 protons.

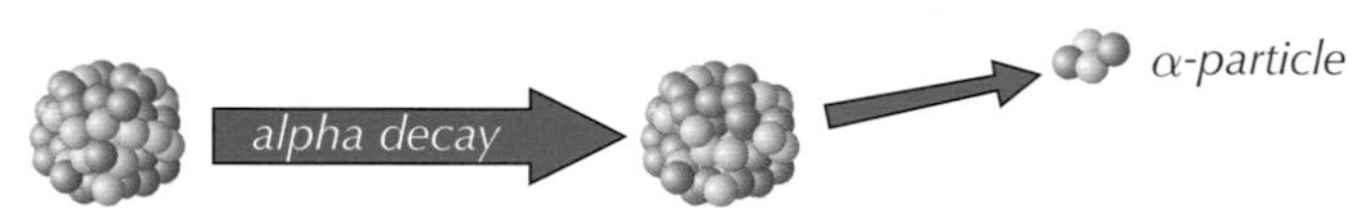

The nuclear equation for this decay looks like this:

$$^{238}_{92}U \rightarrow \, ^{234}_{90}Th + \, ^{4}_{2}He$$

On the left-hand side:

- The mass number is 238.
- The atomic number is 92.

On the right-hand side:

- The total of the mass numbers is: 234 + 4 + 0 = 238.
- The total of the atomic numbers is: 90 + 2 + 0 = 92.

So both sides of the equation balance.

Example **Higher**

Balance the following equation: $^{238}_{94}Pu \rightarrow \, ^{234}_{\dots}U + \, ^{\dots}_{2}He$

Make these equations balance: 238 → 234 + ...

94 → ..... + 2

Balancing mass numbers, 238 = 234 + **4**, so the mass number of He is 4.

Balancing atomic numbers, 94 = **92** + 2, so the atomic number of U is 92.

The full equation is:

$$^{238}_{94}Pu \rightarrow \, ^{234}_{92}U + \, ^{4}_{2}He$$

Exam Tip **H**
You won't have to work out what the elements are (e.g. Pu, U) in nuclear equations. You only need to be able to balance the atomic and mass numbers and identify the type of decay (alpha or beta).

Balancing nuclear equations is pretty similar for beta decay too.

Example **Higher**

Carbon-14 can decay into nitrogen-14 by emitting a beta particle (when a neutron turns into a proton).

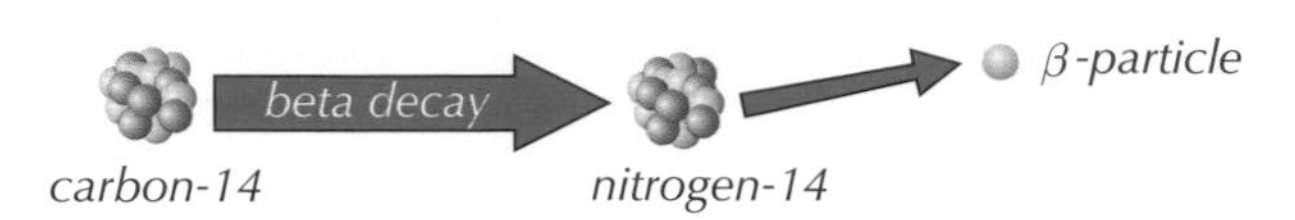

The equation is:

$$^{14}_{6}C \rightarrow ^{14}_{7}N + ^{0}_{-1}e$$

and the mass and atomic numbers balance on each side. Brill.

Electric and magnetic fields

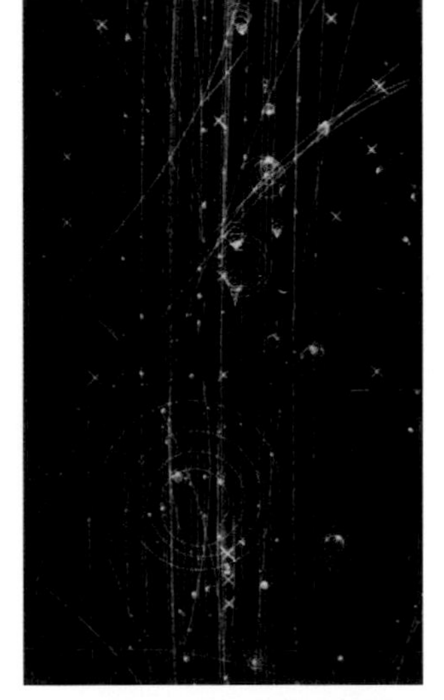

Figure 5: A bubble chamber image showing beta particles (yellow tracks) spiralling in a magnetic field. Bubble or cloud chambers are what scientists use to show the paths of particles.

Both alpha and beta particles are charged. Because of this, when travelling through a magnetic or electric field, they'll both be deflected. Alpha particles have a positive charge and beta particles have a negative charge, they're deflected in opposite directions because of their opposite charges. Alpha particles are deflected less than beta particles (see Figure 6).

Gamma radiation is an electromagnetic (EM) wave and has no charge, so it doesn't get deflected by electric or magnetic fields.

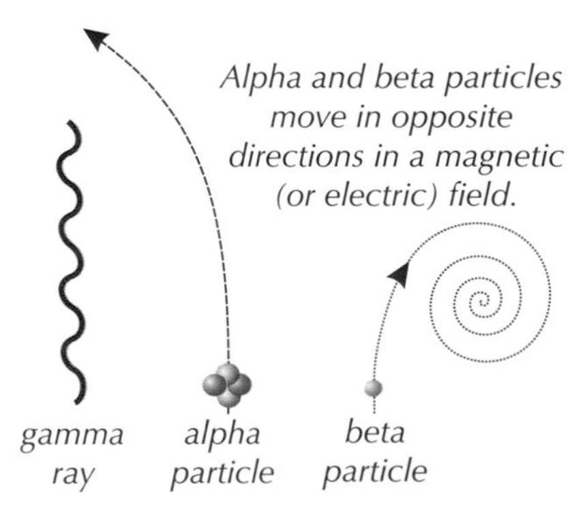

Figure 6: A diagram to show the behaviour of alpha, beta and gamma radiation in a magnetic field.

Higher

Alpha particles have a larger charge than beta particles, and feel a greater force in magnetic and electric fields. But because they have a much greater mass than beta particles, they are deflected less.

Practice Questions — Fact Recall

Q1 What does it mean if a substance is radioactive?

Q2 How can you change the rate of radioactive decay?

Q3 Name the three types of ionising radiation given out by radioactive substances.

Q4 Describe what each type of radiation named in Q3 is made of.

Q5 Which is the most strongly ionising radiation? Which will penetrate furthest through a material? Which will penetrate the least through air?

Q6 What two numbers need to be the same on both sides of a nuclear equation?

Q7 Which type of ionising radiation is not deflected by a magnetic or electric field?

Q8 Which type of ionising radiation is deflected the most by a magnetic or electric field?

Q9 Explain your answer to Q8.

Practice Questions — Application

Q1 This diagram shows the paths of three types of radiation, A, B and C, being directed towards a human hand and a thick metal sheet.

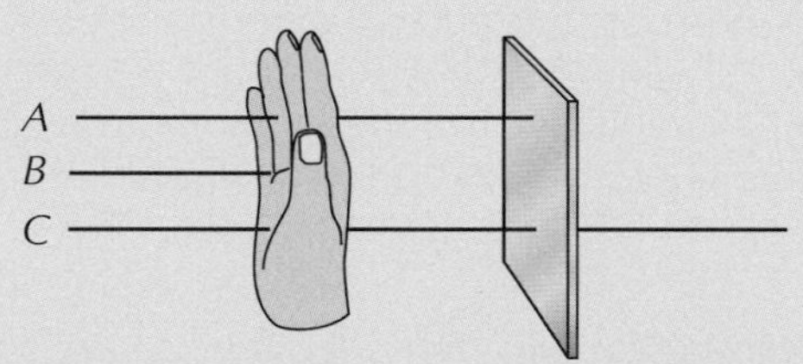

a) Which radiation (A or B) is more penetrating? How can you tell?

b) Which radiation (A or B) is most likely to be alpha radiation. Explain why.

c) Explain what radiation C is likely to be and how you know.

Q2 Americium-241 decays into neptunium-237.
The nuclear equation for this decay is:

$$^{241}_{95}\text{Am} \rightarrow \, ^{237}_{93}\text{Np} + \, ^{4}_{2}\text{He}$$

What type of decay is this — alpha or beta?

Q3 Radium-228 decays into actinium-228 by emitting an electron.

a) What is the name of this decay?

b) The incomplete nuclear equation for this decay is:

$$^{\dots\dots}_{88}\text{Ra} \rightarrow \, ^{228}_{\dots\dots}\text{Ac} + \, ^{0}_{-1}\text{e}$$

Complete the equation.

4. Half-life

Radioactive samples give out less and less radiation over time, but they never stop giving out radiation altogether.

Learning Objectives:
- Know that radioactive half-life is the average time it takes for the number of nuclei of a radioactive isotope in a sample to halve.
- Know that half-life of a radioactive sample can be found by measuring the time it takes for the count rate to reach half its initial level.

Specification Reference P2.5.2

Radioactive half-life

The radioactivity of a sample always decreases over time. This is pretty obvious when you think about it. Each time a decay happens and an alpha, beta or gamma is given out, it means one more radioactive nucleus has disappeared.

Obviously, as the unstable nuclei all steadily disappear, the **activity** (the number of nuclei that decay per second) will decrease. So the older a sample becomes, the less radiation it will emit.

Tip: Remember, the plural of nucleus is nuclei.

How quickly the activity drops off varies a lot. For some substances it takes just a few microseconds before nearly all the unstable nuclei have decayed, whilst for others it can take millions of years.

The problem with trying to measure this is that the activity never reaches zero, which is why we have to use the idea of **half-life** to measure how quickly the activity drops off.

Learn this definition of half-life:

Tip: Remember, an unstable isotope will decay to become stable. This means it is radioactive.

> Half-life is the average time it takes for the number of nuclei of a radioactive isotope in a sample to halve.

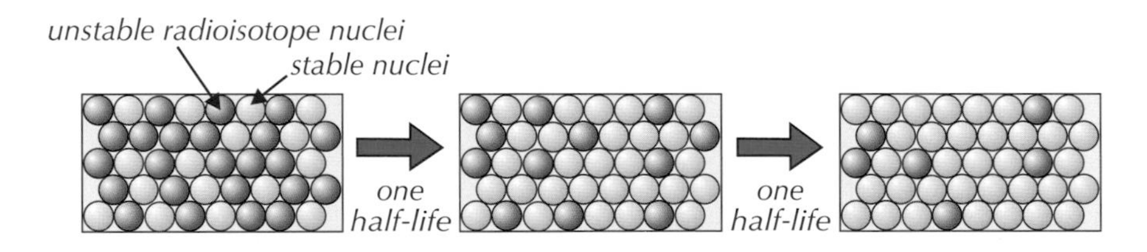

Figure 1: *A diagram showing how the number of unstable nuclei in a radioactive sample decreases over two half-lives.*

In other words, it is the time it takes for the count rate (the number of radioactive emissions detected per unit of time) from a sample containing the isotope to fall to half its initial level.

Tip: Count rate is just a measure of the activity of a radioactive sample.

- A short half-life means the activity falls quickly, because lots of the nuclei decay quickly.
- A long half-life means the activity falls more slowly because most of the nuclei don't decay for a long time — they just sit there, basically unstable, but kind of biding their time.

Calculating half-life

You can work out the half-life of a radioactive isotope if you're given a little information. Or if you know the half-life, you can work out how long it will take for the activity to drop a certain amount.

Half-life is maybe a little confusing, but exam calculations on it are straightforward so long as you do them slowly, step by step. Like this one:

Example

The activity of a radioisotope is 640 cpm (counts per minute). Two hours later it has fallen to 80 cpm. Find the half-life of the sample.

You must go through it in short simple steps like this:

initial count		*after one half-life*		*after two half-lives*		*after three half-lives*
↓		↓		↓		↓
640	(÷2)	320	(÷2)	160	(÷2)	80

It takes three half-lives for the activity to fall from 640 to 80. Hence two hours represents three half-lives, so the half-life is 120 mins ÷ 3 = 40 minutes.

Tip: A radioisotope is just a radioactive isotope.

Tip: Counts per minute (or counts per second) is a measure of radioactive activity. It measures activity by how many 'counts' of ionising radiation are absorbed by a detector per minute (or per second). You might also be given activity in becquerels (Bq). 1 Bq means one nucleus decaying per second.

Using graphs

You can plot or use a graph of radioactive activity against time to work out the half-life of a radioactive isotope.

The data for the graph will usually be several readings of activity which may have been taken with a **Geiger counter** — a particle detector that measures activity.

The graph will always be shaped like the one shown in Figure 3 (see next page).

The half-life is found from the graph by finding the time interval on the bottom axis corresponding to a halving of the activity on the vertical axis.

Example

Figure 3 shows how the activity of a radioactive sample decreases with time. The half-life of the graph can be found as follows:

- The initial activity is 80, so after one half-life it will be 40 (and after two it will be 20 and after three it will be 10).
- To find the half-life of the sample, draw a line from 40 on the activity axis across to the curve and down to the time axis (green dotted line). This tells you that the half-life is 4 hours.
- You can check you were right by doing the same for an activity of 20 and checking that you get a time of 8, and so on...

Figure 2: *You can do an experiment to simulate half-life using cubes with one black face. The cubes represent unstable nuclei and if they land black-side up, they have 'decayed'. Take note of how many cubes you start with and throw them all, removing any that 'decay'. Then throw the rest again. Plotting your results on a graph will allow you to calculate the 'half-life' in 'number of throws'.*

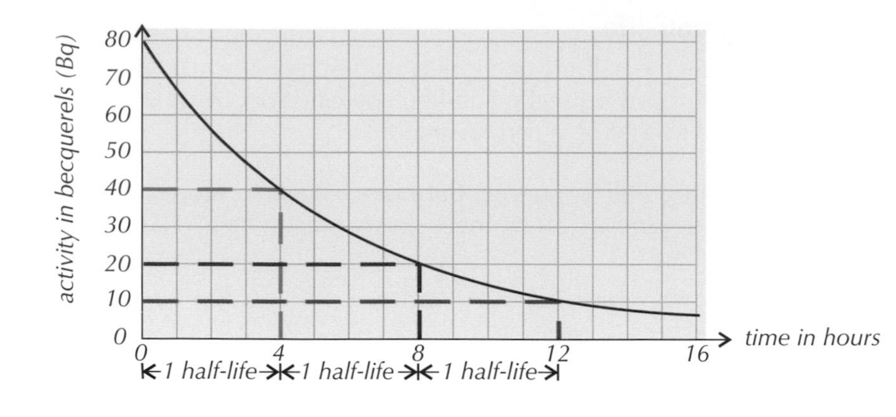

Figure 3: *A graph of activity against time for a radioisotope.*

Practice Questions — Fact Recall

Q1 Why can we not measure the time it takes for a radioactive sample to decay completely?

Q2 Write down two definitions of half-life.

Practice Questions — Application

Q1 A radioactive source with a half-life of 15 minutes has an initial count rate of 240 cpm. What will the count rate be after 1 hour?

Q2 A radioactive source has an initial count rate of 16 cpm and after 2 hours it has decreased to 4 cpm. What is the half-life of this source?

Q3 Find the half-life of the radioisotope from this graph of the activity of the radioisotope against time.

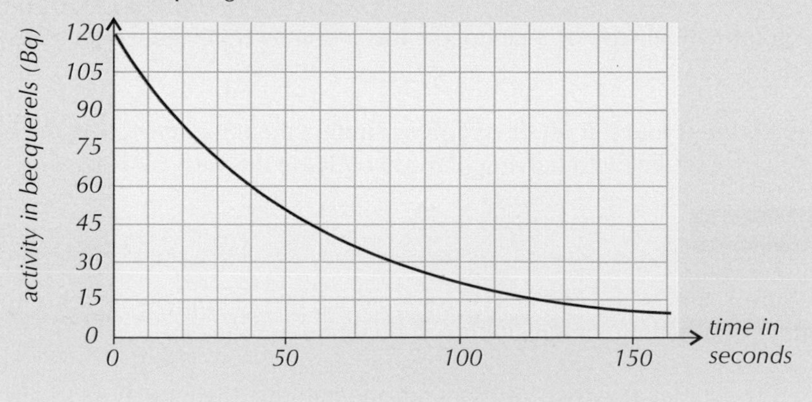

Tip: Make sure you read the axes carefully — you don't want to be saying the half-life is 'so many' hours when it's actually 'so many' seconds.

5. Exposure to Radiation

Where you live and what you do as a job can affect how much radiation you are exposed to, so you need to be aware of where it comes from.

Learning Objectives:

- Know that background radiation is radiation that is all around us, and know where it comes from.
- Know the effects of living in certain locations or having certain jobs on the level of background radiation and radiation dose that people receive.

Specification Reference
P2.5, P2.5.2

What is radiation dose?

You'll see later that radiation can cause damage to humans, including cancer or even death (see page 318). How likely you are to suffer damage if you're exposed to nuclear radiation depends on the radiation dose.

Radiation dose is the amount of energy absorbed by your body from the radiation. It depends on the type and amount of radiation you've been exposed to. The higher the radiation dose, the more at risk you are of developing cancer.

Background radiation

Background radiation is radiation that is present at all times, all around us, wherever you go. The background radiation we receive comes from many sources, including:

- Radioactivity of naturally occurring unstable isotopes which are all around us — in the air, in food, in building materials and in the rocks under our feet.
- Radiation from space, which is known as **cosmic rays**. These come mostly from the Sun.
- Radiation due to man-made sources, e.g. fallout from nuclear weapons tests, nuclear accidents (such as Chernobyl — see Figure 1) or dumped nuclear waste.

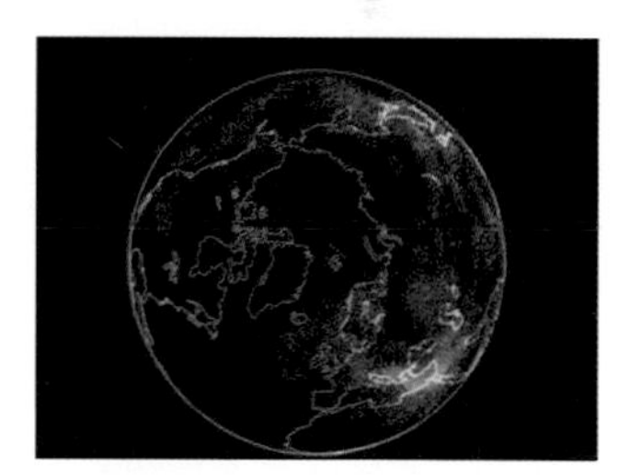

Figure 1: A simulation of the radiation (pink) in the northern hemisphere ten days after the Chernobyl disaster in which a nuclear power plant in the Ukraine exploded in 1986 and released lots of radiation.

Example

Figure 2 shows that more than half of the background radiation in the UK comes from radon gas produced by rocks and only 1% comes from the nuclear industry.

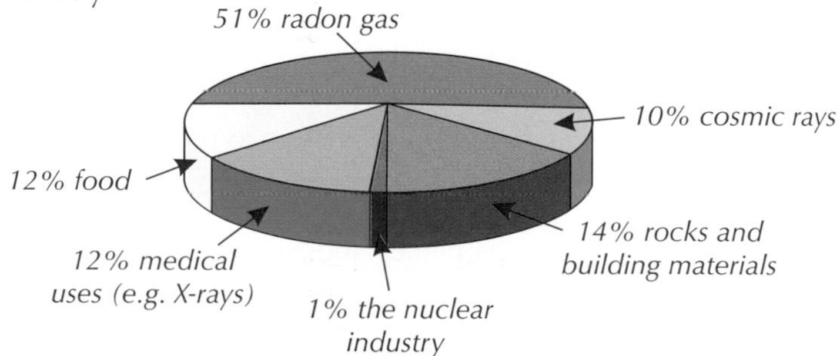

Figure 2: A pie chart showing the relative proportions of background radiation in the UK from different sources.

Effect of location and occupation

The amount of radiation you're exposed to (and hence your radiation dose) can be affected by your location and occupation.

Figure 3: A radon detector in the home. Radioactive radon gas can become trapped in a home. A radon detector can tell you if your house has a dangerous level of radon and a radon outlet pipe can be used to keep the level down.

Location

Examples

- Certain underground rocks (e.g. granite) can cause higher levels of radiation at the surface, especially if they release radioactive radon gas, which tends to get trapped inside people's houses.

Figure 4: A map of the United Kingdom showing radiation from rocks. The scale shows how the radiation from rocks in different areas varies.

- People who live at high altitudes are exposed to more background radiation in the form of cosmic rays than people who live at sea level.

Occupation

Tip: Uranium is mined to use as a fuel for nuclear power stations — see page 328.

Examples

- Nuclear industry workers and uranium miners are typically exposed to 10 times the normal amount of radiation. They wear protective clothing and face masks to stop them from touching or inhaling the radioactive material, and monitor their radiation doses with special radiation badges and regular check-ups.

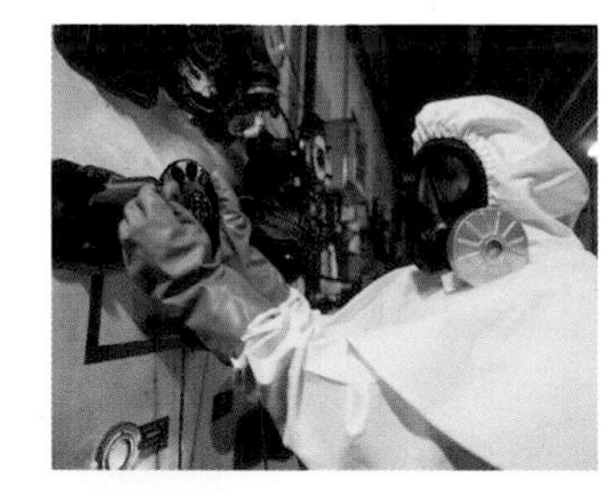

Figure 5: A nuclear power station worker wearing a radiation suit.

- Radiographers work in hospitals using ionising radiation and so have a higher risk of radiation exposure. They wear lead aprons and stand behind lead screens to protect them from prolonged exposure to radiation.
- At high altitudes (e.g. in jet planes) the background radiation increases because of more exposure to cosmic rays. That means pilots and crew have an increased risk of getting some types of cancer.
- Underground (e.g. in mines, etc.) the radiation dose increases because of the rocks all around, posing a risk to miners.

Practice Questions — Fact Recall

Q1 Give three main sources of background radiation.

Q2 Why do people living in locations with certain underground rocks get a higher radiation dose than people living in other areas?

Q3 Name four occupations in which workers are exposed to more radiation than in other occupations. Explain why these workers are exposed to more radiation.

Practice Question — Application

Q1 An astronaut working aboard the International Space Station (ISS), which orbits the Earth, is worried that his job puts him at risk of a higher dose of background radiation.

a) What source of background radiation is likely to be higher on board the ISS than on Earth? Explain why.

b) The crew of the ISS are regularly changed. Suggest why.

6. Dangers of Radioactivity

Learning Objectives:

- Know about the dangers linked to the different types of nuclear radiation and be able to evaluate the potential hazards that are associated with the use of nuclear radiation.
- Be able to evaluate the safety precautions that can be taken to reduce exposure to radiation.

Specification References
P2.5, P2.5.2

So you've seen that your radiation dose can depend on what you do and where you live... but why do we care? This topic's all about what radiation actually does to you and what precautions you should take if you have to work with it.

Effect of radiation on living cells

Ionising radiation can be very harmful to living cells. Alpha, beta and gamma radiation will enter living cells and collide with molecules. These collisions cause ionisation, which damages or destroys the molecules.

Lower doses tend to cause minor damage without killing the cell. This can give rise to mutant cells which divide uncontrollably — see Figure 1. The cells keep dividing, making more cells and forming a tumour — this uncontrolled cell division is cancer.

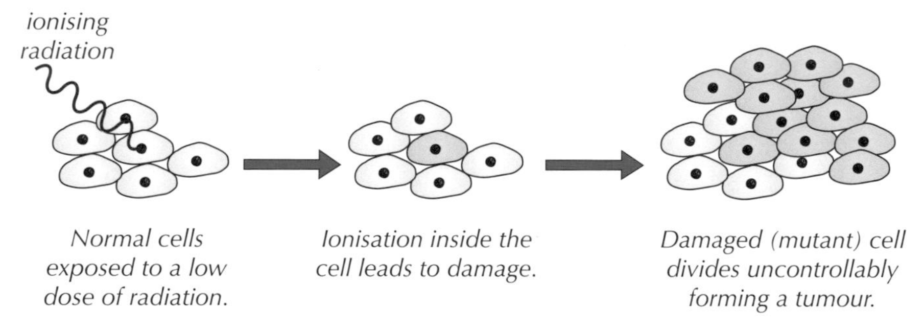

Figure 1: *A cell being damaged by a low dose of radiation, leading to it multiplying uncontrollably.*

Higher doses tend to kill cells completely, which causes radiation sickness if a lot of body cells are killed at once.

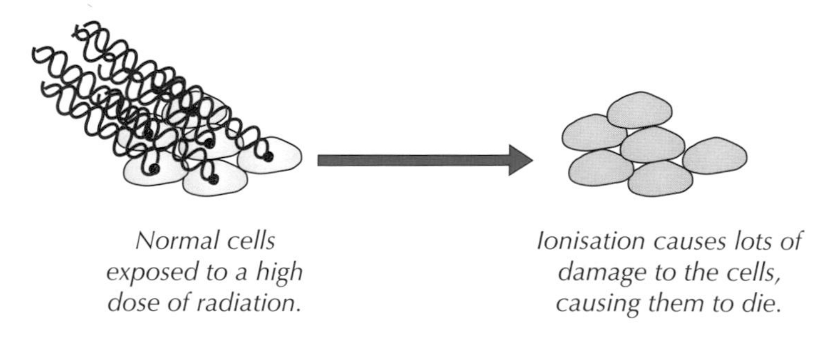

Figure 2: *Cells being killed by a high dose of radiation.*

The extent of the harmful effects of radiation depends on two things:

- How much exposure you have to the radiation (see page 315).
- The energy and penetration of the radiation, since some types are more hazardous than others (see page 307-308).

Which type of radiation is the most dangerous?

Outside the body, beta and gamma sources are the most dangerous. This is because beta and gamma can get inside to the delicate organs, whereas alpha is much less dangerous because it can't penetrate the skin.

Examples

- Gamma radiation is very dangerous to people's health in the event of a radiation leak or nuclear disaster because it can travel so far and every organ in your body is exposed to it.
- Beta radiation doesn't penetrate as much as gamma, but most beta particles can penetrate into your skin a little, and possibly damage your skin and eyes. Some more energetic beta particles can penetrate further into the skin and reach your organs.

Inside the body, an alpha source is the most dangerous. Inside the body alpha sources do all their damage in a very localised area and are highly ionising. Beta and gamma sources on the other hand are less dangerous inside the body because they mostly pass straight out without doing much damage.

Examples

- Radioactive radon gas (see page 316) mostly undergoes alpha decay. This means that radon gas in the home is not that dangerous if it stays outside the body. But radon gas becomes very dangerous when inhaled into the body and can cause cancers by damaging cells inside the body.
- Radioactive polonium-210 is present in cigarette smoke. It is an alpha emitter and cigarette tar causes it to become trapped in the lungs and airways, where it bombards cells with a high dose of highly ionising alpha radiation.

Safety precautions

Obviously radioactive materials need to be handled carefully. But in the exam they might ask you to evaluate some specific precautions that should be taken when handling radioactive materials. Here are a few:

- When conducting experiments, use radioactive sources for as short a time as possible so your exposure is kept to a minimum.
- Never allow skin contact with a source. Always handle with tongs.
- Hold the source at arm's length to keep it as far from the body as possible. This will decrease the amount of radiation that hits you, especially for alpha particles as they don't travel far in air.
- Keep the source pointing away from the body and avoid looking directly at it.

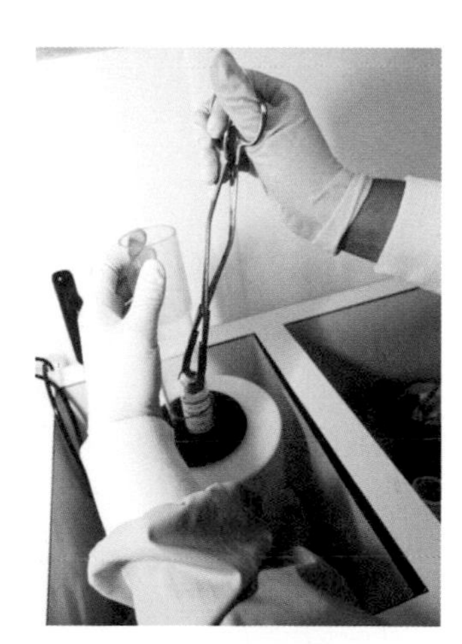

Figure 3: *Gloved hands handling a radioactive substance with tongs. The substance is being removed from its lead storage container.*

Lead absorbs all three types of radiation (though a lot of it is needed to stop gamma radiation completely) so it can be used to protect you from radiation.

- Always store radioactive sources in a lead box and put them away as soon as the experiment is over.
- Medical professionals who work with radiation every day (such as radiographers — see page 322) wear lead aprons and stand behind lead screens for extra protection because of its radiation-absorbing properties.
- When someone needs a medical procedure that uses radiation, only the area of the body that needs to be treated is exposed to radiation. The rest of the body is protected with lead or other radiation-absorbing materials.

Practice Questions — Fact Recall

Q1 Explain how radiation can cause cancer.

Q2 How can radiation cause cell death?

Q3 Which type(s) of ionising radiation is most dangerous inside the body? Why?

Q4 Which type(s) of ionising radiation is most dangerous outside the body? Why?

Q5 Give four precautions you should take when handling a radioactive source.

Q6 Name a material that absorbs all three types of radiation.

Practice Question — Application

Q1 Marie Curie was a scientist who won Nobel prizes in Chemistry and Physics for her work on radioactivity. She was unaware of the health risks of radiation and took no health precautions, often carrying around test tubes of radioactive isotopes in her pocket. She died in 1934 from a disease thought to be caused by exposure to radiation.

a) Explain why carrying radioactive isotopes in your pocket would be dangerous.

b) Marie Curie's papers and even her cookbook are still radioactive. Explain why they must be kept in lead boxes.

c) Anyone who handles Marie Curie's papers must sign a consent form saying that they are doing so at their own risk.

Suggest some safety measures that someone who is going to handle the papers should take and explain how they would minimise the radiation dose received by the person whilst handling them.

7. Uses of Radioactivity

Ionising radiation gets loads of bad press, but it is pretty essential in all sorts of everyday situations from detecting fires to sterilising food. And while it can cause cancer, it can also help to treat it.

Learning Objectives:

- Know some of the ways the different types of nuclear radiation can be used.
- Understand why each type of radiation is appropriate for different uses.

Specification References
P2.5, P2.5.2

Smoke detectors

Smoke detectors use alpha radiation to work. A weak source of alpha radiation is placed in the detector, close to two electrodes. The alpha particles cause ionisation of molecules in the air by knocking off electrons, so a current can flow between the electrodes. If there is a fire then smoke will absorb the radiation — so the current stops and the alarm sounds.

Beta or gamma sources should never be used as their range is too long, so you could be exposed to radiation in your home. A alpha source with a long half-life should be used so that it doesn't need replacing too often.

Figure 1: *A radioactive alpha source inside a smoke detector, marked with the hazard symbol for radioactivity.*

Tip: There's more on half-life on page 312.

Medical tracers

Certain radioactive isotopes can be injected into people (or they can just swallow them) and their progress around the body can be followed using an external detector. These isotopes are known as medical tracers. A computer converts the reading from the external detector to a display showing where the strongest reading is coming from.

Example

A well-known example is the use of iodine-131, which is absorbed by the thyroid gland in the neck just like normal iodine-127, but it gives out gamma radiation. The radiation can be detected to indicate whether the thyroid gland is taking in iodine as it should.

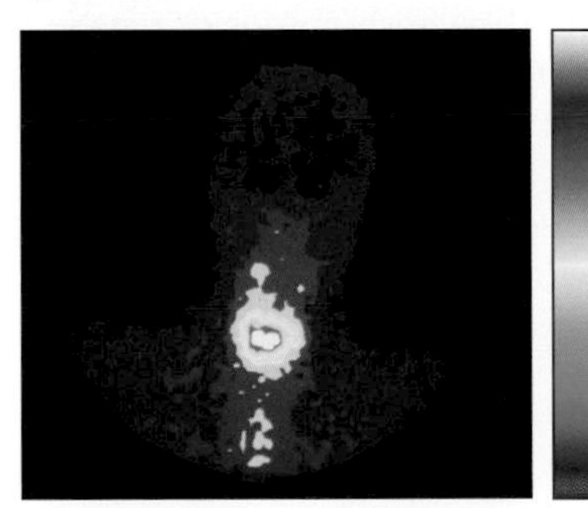

Figure 2: *An image of the gamma radiation detected from a person who has been injected with gamma-emitter iodine-131. The image shows that most gamma radiation is coming from the thyroid, indicating that the iodine-131 has collected there.*

Tip: The intensity of gamma radiation means the amount detected per unit time.

All isotopes which are taken into the body must be gamma or beta emitters, so that the radiation passes out of the body. Alpha sources should never be used as they are highly ionising and do their damage in a localised area — see page 319. The source should only last a few hours too, so that the radioactivity inside the patient quickly disappears (i.e. they should have a short half-life).

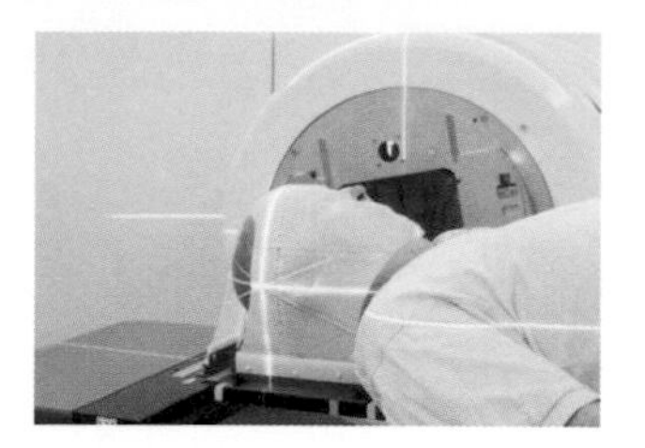

Figure 3: A male undergoing radiotherapy for brain cancer. The laser crosshair marks the point where the radiation should be focused, and a head brace is worn to keep the head perfectly still.

Radiotherapy

Radiotherapy is the treatment of cancer using ionising radiation, e.g. gamma rays. Since high doses of radiation will kill all living cells (page 318), including cancer cells.

The radiation has to be directed carefully and at just the right dosage so as to kill the cancer cells without damaging too many normal cells.

A fair bit of damage is done to normal cells though, which makes the patient feel very ill. But if the cancer is successfully killed off in the end, then it's worth it.

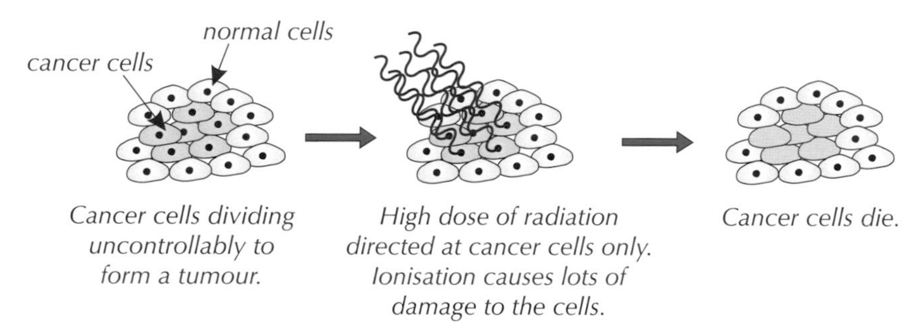

Figure 4: Radiation being used to kill cancer cells.

Sterilisation

Tip: Microbes are living organisms that break down food, causing it to look, taste or smell bad.

Tip: Irradiation just means exposing something to radiation.

Food can be exposed to a high dose of gamma rays which will kill all microbes, keeping the food fresh for longer. Medical instruments can be sterilised in just the same way, rather than by boiling them.

The great advantage of irradiation over boiling is that it doesn't involve high temperatures, so things like fresh apples or plastic instruments can be totally sterilised without damaging them. Food sterilised in this way is not radioactive afterwards, so it's perfectly safe to eat.

The isotope used for this needs to be a very strong emitter of gamma rays with a reasonably long half-life (at least several months) so that it doesn't need replacing too often.

Example

Irradiation of fruit can prolong its life for many days. In Figure 5, the strawberries that haven't been irradiated have gone mouldy due to the action of microbes. However, the strawberries that have been irradiated still look fresh several days later because the microbes have been killed.

Figure 5: Strawberries that have been irradiated (left) and that haven't (right). Both of them have been left for several days.

Practice Questions — Fact Recall

Q1 Why would it be dangerous to use a beta source in a smoke alarm?

Q2 Explain how medical tracers work. Which types of ionising radiation sources can be used and why?

Q3 What is radiotherapy? What sort of radiation does it use — alpha, beta or gamma?

Practice Question — Application

Q1 Radioactivity can be used to measure the thickness of paper during manufacture. A beta source is placed on one side of the paper, and a detector detects how much beta radiation gets through it.

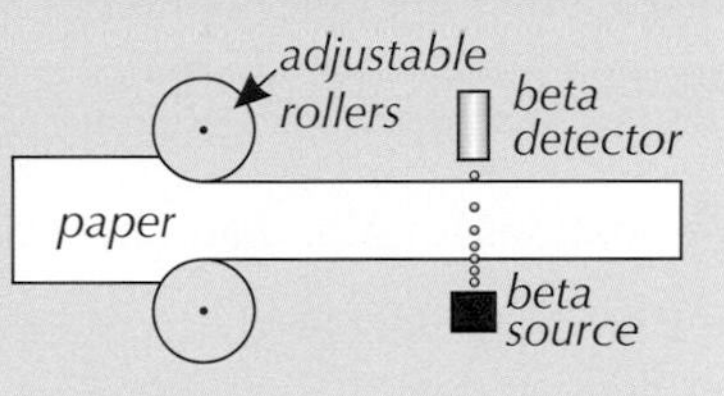

If too much is getting through the paper is too thin and if too little gets through it is too thick, so the rollers are adjusted.

a) Explain why this process couldn't use:

(i) an alpha source. (ii) a gamma source.

b) A beta source with quite a long half-life is used. Explain why.

Exam Tip
In the exam you could be asked to explain why certain radioactive sources are chosen for certain tasks. Just think about the properties of each one (p.307-308 and p.312), and how that would make them useful.

Section Checklist — Make sure you know...

Rutherford Scattering

- ☐ That the plum pudding model suggested that the atom was a sphere of positive charge with negatively-charged electrons stuck in it, like plums in a pudding.
- ☐ How the results of the Rutherford scattering experiments showed that the atom must contain a small, positively-charged nucleus at the centre and how this led to the nuclear model of the atom.

Atoms and Isotopes

- ☐ That in the nuclear model of the atom, the atom has a small, central nucleus containing protons and neutrons, with electrons moving around outside of the nucleus.
- ☐ The relative charges and masses of electrons, protons and neutrons.
- ☐ That an atom has no overall charge because the numbers of protons and electrons are equal.
- ☐ That an ion is an atom with fewer or more electrons than protons, giving it an overall charge.
- ☐ That the atomic number of an atom is the number of protons in its nucleus and the mass number of an atom is the number of protons and neutrons in its nucleus.
- ☐ That every atom of an element has the same number of protons (atomic number).
- ☐ That isotopes are atoms of the same element with the same atomic number and different mass numbers.

cont...

Radioactivity

- ❑ That a radioactive substance will undergo radioactive decay, where it gives out radiation from the nuclei of its atoms.
- ❑ That radioactive decay is completely random — it happens all the time no matter what you do to a radioactive substance.
- ❑ That alpha decay is the process of a nucleus giving out an alpha particle, which is made up of two protons and two neutrons. It is strongly ionising and weakly penetrating.
- ❑ That beta decay is the process of a nucleus giving out a beta particle, which is an electrons. It is moderately ionising and moderately penetrating.
- ❑ That gamma decay is the process of a nucleus giving out gamma rays, which are short-wavelength electromagnetic waves. Gamma rays are weakly ionising and strongly penetrating, passing straight through air.
- ❑ H How to balance nuclear equations for alpha and beta decay.
- ❑ That alpha and beta particles are both deflected (in opposite directions) by electric and magnetic fields but gamma rays aren't deflected at all.
- ❑ That beta particles are deflected more than alpha particles in an electric or magnetic field.
- ❑ H Why beta particles are deflected more than alpha particles by an electric or magnetic field.

Half-life

- ❑ That radioactive half-life is the average time it takes for the number of nuclei in a radioactive isotope sample to halve, or the time it takes for the count rate to reach half of its initial level.

Exposure to Radiation

- ❑ That background radiation is radiation that is all around us and comes from e.g. naturally-occuring isotopes on the Earth, radiation from space and man-made radiation from the nuclear industry.
- ❑ That your occupation and location can affect the radiation dose you receive, and what precautions you can take to make sure you're not exposed to a high dose in your job or home.

Dangers of Radioactivity

- ❑ That radiation can harm or kill living cells, leading to cancer or radiation sickness.
- ❑ That beta and gamma sources are the most dangerous sources outside of the body as they can penetrate into your delicate organs. But alpha is most dangerous when inside the body as it is highly ionising and does very localised damage.
- ❑ How to evaluate the precautions that should be taken when handling radiation including how lead can be used to absorb radiation.

Uses of Radioactivity

- ❑ The uses of different types of radiation and why certain radiation is suitable for certain jobs.

Exam-style Questions

1 The diagram shows two atoms.

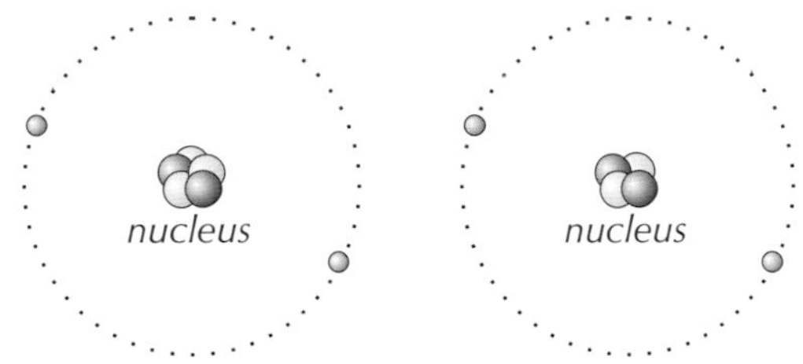

1 (a) Put these three words into the following sentences.
You may only use each word once.

protons | neutrons | electrons

The nucleus contains __________ and __________.

The numbers of protons and __________ in a neutral atom are equal.

(2 marks)

1 (b) The two atoms shown are isotopes of each other. Describe the similarities and differences in the nuclei of two different isotopes of the same element.

(1 mark)

2 In March 2011, the Fukushima nuclear power plant in Japan was damaged by a tsunami and leaked some nuclear radiation into the air. One of the radioactive isotopes that was leaked in this incident was caesium-137, which has a half-life of 30 years.

2 (a) Describe what it means for caesium-137 to have a half-life of 30 years.

(1 mark)

2 (b) Shortly after the disaster, the Japanese government decided to evacuate all people from their homes within a 12 mile radius of the power plant, because the background radiation was higher than average due to the disaster.

2 (b) (i) Name **two** sources of background radiation, other than man-made nuclear sources.

(2 marks)

2 (b) (ii) No one was allowed to move back into any of these homes until at least one year later. Suggest why it takes such a long time for evacuated areas to be considered safe after a nuclear disaster.

(1 mark)

2 (c) Caesium-137 decays into barium-137.
The following incomplete equation shows this decay:

$$^{137}_{55}\text{Cs} \longrightarrow {}^{137}_{\dots\dots}\text{Ba} + {}^{0}_{-1}\text{e}$$

2 (c) (i) What type of radiation is being given out in this decay?

(1 mark)

2 (c) (ii) Complete the nuclear equation for this decay.

(1 mark)

3 This incomplete table gives some information about three types of ionising radiation.

Radiation type:	**Made up of:**	**Stopped by:**
Alpha particles		*Thin paper*
	Electrons	*Thin aluminium*
Gamma rays	*Short-wavelength EM waves*	*Thick lead*

3 (a) (i) Complete the table.

(2 marks)

3 (a) (ii) Alpha sources are the most dangerous radioactive sources when inside the body. Explain why.

(1 mark)

3 (b) Nuclear workers wear radiation dose badges like the one shown. Developing the photographic film inside can tell the workers how high a radiation dose they have had in the time they've been wearing it, and what sort of radiation they've been exposed to.

3 (b) (i) Why do nuclear workers need to monitor their radiation dose?

(1 mark)

3 (b) (ii) Suggest **two** other precautions that nuclear workers should take to control their radiation dose.

(2 marks)

4 *In this question you will be assessed on the quality of your English, the organisation of your ideas and your use of appropriate specialist vocabulary.*

Radioactive tracers can be used in industry to detect cracks in underground pipes. The substance that the pipe carries has a radioactive isotope put in it, and then a radiation detector on the ground is moved along above the pipe, as shown.

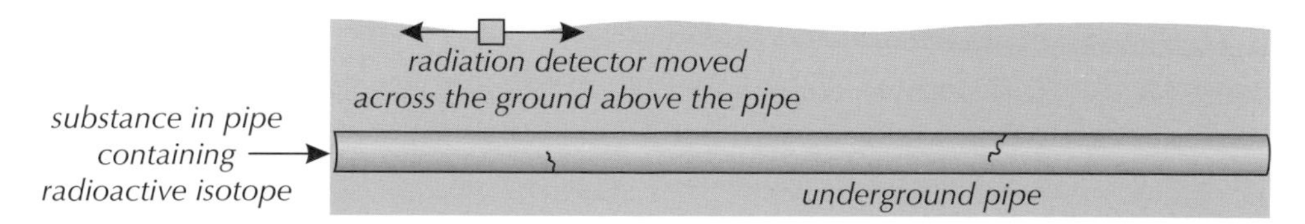

Describe how industry workers would be able to tell where there was a crack in the pipe. Explain what type of radiation the isotope in the pipe should emit and what the half-life of the source should be.

(6 marks)

1. Nuclear Fission

Nuclear fission is used in nuclear power stations to generate electricity. Read on to find out lots more about nuclear fission and how it works...

What is nuclear fission?

Nuclear fission is when an atomic nucleus splits up to form two smaller nuclei. This process releases lots of energy and as a result, it is used in nuclear power stations to generate electricity. The atom that's split in nuclear power stations is usually uranium-235, though sometimes it's plutonium-239.

For nuclear fission to happen, a slow-moving neutron must be absorbed into the uranium or plutonium nucleus. The addition of a neutron makes the nucleus unstable, causing it to split and form two new smaller nuclei. These new nuclei are usually radioactive because they have the "wrong" number of neutrons in them.

Example

When a plutonium-239 nucleus absorbs a neutron, it might split and form a strontium nucleus and a barium nucleus — see Figure 1. These are both radioactive.

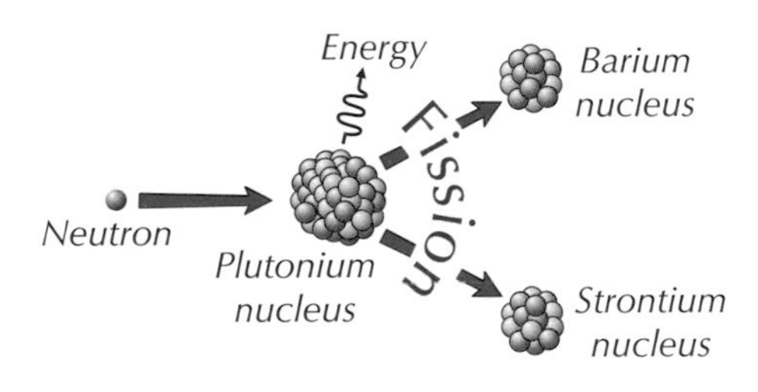

Figure 1: *Nuclear fission of a plutonium nucleus.*

Learning Objectives:

- Know that the splitting of an atomic nucleus into two smaller nuclei is called nuclear fission.
- Know that the process of nuclear fission releases energy.
- Know that the main fuels used in nuclear power stations are uranium-235 and plutonium-239.
- Know that a uranium-235 or plutonium-239 nucleus needs to absorb a neutron for fission to happen.
- Know how the fission of a nucleus can lead to a chain reaction and be able to sketch a diagram to show this.
- Understand how nuclear fission is used to generate electricity.
- Understand the advantages and disadvantages of using nuclear fission to generate electricity.

Specification Reference P2.6.1

Chain reactions

Each time a uranium or plutonium nucleus splits up, it spits out two or three neutrons, which might go on to hit other nuclei and cause them to split also. So one nucleus undergoing nuclear fission can cause other nuclei to undergo nuclear fission, which can then cause even more nuclei to undergo nuclear fission — the reaction keeps on going. This is known as a **chain reaction** (see Figure 2).

Tip: Nuclear processes (like nuclear fission) release much more energy than chemical processes do. That's why nuclear bombs are so much more powerful than ordinary bombs (which rely on chemical reactions).

Exam Tip
In the exam you might have to draw or label a diagram showing how a chain reaction might occur, so make sure you understand this diagram.

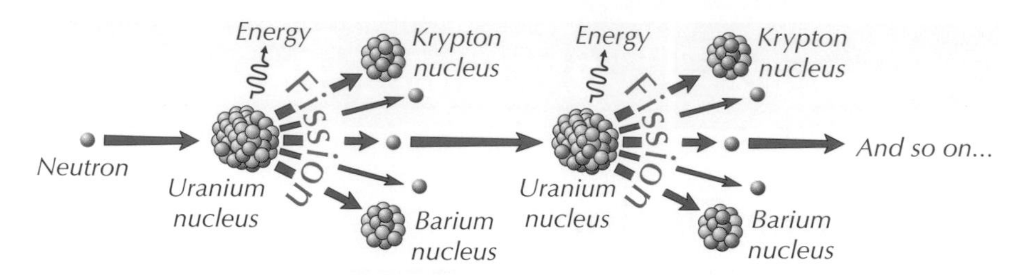

Figure 2: A chain reaction that can occur when uranium undergoes nuclear fission.

Nuclear power stations

Nuclear power stations generate electricity using nuclear reactors. In a nuclear reactor, a controlled chain reaction takes place in which uranium-235 or plutonium-239 nuclei split up and release energy in the form of heat. This heats a coolant (usually water or an inert gas) which is pumped to a boiler. Here the heat is transferred to water to make steam, which is used to drive a steam turbine connected to an electricity generator. The coolant is then pumped back to the reactor and the process continues — see Figure 4.

Figure 3: Fuel rods being loaded into a nuclear reactor.

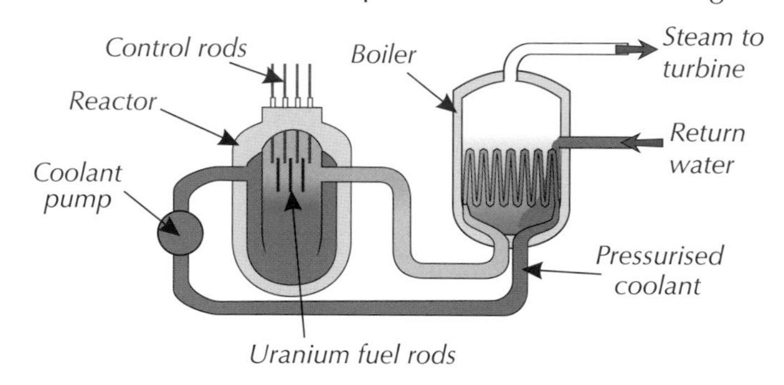

Figure 4: The structure of a nuclear reactor and boiler in a nuclear power station.

Tip: The control rods absorb neutrons, so that there are less neutrons about to cause another nucleus to undergo fission. This stops the reaction from happening too quickly and the reactor overheating.

HOW SCIENCE WORKS

The main problem with nuclear power is with the disposal of waste. The products left over after nuclear fission are highly radioactive, so they can't just be thrown away. They're very difficult and expensive to dispose of safely.

Tip: See pages 318-320 for more on radioactivity and why it can be dangerous.

Nuclear fuel is cheap but the overall cost of nuclear power is high due to the cost of the power plant and final decommissioning. Dismantling a nuclear plant safely takes decades. Nuclear power also carries the risk of radiation leaks from the plant or a major catastrophe like Chernobyl.

Practice Questions — Fact Recall

Q1 What is nuclear fission?

Q2 What are the two most common fuels used in nuclear power stations?

Q3 What must happen for a nucleus to undergo nuclear fission?

Q4 Explain how a nuclear fission chain reaction can happen.

Q5 a) Describe how nuclear fission can be used to generate electricity.

b) What problems are there with using nuclear fission to release energy and generate electricity?

2. Nuclear Fusion

Don't worry — this isn't a déjà vu. Nuclear fission and nuclear fusion may sound similar but they're actually different things... and you need to know about both of them.

Learning Objectives:
- Know that the process of two nuclei joining together to form one larger nucleus is called nuclear fusion.
- Be able to compare the use of nuclear fission and nuclear fusion as energy sources in electricity generation.
- Understand why it has not yet been possible to develop a fusion reactor to generate electricity.

Specification Reference P2.6.2

What is nuclear fusion?

Two nuclei (e.g. hydrogen) can join to create a larger nucleus — this is called **nuclear fusion** (see Figure 1).

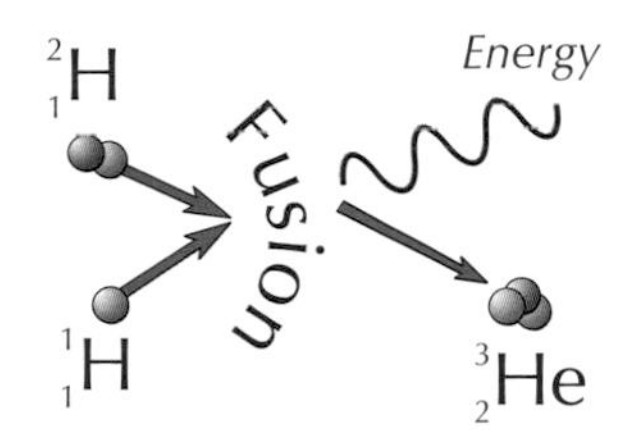

Figure 1: *A diagram to show the formation of a helium nucleus from the nuclear fusion of two hydrogen nuclei. Energy is released in this process.*

Fusion releases a lot of energy (more than fission for a given mass) — all the energy released in stars comes from fusion (see page 330). So people are trying to develop fusion reactors to generate electricity.

Fusion reactors

HOW SCIENCE WORKS

Fusion doesn't leave behind a lot of radioactive waste like fission does, so a fusion reactor wouldn't have the same problem of waste disposal that fission reactors have. There's also plenty of hydrogen knocking about to use as fuel, so if a fusion reactor could be invented it would go a long way to solving the world's energy problems.

The big problem is that fusion can only happen at really high temperatures — millions of degrees. You can't hold the hydrogen at the high temperatures and pressures required for fusion in an ordinary container — you need an extremely strong magnetic field.

There are a few experimental reactors around, but none of them are generating electricity yet. At the moment it takes more power to get up to temperature than the reactor can produce.

Figure 2: *The inside of an experimental fusion reactor.*

Exam Tip
You might get asked to compare the use of nuclear fission (see page 327) and nuclear fusion to generate electricity in the exam — make sure you know the advantages and disadvantages of each.

Practice Questions — Fact Recall

Q1 What is nuclear fusion?

Q2 For a given mass of fuel, which generates more energy — nuclear fusion or nuclear fission?

Q3 What are the advantages and disadvantages of generating electricity using nuclear fusion instead of nuclear fission?

3. The Life Cycle of Stars

Learning Objectives:
- Know that energy is released in stars by nuclear fusion.
- Know the role of gravity in the formation of stars and planets.
- Know that a balance between outwards pressure from fusion and inwards force due to gravity makes main sequence stars stable.
- Know how stars can keep emitting large amounts of energy over millions of years.
- Know the life cycle of a star given its approximate size.
- Understand how the life cycle of stars has resulted in the formation and distribution of elements in the Universe.

Specification Reference P2.6.2

Nuclear fusion happens in stars — that's why stars give out so much heat and light. This topic is all about how stars are formed and what happens to stars once all of their fuel runs out.

The formation of stars

Stars initially form from clouds of dust and gas. The force of gravity makes the gas and dust spiral in together to form a **protostar**. Within the protostar, gravitational energy is converted into heat energy, so the temperature rises.

When the temperature gets high enough, hydrogen nuclei begin to undergo nuclear fusion to form helium nuclei and give out massive amounts of heat and light. At this point, a star is born. Smaller masses of gas and dust around the star may also be pulled together to make planets that orbit the star.

Main sequence stars

Once a star has been formed, it immediately enters a long stable period, where the heat created by the nuclear fusion provides an outward pressure to balance the force of gravity pulling everything inwards. The star maintains its energy output for millions of years due to the massive amounts of hydrogen it contains. In this stable period it's called a **main sequence star** and it lasts several billion years.

Tip: The Sun is a main sequence star in the middle of this stable period.

Eventually the hydrogen begins to run out and the star starts to fuse helium, followed by other heavier elements — anything up to iron, depending on how massive the star is. Stars (and their life cycles) produce all naturally occurring elements in the Universe — when the Universe was young and didn't contain stars, it only contained hydrogen.

The death of stars

Exactly what happens to a star as it starts to run out of fuel and dies depends on how big the star is.

Figure 1: A star cluster — the orange star in the centre is a red giant.

Stars about the size of the Sun

A small star that is about the size of the Sun will expand into a **red giant** when it starts to run out of hydrogen. It becomes red because the surface cools.

It will then become unstable and eject its outer layer of dust and gas as a planetary nebula. This leaves behind a hot, dense solid core — a **white dwarf**, which just cools down to a **black dwarf** and eventually disappears from sight (see Figure 3 on the next page).

Stars larger than the Sun

Stars that are larger than the Sun expand into **red super giants** when they start to run out of hydrogen. Red super giants are much bigger and burn for much longer than regular red giants. They expand and contract several times, forming elements as heavy as iron in various nuclear reactions.

Eventually they explode in a **supernova**, forming elements heavier than iron and ejecting them into the Universe to form new planets and stars.

The exploding supernova throws the outer layers of dust and gas into space, leaving a very dense core called a **neutron star**. If the star is big enough, it will become a **black hole** instead of a neutron star — see Figure 3.

Figure 2: The remnants of a supernova.

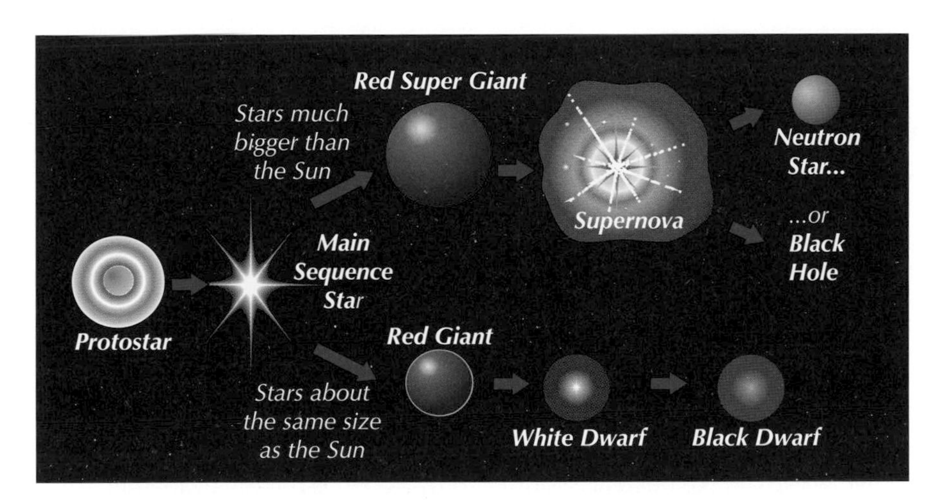

Figure 3: A flow diagram to show the life cycles of stars that are about the same size of the Sun and stars much bigger than the Sun.

Tip: Black holes don't emit any light, so you can't actually see them.

Practice Questions — Fact Recall

Q1 How are stars and planets formed?

Q2 By what process is energy released in stars?

Q3 a) Explain why main sequence stars are stable.

b) How can stars continue outputting energy for millions of years?

Q4 VV Cephei is a star that is much larger than the Sun. When VV Cephei dies, will it form a white dwarf or a neutron star?

Q5 a) Hydrogen was the only element present in the early Universe. How did other elements form and get spread through the Universe?

b) Describe the stages that a star the same size as the Sun will go through when it stops being a main sequence star.

Section Checklist — Make sure you know...

Nuclear Fission

- ❑ That nuclear fission is when an atomic nucleus splits up to form two smaller nuclei — this process releases lots of energy and so can be used to generate electricity.
- ❑ That uranium-235 and plutonium-239 will undergo nuclear fission and are used in nuclear power stations as fuels.
- ❑ That nuclear fission happens when a (slow-moving) neutron is absorbed into the nucleus of an atom, causing it to become unstable and split in two.
- ❑ That nuclear fission of a nucleus can initiate a chain reaction, because when a nucleus splits neutrons are released that can cause other nuclei to undergo nuclear fission.
- ❑ How to sketch and label a diagram showing how a chain reaction of nuclear fission can happen.
- ❑ That in nuclear power stations, the energy from nuclear fission is used to heat water. This generates steam that is used to turn a turbine which is connected to an electricity generator.
- ❑ That generating electricity from nuclear fission involves problems with the cost of building and decommissioning power stations, waste disposal, and the risk of radiation leaks or nuclear disasters.

Nuclear Fusion

- ❑ That nuclear fusion is when two nuclei (e.g. hydrogen nuclei) join to create a larger nucleus, and that this process releases lots of energy (even more energy than nuclear fission for a given mass).
- ❑ That nuclear fusion reactors would be an excellent way to generate electricity because fusion doesn't leave behind lots of radioactive waste (unlike nuclear fission) and hydrogen is readily available.
- ❑ That nuclear fusion only happens at really high temperatures (millions of degrees) — so at the moment, it takes more energy to heat a fusion reactor up to the right temperature than the reactor could produce.
- ❑ The advantages and disadvantages of using nuclear fusion and nuclear fission in electricity generation.

The Life Cycle of Stars

- ❑ That stars are formed when gravity causes gas and dust to come together and form a protostar.
- ❑ That protostars eventually become so hot that nuclear fusion starts, forming a main sequence star.
- ❑ That main sequence stars are stable because nuclear fusion inside them provides an outward pressure that balances the inward pull of gravity.
- ❑ That main sequence stars can be stable for millions of years because they are made up of huge amounts of hydrogen and so can undergo nuclear fusion for a very long time.
- ❑ That early Universe only contained hydrogen, the rest of the elements have been produced by stars.
- ❑ That stars around the size of the Sun form red giants, and eventually form white dwarfs that cool to form black dwarfs.
- ❑ That elements as heavy as iron are formed by nuclear fusion in stable stars and elements heavier than iron are formed in supernovae. Elements have been spread through the Universe by supernovae.
- ❑ That stars bigger than the Sun form red super giants that eventually explode in a supernova and form neutron stars or black holes.

Exam-style Questions

1 A nuclear power station uses the energy released when uranium-235 nuclei split in two to generate electricity.

1 (a) (i) Give the term used to describe the splitting of an atomic nucleus.

(1 mark)

1 (a) (ii) Give the name of the particle that must be absorbed into the nucleus of a uranium-235 atom in order for it to split.

(1 mark)

1 (b) The reaction that occurs in a nuclear reactor is a chain reaction.
Complete the diagram below to illustrate how a chain reaction occurs.

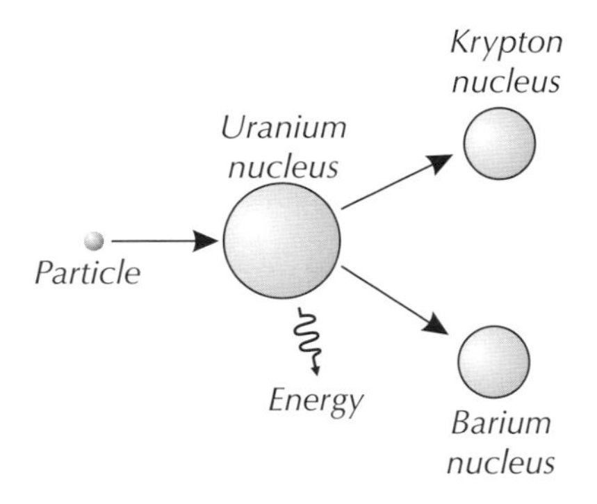

(2 marks)

1 (c) The by-products of nuclear fission in power stations are radioactive themselves.
Explain why this is a problem for nuclear power stations.

(2 marks)

2 *In this question you will be assessed on the quality of your English, the organisation of your ideas and your use of appropriate specialist vocabulary.*

Star A is a main sequence star that is much larger than the Sun.

Describe all the possible stages in the life cycle of star A after its main sequence has ended.

(6 marks)

1. Controlled Assessment Structure

To get your GCSE, you'll need to do a controlled assessment as well as all your exams. This section tells you all about the controlled assessment and what you'll have to do.

Tip: There's loads of information in the How Science Works section that'll help you with your controlled assessment so have a look at pages 2-16 before you get started.

What is the controlled assessment?

The controlled assessment is a type of test that you'll sit during your Science lessons at school. The assessment is known as an **investigative skills assessment (ISA)** and it'll involve doing some research and some practical work, as well as answering some questions on two exam papers. The controlled assessment is designed to test your How Science Works skills, not your knowledge and understanding of specific topics. So it's a good chance for you to show that you're really good at science and not just good at memorising facts.

What you'll have to do

There are five things that you'll need to do as part of the controlled assessment:

- First of all, you'll be given the outline of an investigation and you'll have to go away, come up with a **hypothesis** and plan an experiment.
- Next you'll have to sit an exam paper which will ask you questions about the research that you've done and the method you've chosen.
- Then you'll actually get to carry out the experiment that you've planned (or a similar one) and record some results.
- Once you've done the experiment you'll be given some time to process the data that you've got — you'll get to calculate some averages and draw some pretty graphs.
- Finally, you'll do another exam paper which will ask you questions about your experiment, your results and your conclusions, and ask you to compare your method and results to other people's and to case studies that you'll see.

***Figure 1**: A student conducting an experiment.*

Tip: The controlled assessment might feel more informal, but you should take it just as seriously as all your other exams.

What is the controlled assessment worth?

The controlled assessment is worth 25% of the total marks for your GCSE. It is just as important as the other exams you'll do, even though you're doing some (or all) of it in class and not in an exam hall. Don't worry though, there's loads of stuff over the next few pages to help you prepare.

2. Planning and Research

The first step of the controlled assessment is to do some research and plan your experiment. Here's what you need to know...

What you'll be told

At the very beginning of your controlled assessment, your teacher will give you the context of an investigation. This context will usually be a problem that a scientist might come across out in the real world.

Example

The context for your investigation could be something like:

"A drug company is developing a new antacid (a drug used to treat indigestion). The company wants to know how pH affects the rate of protein digestion catalysed by the enzyme pepsin. This could help them to create an antacid that is effective at treating indigestion, but that doesn't affect the digestion of proteins in the stomach too much."

What you need to do

Once you've been told the context of your investigation, you'll need to do some research, then come up with a hypothesis (see next page) and two possible methods for an experiment to solve the problem that's been outlined. You should also research the context of the experiment a bit, so you understand why your investigation will be useful.

Tip: You need to research two methods that you could use to investigate the problem, but you only need to look into one in detail.

Example

If you were given the context in the example above, you'd need to do a bit of research to find out the following:

- How you would expect pH to affect the digestion of protein catalysed by pepsin — this'll let you come up with a suitable hypothesis.
- What experiments you could do to investigate the effect of pH on the digestion of protein catalysed by pepsin — this'll involve finding a suitable reaction to use and finding a way of measuring the rate of protein digestion catalysed by pepsin.

You also need to make sure you fully understand why it's useful to know how pH affects the digestion of protein catalysed by the enzyme pepsin.

Tip: Although your teacher will give you a context for the experiment, you'll have to do all the research on your own.

When you're researching your method you need to think about what **hazards** might be associated with the experiment and what you need to do to make sure your experiment is a **fair test** (there's more on this on page 340). You should also think about what equipment you'll need and what recordings you'll need to make.

Tip: You might be given time to do your planning research in a lesson or you might be given it to do for homework.

Where to find information

Exam Tip
As you're doing your research, think about why you've found a particular source useful. Was the explanation really clear? Or was there a helpful diagram? You could get asked about this in the exam.

There are lots of places where you can find information. Textbooks are an excellent place to start. Your teacher might be able to provide these or you could get some from the library. The internet can also be an excellent source of information.

When you're doing your research, make sure you look at a variety of resources — not just one book or website. Also, make sure you jot down exactly where you've found your information. You will be asked about the research you've done in your first ISA test and just saying you used 'a textbook' or 'the internet' won't be good enough — you'll need to give the names of any textbooks and their authors, and the names of any websites that you used.

How to write a good hypothesis

Tip: See page 2 for lots more on hypotheses.

Writing a really good hypothesis is important at this stage in the controlled assessment. A hypothesis is a specific statement about the things that you'll be testing and the result you're expecting to get.

Examples

These are all hypotheses:

- There is a link between the reactivity of a metal and the number of electrons it has in its outer shell.
- Drinking a sports drink following a period of prolonged exercise will rehydrate you faster than just drinking water.
- The extension of a rubber band increases with the load applied to it.

Tip: The independent variable is the factor you'll change, the dependent variable is the factor that you'll measure.

To get good marks for your hypothesis you need to make sure it's clear and that it includes an independent and a dependent variable.

Example

If the context of your investigation was finding out how pH affects the rate of protein digestion catalysed by pepsin (see previous page), your hypothesis could be:

"If pH increases, the rate of protein digestion catalysed by the enzyme pepsin will decrease."

This hypothesis is clear and the key variables (pH and the rate of protein digestion catalysed by pepsin) have been identified.

Your hypothesis should be based on the information that you have researched.

Example

If you research antacids, you will find that they increase the pH of the stomach. If you research pepsin and protein digestion, you should find that pepsin works best in quite acidic conditions (around pH 2). This is good justification for the hypothesis that if pH increases, the rate of protein digestion catalysed by the enzyme pepsin will decrease.

Taking notes

As you're doing your research, you need to make some notes. You'll be given a sheet of A4 paper on which to make your notes and you'll be able to take these notes into your ISA tests with you — so it's in your interest to make them top notch. This example shows you what your notes sheet might look like and highlights the kind of notes you might make.

Example

Hypothesis:
If pH increases, the rate of protein digestion catalysed by the enzyme pepsin will decrease.

Research Sources:
The Science of Digestion by M. Hungary. Published by RVN (no diagram, but control variables listed).
www.biofactopedia.com/enzymes (good diagram)

Method(s):
Add egg white suspension to solutions of different pHs (measure the pH using a pH meter). Add pepsin solution and start the stopwatch.

Time how long it takes for the cloudy solution to go clear. Do 2 repeats.

Fair test: use the same volumes of pepsin solution and egg white suspension in each test tube. Carry out each test at the same temperature.

Equipment:

Test tubes	Measuring cylinders
Egg white suspension	Stopwatch
pH meter	1% pepsin solution
Pipettes	1 M hydrochloric acid (pH 0)
Acidic buffer (pH 2)	Acidic buffer (pH 6)
Acidic buffer (pH 4)	Alkaline buffer (pH 8)
Water bath	

Risk Assessment Issues:
Hydrochloric acid can burn if it touches the skin. Buffers and enzymes may irritate the skin. Wear gloves and goggles.

Relating the investigation to the context:
If increasing the pH does decrease the rate of protein digestion catalysed by pepsin, then the drug company should try to adjust the antacids to produce a pH which relieves indigestion, but that doesn't affect protein digestion in the stomach too much.

Tip: You shouldn't write a really detailed method at this stage — in fact, your notes will be checked before you go into the ISA tests to make sure you've not gone into too much detail. Just jot down the main points of the method(s) you could use to help jog your memory.

Tip: You will need to explain how you are making your experiment a fair test in the first ISA test, so you should have researched the variables that will need to be controlled and the ways you will control them — making a brief note of them here.

3. Section 1 of the ISA Test

After you've done your planning, you'll do Section 1 of the ISA test. This asks you questions about the research that you've done and the method you'll use.

Hypotheses and variables

Exam Tip
You're allowed to take one A4 page of your research notes into the ISA test with you.

In Section 1 of the ISA test you'll be asked to give your hypothesis and explain how you'll test it. Your hypothesis should include an independent variable and a dependent variable. You could be asked to identify these.

Example

In my investigation, the independent variable is the pH of the test solution and the dependent variable is the time it takes for the test solution to go clear (i.e. for the egg white protein to be digested).

Have a look at page 7 to help you work out what the different variables in your experiment are.

You could also be asked to explain why you made this hypothesis. If so, you need to give reasons that are backed up by facts from your research.

How to write a good method

In this part of the assessment you'll almost certainly be asked to write down a description of the method you're going to use to test your hypothesis. You need to give a clear and detailed description of how you would carry out your experiment. You must remember to include things like:

Exam Tip
You need to make sure you use correct spelling, punctuation and grammar too, otherwise you won't get full marks.

1. A list of all the equipment you're going to need.
2. A logical, step-by-step guide as to what you're going to do, including an explanation of what you're going to measure and how you're going to measure it.
3. What control variables you're going to regulate and how you're going to regulate them.
4. What hazards there are and how you're going to make sure the experiment is safe.

1. The equipment list

Your method should start with a list of the equipment that you'll need.

Example

To do the experiment into the effect of pH on the rate of protein digestion catalysed by pepsin, you'd need the following equipment:

- Some 1 M hydrochloric acid, acidic buffer (pH 2), acidic buffer (pH 4), acidic buffer (pH 6) and alkaline buffer (pH 8) for changing the pH of the test solution.

- Measuring cylinders for measuring out the above solutions.
- 15 test tubes.
- Some egg white suspension (substrate) and 1% pepsin solution (enzyme).
- Pipettes to measure out the pepsin solution and the egg white suspension.
- A water bath to control the temperature.
- A pH meter to measure the pHs of the test solutions.
- A stopwatch to measure the time it takes for the test mixture to go clear.

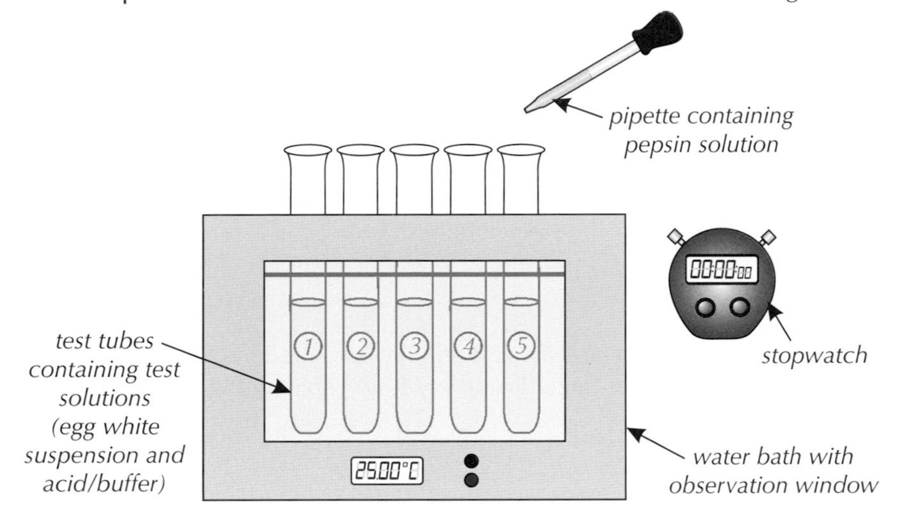

Figure 1: *Diagram of some of the equipment needed for this investigation.*

Tip: You can include a labelled diagram of the apparatus you're going to use if you want to, but you don't have to.

Tip: It's OK to give your method as a numbered list — this is an easy way to make sure you cover all the points in the right order.

2. Describing the method

Once you've written your equipment list, you should then write down exactly what you're going to do, listing the steps in the order that you're going to do them. Here's an example of a method.

Example

1. Use measuring cylinders to measure out 5 ml each of 1 M hydrochloric acid, acidic buffer (pH 2), acidic buffer (pH 4), acidic buffer (pH 6) and alkaline buffer (pH 8), and place each solution into a separate test tube.
2. Label each test tube accordingly, then put them in a water bath set to 25 °C.
3. Use a pipette to add 5 ml of egg white suspension to each test tube.
4. Measure (and then record) the pH of each test tube using the pH meter.
5. Then, use the pipette to add 10 ml of pepsin solution to the first test tube and simultaneously start the stopwatch.
6. Time how long it takes for the solution in the test tube to go clear.
7. Repeat steps 5 and 6 for each test tube.
8. Record the results in a table.
9. Repeat the whole experiment twice more and average the results.

Tip: Never just say you're going to do something, always say how you're going to do it. E.g. don't just say you're going to measure the pH — say you're going to measure the pH using a pH meter.

Tip: Don't forget to repeat your experiment. This will help you to spot anomalous results and let you calculate means, which will make your results more accurate and reduce the impact of errors.

3. Controlling the variables

To make your experiment a **fair test**, you need to make sure you control all of the variables. You'll probably be asked to write about how you're going to do this as part of your method.

Tip: There's more on fair tests and controlling variables on pages 7-8.

Example

In my experiment, the control variables are the temperature the experiment is carried out at, the volume of pepsin solution used and the volume of the egg white suspension. I will control the temperature using a water bath and keep the volumes of pepsin solution and egg white suspension the same for each test.

Things that you might need to watch out for in other experiments include things like keeping the concentrations of the reactants the same and allowing reactions to continue for the same length of time.

4. Hazards

There will always be hazards associated with any experiment. In your method you should identify these hazards and say how you're going to reduce any risk.

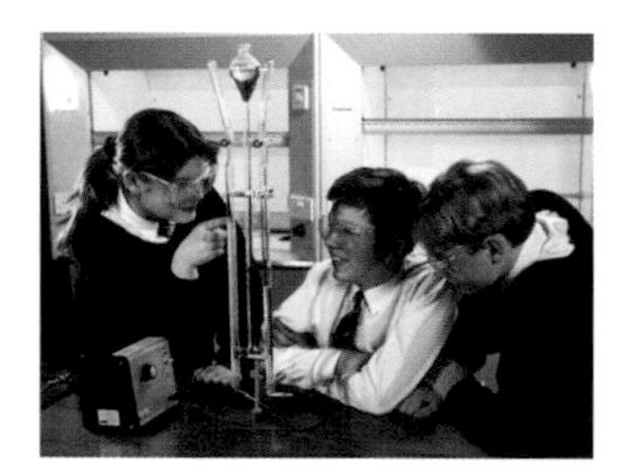

***Figure 1**: Students wearing safety goggles.*

Example

In my experiment, the main hazard is the use of hydrochloric acid, which is corrosive and can burn the skin. Also the buffers and pepsin solution are irritants, so when doing this experiment safety goggles and gloves should be worn to protect the eyes and skin.

There are lots of other hazards that you might need to watch out for. See page 9 for more.

Method selection

During your research you will have investigated at least two methods that you could use. You may be asked to explain why you chose the method you did. Think about things like equipment choices, whether it is practical to do in class, how long it'll take to do and anything else that made you choose it.

Preliminary investigations

In this part of the test, you could be asked how a preliminary investigation (or a trial run) could have been useful. Trial runs are useful for working out what range of values would be best to use and the intervals between the values.

Tip: See pages 8-9 for lots more information on trial runs and why they are useful.

Example

In this experiment, a trial run could have been useful to:

- Work out the amount of pepsin solution and egg white suspension to use, in order to make sure the reaction happens quickly enough. This would involve testing a range of volumes to see which ones give a good reaction speed — you don't want to be waiting around forever.

- Work out how long to watch the reaction for — e.g. if it looks likely that the test solution isn't going to go clear at all, a sensible amount of time to wait for must be decided.

Table of results

In this part of the test, you will also need to draw a table for your results that you can fill in when you do the experiment. There are a few things to remember when drawing tables of results:

- Make sure you include enough rows and columns to record all of the data you need to. You might also need to include a column for processing your data (e.g. working out an average).
- Make sure you give each column a heading so you know what's going to be recorded where.
- Make sure you include units for all your measurements.

Tip: You don't have to draw your table of results by hand — you can use a computer instead.

Here's an example of a jolly good table for results.

Example

Test tube	Test solution	Repeat	pH	Time taken for test solution to go clear (mins)	Mean time taken for test solution to go clear (mins)
1	Hydrochloric acid (pH 0)	1			
		2			
		3			
2	Acidic buffer (pH 2)	1			
		2			
		3			
3	Acidic buffer (pH 4)	1			
		2			
		3			
4	Acidic buffer (pH 6)	1			
		2			
		3			
5	Alkaline buffer (pH 8)	1			
		2			
		3			

Tip: Your table for results won't look exactly like this one. For example, you might need more or fewer rows and columns depending on what kind of data you're collecting.

4. Doing the Experiment

If your plan isn't too outrageous, you'll then get to actually do the experiment you've planned. So grab your safety goggles and your lab coat...

Tip: If you're given an alternative method it doesn't necessarily mean your method was bad — it could be that your teacher thinks there are too many different methods in the class or that your school doesn't have the right equipment.

Good laboratory practice

When it comes to actually doing the investigation, you might be allowed to do the one you planned, or you might be given another method to use by your teacher. When you're doing your experiment it's important that you use good laboratory practice. This means working safely and accurately.

To ensure you get good results, make sure you do the following:

- Measure all your quantities carefully — the more accurately you measure things the more accurate your results will be.
- Try to be consistent — for example, if you need to stir something, stir every sample for the same length of time.
- Don't let yourself get distracted by other people — if you're distracted by what other people are doing you're more likely to make a mistake or miss a reading.

As you're going along, make sure you remember to fill in your table of results — it's no good doing a perfect experiment if you forget to record the data.

Figure 1: *A student working in a laboratory.*

Tip: See pages 12-14 for more on processing your results and calculating averages.

Tip: Your graph will be marked along with your exam papers so make sure it's nice and neat and all your axes are properly labelled.

Processing your results

Once you've got your data you might need to process it. This could involve calculating the mean (by adding all your data together and dividing by the number of values) or working out a change in something (by subtracting the start reading from the end reading).

Then you'll need to plot your data on a graph. It's up to you what type of graph you use. See pages 12-14 for more information on how to draw a good graph.

Things to think about

As you're doing the experiment there are some things you need to think about:

- Is the equipment you're using good enough?
- Is there anything you would do differently if you could do the experiment again?
- Have you got any anomalous results (see page 11) and, if so, can you think what might have gone wrong?
- Do the results you've got support your initial hypothesis?

These are all things that you could get asked about in the second part of your ISA, so it's a good idea to think about them while the experiment is still fresh in your mind.

5. Section 2 of the ISA Test

Once you've done your experiment and processed the results it's time for the final part of your controlled assessment — Section 2 of the ISA test.

Making conclusions

In Section 2 of the ISA test you will be asked to draw conclusions about your data. You could be asked what your data shows, or whether it supports your initial hypothesis. When drawing conclusions it's important to back them up with data from your results. You should describe the general trend(s) in the data, but also quote specific numerical values.

Tip: Remember, there's loads of information on processing data and making conclusions in the How Science Works section. Make sure you are really familiar with pages 12-16 before you go into your ISA tests.

Example

"Do your results support your initial hypothesis?"

Yes, because the general pattern of results was that as pH increased the time it took for the test solution to go clear also increased. For example, when using acidic buffer (pH 2), the average time it took for the test solution to go clear was 6.50 minutes, whereas when using alkaline buffer (pH 8), the test solution still hadn't gone clear after 20 minutes. So overall, increasing the pH decreased the rate of protein digestion catalysed by the enzyme pepsin.

Tip: It doesn't matter if the answer to this question is yes or no — the important thing is that your results support your conclusion.

Comparing results

In Section 2 of the test you will probably be asked to compare your results with the results of other people in your class. This lets you see what similarities or differences there are between sets of results, and allows you to determine if your results are reproducible. If everyone in the class did the same experiment and got similar results to you, then your experiment is reproducible. If everyone got different results to you, your results aren't reproducible. It's OK to say your results aren't reproducible, though you should try to suggest why. And as always, back up anything you say by quoting some data.

Tip: Sharing results with the rest of your class gives you more data to calculate means from, which will make them more accurate.

Improving your method

In this part of the assessment, you might be given the opportunity to evaluate the experiment — in other words, to say how you would improve the experiment if you did it again.

Example

- You could say that it would be better to use equipment with a higher resolution, so you could detect smaller changes and get more precise results.
- You could say that you'd carry out more repeats to check the repeatability and increase the accuracy of the results.
- You could say that you'd use a better technique (e.g. using a mechanical stirrer to ensure that the water in the water bath was at the same temperature throughout) to help make your experiment a fair test.

Tip: When suggesting an improvement to the method, it's really important that you explain how the improvement would give you better data next time.

Tip: See page 10 for more on resolution.

Anomalous results

Tip: See page 11 for more information on anomalous results.

You could be asked whether or not there are any anomalous results in your data. Anomalous results are results that don't seem to fit with the rest of the data. If you're asked about anomalous results make sure you quote the result and explain why you think it is anomalous.

Tip: You could also be asked to suggest a reason for an anomalous result, e.g. in this case too little egg white suspension could have been added by mistake.

Example

I think the time it took for the test solution to go clear for acidic buffer (pH 4) at repeat 2 (4.5 minutes) was an anomalous result because it doesn't seem to fit with the rest of the data (it's too fast).

If you don't have any anomalous results, that's fine — just make sure you explain why you're sure none of your results are anomalous.

Example

I don't think there were any anomalous results in my data. An anomalous result is one that doesn't seem to fit with the rest of the data and all of my data points were very close to the line of best fit when plotted on a graph.

Analysing other data sources

Exam Tip
The important thing when analysing other data sources is to read the question carefully and make sure you answer it — don't just describe the data without referring back to the original question.

In this final part of the controlled assessment you won't only get asked about your own data. You'll also be given some case studies to look at and be asked to analyse that data as well. You could be asked to compare this data to your own data and point out similarities and differences. Or you could be asked whether this data supports or contradicts your hypothesis.

As with making conclusions about your own data, when you're answering questions about these secondary sources it's crucial that you quote specific pieces of data from the source. You shouldn't blindly trust the data in these sources either — you should think as critically about this data as you did about your own data. Don't assume that it's better than yours and be on the look out for mistakes.

Applying your results to a context

Another thing you could be asked to do is explain how your results can be applied to a particular context. This means thinking of a practical application of what you've found out. You should have done some research on this in the planning part of the controlled assessment. You can use the notes you made then to help you answer questions like this.

Example

We found out that, overall, increasing the pH decreased the rate of protein digestion catalysed by the enzyme pepsin. Applying this to the context of antacids — if an antacid causes the pH of the stomach to rise too high, it could affect the digestion of proteins in the stomach. A drug company could use this information to produce an antacid that creates a pH of around 3-4. This would increase the pH of the stomach, which would help relieve indigestion, but wouldn't decrease the rate of protein digestion too much.

1. The Exams

Sadly, to get your Additional Science GCSE you have to sit some exams. And that's what these pages are about — what to expect in your exams.

> **Exam Tip**
> Make sure you have a good read through these pages. It might not seem all that important now but you don't want to get any surprises just before an exam.

Assessment for GCSE Additional Science

To get your GCSE in Additional Science you'll have to do some exams that test your knowledge of biology, chemistry, physics and How Science Works. All the content that you need to know is in this book — there's even a dedicated How Science Works section on pages 2-16.

You'll also have to do a Controlled Assessment (also known as an 'ISA'). There's more about this on pages 334-344.

The exams

There are two different ways you can be assessed — Route 1 and Route 2. Remember that, whichever route you're taking, you could be asked questions on How Science Works in any of your exams. Also, you're allowed to use a calculator in all of your exams, so make sure you've got one.

> **Exam Tip**
> Route 1 and Route 2 cover exactly the same material — the content is just split up differently for the exams.

Route 1

If you're following Route 1, you'll sit separate exams for biology, chemistry and physics. Here's how it works...

Route 1

Unit 1 Exam	Unit 2 Exam	Unit 3 Exam
The Unit 1 exam is on Biology 2. This is covered on pages 17-109 of this book.	The Unit 2 exam is on Chemistry 2. This is covered on pages 110-199 of this book.	The Unit 3 exam is on Physics 2. This is covered on pages 200-333 of this book.
Exam Length: 1 hour Marks: 60 Worth: 25%	Exam Length: 1 hour Marks: 60 Worth: 25%	Exam Length: 1 hour Marks: 60 Worth: 25%

Route 2

If you're doing Route 2, you'll sit two exams that each contain a mixture of biology, chemistry and physics questions.

Exam Tip
If you don't know which route you're doing ask your teacher, so you can revise the right stuff for the right exam.

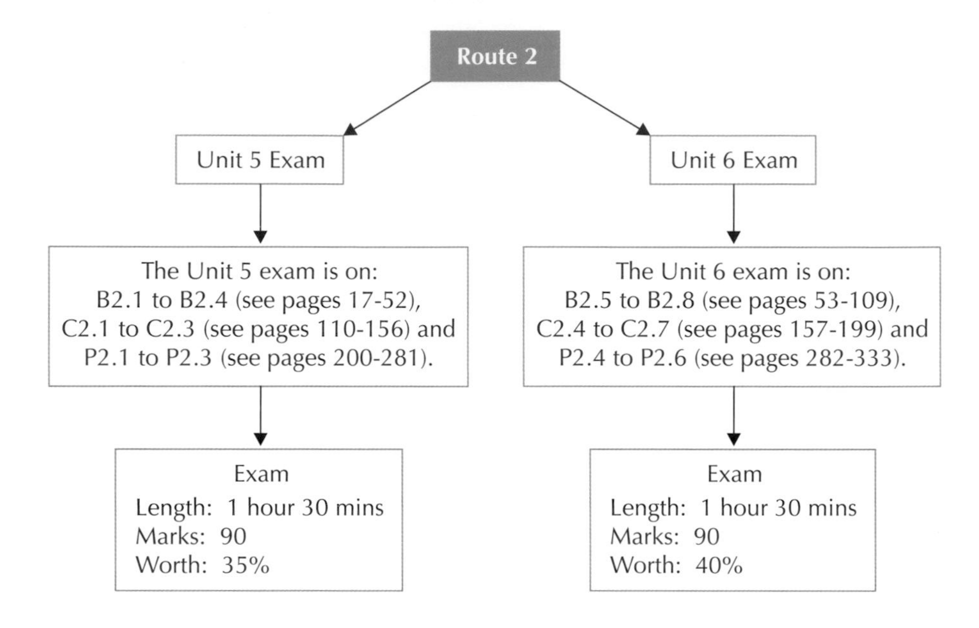

Controlled assessment (ISA)

As well as your exams, you'll have to do a controlled assessment.
The controlled assessment involves a test made up of two sections, which will be based on a practical investigation that you've researched, planned and carried out.

Exam Tip
It doesn't matter what exam route you're taking for this — <u>everyone</u> has to do a controlled assessment.

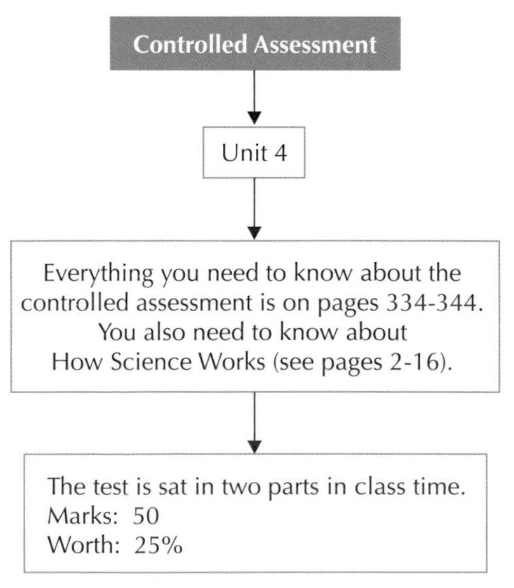

Exam Tip
As well as the test, you'll have to do some research and carry out a practical investigation for your controlled assessment.

2. Exam Technique

Knowing the science is vitally important when it comes to passing your exams. But having good exam technique will also help. So here are some handy hints on how to squeeze every mark you possibly can out of those examiners.

Time management

Good time management is one of the most important exam skills to have — you need to think about how much time to spend on each question. Check out the length of your exams (you'll find them on the previous pages and on the front of your exam papers). These timings give you about 1 minute per mark. Try to stick to this to give yourself the best chance to get as many marks as possible.

Exam Tip
If a question is only worth 1 mark, don't waste time writing more than you need to.

Don't spend ages struggling with a question if you're finding it hard to answer — move on. You can come back to it later when you've bagged loads of other marks elsewhere. Also, you might find that some questions need a lot of work for only a few marks, while others are much quicker — so if you're short of time, answer the quick and easy questions first.

Example

The questions below are both worth the same number of marks but require different amounts of work.

1 **(a)** Name **two** factors that affect the rate of a reaction.

(2 marks)

2 **(a)** Draw a dot and cross diagram to show how the outer electrons of the atoms in a molecule of methane are arranged.

(2 marks)

Question 1 (a) only asks you to write down two factors — if you can remember them this shouldn't take you too long.

Question 2 (a) asks you to draw a diagram — this may take you a lot longer than writing down a couple of factors.

So, if you're running out of time it makes sense to do questions like 1 (a) first and come back to 2 (a) if you've got time at the end.

Exam Tip
Don't forget to go back and do any questions that you left the first time round — you don't want to miss out on marks because you forgot to do the question.

Making educated guesses

Make sure you answer all the questions that you can — don't leave any blank if you can avoid it. If a question asks you to tick a box, circle a word or draw lines between boxes, you should never, ever leave it blank, even if you're short on time. It only takes a second or two to answer these questions, and even if you're not sure what the answer is you can have a good guess.

Exam Tip
If you're asked, for example, to tick two boxes, make sure you only tick two. If you tick more than two, you won't get the marks even if some of your answers are correct.

Example

Look at the question below.

1 (a) Which of the following cell parts are found in plant cells but not animal cells? Tick **two** boxes.

Chloroplast ☐ Nucleus ☐

Cell membrane ☐ Vacuole ☐

(2 marks)

Say you knew that only plant cells contain chloroplasts, and that most animal cells have a nucleus, but weren't sure about the others.

You can tick chloroplast — you know they're only in plants. If most animal cells have a nucleus they can't be found only in plants, so leave that box blank. That leaves you with cell membranes and vacuoles. If you're not absolutely sure which is plant-only and which isn't, just have a guess. You won't lose any marks if you get it wrong and there's a 50% chance that you'll get it right.

Command Words

Command words are just the bits of a question that tell you what to do. You'll find answering exam questions much easier if you understand exactly what they mean, so here's a brief summary of the most common ones:

Exam Tip
When you're reading an exam question, you might find it helpful to underline the command word. It can help you work out what type of answer to give.

Command word:	What to do:
Give / Name / State / Write down	Give a brief one or two word answer, or a short sentence.
Complete	Write your answer in the space given. This could be a gap in a sentence or table, or you might have to finish a diagram.
Describe	Write about what something's like, e.g. describe the trend in a set of results.
Explain	Make something clear, or give the reasons why something happens. The points in your answer need to be linked together, so you should include words like because, so, therefore, due to, etc.
Calculate	Use the numbers in the question to work out an answer.
Suggest	Use your scientific knowledge to work out what the answer might be.
Compare	Give the similarities and differences between two things.
Evaluate	Give the arguments both for and against an issue, or the advantages and disadvantages of something. You may also need to give an overall judgement.

Exam Tip
It's easy to get describe and explain mixed up, but they're quite different. For example, if you're asked to describe some data, just state the overall pattern or trend. If you're asked to explain data, you'll need to give reasons for the trend.

Some questions will also ask you to answer 'using the information provided' (e.g. a graph, table or passage of text) — if so, you must refer to the information you've been given or you won't get the marks.

3. Question Types

If all questions were the same, exams would be mightily boring. So really, it's quite handy that there are lots of different question types. Here are just a few...

Exam Tip
You'll need to use black ink or a black ball-point pen to write your answers, so make sure that you've got a couple ready for the exam.

Quality of written communication (QWC)

All of the exams you take for GCSE Additional Science will have at least one 6 mark question that assesses your quality of written communication — this just means that the examiner will assess your ability to write properly. This may seem like a bit of a drag, but you will lose marks if you don't do it. Here are some tips on how to get all the marks you can...

- Make sure your scribble (sorry, writing) is legible.
- Be careful with your spelling, punctuation and grammar — they need to be accurate.
- Make sure your writing style is appropriate for an exam. You need to write in full sentences and use fairly formal language. For example, the sentence "ionic compounds have high melting points" is an appropriate style. "It needs to be proper hot for an ionic compound to melt" isn't — it's too informal.
- Organise your answer clearly. The points you make need to be in a logical order.
- Use specialist scientific vocabulary whenever you can. For example, if you're describing photosynthesis you'd need to use scientific terms like chlorophyll and glucose. You also need to use these terms correctly — it's no good knowing the words if you don't know what they mean.

Exam Tip
Make sure you write enough to get all the marks that are available. QWC questions are worth six marks, so a one sentence answer isn't likely to be enough — you'll need to write at least a paragraph or two.

You'll be told which questions will be used to assess the quality of your written communication. On the front of your exam paper it will say something like 'Question 2 should be answered in continuous prose' — and that's the question where your writing will be assessed. There'll also be a reminder when you get to the question itself. It'll say something like:

In this question you will be assessed on the quality of your English, the organisation of your ideas and your use of appropriate specialist vocabulary.

Exam Tip
You should really be doing these things all the way through your exam — but they're particularly important in the QWC questions, so it's worth taking special care with them there.

Evaluating information

In the exam, you may be given some information to read and then be asked to evaluate it.

Example

Filament bulbs and LEDs can both be used for lighting. You may be given some information on how expensive filament bulbs and LEDs are, how much power they use and how long they last for. You could then be asked to evaluate the use of filament bulbs and LEDs for lighting a certain place.

Exam Tip
To make your comparisons clear, it's good to use words like: however, whereas, more, less, better than, worse than, etc.

In the previous example, you're basically being asked to compare the use of the two types of lamp — including the advantages and disadvantages of each. This means you need to do more than just pick out relevant information from the question and repeat it in your answer — you need to make clear comparisons between the two.

Example

If the information tells you that filament bulbs last for around 2000 hours and that LEDs will last for around 15 000 hours, you need to say in your answer that "filament bulbs last for a much **shorter** length of time than LEDs". It's even better to say that "LEDs will last around **13 000 more** hours than filament bulbs".

Exam Tip
Even if you're not specifically asked to give a conclusion in your answer, it's still worth writing one — you could pick up marks.

The question may ask you to write a conclusion too, e.g. make an overall judgement about which type of lamp is best. If so, you must include a conclusion in your answer and you must back it up with evidence from the question.

Calculations

Questions that involve a calculation can seem a bit scary. But they're really not that bad. Here are some tips to help you out...

Showing working

The most important thing to remember is to show your working. You've probably heard it a million times before but it makes perfect sense. It only takes a few seconds more to write down what's in your head and it might stop you from making silly errors and losing out on easy marks. You won't get a mark for a wrong answer but you could get marks for the method you used to work out the answer.

Figure 1: *A calculator. Under the pressure of an exam it's easy to make mistakes in calculations, even if they're really simple ones. So don't be afraid to put every calculation into the calculator.*

Units

Make sure you always give units for your answer when you're asked for them. You could get a mark for getting the units right even if you haven't managed to do the calculation.

Significant figures

The first significant figure (s.f.) of a number is the first digit that isn't a zero. The second, third and fourth significant figures follow on immediately after the first (even if they're zeros). If you need to round an answer to a calculation, give it to the lowest number of significant figures given in the question data. You should write down the number of significant figures you've rounded to after your answer.

Example

Say you need to round 0.4573 kg to two significant figures. The first digit that isn't a zero is 4, so that's the first significant figure, and the second is 5. The third significant figure is a 7, so round the second significant figure up from 5 to 6. Bob's your uncle, you've got 0.4573 kg = 0.46 kg (to 2 s.f.).

Standard form **Higher**

You need to be able to work with numbers that are written in standard form. Standard form is used for writing very big or very small numbers in a more convenient way. Standard form must always look like this:

This number must always be between 1 and 10. → $A \times 10^n$ ← *This number is the number of places the decimal point moves.*

Exam Tip
Your calculator might give you an answer in standard form.

You can write numbers out in full rather than in standard form by moving the decimal point. Which direction to move the decimal point, and how many places to move it depends on the value of 'n'. If 'n' is positive, the decimal point needs to move to the right. If 'n' is negative the decimal point needs to move to the left.

Examples

Here's how to write out 6.7×10^3 in full.

- Work out which way the decimal point needs to move, by looking at the 'n' number. Here it's a positive number (3) so the decimal point needs to move to the right.
- Then count the number of places the decimal point has to move to the right. In this example it's three:

1 2 3

$$6.7 \times 10^3 = 6700.$$

- So 6.7×10^3 is the same as 6700.

Exam Tip
You need to add a zero into any space left by the decimal point moving.

Here's how to write out 9.1×10^{-4} in full.

- 'n' is a negative number (–4) so the decimal point needs to move to the left.
- Count four places to the left.

4 3 2 1

$$9.1 \times 10^{-4} = .00091$$

- So 9.1×10^{-4} is the same as 0.00091.

The key things to remember with numbers in standard form are...

- When 'n' is positive the number is big.
  The bigger 'n' is, the bigger the number is.
- When 'n' is negative the number is small.
  The smaller 'n' is (the more negative), the smaller the number is.
- When 'n' is the same for two or more numbers, you need to look at the start of each number to work out which is bigger. For example, 4.5 is bigger than 3.0, so 4.5×10^5 is bigger than 3.0×10^5.

Formula triangles

Formula triangles are extremely useful tools for lots of tricky maths problems.

- If three terms are related by a formula that looks like:

$$F = m \times a \qquad \text{or} \qquad a = \frac{F}{m}$$

then you can put them into a formula triangle like this:

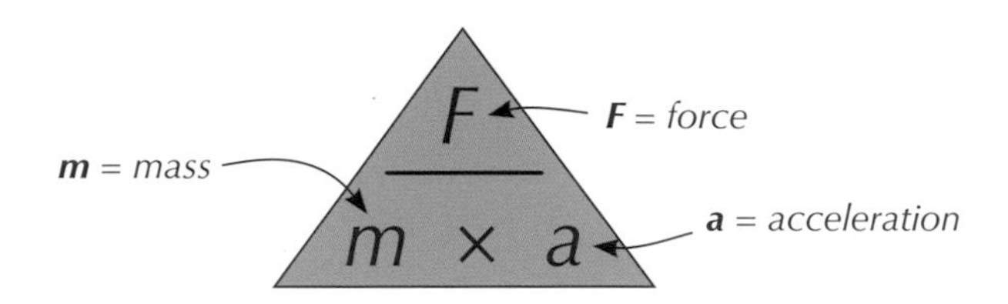

Figure 2: *The formula triangle for F = m × a — F on the top and m × a on the bottom.*

- If there are two terms multiplied together in the formula, then they must go on the bottom of the formula triangle (and so the other one must go on the top).
- If there's one term divided by another in the formula, then the one on top of the division goes on top in the formula triangle (and so the other two must go on the bottom — it doesn't matter which way round).
- To use the formula triangle, put your thumb over the term you want to find and write down what's left showing. This gives you your formula (for example $m = F \div a$).

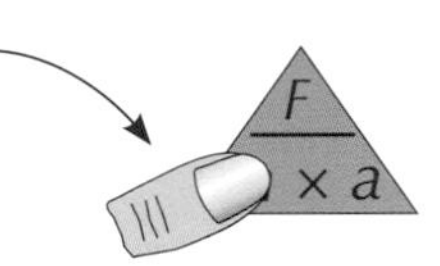

- Then put in the values for the other two terms and work out the term you don't know.

Exam Tip
If you're not sure you've done this right, change one of the numbers and check that what it does to the answer is sensible.

For example, if you increase the value for energy in your formula and the power decreases, you'll know you must have got it the wrong way round.

Example

If you want to work out power, but you only have this formula:

energy transferred (E) = power (P) × time taken (t)

...then you can turn it into a formula triangle.

- As P is multiplied by t, E goes on top, leaving $P \times t$ on the bottom.

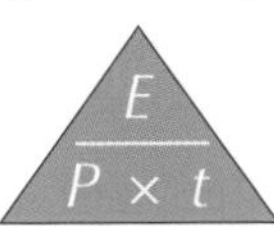

- Covering P leaves $E \div t$.
- So, power = energy transferred ÷ time.
- Then you just need to slot in the values you have (for E and t) and calculate the value of P.

Answers

Biology 2

Biology 2.1 Cells and Simple Cell Transport

1. Cell Structure

Page 18 — Fact Recall Questions

Q1 the nucleus
Q2 In the cytoplasm.
Q3 respiration
Q4 A cell wall, a permanent vacuole and chloroplasts.
Q5 A yeast cell has a nucleus, cytoplasm, and a cell membrane surrounded by a cell wall.
Q6 E.g. in a yeast cell the genetic material is contained within a nucleus, whereas in a bacterial cell the genetic material floats in the cytoplasm. / A yeast cell has a nucleus and a bacterial cell doesn't.

2. Specialised Cells

Pages 20-21 — Application Questions

Q1 E.g. you'd expect to find a lot of ribosomes because they make proteins.
The function of a gastric chief cell is to secrete proteins — and ribosomes are where proteins are made in the cell. So it makes sense that you'd find a lot of ribosomes in a gastric chief cell.
Q2 a) C is most likely to be the correct structure of a root hair cell because this cell has a thin cell wall (unlike cell A), which should make it easier for water and mineral ions to be absorbed from the soil. Also cell C doesn't have any chloroplasts (unlike cell B), which are not needed because the root hair cells are in the soil and so can't photosynthesise/absorb light.
b) The cell's long extension gives it a bigger surface area for absorbing water and nutrients.
Q3 E.g. the folds in the cell membrane give the cells a large surface area for absorbing food molecules efficiently. Lots of mitochondria provide the energy from respiration needed to absorb food molecules.
This question is pretty tricky — you need to think about the unusual shape of the cell and look at the things it contains. Cells that need to absorb things tend to have a large surface area (e.g. like red blood cells and palisade leaf cells), so look for anything about the cell that increases its surface area. You also know that the cell needs energy — so look for mitochondria, which are the site of respiration (a process which releases energy).

3. Diffusion

Page 24 — Application Questions

Q1 Inside respiring cells. The carbon dioxide molecules must be diffusing from an area of higher concentration (inside respiring cells) to an area of lower concentration (the bloodstream).
Q2 a) The smoke particles diffuse from where there is a high concentration (near the stage), to where there is a low concentration (at the opposite end of the hall).
b) There are already some smoke particles in the air the second time the smoke machine is set off, whereas there weren't the first time. This means there is a smaller difference in the concentration of the smoke particles at each end of the hall, so the rate of diffusion is slower the second time.

Biology 2.2 Tissues, Organs and Organ Systems

1. Cell Organisation

Pages 27-28 — Fact Recall Questions

Q1 a) differentiation
b) true
Q2 a) A group of similar cells that work together to carry out a particular function.
b) To make and secrete substances such as enzymes and hormones.
c) e.g. muscular tissue and epithelial tissue
Q3 A group of different tissues that work together to perform a certain function.
Q4 organ system
Q5 A is the salivary glands, which produce digestive juices.
B is the liver, which produces bile.
C is the stomach, where food is digested.
D is the pancreas, which produces digestive juices.
E is the small intestine, where food is digested and soluble food molecules are absorbed.
F is the large intestine, which absorbs water from undigested food, leaving faeces.

Page 28 — Application Questions

Q1 Glandular tissue, because this sort of tissue secretes hormones.
The hypophysis is actually just another name for the pituitary gland. You didn't need to know that to answer the question though.
Q2 A tissue, because it consists of a group of similar cells that work together to perform a particular function.

Q3 a) It contracts, to move the fertilised egg cell along the fallopian tube to the uterus.
b) An organ, because it consists of a group of different tissues that work together to perform a certain function.
c) egg cell, muscular tissue, uterus, reproductive system

2. Plant Tissues and Organs

Page 30 — Fact Recall Questions

Q1 e.g. stems, roots, leaves
Q2 mesophyll tissue
Q3 To transport things like water, mineral ions and sucrose around the plant.
Q4 epidermal tissue
Remember, 'epidermal tissue' is found in plants and 'epithelial tissue' is found in animals — they're very similar words, so be careful you don't get them mixed up in the exam.

Pages 31-32 — Biology 2.1-2.2

Exam-style Questions

1 a) A — cell wall ***(1 mark)***. B — nucleus ***(1 mark)***. C — cytoplasm ***(1 mark)***. D — cell membrane ***(1 mark)***.
b) A yeast, because it has a nucleus / its genetic material is not floating free in the cytoplasm ***(1 mark)***.
2 a) i) small intestine ***(1 mark)***
ii) A is the salivary glands ***(1 mark)***. B is the pancreas ***(1 mark)***. The role of both of these organs is to produce digestive juices ***(1 mark)***.
b) Any two from: e.g. muscular tissue ***(1 mark)***, which moves the stomach wall to churn up food ***(1 mark)***. / Glandular tissue ***(1 mark)***, which makes digestive juices to digest food ***(1 mark)***. / Epithelial tissue ***(1 mark)***, which covers the outside and inside of the stomach ***(1 mark)***.
3 a) A cell which carries out a particular function ***(1 mark)***.
b) A tissue ***(1 mark)*** because it shows several similar cells that work together to carry out a particular function ***(1 mark)***.
c) E.g. it has long extensions so it can carry electrical signals further in the body. / It has branched ends so it can carry electrical signals to several different body cells at once ***(1 mark)***.
4 a) epidermal tissue ***(1 mark)***
b) Mesophyll tissue ***(1 mark)***. Having lots of chloroplasts suggests that the cells are adapted for photosynthesis ***(1 mark)*** and it is in the mesophyll tissue that most photosynthesis takes place ***(1 mark)***.

c) i) There must be a higher concentration of carbon dioxide outside the cell than inside ***(1 mark)***. This is because when particles diffuse, they move from an area of high concentration to an area of low concentration ***(1 mark)***.
ii) A decrease in the concentration of carbon dioxide in the air spaces outside the leaf cells would reduce the rate of diffusion of carbon dioxide into the cells ***(1 mark)***. This is because the difference between the concentration of carbon dioxide inside the cells and outside the cells would be smaller ***(1 mark)***.

Biology 2.3 Photosynthesis

1. The Basics of Photosynthesis

Page 34 — Fact Recall Questions

Q1 glucose
Q2 a) chloroplasts
b) It absorbs light energy.
Q3

$$\text{carbon dioxide + water} \xrightarrow{\text{light energy}} \text{glucose + oxygen}$$

Q4 carbon dioxide
Q5 oxygen

Page 34 — Application Questions

Q1 Plant C. It received the most hours of sunlight, so it will have photosynthesised for longer. As photosynthesis produces glucose, it will have produced the most glucose.
Q2 3, because this type of plant cell contains the most chloroplasts. Chloroplasts contain chlorophyll, which is needed for plants to photosynthesise.

2. The Rate of Photosynthesis

Page 38 — Fact Recall Question

Q1 a) A factor which stops photosynthesis from happening any faster.
b) e.g. light intensity, carbon dioxide level, temperature

Page 38 — Application Questions

Q1

Environmental conditions	Most likely limiting factor
Outside on a cold winter's day.	temperature
In an unlit garden at 1:30 am, in the UK, in summer.	light
On a windowsill on a warm, bright day.	carbon dioxide concentration

Q2 a) oxygen
b) Any two from: e.g. he kept the flasks at the same temperature. / He put flasks the same distance from the light source. / He used the same amount of pondweed in both flasks. / He took the pondweed from the same plant.

Different plants may photosynthesise at different rates, so taking the pondweed from the same plant helps to make the experiment a fair test.

c) Because before point X, increasing the light intensity increases the rate of photosynthesis.
d) Because carbon dioxide concentration is limiting the rate of photosynthesis in Flask A.
Flask A has a lower carbon dioxide concentration than Flask B but all the other variables that could affect the rate of photosynthesis are the same for both flasks. Therefore the reason why the rate of photosynthesis levels off at a lower level in Flask A, is most likely to be because of the lower carbon dioxide concentration in this flask.

3. Artificially Controlling Plant Growth

Page 41 — Fact Recall Questions

Q1 E.g. so that they can create the ideal conditions for photosynthesis. This means that their plants photosynthesise faster, so a decent crop can be harvested much more often.
Q2 e.g. carbon dioxide concentration

Page 41 — Application Questions

Q1 a) 30 ÷ 8 = **3.75 cm per week**.
b) 17.5 ÷ 8 = **2.19 cm per week**.

Graphs like this with two y-axes can be tricky — just take your time and make sure you're reading the value off the correct axis.

Q2 Carbon dioxide concentration. Light, temperature and carbon dioxide concentration can all affect the rate of photosynthesis, which affects growth rate. The graph shows that there was very little difference in the temperature of each greenhouse throughout the experiment, and both greenhouses were exposed to the same amount of light. Therefore it's most likely to be the extra carbon dioxide produced by the paraffin heater in Greenhouse A which caused the higher average growth rate of plants in this greenhouse.
Q3 E.g. the cost of running the heaters.

4. How Plants and Algae Use Glucose

Page 43 — Fact Recall Questions

Q1 respiration
Q2 making strong cell walls
Q3 nitrate ions
Q4 as lipids/fats and oils
Q5 Starch is insoluble, so it doesn't draw in water and cause the cells to swell up.

Biology 2.4 Organisms and Their Environment

1. Distribution of Organisms

Page 45 — Fact Recall Questions

Q1 Where organisms are found in a particular area.
Q2 E.g. temperature / availability of water / availability of oxygen / availability of carbon dioxide / availability of nutrients / availability of light.

2. Studying Distribution

Page 49 — Fact Recall Questions

Q1 E.g. you would place the quadrat on the ground at a random position in the first sample area and count the number of the organisms within the quadrat. You would then repeat this many times. Next you would repeat this whole process in the second sample area. Finally you would work out an average number of organisms per quadrat or the population size in each sample area and compare the results.
Q2 Add all the values in the data set together and divide the total by the number of values you have.
Q3 The value which occurs most often.
Q4 The middle value when the data is in order of size.
Q5 A line can be marked out across the area you want to study and all of the organisms that touch the line can be counted. / Data can be collected using quadrats placed along the line.
Q6 E.g. by using a large sample size.

Page 50 — Application Question

Q1 a) i) 1 + 5 + 5 + 20 + 43 + 37 = 111
111 ÷ 6 = **18.5**
ii) 5
iii) 5 + 20 = 25
25 ÷ 2 = **12.5**

Remember the mean is the average you get by adding together all the values in the data and dividing it by the number of values that you have, the mode is the most common value, and the median is the middle value when the data is in order of size.

b) End B, as the amount of bulrushes is lower here and you would expect there to be fewer bulrushes further away from the pond as they prefer moist soil or shallow water.
c) It decreases the validity of her study. If she didn't control the other variables that could affect the distribution of bulrushes in her garden, it means she can't conclude that moist soil and shallow water cause bulrushes to grow best.
d) E.g. there will be fewer bulrushes in the area closer to the pond because the pond is decreasing in size.

Pages 51-52 — Biology 2.3-2.4

Exam-style Questions

1 a) i) 55 + 41 + 57 = 153
153 ÷ 3 = **51**
(2 marks for correct answer, otherwise 1 mark for correct working)

ii) The number of limpets increases as you move away from the water's edge, and then begins to decrease after the position of quadrat 3 ***(1 mark)***. The low number of limpets in quadrats closest to the water's edge could be due to competition for space from other organisms ***(1 mark)***. The decrease in the number of limpets after quadrat 3 could be due to there being less water available further from the water's edge, which increases the limpets' chance of drying out ***(1 mark)***.

iii) This would increase their sample size ***(1 mark)*** which would make their samples more representative of the population at each distance ***(1 mark)***.

b) i) To increase the validity of their results ***(1 mark)***.

ii) Any two from: e.g. a difference in temperature / a difference in the availability of water / a difference in the availability of oxygen / a difference in the availability of nutrients ***(1 mark for each correct answer)***.

2 a) i) in the chloroplasts ***(1 mark)***

ii)
$$\text{carbon dioxide + water} \xrightarrow{\text{light energy}} \text{glucose + oxygen}$$
(1 mark for each correct answer)

b) i) B. It took the shortest time for all of the discs to be floating ***(1 mark)*** suggesting that photosynthesis was happening the fastest in this condition ***(1 mark)***.

ii) Increasing the light intensity will increase the rate of photosynthesis up to a point ***(1 mark)***. However, past this point increasing the light intensity will have no further effect on the rate of photosynthesis ***(1 mark)*** as other limiting factors may come into play, such as carbon dioxide concentration ***(1 mark)*** and temperature ***(1 mark)***.

iii) It should take less than 18 minutes because the rate of photosynthesis should be faster ***(1 mark)***, as there is more carbon dioxide available in the solution for photosynthesis ***(1 mark)***.

c) How to grade your answer:

0 marks:
No relevant information is given.

1-2 marks:
One or two uses of glucose by a plant are described.

3-4 marks:
Three or four uses of glucose by a plant are described. The answer has a logical structure and spelling, grammar and punctuation are mostly correct.

5-6 marks:
At least five uses of glucose by a plant are described. The answer has a logical structure and uses correct spelling, grammar and punctuation.

Here are some points your answer may include:
Some of the glucose is used for respiration.
Some glucose is converted into cellulose which is used to make strong cell walls.
Some glucose is combined with nitrate ions from the soil to make proteins.
Some glucose is converted into starch for storage.
Some glucose is converted into lipids (fats and oils) for storage.

Biology 2.5 Proteins — Their Functions and Uses

1. Proteins and Enzymes

Page 55 — Fact Recall Questions

Q1 a) The folding up of the long chains of amino acids that make up the protein.
b) So that other molecules can fit into the protein and the protein can carry out its function.

Q2 Any three from: e.g. structural components of tissues/ muscles / hormones / antibodies / catalysts/enzymes.

Q3 A catalyst is a substance which increases the speed of a reaction, without being changed or used up in the reaction.

Q4 False
Different enzymes work best at different pHs.

Page 55 — Application Question

Q1 It should slow down the rate of reaction.
This is because heating hexokinase up to a high temperature/50 °C will probably cause the bonds in hexokinase to break and the enzyme to lose its shape. This would mean that glucose will no longer be able to fit into hexokinase and the reaction won't be catalysed.
For questions like this you just need to apply your own knowledge — e.g. that enzymes lose their shape at high temperatures and that enzymes need their unique shape to work — to the specific enzyme named in the question.

2. Digestion

Page 58 — Fact Recall Questions

Q1 By specialised cells in the glands and in the gut lining.

Q2 False
Digestive enzymes catalyse the breakdown of big molecules into smaller molecules, e.g. protease enzymes catalyse the breakdown of proteins into amino acids.

Q3 amylase

Q4 In the stomach, the pancreas and the small intestine.

Q5 lipases

Q6 a) The stomach produces hydrochloric acid, which creates acidic conditions for pepsin/enzymes in the stomach to work in.
b) Bile is released into the small intestine. There, it neutralises the stomach acid and creates the ideal alkaline conditions for enzymes in the small intestine to work in.

Page 59 — Application Questions

Q1

	Amylase	Proteases	Lipases	Bile
Made where?	B, F, G	D, F, G	F, G	C
Work(s) where?	A, G	D, G	G	G

Make sure you learn where digestive enzymes and bile are produced and where they work — you can pick up easy marks with this information in the exam. However, it's easy to get things mixed up, so watch out. E.g. bile is made in the liver but stored in the gall bladder — make sure you don't get those two organs mixed up.

Q2 The photograph shows that in the test tubes with hydrochloric acid only and pepsin only (test tubes 1 and 2), the meat hasn't been fully digested. However, in the test tube with both pepsin and hydrochloric acid (test tube 3) the meat sample has been completely digested. This has happened because to digest meat, which contains protein, pepsin (a protease enzyme) is needed. Also, pepsin in the stomach works best under acidic conditions, which are provided by hydrochloric acid released by the stomach. Therefore the meat was only broken down in the test tube that had both the pepsin and the acidic conditions.

3. Enzymes in Home and Industry

Page 62 — Fact Recall Questions

Q1 a) proteases and lipases
b) Proteases help break down proteins. Lipases help break down fats/lipids.

Q2 E.g. they don't work well at high temperatures. / They might not work very well in very acidic or alkaline tap water. / They can irritate sensitive skin.
Enzymes are the 'biological' bit of biological detergents. So, biological detergents usually don't work well at high temperatures or extremes of pH because the enzymes are denatured and so won't work anymore.

Q3 It means that the baby foods contain proteins that have already been partially broken down by enzymes, so that they are easier for babies to digest.

Q4 carbohydrase

Q5 E.g. the reaction that turns glucose syrup into fructose syrup.

Page 62 — Application Questions

Q1 Sarah should buy non-biological washing powder because the enzymes in biological washing powders usually denature at high temperatures, so they may not work as well on a hot wash. Also, biological washing powder may irritate sensitive skin like Sarah's.
John should buy biological washing powder because it's more effective at lower temperatures than non-biological washing powders. This means he can save energy and money by putting his washing machine on a lower temperature cycle.

Q2 a) The manufacturer should use fructose syrup in Diet Lem-Fizz because it is sweeter than glucose syrup, so a smaller amount is needed.
b) Fructose syrup can be made from glucose syrup using an isomerase enzyme.

Biology 2.6 Aerobic and Anaerobic Respiration

1. Aerobic Respiration

Page 65 — Fact Recall Questions

Q1 enzymes

Q2 Respiration using oxygen. / The process of releasing energy from glucose using oxygen.

Q3 E.g. mammals use energy to build larger molecules from smaller ones, to contract muscles and to keep their body temperature steady.

Q4 E.g. sugars and nitrates.
Plants use energy from respiration to make sugars, nitrates and other nutrients into amino acids. They then use amino acids to make proteins.

Page 65 — Application Questions

Q1 mitochondrion/mitochondria
'Mitochondrion' is the singular of mitochondria.

Q2 a) oxygen
b) water / energy
c) energy / water

2. Exercise

Page 67 — Fact Recall Questions

Q1 During exercise, your breathing rate and depth both increase.

Q2 a) muscles
b) During exercise, glycogen in the muscles is converted back to glucose to provide more energy.
Energy is released from glucose via respiration.

Page 67 — Application Questions

Q1 Charlotte's heart rate has increased to increase blood flow to the muscles. This means that the muscles receive more oxygen and glucose for respiration, and can get rid of more carbon dioxide.

Q2 a) Samir's breathing rate increases from 16 breaths per minute at rest, to 44 breaths per minute by the end of the race. By eight minutes after the race Samir's breathing rate has decreased back to 16 breaths per minute.

b) During the race, Samir's breathing rate increases to provide more oxygen for respiration, so that more energy is released to keep his muscles contracting. By eight minutes after the race his breathing rate has decreased back to its resting level. This is because his muscle activity has decreased and his body doesn't need as much energy from respiration, so he doesn't need to take in as much oxygen.

3. Anaerobic Respiration

Page 69 — Fact Recall Questions

Q1 The body uses anaerobic respiration during vigorous exercise when it can't get enough oxygen to the muscles for aerobic respiration.

We're not respiring by anaerobic respiration all the time — just when increased muscle activity means we can't get oxygen to our muscles fast enough for them to respire aerobically.

Q2 Anaerobic respiration is the incomplete breakdown of glucose which produces lactic acid. (It takes place in the absence of oxygen.)

Q3 a) It's when muscles get tired and stop contracting efficiently.

b) E.g. build up of lactic acid.

Q4 Oxygen debt is when, after vigorous exercise, a person has to "repay" the oxygen that they didn't get to their muscles in time, because their lungs, heart and blood couldn't keep up with the demand earlier on.

Pages 70-71 — Biology 2.5-2.6

Exam-style Questions

1 a) i) a protein ***(1 mark)***

ii) To act as a biological catalyst. / To speed up the rate of a reaction (in a living organism) without being changed or used up itself ***(1 mark)***.

b) How to grade your answer:

0 marks:
No relevant information is given.

1-2 marks:
There is a brief description of the function of at least one type of digestive enzyme, but where it's made or where it works may not be covered.

3-4 marks:
There is a description of the function of at least two types of digestive enzyme, with mention of where they are made or where they work. The answer has a logical structure and spelling, grammar and punctuation are mostly correct.

5-6 marks:
There is a detailed description of the function of three types of digestive enzyme, including where each of them is made and where each of them works in the digestive system. The answer has a logical structure and uses correct spelling, grammar and punctuation.

Here are some points your answer may include:
Amylase is a digestive enzyme that catalyses the conversion of starch into sugars. Amylase is made in the salivary glands, the pancreas and the small intestine. It works in the mouth and the small intestine.
Protease enzymes are digestive enzymes that catalyse the conversion of proteins into amino acids. Proteases are made in the stomach, the pancreas and the small intestine. They work in the stomach and the small intestine.
Lipase enzymes are digestive enzymes that catalyse the conversion of lipids into glycerol and fatty acids. Lipases are made in the pancreas and the small intestine. They work in the small intestine.

2 a) i) B, because it has a higher peak enzyme activity ***(1 mark)***.

ii) Above 80 °C the enzyme activity of each enzyme decreases ***(1 mark)***. This is because the high temperatures cause the enzymes to become denatured / the enzymes' shapes to change so that they can't catalyse the reaction ***(1 mark)***.

b) Fructose syrup is sweeter than glucose syrup ***(1 mark)***, so it can be used in smaller amounts, which is good for slimming foods ***(1 mark)***.

c) Any three from: e.g. they're specific, so they only catalyse the reaction that you want them to. / They allow reactions to happen at lower temperatures and pressures and so at a lower cost as it saves energy. / Enzymes work for a long time, so after the initial cost of buying them, you can continually use them. / They are biodegradable and therefore cause less environmental pollution. ***(1 mark for each correct answer)***

3 a) i) (151 + 163 + 154) / 3 = **156 beats per minute** ***(1 mark for correct working, 1 mark for correct answer)***

Make sure that you always include units in your answer — in this case, the units are beats per minute.

ii) Because the student was respiring anaerobically ***(1 mark)*** so will have had an oxygen debt ***(1 mark)***. This means his heart rate had to remain high to keep blood flowing through the muscles ***(1 mark)*** to deliver oxygen to them ***(1 mark)***, in order to get rid of lactic acid by oxidising it to carbon dioxide and water ***(1 mark)***.

b) E.g. making larger molecules from smaller ones ***(1 mark)***. Keeping the body at a steady temperature ***(1 mark)***

4 a) i) glucose + oxygen
→ carbon dioxide + water + energy
(1 mark for glucose and oxygen on the left-hand side of the equation, 1 mark for carbon dioxide and water on the right)
ii) constantly/all the time ***(1 mark)***
b) Anaerobic respiration releases less ATP than aerobic respiration, which shows that it releases less energy ***(1 mark)***. This is because glucose is not completely broken down in anaerobic respiration ***(1 mark)***.

Biology 2.7 Cell Division and Inheritance

1. DNA

Page 74 — Fact Recall Questions

Q1 Deoxyribonucleic acid
Q2 (long molecules of) DNA
Q3 It has a double helix structure.
Q4 By telling the cell what order to put amino acids in.
Q5 Because everyone's DNA fingerprint is unique (except identical twins).

Page 74 — Application Questions

Q1 a) Suspect B because their DNA exactly matches the DNA of the blood found at the crime scene.
b) No. The DNA match only provides evidence that suspect B was probably at the crime scene, not that they committed the crime.
Q2 Suspects A and D as their DNA fingerprints are identical.

2. Cell Division — Mitosis

Page 76 — Fact Recall Questions

Q1 two
Q2 For growth, to replace damaged cells and for asexual reproduction.
Q3 one

Page 76 — Application Questions

Q1 genetically identical
Mitosis produces cells that are genetically identical to the parent cells.
Q2 two
If a cell has two sets of chromosomes it means that it will have two copies of each chromosome.

3. Cell Division — Meiosis

Page 79 — Fact Recall Questions

Q1 one
Q2 In the reproductive organs/the testes and the ovaries in humans.
Q3 By repeatedly dividing by mitosis.
Q4 two
Q5 four
Q6 False
Gametes are all genetically different.

Page 79 — Application Questions

Q1 a) 39
b) 38
c) 32
Q2 a) i) Before the first division, the cell duplicates its DNA.
This creates X-shaped chromosomes, where each 'arm' of the chromosome has the same DNA.
ii) It would only have one set of chromosomes. (It should have two sets of chromosomes.)
b) Any three from: e.g. mitosis occurs in body cells, meiosis occurs in cells of the reproductive organs only. / Mitosis produces body cells, meiosis produces gametes. / Mitosis is used for growth, cell replacement or asexual reproduction, meiosis is used for gamete production. / Mitosis involves one cell division, meiosis involves two. / Two new cells are produced when a cell divides by mitosis, four new cells are produced when a cell divides by meiosis. / Mitosis produces cells which have two sets of chromosomes in them, meiosis produces cells that only contain one set of chromosomes.

4. Stem Cells

Page 82 — Fact Recall Questions

Q1 In most animal cells, the ability to differentiate is lost at an early stage, whereas lots of plant cells don't ever lose this ability.
Q2 An undifferentiated cell that has the potential to differentiate into different types of cell.
Q3 any type of cell
Q4 E.g. in the bone marrow.

Page 82 — Application Questions

Q1) a) Stem cells could be made to differentiate into neurones, which could replace the damaged/dead neurones.
b) E.g. producing nerve cells to replace damaged tissue in people with paralysis. / Producing beating heart muscle cells for people with heart disease. / Producing insulin-producing cells for people with diabetes.
Q2 Because the embryos leftover from fertility clinics will be destroyed anyway.
Q3 E.g. because the embryo still has the potential to develop life before this point.

5. X and Y Chromosomes

Page 86 — Fact Recall Questions

Q1 one
Q2 False
Half carry X chromosomes, and half carry Y chromosomes.
Q3 females

Page 86 — Application Questions

Q1

Rachael XX   Henry XY

Gametes: X X X Y

Offspring: XX female, XX female, XY male, XY male

Q2 50% or 50:50 or ½.

Q3 No. There is always a 50% chance of having a boy and a 50% chance of having a girl at each pregnancy.

Q4

Rachael's gametes

	X	X	
	XX	XX	X
	XY	XY	Y

Henry's gametes

6. The Work of Mendel

Page 89 — Fact Recall Questions

Q1 Characteristics in plants are determined by "hereditary units". Hereditary units are passed on from both parents, one unit from each parent. Hereditary units can either be dominant or recessive — if an individual has both the dominant and the recessive unit for a characteristic, the dominant characteristic will be expressed.

Q2 genes

Q3 No one knew about genes or DNA when Mendel was still alive, so the significance of his work wasn't realised until after he had died.

These days people recognise Mendel as one of the founding fathers of genetics. He was just a bit ahead of his time. Poor Mendel.

Page 89 — Application Question

Q1

Seed colour of pea plant	Type of hereditary unit		
	Just green	Just yellow	Both green and yellow
Green	✓	✗	✗
Yellow	✗	✓	✓

The yellow hereditary unit is dominant, so if the pea plant has both yellow and green hereditary units its seeds will be yellow. If the plant just has yellow hereditary units its seeds will also be yellow. For its seeds to be green, the plant has to have two of the green hereditary units.

7. Alleles and Genetic Diagrams

Page 94 — Fact Recall Questions

Q1 Different versions of the same gene.

Q2 The allele for the characteristic that's shown if two different alleles for the same gene are present.

Q3 When an organism has two alleles for a particular gene that are the same, e.g. TT.

Q4 The characteristics you have.

Page 94 — Application Questions

Q1 a) a rough coat

You need to have worked out from the letters that the rough coat allele (R) is dominant over the smooth coat allele (r).

b) i) E.g.

Parents' phenotypes: female rough coat, male rough coat

Parents' genotypes: Rr, Rr

Gametes' alleles: R, r, R, r

Offspring's genotypes: RR, Rr, Rr, rr

You could have drawn a Punnet square here too.

ii) 1 in 4 or 25%

Q2 a) heterozygous

b) ss

c) SS

8. Genetic Disorders

Page 98 — Fact Recall Questions

Q1 cystic fibrosis

Q2 recessive

You need to have two recessive alleles for cystic fibrosis to be a sufferer of the disease.

Q3 extra fingers or toes

Q4 E.g. to see if the embryo carries a genetic disorder.

Page 98 — Application Questions

Q1 a) Ff

b) ff

Q2 a) Because there are no carriers of the disease, just sufferers.

b) a purple circle

c) i) dd

ii) Dd

You know from the diagram that Kate is a sufferer of polydactyly, so she must have at least one copy of the dominant allele 'D'. You also know that she doesn't have two copies of the dominant allele, as her father Clark is not a sufferer, so she couldn't have inherited a second 'D' allele from him. Therefore her genotype must be Dd.

d) *Lois's alleles*

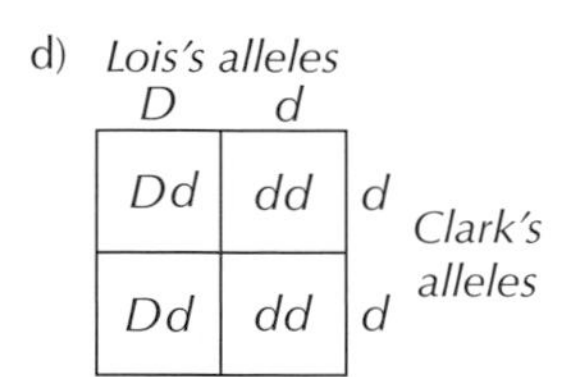

e) i) E.g

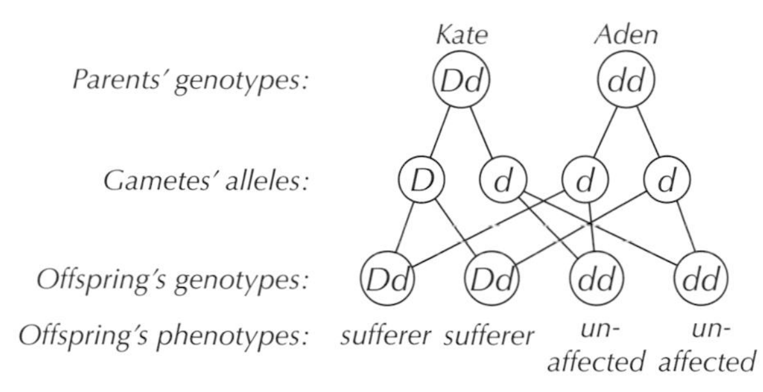

ii) The probability of the new baby having polydactyly is 50%/1 in 2.

Pages 101-102 — Biology 2.7

Exam-style Questions

1 a) Male 1 because bands 7, 11 and 12 match bands 1, 5 and 6 in the child's DNA sample ***(1 mark)*** whereas none of Male 2, Male 3 or Male 4's bands match those in the child's DNA sample ***(1 mark)***.

b) Bands 2, 3 and 4 ***(1 mark)***. You get half of your DNA from your father and half from your mother ***(1 mark)***, so you'd expect the mother to share the remaining bands on the child's DNA fingerprint ***(1 mark)***.

2 a) i) E.g.

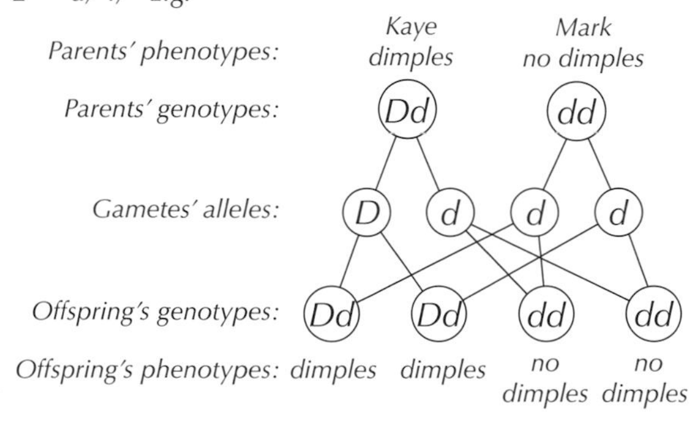

(1 mark for correctly identifying Mark's genotype, 1 mark for correctly identifying possible genotypes of the offspring.)

You could have drawn a Punnett square to answer this question instead.

ii) The baby has a 50%/1 in 2 chance of having dimples ***(1 mark)***.

b) XY ***(1 mark)***

Males have the XY chromosome combination, females have the XX chromosome combination.

c) Because the baby has been produced via sexual reproduction ***(1 mark)***. In sexual reproduction, two gametes fuse ***(1 mark)*** bringing together two different sets of chromosomes (one from the mother and one from the father) to form the new individual ***(1 mark)***.

3 a)

Statement	Mitosis	Meiosis
Only occurs in the reproductive organs.		✓
It produces gametes.		✓
It produces body cells.	✓	

(1 mark for each correct answer)

b) i) $2 \div 0.5 = 4$ divisions

2^4 (or $2 \times 2 \times 2 \times 2$) = 16 cells

(1 mark for correctly calculating that 4 divisions will take place in 2 hours, 1 mark for 16 cells.)

There will be 4 divisions in two hours, so 1 cell will become 2 cells in the first division, 2 cells will become 4 cells in the second division, 4 cells will then become 8, and 8 cells will become 16.

ii) genetically identical ***(1 mark)***

4 a) Cystic fibrosis is a genetic disorder ***(1 mark)***, which affects the cell membranes ***(1 mark)***.

b) Homozygous, because he is a sufferer of a recessive disorder ***(1 mark)***.

c) E.g.

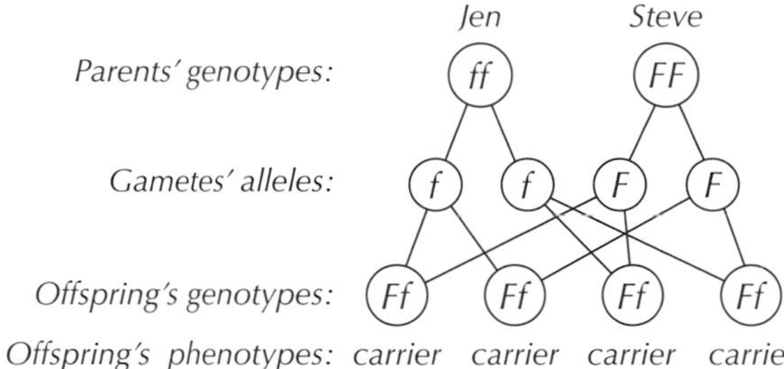

(1 mark for correctly identifying the parents' genotypes, 1 mark for correctly identifying possible genotypes of the offspring.)

No, because to suffer from cystic fibrosis you need to have the genotype ff ***(1 mark)***. Jen and Steve's offspring will only have the genotype Ff, so they could only be carriers, not sufferers ***(1 mark)***.

You could have drawn a Punnett square to answer this question instead.

d) Ff ***(1 mark)***. For a child to have cystic fibrosis, both parents must carry the cystic fibrosis allele ***(1 mark)***, as it is a recessive disorder ***(1 mark)***.

Tony is a carrier so his alleles must be Ff. As their child has cystic fibrosis (ff) it must have inherited a cystic fibrosis allele from both Tony and Bex, as it's a recessive disorder. Bex doesn't suffer from cystic fibrosis, then she must be a carrier (Ff).

Biology 2.8 Fossils and Speciation

1. Fossils

Page 105 — Fact Recall Questions

Q1 The remains of an organism from many years ago that are found in a rock.

Q2 That organisms lived ages ago and how today's species have evolved over time.

Q3 Early organisms were soft-bodied and soft tissue tends to decay away completely, without forming fossils. Plus fossils that did form millions of years ago may have been destroyed by geological activity, e.g. the movement of tectonic plates. So the fossil record is incomplete.

Page 105 — Application Question

Q1 A E.g. an organism (or organisms) burrowed into soft material. The material later hardened around the burrows to form casts in the rock.

B E.g. the hard shell of the snail decayed away slowly. It was gradually replaced by minerals as it decayed, forming a rock-like substance shaped like the shell.

C E.g. a leaf became buried in a soft material. The material later hardened around the leaf, which decayed, leaving a cast of itself in the rock.

D E.g. the mammoth died and it's body became trapped in frozen ground. It was too cold for decay microbes to work, so the mammoth's body was preserved.

2. Extinction and Speciation

Page 108 — Fact Recall Questions

Q1 Any two from: e.g. the environment changes too quickly. / A new predator kills them all. / A new disease kills them all. / They can't compete with another (new) species for food. / A catastrophic event happens that kills them all. / A new species develops.

Q2 The development of a new species.

Q3 E.g. due to the formation of a physical barrier.

Q4 Because they have a wide range of alleles.

Q5 When individuals from different populations have changed so much that they can no longer interbreed to produced fertile offspring.

Page 109 — Biology 2.8 Exam-style Questions

1 a) Populations of the original squirrel species became separated/isolated by the formation of the canyon ***(1 mark)***. Each population showed variation because they had a wide range of alleles ***(1 mark)***. In each population, individuals with characteristics that made them better adapted to their environment were more likely to survive and breed successfully ***(1 mark)***. So the alleles that controlled beneficial characteristics were more likely to be passed onto the next generation ***(1 mark)***. Eventually individuals from the different populations changed so much that they were unable to interbreed to produce fertile offspring ***(1 mark)***.

Remember, the main steps leading to speciation are: isolation, genetic variation in the isolated populations, natural selection causing different characteristics and therefore different alleles to become more common in each population, populations change and are unable to interbreed.

b) Individuals from bird species X were able to fly across the canyon ***(1 mark)***, so there were no isolated populations ***(1 mark)***.

Something that's a physical barrier for one species won't necessarily be a barrier for another. It depends on things like the size of the organisms involved, how they move around, how many of them there are, etc.

c) i) The hard shells won't have decayed easily so they will have lasted a long time when buried ***(1 mark)***. As the shells did decay, they will have been gradually replaced by minerals, forming a rock-like substance shaped like the original shells ***(1 mark)***.

ii) Soft tissue tends to decay away completely without forming fossils ***(1 mark)***.

iii) E.g. by geological activity / they may have been crushed by the movements of tectonic plates ***(1 mark)***.

Chemistry 2

Chemistry 2.1 Structure and Bonding

1. Bonding in Compounds

Page 110 — Fact Recall Questions

Q1 A compound is a substance that's formed when atoms of two or more elements are chemically combined.

Q2 E.g. covalent bonding and ionic bonding.

Q3 So that they can have a full outer shell of electrons/a stable electronic structure/the electronic structure of a noble gas.

Q4 By atoms sharing electrons.

2. Ionic Bonding

Page 115 — Fact Recall Questions

Q1 Ionic bonding is a strong electrostatic attraction between oppositely charged ions that holds ions in an ionic compound together.

Q2 Group 6 and Group 7.

Q3 Positively charged ions.

Q4 They gain electrons.

Q5 1^+

Q6 1^-

Q7 a)

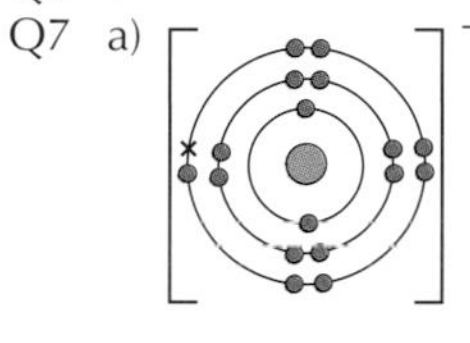

b)

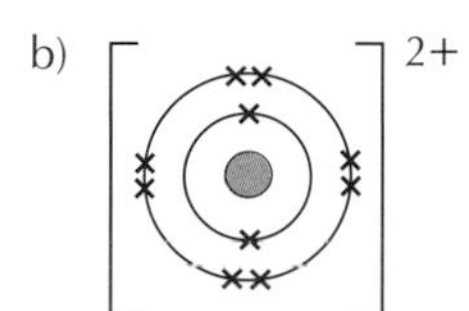

c)

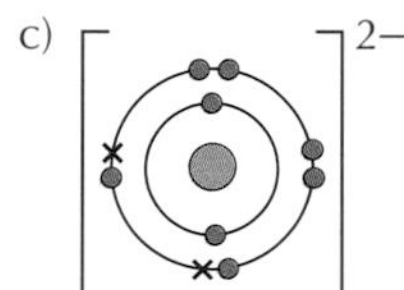

d)

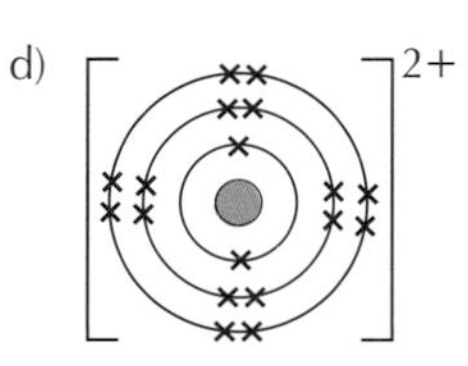

It doesn't matter if you've used dots AND crosses to show the electrons in the ions, or if you've used all dots or all crosses. The important thing is that you've got the right number of electrons.

Q8 An ionic compound is a giant structure made of ions. The ions are held together in a lattice by electrostatic forces of attraction acting in all directions.

Page 115 — Application Questions

Q1 a) Rb^+
b) Br^-
c) Ba^{2+}
d) S^{2-}

Q2 a) Sodium loses one electron to form Na^+ ions. Bromine gains one electron to form Br^- ions. $(+1) + (-1) = 0$, so the charges are balanced with one ion of each and the formula is **NaBr**.
b) Calcium loses two electrons to form Ca^{2+} ions. Fluorine gains one electron to form F^- ions. $(+2) + (-1) + (-1) = 0$, so the charges are balanced with one ion of calcium and two ions of fluorine. So the formula is **CaF_2**.
c) Sodium loses one electron to form Na^+ ions. Oxygen gains two electrons to form O^{2-} ions. $(+1) + (+1) + (-2) = 0$, so the charges are balanced with two ions of sodium and one ion of oxygen. So the formula is **Na_2O**.
d) Calcium loses two electrons to form Ca^{2+} ions. Oxygen gains two electrons to form O^{2-} ions. $(+2) + (-2) = 0$, so the charges are balanced with one ion of each and the formula is **CaO**.

Q3 a) K^+ ions and I^- ions.
b) $(+1) + (-1) = 0$, so the charges are balanced with one ion of each and the formula is **KI**.
c) E.g. potassium has one electron in its outer shell and iodine has seven electrons in its outer shell. When they react, the electron in the outer shell of the potassium atom is transferred to the iodine atom. A positively charged potassium ion and a negatively charged iodide ion are formed. They both have full outer shells of electrons.

Q4 E.g. magnesium has two electrons in its outer shell. Chlorine has seven electrons in its outer shell. When they react, the magnesium atom gives up its outer electrons and forms an Mg^{2+} ion. Chlorine atoms accept one electron each to form Cl^- ions. Chloride ions and magnesium ions have stable electronic structures. Because the magnesium ions and chloride ions are oppositely charged they are strongly attracted to each other, and this strong electrostatic attraction, known as ionic bonding, holds them together in the ionic compound magnesium chloride.

3. Covalent Bonding

Page 119 — Fact Recall Questions

Q1 A shared pair of electrons.

Q2 a) Hydrogen chloride
b) Water

Q3 a)

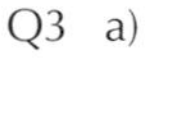

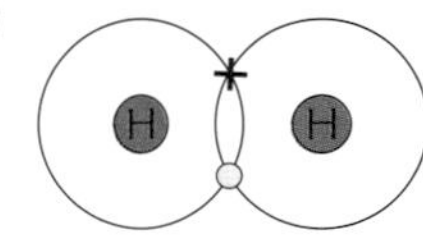

b)

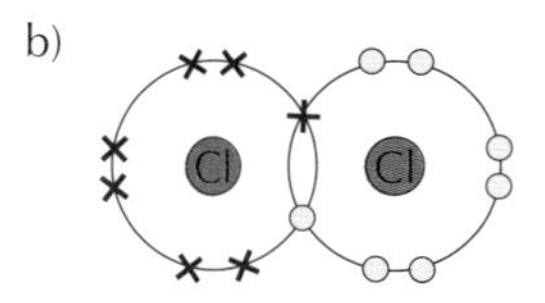

c)

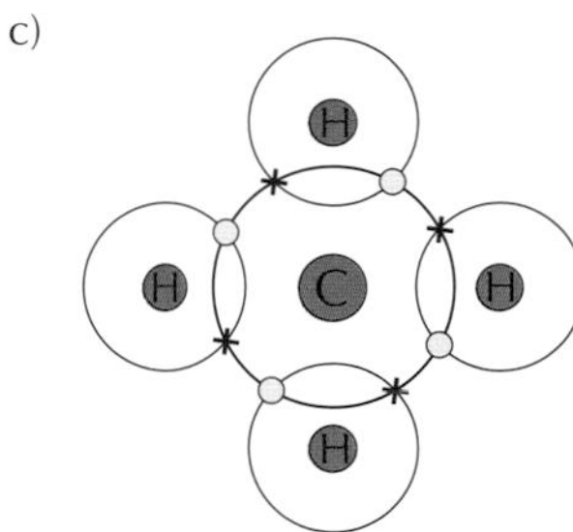

Q4 a) Cl—Cl

b)
```
    H
    |
H—N—H
```

c) O=O

Q5 Two pairs of electrons shared between two atoms.

Q6 E.g. silicon dioxide and diamond.

Page 119 — Application Questions

Q1 'A' has seven electrons in its third shell, so needs one more to have a full outer shell. Hydrogen has one electron in its outer shell, so needs one more to have a full outer shell. Hydrogen and element A both share one of their electrons so that both atoms have a full outer shell, forming a single covalent bond.

Q2 a) Molecule A contains a double bond — there are two pairs of electrons shared between two atoms in this molecule.

There are actually two double bonds in molecule A.

b) O=C=O

4. Metallic Bonding

Page 120 — Fact Recall Questions

Q1 Metals are giant structures, with atoms arranged in a regular pattern.

Q2 Electrons that aren't associated with a particular atom or bond — they're free to move through the whole structure.

Q3 a) Electrostatic forces.

b) Electrostatic forces exist in a metal because there are delocalised electrons and positive metal ions.

Chemistry 2.2 Structure, Properties and Uses of Substances

1. Ionic Compounds

Page 122 — Fact Recall Questions

Q1 High melting points. The electrostatic forces of attraction between the ions in an ionic compound are very strong, so it takes a lot of energy to overcome this attraction and melt the compound.

Q2 When ionic compounds are dissolved in water the ions separate and are free to move in solution, so they can carry an electric current.

2. Covalent Substances

Page 125 — Fact Recall Questions

Q1 A molecule made up of only a few atoms.

Q2 Covalent bonding.

Q3 Any three from: e.g. hydrogen / chlorine / hydrogen chloride / methane / ammonia / water / oxygen.

Q4 The forces of attraction between the molecules/ intermolecular forces are very weak. So the molecules are easily parted from one another — little energy is needed to break them.

Q5 Diamond has a giant structure where all the carbon atoms are bonded to each other by strong covalent bonds. Lots of energy is required to overcome these bonds and melt diamond.

Q6 b) and c)

Q7 It can conduct heat and electricity.

Page 125 — Application Questions

Q1 It is very hard.

Q2 The layers in graphite can slide over each other so it is slippery.

Q3 a) B

b) C

c) A

3. Metallic Structures

Page 126 — Fact Recall Questions

Q1 The atoms in metals are arranged in layers that are able to slide over each other. This allows the metal to be bent.

Q2 Metals have delocalised electrons that are able to move through the whole structure. They carry heat energy, allowing the metal to conduct heat.

Q3 Alloys are made from more than one element, so they contain atoms of different sizes. The atoms of the element that is added to the metal distort the layers of metal atoms, making it more difficult for them to slide over each other.

4. New Materials

Page 129 — Fact Recall Questions

Q1 c)

Q2 E.g. nitinol.

Q3 1–100 nanometres across.

Q4 E.g. new industrial catalysts / highly specific sensors / strong, light building materials / new cosmetics / lubricant coatings / in electric circuits for computer chips / delivering drugs into the body / reinforcing materials (e.g. graphite in tennis rackets).

Q5 B

Fullerenes are based on hexagonal rings of carbon atoms.

Q6 E.g. new industrial catalysts / lubricant coatings / delivering drugs into the body / reinforcing materials (e.g. graphite in tennis rackets).

5. Polymers

Page 132 — Fact Recall Questions

Q1 A thermosetting polymer.

Q2 A thermosoftening polymer.

Q3 Thermosetting polymers have strong cross-links between the polymer chains. These forces are difficult to overcome so thermosetting polymers are strong, hard and rigid. The intermolecular forces between the polymer chains in thermosoftening polymers are much weaker. There are no cross-links, between the chains and the forces are easily overcome, so thermosoftening polymers melt easily and can be remoulded.

Q4 E.g. the reaction conditions. / The temperature at which the polymer was formed. / The pressure at which the polymer was formed. / The catalyst used when the polymer was formed.

Q5 E.g. low density (LD) polythene and high density (HD) polythene.

It doesn't matter whether you've put polythene or poly(ethene) here — both are correct.

Page 132 — Application Questions

Q1 A thermosetting polymer. E.g. kitchenware such as ladles and spatulas needs to be able to withstand heat without melting. Thermosetting polymers don't melt when heated, so melamine resin is likely to be a thermosetting polymer.

Q2 A thermosoftening polymer. E.g. thermosoftening polymers soften when they are heated and can be remoulded.

Q3 a) E.g. expanded polystyrene. The polymer will need to be able to absorb shocks to protect the glassware, and be lightweight so that it can be moved around easily.

b) E.g. poly(methyl methacrylate). The polymer needs to be transparent so that the spectators can see through it and shatter-resistant so that it doesn't break if it gets hit.

c) E.g. expanded polystyrene. The polymer needs to be a poor conductor of heat so that it traps heat inside the house.

d) E.g. polyvinyl chloride. The polymer needs to be rigid so that it can hold its shape and it needs to be strong so that it can carry the material that flows through it.

Pages 134-136 — Chemistry 2.1-2.2
Exam-style Questions

1 a)

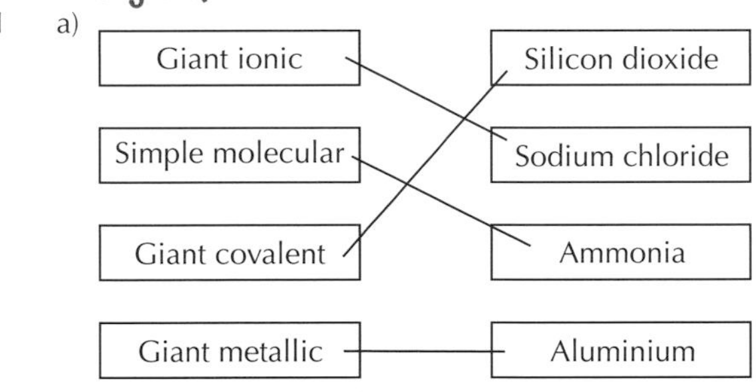

(1 mark for each correct line drawn).

b) i) Simple molecular ***(1 mark).***

ii) Giant metallic ***(1 mark).***

iii) Giant covalent ***(1 mark).***

iv) Giant ionic ***(1 mark).***

2 a) i) Covalent bonding ***(1 mark).***

ii) Chlorine is made of simple molecules ***(1 mark)*** and so the intermolecular forces between molecules are weak ***(1 mark).*** This means not much energy is needed to overcome them/ chlorine has a low boiling point ***(1 mark).***

b) i) Lithium loses one electron ***(1 mark)*** and chlorine gains one electron ***(1 mark).*** This happens so that both lithium and chlorine can achieve a full outer shell of electrons/a stable electronic structure ***(1 mark).***

ii)

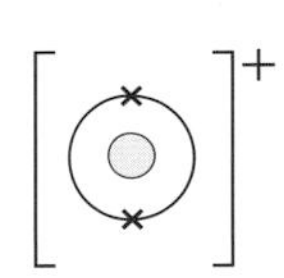

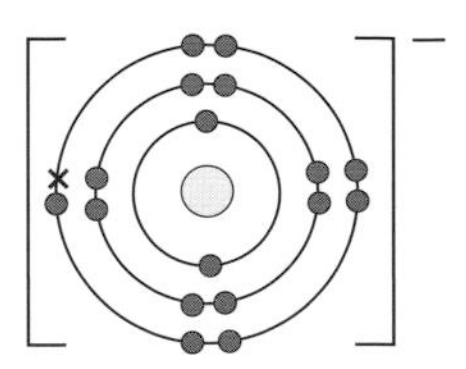

(1 mark for correct electron arrangement for a sodium ion, 1 mark for correct electron arrangement for a chloride ion. 1 mark for both charges shown correctly.)

iii) LiCl ***(1 mark).***

Lithium loses one electron so has a charge of +1, chlorine gains one electron so has a charge of −1. (+1) + (−1) = 0, so you only need one of each ion to balance out the charges.

c) Lithium chloride is an ionic compound so consists of oppositely charged ions held together by strong electrostatic forces ***(1 mark).*** A lot of energy is required to overcome these forces and melt the compound ***(1 mark).***

3 a) Thermosoftening polymer ***(1 mark).***

You're told that polycaprolactone melts so it must be a thermosoftening polymer — thermosetting polymers don't melt when they're heated.

b) i) When a covalent bond forms, atoms share a pair of electrons ***(1 mark)*** so that they've both got full outer shells of electrons/stable electronic structures ***(1 mark).***

ii) Polycaprolactone has weak intermolecular forces between its polymer chains ***(1 mark).*** It's these forces that need to be overcome to melt the polymer, and not much energy is required to do this ***(1 mark).***

c) Thermosetting polymers contain cross-links between polymer chains ***(1 mark)*** so they do not soften when they are heated ***(1 mark).*** This means they cannot be melted down and made into new shapes ***(1 mark).***

d) E.g. silicon dioxide / graphite / diamond ***(1 mark)***

4 a) How to grade your answer:

0 marks:
No relevant details of the arrangement of atoms or bonding in diamond or graphite are given.

1-2 marks:
Brief description of the arrangement of atoms or the bonding in both substances, or the arrangement of atoms and the bonding in one substance.

3-4 marks:
The arrangement of atoms and the bonding in diamond and graphite are described. The answer has some structure and spelling, grammar and punctuation are mostly correct. Some specialist terms are used.

5-6 marks:
The arrangement of atoms and the bonding in diamond and graphite are described in detail. The answer has a logical structure and uses correct spelling, grammar and punctuation. Relevant specialist terms are used correctly.

Here are some points your answer may include:

In diamond, each carbon atom forms four covalent bonds.
This makes diamond a hard, rigid, giant covalent structure.
In graphite, each carbon atom only forms three covalent bonds.
This results in layers of carbon atoms.
The layers are held together by weak intermolecular forces/aren't covalently bonded to each other.
The layers can slide over each other making graphite soft and slippery.

b) Carbon nanotubes have different properties to bulk carbon ***(1 mark)***. Carbon nanotubes contain carbon atoms arranged into hexagons ***(1 mark)***.

A nanoparticle is made out of a few hundred atoms, not thousands, and carbon nanotubes have a high surface area to volume ratio. Unfortunately, if you've ticked more than 2 boxes for this question you can't have any marks.

5 a) The electrons in the outer shells of silver atoms are delocalised ***(1 mark)***, so they are free to move throughout the whole metal, carrying electric charge ***(1 mark)***.

b) i) Diagram B — sterling silver is an alloy so contains atoms of different elements ***(1 mark)***.

ii) Sterling silver is harder — in pure silver the atoms are arranged in layers that can slide over each other making the metal soft ***(1 mark)***. In sterling silver other atoms have been added that disrupt the layers, preventing them from sliding over each other ***(1 mark)***.

Chemistry 2.3 Quantitative Chemistry and Analysis

1. Atoms and Isotopes

Page 138 — Fact Recall Questions

Q1 a) The atomic number tells you how many protons there are in the atom.

b) The mass number tells you the total number of protons and neutrons in the atom.

Q2 Subtract the atomic number from the mass number.

Q3 a) 1

b) very small

c) 1

Q4 Isotopes are different atomic forms of the same element, which have the same number of protons but a different number of neutrons.

Page 138 — Application Questions

Q1 a) 8 protons, 8 neutrons

b) 13 protons, 14 neutrons

c) 23 protons, 28 neutrons

d) 47 protons, 61 neutrons

Q2 A is the isotope.

You know A is the isotope because it has the same number of protons (17) but a different number of neutrons (20 as opposed to 18).

2. Relative Formula Mass

Page 140 — Fact Recall Questions

Q1 The mass of atoms of that element measured relative to atoms of carbon-12.

Q2 If more than one stable isotope of an element exists, the relative atomic mass of that element is the average relative atomic mass of all the isotopes, taking into account how much of each isotope there is.

Q3 By adding together the relative atomic masses of all the atoms in the compound.

Q4 $\text{Number of moles} = \frac{\text{Mass in g (of element or compound)}}{M_r \text{ (of element or compound)}}$

Page 141 — Application Questions

Q1 a) 9

b) 31

c) 65

d) 63.5

Q2 a) $16 \times 2 = \mathbf{32}$

b) $39 + 16 + 1 = \mathbf{56}$

c) $1 + 14 + (3 \times 16) = \mathbf{63}$

d) $40 + 12 + (3 \times 16) = \mathbf{100}$

Q3 a) A_r of K = 39
moles = mass ÷ A_r = 19.5 ÷ 39 = **0.5 moles**

b) M_r of NaCl = 23 + 35.5 = 58.5
moles = mass ÷ M_r = 23.4 ÷ 58.5 = **0.4 moles**

c) M_r of SO_2 = 32 + (2 × 16) = 64
moles = mass ÷ M_r = 76.8 ÷ 64 = **1.2 moles**

d) M_r of $CuSO_4$ = 63.5 + 32 + (4 × 16) = 159.5
moles = mass ÷ M_r = 31.9 ÷ 159.5 = **0.2 moles**

Q4 a) A_r of Ni = 59
mass = moles × A_r = 0.8 × 59 = **47.2 g**

b) M_r of MgO = 24 + 16 = 40
mass = moles × M_r = 0.5 × 40 = **20 g**

c) M_r of NH_3 = 14 + (3 × 1) = 17
mass = moles × M_r = 1.6 × 17 = **27.2 g**

d) M_r $Ca(OH)_2$ = 40 + (2 × (16 + 1)) = 74
mass = moles × M_r = 1.4 × 74 = **103.6 g**

3. Formula Mass Calculations

Page 144 — Fact Recall Questions

Q1 $\% \text{ mass} = \frac{A_r \times \text{No. of atoms}}{M_r} \times 100$

Q2 The simplest possible whole number ratio of atoms of each element within that compound.

Q3 List all the elements in the compound and write their experimental masses underneath them. Divide each mass by the A_r of that element. Take the numbers you end up with and divide each of them by the smallest number. If any of your answers are not whole numbers, multiply everything up to get the lowest possible whole number ratio.

Page 144 — Application Questions

Q1 a) A_r of H = 1
M_r of HCl = 1 + 35.5 = 36.5
% mass of hydrogen = (1 ÷ 36.5) × 100 = **2.7%**

b) A_r of Na = 23
M_r of NaOH = 23 + 16 + 1 = 40
% mass of sodium = (23 ÷ 40) × 100 = **57.5%**

c) A_r of Al = 27
M_r of Al_2O_3 = (2 × 27) + (3 × 16) = 102
% mass of aluminium = ((2 × 27) ÷ 102) × 100
= **52.9%**

d) A_r of O = 16
M_r of $Cu(OH)_2$ = 63.5 + (2 × (16 + 1)) = 97.5
% mass of oxygen = ((16 × 2) ÷ 97.5) × 100
= **32.8%**

Q2

N	O
5.6	12.8
$\frac{5.6}{14} = 0.4$	$\frac{12.8}{16} = 0.8$
$\frac{0.4}{0.4} = 1$	$\frac{0.8}{0.4} = 2$

The empirical formula is NO_2.

Q3

C	H
80	20
$\frac{80}{12} = 6.67$	$\frac{20}{1} = 20$
$\frac{6.67}{6.67} = 1$	$\frac{20}{6.67} = 3$

The empirical formula is CH_3.

Q4

C	H	O
10.8	2.4	9.6
$\frac{10.8}{12} = 0.9$	$\frac{2.4}{1} = 2.4$	$\frac{9.6}{16} = 0.6$
$\frac{0.9}{0.6} = 1.5$	$\frac{2.4}{0.6} = 4$	$\frac{0.6}{0.6} = 1$
3	8	2

The empirical formula is $C_3H_8O_2$.

Q5

Fe	O	H
52.3	44.9	2.8
$\frac{52.3}{56} = 0.93$	$\frac{44.9}{16} = 2.8$	$\frac{2.8}{1} = 2.8$
$\frac{0.93}{0.93} = 1$	$\frac{2.8}{0.93} = 3$	$\frac{2.8}{0.93} = 3$

The empirical formula is FeO_3H_3 or $Fe(OH)_3$.

4. Calculating Masses in Reactions

Page 147 — Application Questions

Q1 $2KBr + Cl_2 \rightarrow 2KCl + Br_2$
M_r of 2KBr = 2 × (39 + 80) = 238
M_r of 2KCl = 2 × (39 + 35.5) = 149
238 g of KBr reacts to give 149 g of KCl
(÷ 238) 1 g of KBr reacts to give 0.626 g of KCl
(× 36.2) 36.2 g of KBr reacts to give **22.7 g** of KCl

Q2 $6HCl + 2Al \rightarrow 2AlCl_3 + 3H_2$
M_r of 6HCl = 6 × (1 + 35.5) = 219
M_r of $2AlCl_3$ = 2 × (27 + (3 × 35.5)) = 267
219 g of HCl reacts to give 267 g of $AlCl_3$
(÷ 219) 1 g of HCl reacts to give 1.22 g of $AlCl_3$
(× 15.4) 15.4 g of HCl reacts to give **18.8 g** of $AlCl_3$

Q3 $CaCO_3 + H_2SO_4 \rightarrow CaSO_4 + H_2O + CO_2$
M_r of $CaCO_3$ = 40 + 12 + (3 × 16) = 100
M_r of $CaSO_4$ = 40 + 32 + (4 × 16) = 136
100 g of $CaCO_3$ reacts to give 136 g of $CaSO_4$
(÷ 100) 1 g of $CaCO_3$ reacts to give 1.36 g of $CaSO_4$
(× 28.5) 28.5 g of $CaCO_3$ reacts to give **38.8 g** $CaSO_4$

Q4 $HNO_3 + KOH \rightarrow KNO_3 + H_2O$
M_r of KOH = 39 + 16 + 1 = 56
M_r of KNO_3 = 39 + 14 + (3 × 16) = 101
56 g of KOH reacts to give 101 g of KNO_3
(÷ 101) 0.554 g of KOH reacts to give 1 g of KNO_3
(× 25.0) **13.9 g** of KOH reacts to give 25.0 g of KNO_3

Q5 $C_2H_4 + H_2O \rightarrow C_2H_6O$
M_r of C_2H_4 = (2 × 12) + (4 × 1) = 28
M_r of C_2H_6O = (2 × 12) + (6 × 1) + 16 = 46
28 g of C_2H_4 reacts to give 46 g of C_2H_6O
(÷ 46) 0.609 g of C_2H_4 reacts to give 1 g of C_2H_6O
(× 60) **36.5 g** of C_2H_4 reacts to give 60.0 g of C_2H_6O

Q6 $2Fe_2O_3 + 3C \rightarrow 4Fe + 3CO_2$
M_r of $2Fe_2O_3$ = 2 × ((2 × 56) + (3 × 16)) = 320
M_r of 4Fe = 4 × 56 = 224
320 g of Fe_2O_3 reacts to give 224 g of Fe
(÷ 224) 1.429 g of Fe_2O_3 reacts to give 1 g of Fe
(× 32.0) **45.7 g** of Fe_2O_3 reacts to give 32.0 g of Fe

5. Percentage Yield

Page 150 — Fact Recall Questions

Q1 The yield is the amount of product formed in a reaction.

Q2 The percentage yield is the amount of product produced in a reaction, given as a percentage of the predicted yield.

Q3 $\% \text{ yield} = \frac{\text{actual yield}}{\text{predicted yield}} \times 100$

Q4 E.g. The reaction could be reversible. / Some of the product may be lost when it is separated from the rest of the reaction mixture. / There may be some unexpected reactions happening that are using up some of the reactants.

Q5 If the percentage yield is high then fewer resources will be used/less chemicals will be wasted.

Page 150 — Application Questions

Q1 This reaction is reversible, so the yield will not be 100% because there will always be some product converting back to reactants.

Q2 E.g. the new method has a higher percentage yield than the old method, so it will use up less resources/ waste less chemicals and produce less waste.
The new method also works at a lower temperature, so it will save energy, using less fuel and creating less pollution.

Q3 % yield = (28.6 g ÷ 34.6 g) × 100 = **82.7%**
Q4 % yield = (33.4 g ÷ 41.9 g) × 100 = **79.7%**
Q5 % yield = (10.3 g ÷ 15.2 g) × 100 = **67.8%**
Q6 % yield = (4.27 g ÷ 8.45 g) × 100 = **50.5%**

6. Chemical Analysis

Page 153 — Fact Recall Questions

Q1 Put spots of the food colouring on a pencil baseline on some filter paper. Put the paper in a beaker with some solvent, making sure that the baseline is kept above the level of the solvent. The solvent seeps up the paper, taking the dyes with it. Different dyes form spots in different places.
Q2 Any three from: E.g. They are very sensitive/can detect very small amounts of substance. / They are very fast. / The tests can be automated. / They are very accurate.
Q3 A gas is used to carry the mixture through a column packed with solid material. Different substances in the mixture travel through the column at different speeds, so they are separated.
Q4 The relative molecular mass of each of the substances separated in the gas chromatography column.

Page 153 — Application Questions

Q1 C: Three or more — there are 3 spots so there must be at least 3 dyes. But if two different dyes have travelled similar distances their spots could have joined together, so there could be more than 3 dyes.
Q2 a) 4
You know there are 4 compounds in the substance because there are 4 peaks on the chromatogram.
b) 8 minutes

Pages 155-156 — Chemistry 2.3 Exam-style Questions

1 a) i) M_r of Na_2CO_3 = (2 × 23) + 12 + (3 × 16) = 106 ***(1 mark)***
moles = mass ÷ M_r = 25 ÷ 106 = **0.24 moles** ***(1 mark)***
ii) E.g. M_r of Na_2CO_3 = 106 (see above)
M_r of 2NaOH = 2 × (23 + 16 + 1) = 80
106 g of Na_2CO_3 reacts to give 80 g of NaOH
1 g of Na_2CO_3 reacts to give 0.755 g of NaOH
25 g of Na_2CO_3 reacts to give **18.9 g** of NaOH
(2 marks for correct answer, otherwise 1 mark for some correct working)
b) i) % yield = (actual yield ÷ predicted yield) × 100
= (10.4 ÷ 18.9) × 100 = **55%**
(2 marks for correct answer, otherwise 1 mark for writing out the percentage yield calculation correctly)
If you used the value of 22.4 g as the expected yield, you should get a percentage yield of 46.4%. Give yourself full marks if you got this answer.
ii) E.g. some sodium hydroxide will be lost when the solution is filtered to remove the calcium carbonate ***(1 mark)***.
iii) If the percentage yield of a reaction is low, lots of reactants/chemicals/resources will be wasted / the reaction will be unsustainable ***(1 mark)***.

2 a) i) (3 × 1) + 31 + (4 × 16) = **98** ***(1 mark)***
ii) On the gas chromatography read-out there is a peak with the same retention time as phosphoric acid (about 10 minutes) ***(1 mark)***. On the mass spectrometry read-out there is a molecular ion peak with the same M_r as phosphoric acid (98) ***(1 mark)***.
b) % mass = ((A_r × no. of atoms) ÷ M_r) × 100
% mass of carbon = ((12 × 4) ÷ 133) × 100
= **36.1%**
(2 marks for correct answer, otherwise 1 mark for some correct working)
c)

C	H	O
4.8	1.2	3.2
$\frac{4.8}{12} = 0.4$	$\frac{1.2}{1} = 1.2$	$\frac{3.2}{16} = 0.2$
$\frac{0.4}{0.2} = 2$	$\frac{1.2}{0.2} = 6$	$\frac{0.2}{0.2} = 1$

The empirical formula is C_2H_6O.
(3 marks for correct answer, otherwise 1 mark for dividing the masses by the A_rs and 1 mark for finding the ratio 2:6:1)
d) E.g. instrumental methods are more sensitive. / Instrumental methods can be used with very small amounts of sample. / Instrumental methods are much faster than manual methods. / Instrumental methods can be automated. / Instrumental methods are more accurate than manual methods. ***(1 mark)***

Chemistry 2.4 Rates of Reaction

1. Rate of Reaction

Page 160 — Fact Recall Questions

Q1 The two particles must collide with sufficient energy.
Q2 If you increase the concentration of the reactants, the particles will be closer together and so collisions between the particles will be more likely. More frequent collisions means a faster rate of reaction.
Q3 Increasing the temperature increases the frequency of collisions because the particles are moving faster. It also increases the energy of the collisions because the particles are moving faster, so more particles collide with enough energy to react.
Q4 A catalyst is a substance that can increase the rate of a reaction without being changed or used up during the reaction.
Q5 a) E.g. a catalyst increases the rate of a reaction so more product can be produced in the same length of time, which saves money. / Catalysts can allow reactions to work at lower temperatures, which saves energy and money. / Catalysts don't get used up in reactions, so once you've got them you can use them over and over again.
b) E.g. catalysts can be very expensive to buy. / Different reactions require different catalysts. / Catalysts can be poisoned by impurities, so they stop working.

Page 160 — Application Questions

Q1 E.g. the reaction was slowest with the marble chips and fastest with the powdered chalk. This is because the powdered chalk has a much larger surface area than the marble chips. This larger surface area means that there are more collisions between the reacting particles and so the rate of reaction is faster.

Q2 a) At a higher temperature, the rate of reaction will be faster. If the rate of reaction is faster, the factory can make more product in the same amount of time.

b) E.g. they could use a catalyst. / They could increase the concentration of the reactants.

2. Measuring Rates of Reaction

Page 163 — Fact Recall Questions

Q1 $\text{Rate of reaction} = \frac{\text{Amount of reactant used or product formed}}{\text{Time}}$

Q2 E.g. observe a mark through the solution and time how long it takes for the mark to disappear. The quicker the mark disappears, the quicker the reaction.

Q3 a) E.g. gas syringes are usually quite precise and they don't release the gas into the room, which is useful if the gas produced is poisonous. But you can only use this technique to measure the rate of reactions where one of the products is a gas and if the reaction is too vigorous the plunger could blow out of the end of the syringe.

b) E.g. the student could measure the change in mass of the reaction using a mass balance.

Page 163 — Application Questions

Q1 E.g. by directly measuring the amount of carbon dioxide produced over time using a gas syringe. / By measuring the decrease in mass of the reactants as carbon dioxide is given off using a mass balance.

You can use either of these methods for this reaction because one of the products of the reaction is a gas — carbon dioxide. You can tell this from the equation for the reaction that you're given in the question.

Q2 E.g. by putting a mark behind the solution and timing how long it takes for the mark to disappear.

One of the products of this reaction is a solid ($Mg(OH)_2$), which means it will form as a precipitate in the solution.

Q3 $4.3\ cm^3 \div 5.0\ s = \mathbf{0.86\ cm^3/s}$

Q4 $34.31\ g - 32.63\ g = 1.68\ g$

$1.68\ g \div 8.0\ s = \mathbf{0.21\ g/s}$

3. Rate of Reaction Graphs

Pages 165-166 — Application Questions

Q1 Reaction A — reaction A has the steepest curve at the beginning of the reaction. The higher the temperature, the faster the rate of reaction and the steeper the curve.

Q2 Reaction C — reaction C has the shallowest curve at the beginning of the reaction. The lower the concentration of the acid, the slower the rate of reaction and the shallower the curve.

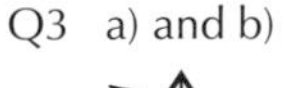
Q3 a) and b)

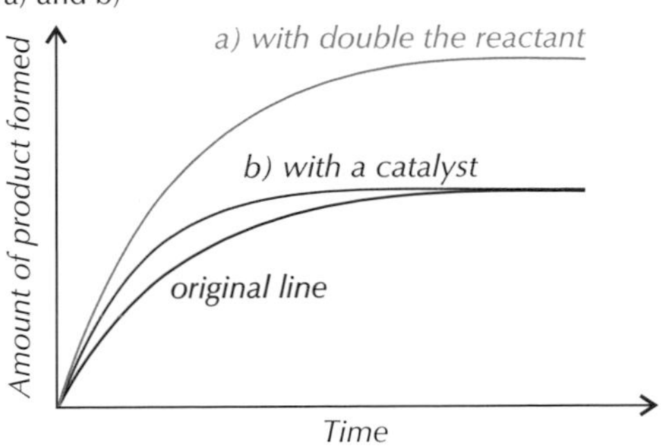

4. Rate of Reaction Experiments

Page 170 — Fact Recall Questions

Q1 E.g. react hydrochloric acid with marble chips. Measure the volume of carbon dioxide produced with a gas syringe. Take readings at regular intervals. Repeat the experiment with crushed marble chips and powdered chalk. The powdered chalk, which has the largest surface, will produce the fastest rate of reaction. The marble chips, which have the smallest surface area, will produce the slowest rate of reaction.

Q2

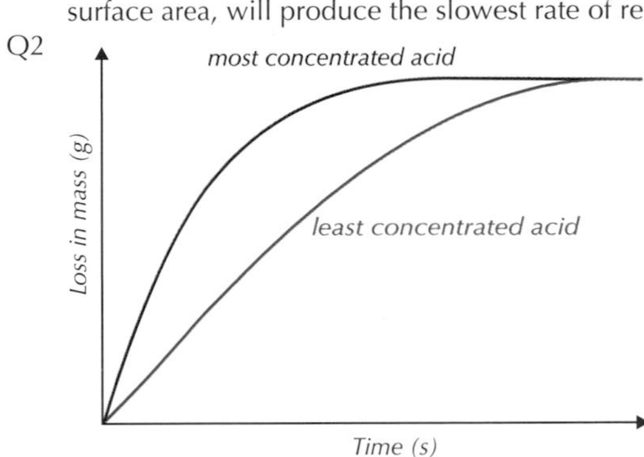

To get this question right you need to draw two curves that start and finish in the same place. The steeper curve should be labelled as the more concentrated acid and the shallower curve should be labelled as the least concentrated acid.

Q3 E.g. the reaction between sodium thiosulfate and hydrochloric acid produces a yellow sulfur precipitate. To measure the rate of the reaction you could put a mark behind the solution and time how long it takes for the mark to disappear.

Chemistry 2.5 Exothermic and Endothermic Reactions

1. Energy Transfer in Reactions

Page 174 — Fact Recall Questions

Q1 a) An exothermic reaction is a reaction that transfers energy to the surroundings.

b) E.g. combustion / neutralisation / some oxidation reactions.

Q2 a) Because endothermic reactions absorb energy from the surroundings.
b) E.g. endothermic reactions are used in some sports injury packs.

Q3 If a reaction is exothermic in the forward direction it must be endothermic in the reverse direction, so the reverse reaction must absorb heat from the surroundings.

Pages 175-176 — Chemistry 2.4-2.5 Exam-style Questions

1 a) E.g. measuring the decrease in mass as the CO_2 is given off using a mass balance ***(1 mark)***.
b) i) 14 minutes ***(1 mark)***

You can tell that the reaction finished after 14 minutes because this is how long it took for the graph to level off.

ii) 12 cm³ of CO_2 was produced in the first 2 minutes, so the rate of reaction was $12 \div 2 =$ **6 cm³/min**.
(2 marks for correct answer, otherwise 1 mark for dividing a volume read from the graph by a time read from the graph).

iii) As the reaction progresses, the reactants get used up, so the concentration of the reactants decreases ***(1 mark)***. This means there are fewer collisions between the reacting particles ***(1 mark)***.

c)

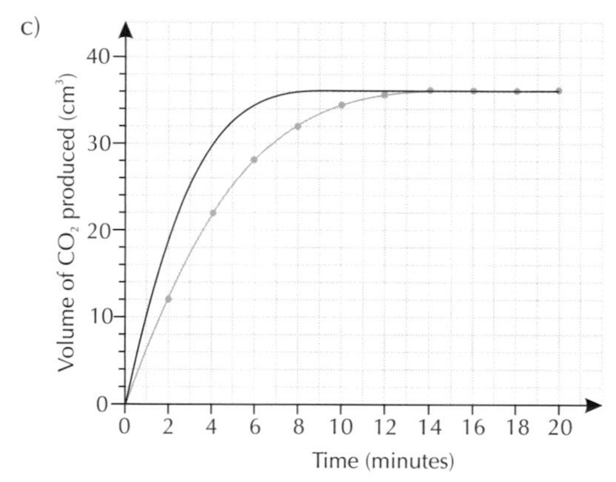

(1 mark for the curve being steeper than the original curve, 1 mark for the curve ending at the same level as the original curve).

2 a) i) A catalyst is a substance that can speed up the rate of a reaction, without being changed or used up ***(1 mark)***.
ii) Advantages: e.g. using a catalyst increases the rate of reaction, so more product can be produced in the same amount of time. / Using a catalyst means the reaction will work at a lower temperature, so energy costs can be reduced. / Using a catalyst means the reaction will work at a lower temperature, which is good for sustainable development.
(1 mark for each, maximum 2 marks).
Disadvantages: e.g. catalysts are expensive to buy. / Catalysts only work with one reaction. / Catalysts can be poisoned by impurities.
(1 mark for each, maximum 2 marks).

If you get a question asking you to discuss the advantages and disadvantages of something, make sure you talk about both. You won't be able to get full marks on the question if you only talk about advantages or only talk about disadvantages.

b) i) Increasing the pressure will increase the rate of reaction ***(1 mark)***.
ii) At higher pressures, the reactant molecules are closer together ***(1 mark)***, so there will be more frequent collisions between the reacting particles ***(1 mark)***.

3 a) exothermic ***(1 mark)***
b) i) The reaction is reversible ***(1 mark)***, so the solid sodium acetate trihydrate that is formed when the hand warmer is activated can be converted back into sodium acetate trihydrate solution ***(1 mark)***.
ii) The conversion of sodium acetate trihydrate solution to solid sodium acetate trihydrate is exothermic, so the reverse reaction (the conversion of solid sodium acetate trihydrate back to sodium acetate trihydrate solution) must be endothermic ***(1 mark)***. This means the hand warmer could be reset by heating it ***(1 mark)***.

Chemistry 2.6 Acids, Bases and Salts

1. pH and Neutralisation

Page 179 — Fact Recall Questions

Q1 E.g. pH is a measure of how acidic or alkaline a solution is.
Q2 pH 7
Q3 a) pHs greater than 7.
b) E.g. an alkali is soluble in water. A base can be either soluble or insoluble in water.
c) $H^+_{(aq)}$ ions make solutions acidic and $OH^-_{(aq)}$ ions make them alkaline.

It's important that you mention that the ions are aqueous. It is only in this state that they can affect the pH of a solution.

Q4 (aq)
Q5 a) Water/$H_2O_{(l)}$.
b) $H^+_{(aq)} + OH^-_{(aq)} \rightarrow H_2O_{(l)}$

Page 179 — Application Questions

Q1 a) Acidic
b) Alkaline
Q2 a) pH 6
b) Blue
Q3 a) Gas
b) Liquid
c) Aqueous
d) Solid
Q4 a) Neutralisation
b) Water/H_2O.

2. Making Salts

Page 183 — Fact Recall Questions

Q1 a) acid + metal → salt + hydrogen

b) Some metals are too reactive to use (e.g. sodium) / Some metals are not reactive enough (e.g. copper).

Only one example metal is required for this question.

Q2 a) Bases

b) acid + metal hydroxide → salt + water

Q3 a) Nitric acid/HNO_3

b) E.g. It is used as a fertiliser. / It is used to supply nitrogen to plants.

Q4 $NH_{3(aq)} + HNO_{3(aq)} \rightarrow NH_4NO_{3(aq)}$

Page 183 — Application Questions

Q1 a) $SnSO_{4(aq)}$

b) Hydrogen gas/H_2

Q2 hydrochloric acid + magnesium hydroxide → magnesium chloride + water

Q3 a) Iron sulfate.

b) Calcium chloride.

Q4 a) Copper nitrate.

b) Potassium sulfate.

Q5 a) $2HCl_{(aq)} + Mg_{(s)} \rightarrow MgCl_{2(aq)} + H_{2(g)}$
The salt is magnesium chloride.

b) $HNO_{3(aq)} + NaOH_{(aq)} \rightarrow NaNO_{3(aq)} + H_2O_{(l)}$
The salt is sodium nitrate.

3. Methods for Making Salts

Page 186 — Fact Recall Questions

Q1 An indicator.

Q2 E.g. first, heat the solution to evaporate most of the water from the salt solution to make it more concentrated. Then leave the rest of the water to evaporate very slowly at room temperature. This process is called crystallisation.

Q3 a) A precipitation reaction.

b) E.g. to remove ions from solutions. / To remove poisonous ions from drinking water. / To remove calcium and magnesium ions from drinking water. / To remove unwanted ions from sewage (effluent).

Page 186 — Application Questions

Q1 a) hydrochloric acid + tin → tin chloride + hydrogen

b) E.g. put the hydrochloric acid in a beaker. Then add the tin and stir. Keep adding the tin until it is in excess. Then filter out the excess tin to get the salt solution ($SnCl_2$) using filter paper and a filter funnel. Finally, you can use crystallisation to get pure crystals of $SnCl_2$ by evaporating water from the solution.

Q2 E.g. you can't produce magnesium carbonate by reacting magnesium sulfate and sodium sulfate because neither of these chemicals contains carbonate ions.

Pages 188-189 — Chemistry 2.6

Exam-style Questions

Q1 a) i) A base ***(1 mark)***

ii) Neutral ***(1 mark)***

iii) An acid ***(1 mark)***

b) i) Hydrogen ions/H^+ ions ***(1 mark)***

ii) Potassium hydroxide ***(1 mark)***

iii) E.g. Niall could add universal indicator to the solution ***(1 mark)***. When the indicator turns green this shows that the solution has become neutral and the reaction has finished ***(1 mark)***.

iv) $H^+_{(aq)} + OH^-_{(aq)} \rightarrow H_2O_{(l)}$
(1 mark for correct equation, 1 mark for correct state symbols).

Q2 a) i) acid + metal oxide → salt + water
(1 mark for each correct product).

ii) A neutralisation reaction ***(1 mark)***.

b) i) Magnesium chloride ***(1 mark)***.

ii) E.g. the reaction will be finished when all the acid has been neutralised and no more magnesium oxide/MgO will react ***(1 mark)***. At this point you'll be able to see the excess magnesium oxide/MgO in the solution ***(1 mark)***.

iii) E.g. first filter the solution to remove the excess magnesium oxide/MgO ***(1 mark)***. Then evaporate most of the water from the salt solution by heating it up ***(1 mark)***. Then leave the remaining water to evaporate slowly at room temperature ***(1 mark)***.

Q3 a) i) $Ba(OH)_2 + 2HCl \rightarrow BaCl_2 + 2H_2O$
(1 mark for correct reactants and products, 1 mark for balancing the equation)

ii) An alkali is a substance with a pH greater than 7/a base ***(1 mark)*** that is soluble in water ***(1 mark)***.

iii) E.g. barium is too reactive. / Barium reacts explosively with acid. / The reaction would be too dangerous ***(1 mark)***.

b) i) Sulfuric acid/H_2SO_4 ***(1 mark)***.

ii) E.g. so that you can separate the barium sulfate from the excess barium chloride at the end of the reaction ***(1 mark)***.

iii) E.g. to remove poisonous ions such as lead from drinking water. / To remove calcium and magnesium ions from drinking water. / To remove unwanted ions during the treatment of effluent (sewage) ***(1 mark for each answer, maximum of 2 marks)***.

Chemistry 2.7 Electrolysis

1. Electrolysis — The Basics

Page 193 — Fact Recall Questions

Q1 a) It breaks down into the elements it's made from.

b) Electrolysis

Q2 Because they contain free ions.

Q3 Electrons are taken away from negative ions at the positive electrode. As the ions lose electrons they become atoms or molecules and are released.

Q4 Positive ions.
Q5 Reduction is a gain of electrons.
Q6 The negative electrode.
Q7 Bromine will form.

Page 193 — Application Questions

Q1 a) (Molten) zinc chloride.
b) The positive electrode.
c) The chloride ions lose one electron each (they are oxidised) and form chlorine molecules.
d) They are reduced.

Q2 Potassium bromide solution contains hydrogen ions, from the water in the solution. Potassium is more reactive than hydrogen so the potassium ions stay in solution and the hydrogen ions are reduced to form hydrogen gas.

Q3 a) $2Br^- \rightarrow Br_2 + 2e^-$ / $2Br^- - 2e^- \rightarrow Br_2$ and $2H^+ + 2e^- \rightarrow H_2$
b) $Cu^{2+} + 2e^- \rightarrow Cu$ and $2O^{2-} \rightarrow O_2 + 4e^-$ / $2O^{2-} - 4e^- \rightarrow O_2$

2. Electrolysis of Sodium Chloride

Page 195 — Fact Recall Questions

Q1 Chlorine and hydrogen.
Q2 E.g. to make soap.
Q3 Hydrogen
Q4 Hydrogen
Q5 The sodium ions remain in solution because they're more reactive than hydrogen. Hydroxide ions from water are also left behind. This means that sodium hydroxide is left in the solution.

3. Electrolysis of Aluminium Ore

Page 196 — Fact Recall Questions

Q1 It allows the aluminium oxide to be melted at a lower temperature, which saves energy, making the process cheaper and easier.
Q2 a) Oxygen
b) Aluminium
Q3 The oxygen that is produced at the positive electrode reacts with the carbon in the electrode. This reaction produces carbon dioxide.

4. Electroplating

Page 198 — Fact Recall Questions

Q1 A process that uses electrolysis to coat the surface of one metal with another metal.
Q2 E.g. copper and silver.
Q3 E.g. decorating other metals. Making objects conduct electricity better.

Page 199 — Chemistry 2.7

Exam-style Questions

1 a) Copper chloride solution ***(1 mark)***.
b) i) Water ***(1 mark)***
ii) Each copper ion gains two electrons/is reduced ***(1 mark)*** and becomes a neutral copper atom ***(1 mark)***.
iii) The hydrogen ions stay in solution ***(1 mark)*** because copper is less reactive than hydrogen ***(1 mark)***.

You can look up how reactive copper is compared to hydrogen using the reactivity series. There's one on page 43, and you'll be given one in the exam too.

c) i) E.g. the production of bleach / the production of plastics ***(1 mark)***.
ii) $2Cl^- \rightarrow Cl_2 + 2e^-$ ***(1 mark for*** $2Cl^-$***, 1 mark for*** $2e^-$***.)***

2 a) Electroplating ***(1 mark)***
b) The ring ***(1 mark)***.
c) Silver nitrate solution ***(1 mark)***.
d) Oxidation is the loss of electrons ***(1 mark)***.

Physics 2

Physics 2.1 Forces and their Effects

1. Distance-Time Graphs

Page 203 — Fact Recall Questions

Q1 The speed of the object.
Q2 *A* — It's increasing (the object is speeding up).
B — It's not changing (the object is moving at a steady speed).
C — It's decreasing (the object is slowing down).
D — It's zero (the object is not moving / stationary).
Q3 Calculate the gradient of the graph during that time period.

Page 203 — Application Questions

Q1 For the first 10 seconds the graph will be curved with an increasing gradient. For the next 5 seconds it will be a sloped straight line.

Q2 a)

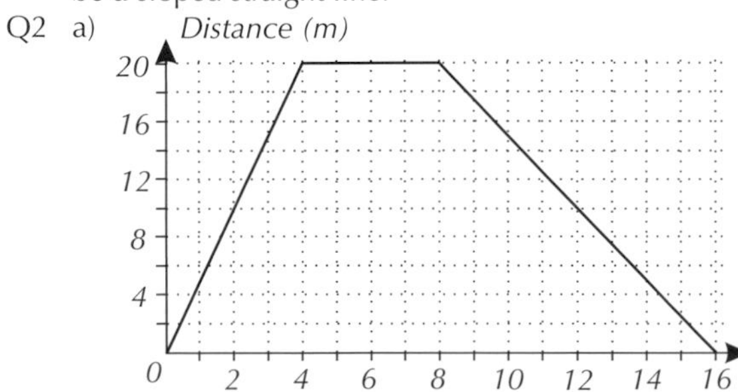

b) Between 4 and 8 seconds.

Q3 a) Between 2 and 4 seconds the object is travelling backwards (towards the start point) at a steady speed.
Between 4 and 8 seconds the object is stationary.
Between 8 and 11 seconds the object is accelerating (away from the start point).

b) $\text{speed} = \text{gradient} = \frac{7-3}{13-11}$
$= \frac{4}{2}$
$= \mathbf{2\ m/s}$

2. Velocity-Time Graphs

Page 207 — Fact Recall Questions

Q1 The speed of an object only tells you how fast it's going. The velocity of an object tells you how fast it's going as well as the direction it's going in.

Q2 Acceleration is a measure of how quickly the velocity is changing.

Q3 $a = \frac{v-u}{t}$
a = acceleration in m/s²
v = final velocity in m/s
u = initial velocity in m/s
t = time in s

Q4 The acceleration (of the object).

Q5 The distance travelled (by the object).

Page 208 — Application Questions

Q1 a) speed
b) speed
c) velocity
d) speed

Q2 $a = \frac{v-u}{t}$
$= \frac{10-25}{5}$
$= \mathbf{-3\ m/s^2}$

Q3 a) **4 m/s**
b) Between 100 and 120 seconds.
It's the part where the graph has a negative gradient (sloping downwards).
c) $\text{acceleration} = \text{gradient} = \frac{8-4}{80-60}$
$= \mathbf{0.2\ m/s^2}$
d) distance travelled between 0 and 20 s
$= \frac{1}{2} \times \text{base} \times \text{height} = \frac{1}{2} \times 20 \times 4$
$= 40\ \text{m}$
distance travelled between 20 and 60 s
$= \text{base} \times \text{height} = (60 - 20) \times 4$
$= 160\ \text{m}$
total distance travelled = 40 + 160 = **200 m**
Remember to break the area into separate shapes if you think it will make the calculation easier.

Q4 $a = \frac{v-u}{t} \Rightarrow u = v - (a \times t)$
$= 7.1 - (0.3 \times 5)$
$= \mathbf{5.6\ m/s}$

3. Resultant Forces

Page 210 — Fact Recall Questions

Q1 The resultant force is the force found by combining all of the forces acting on a single object or at a single point.

Q2 The object will accelerate.

Page 210 — Application Question

Q1 a) Choosing left as the positive direction:
Resultant force = 2000 – 400 – 1500 = 100 N
b) The boat is accelerating. There is a resultant force acting on it.

4. Forces and Acceleration

Page 214 — Fact Recall Questions

Q1 a) Nothing will happen — it will remain stationary.
b) The object will accelerate (start moving) in the direction of the resultant force.
c) The object will keep moving at the same velocity.
d) The object will accelerate.
e) The object will decelerate.

Q2 $F = m \times a$
F = force in N
m = mass in kg
a = acceleration in m/s²

Page 214 — Application Questions

Q1 The resultant force is zero.

Q2 The car without the rock would win — acceleration is equal to force ÷ mass, so a larger mass means a smaller acceleration.

Q3 $a = \frac{F}{m} = \frac{305}{1.5}$
$= \mathbf{200\ m/s^2}$ (to 2 s.f.)

Q4 Resultant force acting on left-hand car:
$F = m \times a = 1200 \times 2.3$
$= 2760\ \text{N}$
Resultant force acting on right-hand car:
$F = m \times a = 820 \times 3.1$
$= 2542\ \text{N}$
The resultant force acting on the **left-hand car** is greater, so that car's engine is providing the greater driving force.
Because the cars are starting from rest you don't need to worry about any other forces affecting the acceleration.

5. Weight and Reaction Forces

Page 217 — Fact Recall Questions

Q1 Mass is just the amount of 'stuff' in an object and is always the same wherever an object is in the universe. Weight is caused by the pull of gravity on an object, and varies depending on where the object is in the universe.

Q2 $W = m \times g$
W = weight in N
m = mass in kg
g = gravitational field strength in N/kg

Q3 ... equal and opposite.

Page 217 — Application Questions

Q1 Earth dog:
$W = m \times g = 6.3 \times 10$
$= 63$ N
Moon dog:
$W = m \times g = 21 \times 1.6$
$= 33.6$ N
So the **Earth dog** has a larger weight.

Q2 The ball will experience a greater acceleration. The tennis racquet will experience an identical reaction force, but its mass is greater so its acceleration will be smaller ($a = \frac{F}{m}$).

6. Friction and Terminal Velocity

Page 221 — Fact Recall Questions

Q1 The resistive forces must be equal to the driving force.
Q2 Drag is the friction experienced by an object moving through a fluid.
Q3 The faster the object's speed, the greater the drag force.
Q4 The car's shape can be changed so that it's more streamlined. The car's power can be increased so that it has a greater driving force.
Q5

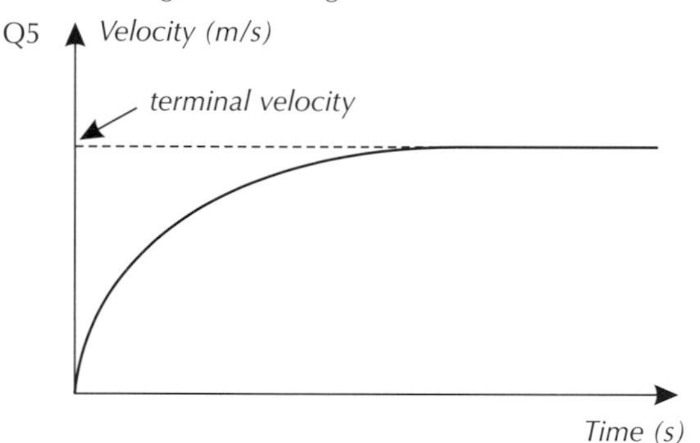

Page 221 — Application Questions

Q1 On Earth, air resistance causes objects to fall at different speeds depending on their shape and size — it has a greater effect on the feather than on the rock. On the Moon there's no air, so there's no air resistance and all objects accelerate due to gravity at the same rate.
Q2 A parachute increases the resistive forces acting on a skydiver at any given speed by increasing his or her area. Resistive forces are proportional to speed, so this causes the speed to drop right down until forces are balanced again.

7. Stopping Distances

Page 224 — Fact Recall Questions

Q1 a) The stopping distance of a vehicle is the distance covered in the time between the driver first spotting a hazard and the vehicle coming to a complete stop. It's the sum of the thinking distance and the braking distance.
b) The thinking distance is the distance the vehicle travels during the driver's reaction time.
c) The braking distance is the distance the vehicle travels after the brakes are applied until it comes to a complete stop.
Q2 Any three of e.g. tiredness / drugs / alcohol / lack of concentration.
Q3 Any three of e.g. ice (or water, oil, leaves etc.) on the road, quality of the tyres, quality of the car's brakes, weather conditions.
Q4 a) Braking
b) Thinking
c) Thinking
d) Braking
e) Thinking
Q5 Work is done by the braking force to convert kinetic energy into other forms of energy, such as thermal energy and a little sound energy.

Page 224 — Application Questions

Q1 Stopping distance = 15 + 38 = **53 m**
Q2 Heavy rain reduces visibility and grip, increasing both the thinking and braking distance, and therefore the stopping distance, of a car. Therefore it's important to leave more room between vehicles to allow for the extra stopping distance.

8. Forces and Elasticity

Page 227 — Fact Recall Questions

Q1 force
Q2 elastic (object)
Q3 elastic potential energy
Q4 $F = k \times e$
F = force in N
e = extension in m
k = spring constant in N/m
Q5 The point at which the extension of an object stops being proportional to the applied force.

Page 227 — Application Question

Q1 2.7 cm = $\frac{2.7}{100}$ m = 0.027 m
$F = k \times e$
$= 69 \times 0.027 =$ **1.9 N** (to 2 s.f.)

Pages 230-232 — Physics 2.1 Exam-style Questions

1 (a) Between 70 and 120 seconds ***(1 mark)***
(b) (i) acceleration = gradient
$= \frac{10 - 6}{40 - 30}$
$=$ **0.4 m/s²**
(3 marks if answer correct, otherwise 1 mark for knowing that the acceleration is given by the gradient and 1 mark for correct calculation.)

You could have also used the formula for acceleration given on page to answer this question, using the graph to find v, u and t.

(ii) $F = m \times a$
$= 980 \times 0.4$
$= \mathbf{392\ N}$
(2 marks if answer correct, otherwise 1 mark for use of correct formula. Allow follow-through from part i).)

(c) distance travelled between 30 and 40 s
$= (\frac{1}{2} \times 10 \times 4) + (10 \times 6)$
$= \mathbf{80\ m}$
(3 marks if answer correct, otherwise 1 mark for attempting to find the correct area and 1 mark for correct calculation.)

(d) Any two from: e.g. the stopping distance is increased because poor visibility due to rainfall increases the time it takes for the driver to react / the stopping distance is increased because wet roads increase braking distance / the stopping distance is increased because rainfall causes a distraction, increasing the thinking distance.
(2 marks available — 1 mark for each correct answer.)

(e) Friction between the brakes and the tyres ***(1 mark)*** does work to convert the kinetic energy of the car ***(1 mark)*** into other forms of energy, such as thermal energy (and a little sound energy) ***(1 mark)***.

2 (a) (i) 0 N ***(1 mark)***
If it's travelling at a steady speed, the resultant force acting on it must be zero.
(ii) air resistance (or drag) ***(1 mark)***

(b) The thinking distance is the distance travelled in the time it takes the driver to react to seeing a hazard ***(1 mark)*** and the braking distance is the distance it takes the truck to stop after the driver has applied the brakes ***(1 mark)***.

(c) (i) By increasing the driving force, more air resistance is needed to balance it at the truck's top speed ***(1 mark)***. Air resistance increases with speed, so a bigger speed is possible before the resistive forces balance the driving force ***(1 mark)***.
(ii) Making the truck more streamlined reduces the air resistance acting on the truck ***(1 mark)***. So the speed at which resistive forces match the driving force becomes bigger ***(1 mark)***.

3 (a) greater than the frictional force due to air resistance ***(1 mark)***.
(b) the same as the frictional force due to air resistance ***(1 mark)***.

(c)
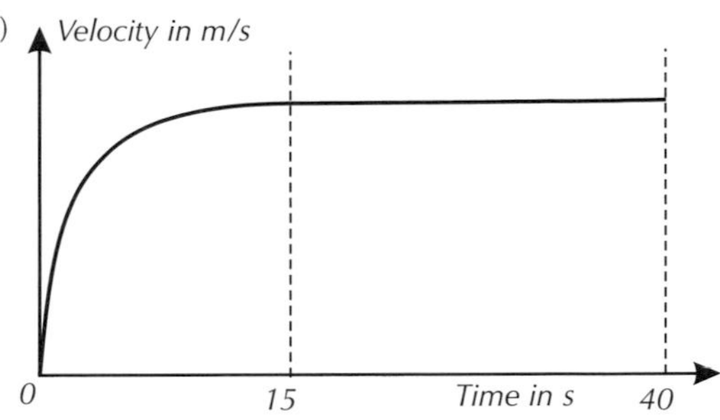

(4 marks available — 1 mark for correctly labelled axes, 1 mark for a line with positive gradient between 0 and 15 seconds, 1 mark if the line is sloped (with decreasing gradient) and 1 mark for a horizontal line between 15 and 40 seconds.)

(d) (i) it will decrease ***(1 mark)***
(ii) they will increase ***(1 mark)***

4 (a) The reaction force is equal in size and in the opposite direction to *F* ***(1 mark)***.

(b) (i) $a = \frac{v - u}{t}$
$= \frac{3 - 0}{1.2}$
$= \mathbf{2.5\ m/s^2}$
(3 marks if answer correct, otherwise 1 mark for using correct formula and 1 mark for substituting the correct numbers.)
(ii) $F = m \times a$
$= 100 \times 2.5$
$= \mathbf{250\ N}$
(3 marks if answer correct, otherwise 1 mark for using the correct formula and 1 mark for using the correct units. Allow follow-through from part (i).)

5 (a) $W = m \times g$
$= 2.1 \times 10$
$= \mathbf{21\ N}$
(2 marks if answer correct, otherwise 1 mark for using correct formula.)

(b) Gravity (or the object's weight) does work on the spring ***(1 mark)*** to change its shape, causing it to store elastic potential energy ***(1 mark)***.

(c) $F = k \times e \Rightarrow k = \frac{F}{e}$
$= \frac{21}{(0.35 - 0.29)}$
$= \mathbf{350\ N/m}$
(4 marks if answer correct, otherwise 1 mark for correct substitution into the formula, 1 mark for finding the extension of the spring and 1 mark for using the correct units.)

Physics 2.2 The Kinetic Energy of Objects

1. Work and Potential Energy

Page 235 — Fact Recall Questions

Q1 Work done is the energy transferred when a force moves an object through a distance.

Q2 $W = F \times d$. W is work done in J, F is force in N and d is distance in m.

Q3 It's the energy that an object has because of its vertical position in a gravitational field.

Q4 $E_p = m \times g \times h$. E_p is gravitational potential energy in J, m is mass in kg, g is gravitational field strength in N/kg and h is height in m.

Page 235 — Application Questions

Q1 $W = F \times d = 250 \times 20 =$ **5000 J**

Q2 $E_p = m \times g \times h = 43\,000 \times 10 \times 10\,600$ = **4 558 000 000 J**

Q3 a) $W = F \times d = 1000 \times 1 =$ **1000 J**

b) $E_p = m \times g \times h = 80 \times 10 \times 1 =$ **800 J**

Q4 Rearranging $W = F \times d$, $d = \frac{W}{F} = \frac{375}{25} =$ **15 m**

Q5 Rearranging $E_p = m \times g \times h$,

$m = \frac{E_p}{g \times h} = \frac{86.4}{10 \times 2.3} =$ **3.8 kg (to 2 s.f.)**

2. Kinetic Energy

Page 238 — Fact Recall Questions

Q1 It's the energy something has because it's moving.

Q2 The large dog has more kinetic energy, because the kinetic energy something has increases with its mass and speed.

Q3 $E_k = ½ \times m \times v^2$. E_k is kinetic energy in J, m is mass in kg and v is speed in m/s.

Page 239 — Application Questions

Q1 a) $E_k = ½ \times m \times v^2 = ½ \times 2 \times 2.1^2 =$ **4.41 J**

b) $E_k = ½ \times m \times v^2 = ½ \times 0.02 \times 0.5^2 =$ **0.0025 J**

c) $E_k = ½ \times m \times v^2 = ½ \times 120 \times 4^2 =$ **960 J**

d) $E_k = ½ \times m \times v^2 = ½ \times 0.05 \times 1^2 =$ **0.025 J**

Q2 $W = ½ \times m \times v^2 = ½ \times 2400 \times 1500^2$
= **2 700 000 000 J**

Remember the work done by the brakes to stop a moving object is equal to the kinetic energy it had before the brakes were applied.

Q3 $W = ½ \times m \times v^2 = ½ \times 0.024 \times 3.5^2 =$ **0.147 J**

Q4 $E_k = m \times g \times h = 0.1 \times 10 \times 2 =$ **2 J**

Q5 Frog: $E_k = ½ \times m \times v^2 = ½ \times 0.240 \times 1.5^2 =$ **0.27 J**
Rat: $E_k = ½ \times m \times v^2 = ½ \times 0.215 \times 1.6^2 =$ **0.2752 J**
The rat has more kinetic energy.

Q6 Rearranging $E_k = ½ \times m \times v^2$,

$m = \frac{2E_k}{v^2} = \frac{2 \times 2.1}{0.25^2} =$ **67.2 kg**

Q7 Rearranging $E_k = ½ \times m \times v^2$,

$v = \sqrt{\frac{2E_k}{m}} = \sqrt{\frac{2 \times 40}{0.0125}} =$ **80 m/s**

Q8 Rearranging $E_p = ½ \times m \times v^2$,

$v = \sqrt{\frac{2E_p}{m}} = \sqrt{\frac{2 \times 450}{1}} =$ **30 m/s**

3. Power

Page 242 — Fact Recall Questions

Q1 Power is the rate of doing work — i.e. how much work is done per second.

Q2 P is power in watts, E is work done or energy transferred in joules and t is time taken in seconds.

Page 242 — Application Questions

Q1 a) $P = \frac{E}{t} = \frac{150}{37.5} =$ **4 W**

b) 79.8 kJ = 79 800 J
$P = \frac{E}{t} = \frac{79\,800}{42} =$ **1900 W**

c) 7215 kJ = 7 215 000 J
9.5 minutes = 570 s
$P = \frac{E}{t} = \frac{7\,215\,000}{570} =$ **13 000 W (to 2 s.f.)**

Q2 $P = \frac{m \times g \times h}{t} = \frac{58 \times 10 \times 45}{50}$
= **522 W**

Q3 $P = \frac{½ \times m \times v^2}{t} = \frac{½ \times 82 \times 8.0^2}{20.5}$
= **128 W**

Q4 a) Rearranging $P = \frac{E}{t}$,
$t = \frac{E}{P} = \frac{1344}{525} =$ **2.56 s**

b) 2.86 kW = 2860 W. Rearranging $P = \frac{E}{t}$,
$t = \frac{E}{P} = \frac{1430}{2860} =$ **0.5 s**

Q5 a) Rearranging $P = \frac{E}{t}$, $E = P \times t = 1240 \times 35$
= **43 400 J**

b) 17 minutes = 1020 s. Rearranging $P = \frac{E}{t}$,
$E = P \times t = 1500 \times 1020 = 1\,530\,000$ J = **1530 kJ**

4. Momentum and Collisions

Page 245 — Fact Recall Questions

Q1 The object's mass and velocity.

Q2 $p = m \times v$. p is momentum in kg m/s, m is mass in kg and v is velocity in m/s.

Q3 In a closed system, the total momentum before an event is the same as after the event.

Page 245 — Application Questions

Q1 a) $p = m \times v = 0.1 \times 0.6 =$ **0.06 kg m/s north**

Don't forget to give a direction.

b) $p = m \times v = 0.008 \times 12 =$ **0.0096 kg m/s left**

c) $p = m \times v = 5.2 \times 8 =$ **41.6 kg m/s down**

Q2 The momentum after the collision will be the same as the momentum before the collision.
Say positive means to the right.
Total momentum before the collision
$= [m_A \times v_A] + [m_B \times v_B] = [98 \times 1.75] + [53 \times -2.31]$
= **49.07 kg m/s to the right**

Q3 The total momentum before and after the event is 0. Momentum depends on mass and velocity, so if the gas canisters's velocity before the explosion is zero, the momentum is 0. Assuming it's a closed system, the total momentum after the explosion will be equal to the momentum before, so it must be 0 as well.

Q4 a) Rearranging $p = m \times v$,

$v = \frac{p}{m} = \frac{3.04}{0.95} = \mathbf{3.2\ m/s\ (south)}$

b) Rearranging $p = m \times v$,

$v = \frac{p}{m} = \frac{1.71}{0.057} = \mathbf{30\ m/s\ (towards\ the\ net)}$

c) Rearranging $p = m \times v$,

$v = \frac{p}{m} = \frac{45\,000}{2000} = \mathbf{22.5\ m/s\ (east)}$

Q5 a) Rearranging $p = m \times v$, $m = \frac{p}{v} = \frac{31.5}{0.75} = \mathbf{42\ kg}$

b) Rearranging $p = m \times v$, $m = \frac{p}{v} = \frac{210}{7.5} = \mathbf{28\ kg}$

Q6 Total momentum before = total momentum after.
Total momentum before = 0
Total momentum after = $[m_{gun} \times v_{gun}] + [m_{bullet} \times v_{bullet}]$

So $0 = [1 \times -2] + [m \times 200]$, so $m = \frac{2}{200} = \mathbf{0.01\,kg}$

Q7 Say positive means to the right.
Total momentum after the collision = $m_{C+D} \times v_{C+D}$
$= [56 + 70] \times -1.5 = -189$ kg m/s
Total momentum before the collision
$= [m_C \times v_C] + [m_D \times v_D]$
$-189 = [56 \times 1.3] + [70 \times v]$, so

$v = \frac{-189 - 72.8}{70} = \mathbf{-3.74\ m/s}$

The minus sign means that means that the skier D moves to the left (because we said positive was to the right).

5. Car Design and Safety

Page 247 — Fact Recall Questions

Q1 Regenerative brakes are brakes that extract energy when they operate, to be stored and used later. They put the vehicle's motor into reverse rather than converting the kinetic energy of the vehicle into heat energy. At the same time, the motor acts as an electric generator, converting kinetic energy into electrical energy that is stored as chemical energy in the vehicle's battery.

Q2 E.g. Crumple zones at the front and back of the car crumple up on impact. The car's kinetic energy is converted into other forms of energy by the car body as it changes shape. Crumple zones increase the impact time, decreasing the force produced by the change in momentum. Side impact bars are strong metal tubes fitted into car door panels. They help direct the kinetic energy of the crash away from the passengers to other areas of the car, such as the crumple zones. Seat belts prevent you from hitting hard surfaces in the car or being thrown out of the car. They also stretch slightly, increasing the time taken for the wearer to stop. This reduces the forces acting in the chest. Some of the kinetic energy of the wearer is absorbed by the seat belt stretching.
Air bags also slow you down more gradually and prevent you from hitting hard surfaces inside the car.

Pages 249-250 — Physics 2.2

Exam-style Questions

1 a) $W = F \times d = 3000 \times 500 =$ **1 500 000 J**
(2 marks for correct answer, 1 mark for substituting values into correct equation if answer is incorrect.)

b) $p = m \times v = 1540 \times 10 =$ **15 400 kg m/s**
(3 marks for correct answer, 2 marks for correct answer with incorrect units, otherwise 1 mark for substituting values into correct equation, 1 mark for correct units if answer incorrect.)

c) i) It decreases to zero ***(1 mark)***.

ii) The car's kinetic energy is transferred to heat energy ***(1 mark)***.

iii) Work done = kinetic energy transferred, so:
$W = E_k$
$= \frac{1}{2} \times m \times v^2 = \frac{1}{2} \times 1540 \times 10^2 =$ **77 000 J**
(3 marks for correct answer, 2 marks for correct answer with incorrect units, otherwise 1 mark for substituting values into correct equation, 1 mark for correct units if answer is incorrect.)

d) Seat belts stretch slightly, increasing the time taken for the wearer to stop ***(1 mark)***. This increases the time over which the momentum of the wearer changes ***(1 mark)***, and so reduces the forces acting in the chest ***(1 mark)***. Also, some of the kinetic energy is absorbed by the seat belt stretching ***(1 mark)***.

2 a) i) $E_p = m \times g \times h = (85 + 10) \times 10 \times 12$
$=$ **11 400 J**
(2 marks for correct answer, 1 mark for substituting values into correct equation if answer incorrect.)

ii) $P = \frac{E}{t} = \frac{11\,400}{18} =$ **630 W (to 2 s.f.)**
(3 marks for correct answer given to 2 significant figures, 2 marks for correct answer, 1 mark for substituting values into correct equation if answer incorrect. Allow follow-through from part i).)

b) Rearranging $E_k = \frac{1}{2} \times m \times v^2$,

$v = \sqrt{\frac{2E_k}{m}} = \sqrt{\frac{2 \times 153.9}{85 + 10}} =$ **1.8 m/s**

(2 marks for correct answer, 1 mark for substituting values into correct equation if answer is incorrect.)

3 a) In a closed system, the total momentum before an event is the same as after the event ***(1 mark)***.

b) Say to the right is positive.
Total momentum before the collision
$= [m_{white} \times v_{white}] + [m_{blue} \times v_{blue}]$
$= [0.16 \times 0.5] + [0.16 \times 0]$
= **0.08 kg m/s to the right**
(3 marks for correct answer, otherwise 1 mark for substituting values into correct equation and 1 mark for correct rearrangement.)

c) Total momentum before the collision
$= 0.08$ kg m/s
Total momentum after the collision
$= [m_{white} \times v_{white}] + [m_{blue} \times v_{blue}]$
$= [0.16 \times 0.1] + [0.16 \times v]$, so
$0.08 = [0.16 \times 0.1] + [0.16 \times v]$

$$v = \frac{0.08 - (0.16 \times 0.1)}{0.16}$$

$=$ **0.4 m/s to the right**

(4 marks for correct answer, otherwise 1 mark for substituting values into correct equation, 1 mark for correct rearrangement and 1 mark for direction correctly stated.)

Physics 2.3 Currents in Electrical Circuits

1. Static Electricity

Page 253 — Fact Recall Questions

Q1 An electrical conductor is a material in which electrical charge can easily move. E.g. metals.

Q2 Negatively charged electrons are rubbed off the first insulator and onto the other insulator, leaving the first insulator with a positive charge.

Q3 a) Repel
b) Repel
c) Attract

Page 253 — Application Question

Q1 a) All her hairs have the same charge (the opposite charge to the hair brush), so they will all repel each other, causing them to stand on end.
b) + 0.5 nC

2. Circuit Basics

Page 255 — Fact Recall Questions

Q1 a)

b)

c)

d)

e)

Q2 A circuit is incomplete if you can't follow a wire from one end of the battery (or other power supply), through any components to the other end of the battery.

Page 255 — Application Questions

Q1 E.g.

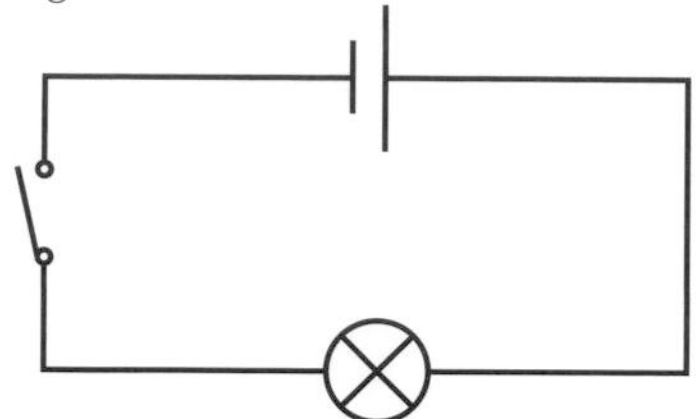

This is just one example of a correct circuit diagram. You could have the components in a different order in the circuit.

Q2 E.g.

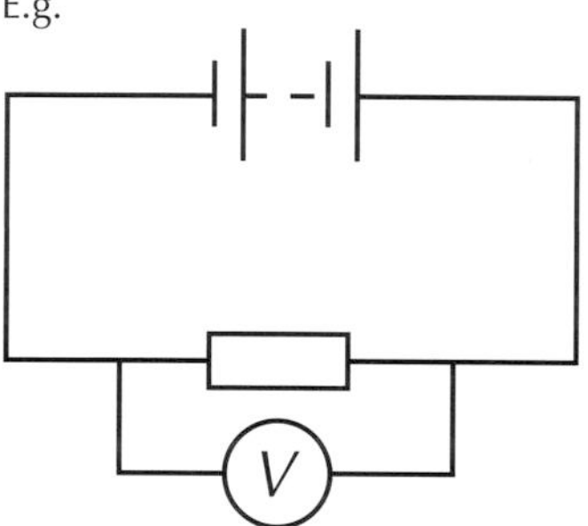

Remember that voltmeters are always connected across a component.

Q3 E.g.

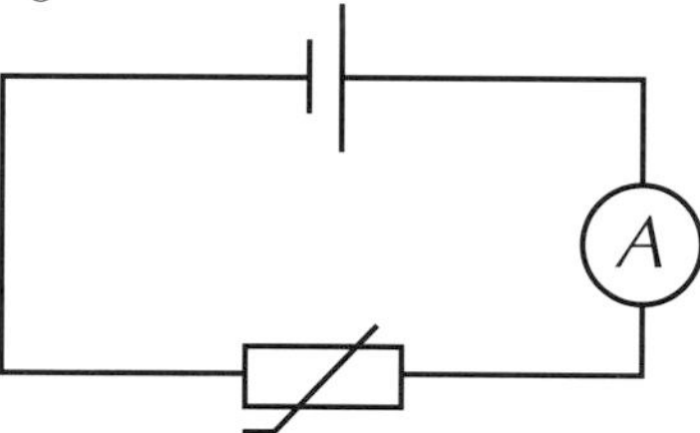

Remember that ammeters are always connected in line with a component.

Q4 Circuit B.
In the rest of the circuits, the lamp is in an incomplete part of the circuit. Don't worry about the extra bits coming off the circuit — as long as there's a complete cycle containing the lamp, current will flow through it and the lamp will light.

3. Current and Potential Difference

Page 258 — Fact Recall Questions

Q1 A flow of electric charge.

Q2 From positive to negative.

Q3 $I = Q \div t$, where I = current in amps (A), Q = charge in coulombs (C) and t = time in seconds (s).

Q4 The work done (the energy transferred, measured in joules, J) per coulomb of charge that passes between two points in an electrical circuit.

Q5 $V = W \div Q$, where V = potential difference in volts (V), W = work done in joules (J) and Q = charge in coulombs (C).

Page 258 — Application Questions

Q1 t = 1 minute = 60 seconds, so
$I = Q \div t$
$= 102 \div 60 =$ **1.7 A**

Q2 a) $I = Q \div t$
$= 60 \div (2 \times 60)$
$=$ **0.5 A**

b) $V = W \div Q$
$= 1440 \div 60$
$=$ **24 V**

Q3 $I = Q \div t$, but you don't have the value for Q yet.
Rearrange $V = W \div Q$, so that $Q = W \div V$
$= 315 \div 6.00$
$= 52.5$ C

So $I = Q \div t$
$= 52.5 \div 37.0 =$ **1.42 A** (to 3 s.f.)

4. Resistance

Page 262 — Fact Recall Questions

Q1 Resistance is anything in a circuit that opposes the flow of current. It is measured in ohms, Ω.

Q2 $V = I \times R$

Q3 E.g.

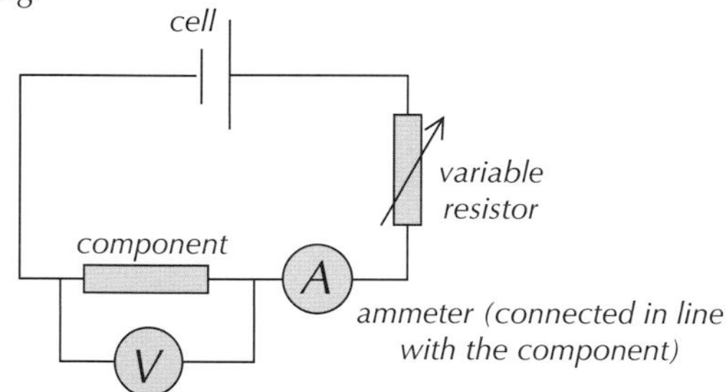

Q4 Calculate the inverse of the gradient (i.e. $1 \div$ gradient) of the graph at any point.

Q5 a) E.g.

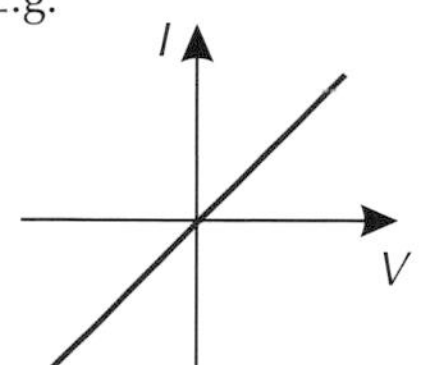

b) E.g.

Q6 As the filament gets hot, the ions in the conductor vibrate more, making it more difficult for the charge-carrying electrons to get through the filament. So the resistance increases and the current decreases.

Page 262 — Application Questions

Q1 $V = I \times R$
$= 0.015 \times 2.0$
$=$ **0.03 V**

Q2 $R = V \div I$
$= 14.4 \div 0.6$
$=$ **24 Ω**

Q3 $R = V \div I$. The gradient is constant, so the resistance is constant, so just pick a point on the line and use the values of V and I to work out the resistance:
E.g. $R = V \div I$
$= 2 \div 0.25$
$=$ **8 Ω**

5. Diodes and LEDs

Page 264 — Fact Recall Questions

Q1 a) The resistance is initially high but drops as V increases, allowing current to flow.

b) The resistance is very high, so current can't flow through a diode in this direction.

Q2

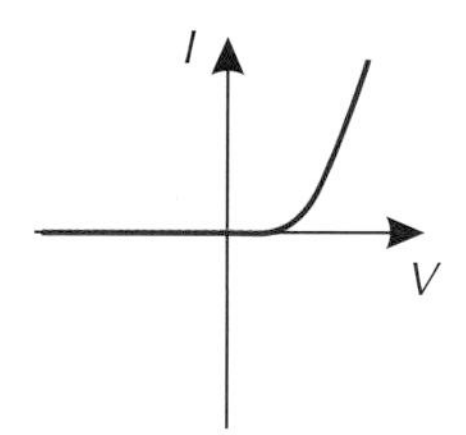

Q3 An LED lights up/emits light when current flows through it in the forward direction.

Q4 E.g. for household lighting / to indicate whether an appliance is switched on / in remote controls / in pill cameras (to illuminate inside the body) / in digital clocks / in LED screens / in traffic lights / in car brake lights.

Page 264 — Application Questions

Q1 No, the LED is connected in the 'reverse' direction and current can only flow in the forwards direction through an LED.
Current flows from positive to negative and so it won't be able to flow through the LED.

Q2 A diode.

Q3 E.g. it is better to use an LED for the standby light because it needs less current to work than a filament bulb, so it uses less energy. It is also more cost efficient as it uses less energy and so costs less to run. LEDs are more expensive to buy than filament bulbs but they have a longer lifetime, so this cost should be offset over time. LEDs are also much smaller than filament lamps and generally produce less light, but this is not an issue for a standby light — you don't want it to light up the room when the main lights are off. Overall, LEDs seem better to use as a standby light for the radio than a filament bulb.

6. LDRs and Thermistors

Page 266 — Fact Recall Questions

Q1 E.g.

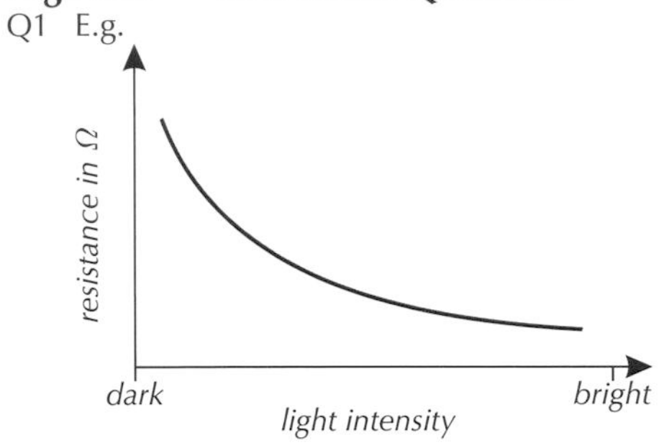

Q2 Increase its temperature.

A thermistor is a temperature dependent resistor — its resistance decreases as the temperature rises.

Q3 a) E.g. automatic night lights / outside lighting / burglar detectors.

b) E.g. thermostats / temperature sensors.

Page 266 — Application Question

Q1 a) A light-dependant resistor (LDR).

b) The cat blocks the light incident on the LDR, so the light intensity drops and the resistance increases, causing the alarm to sound.

7. Series Circuits

Page 271 — Fact Recall Questions

Q1 Components are connected all in a line, end to end.

Q2 Ammeter

Q3 In series and in the same direction as each other (and any other cells in the circuit).

Q4 False, it is shared between the components.

Q5 It is always the same.

Q6 Add up the resistances of all the components.

Page 271 — Application Questions

Q1 a) **1.5 A**

b) $V_1 = I \times R$

$= 1.5 \times 7$

$= \mathbf{10.5\ V}$

c) $V = V_1 + V_2$ so $V_2 = V - V_1$

$= 12 - 10.5$

$= \mathbf{1.5\ V}$

Q2 $V = I \times R$ so $R = V \div I$

$= 1.5 \div 1.5$

$= \mathbf{1\ \Omega}$

8. Parallel Circuits

Page 275 — Fact Recall Questions

Q1 Components are connected to the battery separately to the other components (on their own branches).

Q2 Each branch/component can be turned on and off separately, whereas in series circuits, turning off one component will turn them all off.

Q3 It is the same across each component and across the power supply.

Q4 By adding up the current in every branch.

Page 276 — Application Questions

Q1 a) Find the p.d. across the branch with the resistor in, and it will be the same as the p.d. across the voltmeter. The current through the branch is 0.75 A and the resistance is 8 Ω.

$V = I \times R = 0.75 \times 8 = \mathbf{6\ V}$

Remember, the resistance of an ammeter is so small that you don't need to consider it — you can just pretend that it's not there.

b) The total current in the circuit is 2 A, and the current through the branch with the resistor is 0.75 A. So the current through the bulb is 2 A – 0.75 A = 1.25 A. The voltage across the bulb is 6 V so the resistance can be found by rearranging $V = I \times R$.

$R = V \div I = 6 \div 1.25 = \mathbf{4.8\ \Omega}$

Q2 a) With the switch open, the circuit is just a simple series circuit with two resistors and an ammeter. The current in the circuit is 0.7 A and the total resistance is 12 + 8 = 20 Ω.

$V = I \times R = 0.7 \times 20 = \mathbf{14\ V}$

b) (i) The potential difference is the same on each branch of the parallel part of the circuit. So you can just find the voltage on the lower branch by using the resistance of, and current through resistor R_1.

$V = I \times R_1 = 0.5 \times 8 = \mathbf{4\ V}$

(ii) The total potential difference of the circuit is shared between resistor R_2 and the parallel loop with the other components on it. The potential difference across the parallel loop is 4 V and the total potential difference is 14 V, so the potential difference across resistor R_2 is 14 – 4 = **10 V**.

Pages 279-281 — Physics 2.3

Exam-style Questions

1 a) They lose (negatively charged) electrons ***(1 mark)***.

b) repulsive ***(1 mark)***.

c) The force felt between the positively charged paint droplets and the negatively charged car body is attractive, so the droplets are attracted to the car body ***(1 mark)***. If the paint droplets and car body were uncharged, there would be no electrostatic force between the droplets and the car, so less paint would reach the car body resulting in more waste ***(1 mark)***.

2 a) The rate of flow of charge *(1 mark)*.
b) The potential difference of the battery is the same as the potential difference of the motor *(1 mark)*. So use $V = W \div Q = 210 \div 15 =$ **14 V**
(2 marks available for correct answer to calculation, otherwise 1 mark for substituting the correct values into the correct formula.)
c) i) The components are in parallel so the sum of their currents is equal to the total current, so $A_{total} = A_{motor} + A_{bulb}$
The current passing through the motor is found by $I_{motor} = Q \div t = 15 \div 30 = 0.5$ A.
$0.5\text{ A} + I_{bulb} = 1.2$ A, so $I_{bulb} =$ **0.7 A**
(3 marks for correct answer, otherwise 1 mark for substituting the right values into $I = Q \div t$ to attempt to calculate I_{motor}, 1 mark for finding the current through the motor.)
ii) The potential difference through the filament bulb is the same as the power supply, $V = 14$ V.
$V = I \times R$ so $R = V \div I = 14 \div 0.7 =$ **20 Ω**
(2 marks available for correct answer, otherwise 1 mark for substituting correct values into correct equation. Allow follow through marks from part (b) or (c) (i).)

3 a) A thermistor *(1 mark)*.
b) E.g.

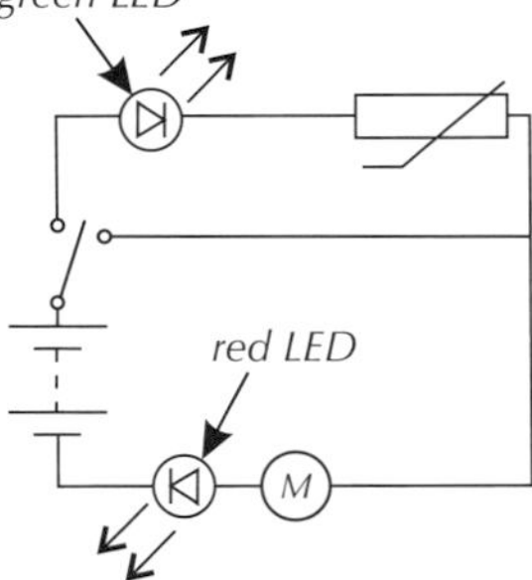

(3 marks available — 1 mark for each LED in the correct stretch of circuit and labelled correctly. 1 mark for both LEDs being connected in the right direction.)
c) As the room gets hotter the resistance of the thermistor will decrease *(1 mark)*. This will allow more current to flow through the circuit and so more current to flow through the fan motor *(1 mark)*.

4 a) The resistance of the variable resistor can be increased or decreased, which will decrease or increase the current in the circuit *(1 mark)*.
b) A resistor *(1 mark)*.
c) Choose a point on the graph, e.g. $I = 0.2$ A when $V = 1$ V. $V = I \times R$ so $R = V \div I = 1 \div 0.2 =$ **5 Ω**
(2 marks for correct answer — otherwise 1 mark for substituting in any correct values of V and I from the graph into the correct equation.)
You could also calculate the gradient of the graph and then do 1 ÷ gradient to find resistance.
d) Graph B *(1 mark)*. A higher resistance means a more shallow gradient *(1 mark)*.
The line should still start at the origin.

Physics 2.4 Mains Electricity and Appliances

1. Mains Electricity

Page 284 — Fact Recall Questions

Q1 Direct current is current that only flows in one direction. It's supplied by lots of power sources, e.g. cells and batteries.
Q2 Alternating current. The direction of a.c. is constantly changing whereas d.c. always flows in one direction.
Q3 The frequency is 50 Hz and the voltage is approximately 230 V.
Q4 The vertical axis is voltage and the horizontal axis is time.
Q5 You divide 1 by the time period in seconds to give the frequency in hertz.
i.e. use $\text{frequency (Hz)} = \frac{1}{\text{time period (s)}}$

Page 284 — Application Questions

Q1 A — Distance from trace to centre line is 2 major divisions and 1 minor division. There are 5 minor divisions in each major division, so 1 minor division = 0.2 major divisions. So the distance from the trace to the centre line = 2.2 (major) divisions.
The gain dial is set at 5 V/div. So p.d. = 2.2 × 5 = **11 V**.
B — Distance from peak p.d. to centre line = 2 divisions. Gain dial is set at 5 V/div.
So peak p.d. = 2 × 5 = **10 V**.
Q2 $\text{frequency} = \frac{1}{\text{time period}} = \frac{1}{0.05} =$ **20 Hz**

2. Electricity in the Home

Page 287 — Fact Recall Questions

Q1 Any six from: e.g. long cables / frayed cables / too many plugs in one socket / cables in contact with something hot or wet / water near sockets / shoving things into sockets / damaged plugs / lighting sockets without bulbs in / appliances without their covers on.
Q2 The live wire is brown, the neutral wire is blue and the earth wire is green and yellow.
Q3 a) The live wire alternates between high positive and negative potential difference. The blue neutral wire is always at 0 V.
b) The earth wire protects the wiring of an appliance and has a safety role — it carries the electricity to earth should something go wrong and the live or neutral wires touch the metal casing of an appliance.
Q4 A three-core cable has a live wire, a neutral wire and an earth wire, whereas a two-core cable just has a live wire and a neutral wire.

Q5

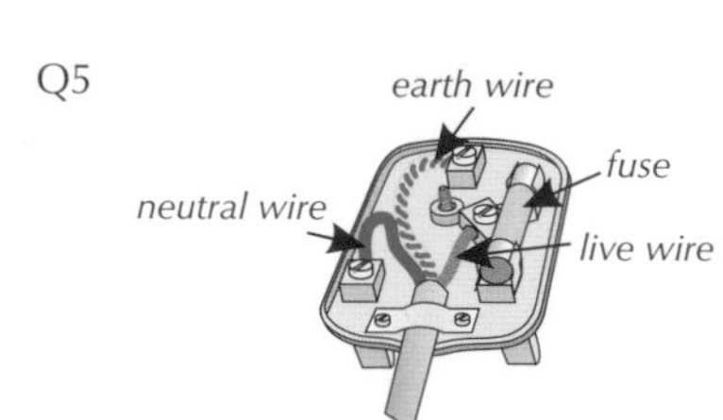

Q6 The metal parts of a plug are made of copper and brass because they are very good conductors. The case, cable grip and cable insulation are made of rubber or plastic because they're insulators and they're flexible.

Page 287 — Application Question

Q1 There are too many plugs in one socket, which could overheat and cause a fire. There are cables on and near water, which could cause an electric shock or electrocution. The cable on the hair dryer is frayed, which could cause an electric shock from exposed wires. There are sockets near water.

3. Safety Devices in Circuits

Page 291 — Fact Recall Questions

Q1 a) A small tube containing a short piece of wire.
b) The fuse melts.

Q2 Advantage: any one from e.g. circuit breakers work much faster than fuses (so they're safer than fuses) / they can be reset with the flick of a switch (so they're more convenient than fuses).
Disadvantage: e.g. they're much more expensive to buy than fuses.

Q3 A fuse should be chosen that is rated as near as possible but just higher than the normal operating current of the appliance.

Q4 The thickness required for a cable increases with the current flowing through the cable. A high-powered appliance is likely to have a larger current flowing through its cable than a low-powered appliance, and so will need a thicker cable.

Q5 A Residual Current Circuit Breaker. It detects the difference in current between the live and neutral wires when a current flows to earth. It cuts off the current by opening a switch.

Q6 An appliance with a plastic (or other insulator) casing and no metal part showing is double insulated — it doesn't need an earth wire because no part of its casing can become live.

4. Energy and Efficiency in Circuits

Page 293 — Fact Recall Questions

Q1 a) Any two from: e.g. a motor / a kettle / a speaker / a bulb.
b) Any two from: e.g.
motor — kinetic energy
kettle — heat (thermal) energy
speaker — sound energy
bulb — light energy

There are loads of options you could give here — these are just the examples that were given in the topic.

Q2 As heat energy.

Q3 More efficient electrical appliances transfer more of their total electrical input into useful energy. They waste less energy which usually means they use less energy overall, which will save you money on energy bills.

Q4 CFLs (compact fluorescent lamps) are energy-saving lamps. They waste much less energy as heat than traditional filament bulbs.

5. Power and Energy Transfer

Page 296 — Fact Recall Questions

Q1 $P = \frac{E}{t}$. P is power in watts, E in energy transferred in joules and t is time in seconds.

Q2 a) power = current × potential difference, $P = I \times V$.
b) Power is measured in watts, current is in amps and potential difference is in volts.
c) You work out the current of the appliance by dividing its power rating by the potential difference of the supply. The fuse needs to be rated just a little higher than the normal current.

Page 296 — Application Questions

Q1 Cooker B will use the most energy in 20 minutes because it has the highest power.

Q2 $P = \frac{E}{t} = \frac{2400}{1300} = \mathbf{1.8\ W\ (to\ 2\ s.f.)}$

Q3 $P = I \times V = 3 \times 230 = \mathbf{690\ W}$

Q4 t = 8 minutes = 480 s, E = 3.6 kJ = 3600 J
$P = \frac{E}{t} = \frac{3600}{480} = \mathbf{7.5\ W}$

Q5 $I = \frac{P}{V} = \frac{900}{230} = 3.9...$ A. A **5 A** fuse should be used.

The fuse should be a bit higher but close to the normal current of the toaster. Common fuses are 3 A, 5 A and 13 A.

Q6 $P = \frac{E}{t} \Rightarrow t = \frac{E}{P} = \frac{300}{15} = \mathbf{20\ s}$

Q7 P = 2.1 kW = 2100 W, t = 30 minutes = 1800 s
$E = P \times t = 2100 \times 1800 = \mathbf{3\,780\,000\ J}$

Q8 Microwave A:
$P = \frac{E}{t} \Rightarrow E = P \times t = 900 \times (4 \times 60) = 216\,000$ J

Microwave B:
$P = \frac{E}{t} \Rightarrow E = P \times t = 650 \times (6 \times 60) = 234\,000$ J

So **microwave B** transfers the most energy.

Remember to convert the time into seconds before carrying out any calculations.

6. Energy Transfer and Charges

Page 298 — Fact Recall Question

Q1 energy transferred = potential difference × charge, $E = V \times Q$. Energy transferred is in joules, potential difference is in volts and charge is in coulombs.

Page 298 — Application Questions

Q1 $E = V \times Q = 5 \times 240 =$ **1200 J**

Q2 $E = V \times Q \Rightarrow V = \frac{E}{Q} = \frac{22}{4} =$ **5.5 V**

Pages 300-301 — Physics 2.4

Exam-style Questions

1 a) i) brown ***(1 mark)***

ii) A double insulated appliance / an appliance with an insulating case ***(1 mark)***. The case cannot become electrically charged, so there is no danger to the device itself or to a person touching the device. ***(1 mark)***.

b) Power = 0.6 kW = 600 W

$I = \frac{P}{V} = \frac{600}{230} = 2.6$ A

A **3 A** fuse should be used.

(1 mark for correctly rearranging the equation, 1 mark for correct substitution, 1 mark for correctly calculating a current of 2.6 A, 1 mark for saying a fuse with a rating slightly above the current calculated should be used.)

c) E.g. when the casing is in contact with the live wire, a large current flows out through the earth wire ***(1 mark)***. The surge in the current melts the fuse when the amount of current is greater than the fuse rating ***(1 mark)***. This breaks the circuit and cuts off the electricity supply ***(1 mark)***.

2 a) The oven has a higher power rating than the dishwasher ***(1 mark)*** so will draw a greater current from the mains supply ***(1 mark)***. The larger the current the thicker the cable needed, so the oven will need a thicker cable ***(1 mark)***.

b) E.g. If there is a fault, a fuse will melt and need to be replaced. A RCCB is operated by a switch and can be turned back on more easily. ***(1 mark)***.

c) i) Power = 10.2 kW = 10 200 W

$t = \frac{E}{P} = \frac{7\,038\,000}{10\,200} =$ **690 s**

(2 marks for correct answer, otherwise 1 mark for correct substitution.)

ii) $Q = \frac{E}{V} = \frac{7\,038\,000}{230} =$ **30 600 C**

(3 marks for correct answer, otherwise 1 mark for correct substitution and 1 mark for identifying the oven is connected to a 230 V supply.)

3 a) i) Alternating current/a.c. ***(1 mark)***. The supply alternates between positive and negative voltage / is constantly changing direction ***(1 mark)***.

ii) Batteries supply a d.c. current, but the oscilloscope shows an a.c. current ***(1 mark)***.

b) Distance from peak p.d. to centre line = 2 divisions.
Gain dial is set at 5 V/div.
So peak p.d. = 2 × 5 = **10 V**
(2 marks for correct answer, otherwise 1 mark for correct working.)

c) 1 full wave cycle = 5 divisions
Timebase is set at 3 ms/div.
So time period = 5 × 3 = 15 ms = 0.015 s

$\text{frequency} = \frac{1}{\text{time period}} = \frac{1}{0.015} =$ **70 Hz (to 1 s.f.)**

(4 marks for correct answer — otherwise 1 mark for correct time period, 1 mark for correct substitution into frequency formula and 1 mark for rounding answer to the correct number of significant figures.)

Physics 2.5 Atomic Structure and Radioactivity

1. Rutherford Scattering

Page 303 — Fact Recall Questions

Q1 According to the model, an atom is made of a positively-charged sphere with tiny negative electrons stuck in it (like plums in a plum pudding).

Q2 Rutherford and Marsden expected that alpha particles fired at thin gold foil would be deflected a very small amount by the electrons in the atoms.

Q3 Most alpha particles passed straight through and the odd one bounced straight back. The fact that most alpha particles passed straight through the foil, showed that most of the atom is empty space. Some positively-charged alpha particles were deflected by the nucleus by a large angle, showing that the nucleus had a large positive charge. Very few alpha particles bounced back, showing that the nucleus is very small.

2. Atoms and Isotopes

Page 306 — Fact Recall Questions

Q1 Protons, neutrons and electrons.

Q2 The electron.

Q3 The relative mass is 1 and the relative charge is 0.

Q4 They are equal. The atom has no overall charge (it's neutral), so the charges must be equal to cancel each other out.

Q5 Atomic number is the number of protons in the nucleus of an atom. Mass number is the number of protons and neutrons in the nucleus of an atom.

Q6 The atomic number is always the same (they have the same number of protons).

Q7 Another atom (of the same element) with the same number of protons (atomic number) but a different number of neutrons (mass number).

Page 306 — Application Question

Q1 a) 17 – 18 = **–1**

Remember, electrons have a negative charge of –1 and protons have an equal positive charge of +1.

b) The particle has an overall charge.

c) They have the same number of protons but a different number of neutrons.

3. Radioactivity

Page 311 — Fact Recall Questions

Q1 It gives out radiation from the nuclei of its atoms all the time, no matter what is done to it.

Q2 You can't, it is random.

Sorry — that was sort of a trick question...

Q3 Alpha, beta and gamma.

Q4 Alpha radiation is made up of alpha particles, which are made up of two protons and two neutrons (a helium nucleus).
Beta radiation is made up of beta particles, which are electrons.
Gamma radiation is made up of gamma rays, which are electromagnetic waves with a very short wavelength.

Q5 The most strongly ionising radiation is alpha radiation. The radiation that will penetrate furthest through a material is gamma radiation.
The radiation that will penetrate the least through air is alpha radiation.

Q6 Atomic number and mass number.

Q7 Gamma rays (they have no charge).

Q8 Beta particles.

Q9 Gamma rays aren't deflected at all because they have no charge, but alpha and beta particles both have a charge, so they are both deflected.
Although beta particles have a smaller charge than alpha particles, their mass is much, much less, so they are deflected more.

Page 311 — Application Questions

Q1 a) Radiation A, as it passes through the hand and radiation B doesn't.

b) Radiation B, as it doesn't even penetrate through the hand.

c) Gamma radiation, as it penetrates through all of the materials.

Q2 Alpha decay.

Q3 a) Beta decay

b) ${}^{228}_{88}Ra \rightarrow {}^{228}_{89}Ac + {}^{0}_{-1}e$

Remember you need to balance the atomic and mass numbers on each side of the equation.

4. Half-life

Page 314 — Fact Recall Questions

Q1 Because the activity never drops to zero.

Q2 Half-life is the average time it takes for the number of nuclei of a radioactive isotope in a sample to halve. Half-life is the time it takes for the count rate from a sample containing the isotope to fall to half its initial level.

Page 314 — Application Questions

Q1 After 1 hour (60 minutes), it will have had 4 half-lives because 60 ÷ 15 = 4.
So it will have halved four times.
After one half-life: 240 ÷ 2 = 120
After two half-lives: 120 ÷ 2 = 60
After three half-lives: 60 ÷ 2 = 30
After four half-lives: 30 ÷ 2 = 15
So the count rate will be **15 cpm**.

Q2 Initial count rate = 16
After one half-life: 16 ÷ 2 = 8
After two half-lives: 8 ÷ 2 = 4
So 2 hours is 2 half-lives. So one half-life is **1 hour**.

Q3 The initial count rate is 120, so after one half-life it will have decreased to 60. Find 60 on the activity axis and follow across to the curve and then down to the time axis.

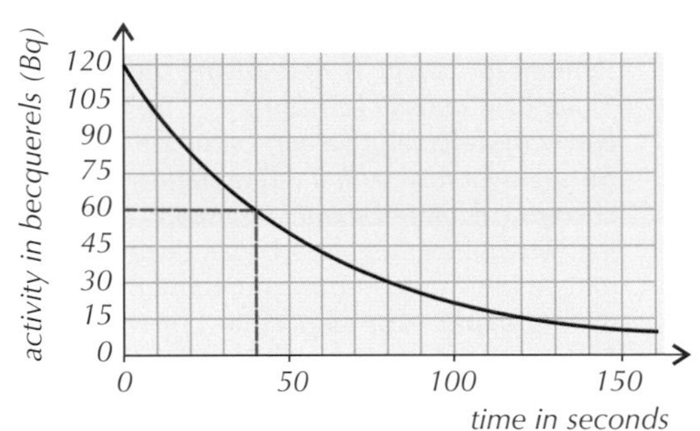

The half-life is **40 seconds**.

5. Exposure to Radiation

Page 317 — Fact Recall Questions

Q1 Naturally occurring unstable isotopes (e.g. in the air, food, building materials and rocks), radiation from space (cosmic rays), and radiation from man-made sources (e.g. nuclear weapons, waste and disasters).

Q2 Certain rocks can cause high levels of radioactive gases at the surface which can get trapped in homes.

Q3 E.g. workers in the nuclear industry/uranium miners — working with radioactive materials exposes them to much more radiation than people in other occupations.
Radiographers — ionising radiation is used in hospitals so radiographers have a higher exposure.
Pilots and cabin crew — they are exposed to more cosmic rays because they work at high altitudes.
Miners — rocks in and around the mines give out radiation.

Page 317 — Application Question

Q1 a) Cosmic rays
b) The astronauts are exposed to a higher dose of radiation on board the ISS than in other occupations. Radiation can be damaging to health, so regularly changing the crew minimises their radiation dose and so minimises the possible health risks.

6. Dangers of Radioactivity

Page 320 — Fact Recall Questions

Q1 Lower doses of radiation can damage cells through ionisation (without killing them), causing them to mutate so that they divide uncontrollably. This is cancer.

Q2 High doses of radiation can kill cells completely, by damaging them so much that they can't repair themselves.

Q3 Alpha radiation is the most dangerous inside the body because it does damage in a localised area and is highly ionising.

Q4 Beta and gamma radiation are the most dangerous outside the body because they can penetrate into your body.

Q5 E.g. minimise your exposure time, never allow skin contact (handle with tongs), hold the source at arm's length and avoid looking at the source or pointing it towards your body.

Q6 E.g. lead.

Page 320 — Application Question

Q1 a) Radioactive isotopes should be kept away from your body to avoid them damaging your cells. A lower dose could cause cancer and a high dose could cause radiation poisoning.
b) Lead absorbs all three types of radiation, so lead boxes should be used to store radioactive materials to stop the radiation leaking out.
c) E.g. any of:
Wear gloves while handing the papers to avoid direct contact with the papers, reducing the radiation dose received.
Use tongs to handle the papers / hold the papers at arms length to increase the distance of the papers from the body. This will reduce the radiation dose as some radiation will be absorbed by the air.
Avoid looking directly at the source (e.g. view the source through a camera image on a screen) to minimise the amount of radiation reaching your head, eyes and body.
Wear a lead apron / stand behind a lead screen. Lead absorbs some of the radiation so the radiation dose will be decreased.
Handle the papers for as short a time as possible to reduce the amount of time the body is exposed to radiation.

7. Uses of Radioactivity

Page 323 — Fact Recall Questions

Q1 Beta radiation has a long range, so it could reach you in your home and expose you to radiation.

Q2 Radioactive isotopes are injected or swallowed and their progress around the body can be followed around the body using an external radiation detector. A computer can produce an image from the detected radiation showing where the radiation is most concentrated. Gamma or beta emitters can be used as they can be detected outside the body.

Q3 Radiotherapy is the killing of cancer cells using high doses of radiation. Gamma radiation is used.

Page 323 — Application Question

Q1 a) (i) Alpha particles would be stopped by the paper.
(ii) Gamma rays would pass straight through the paper, whatever its thickness.
b) So that it doesn't need to be replaced too often.

Pages 325-326 — Physics 2.5

Exam-style Questions

1 (a) The nucleus contains protons and neutrons.
OR
The nucleus contains neutrons and protons.
The numbers of protons and electrons in a neutral atom are equal.
(2 marks for all correct otherwise 1 mark for one correct answer.)
(b) The atoms have the same number of protons (atomic number) but a different number of protons (mass numbers) ***(1 mark)***.

2 (a) The average time it takes for the number of nuclei in a caesium-137 sample to halve is 30 years ***(1 mark)***.
OR
The time it takes for the count rate from a sample of a caesium-137 to fall to half its initial level is 30 years ***(1 mark)***.
(b) (i) Any two from: e.g. cosmic rays (accept radiation from space) / naturally occurring isotopes in food / naturally occurring isotopes in building materials / naturally occurring isotopes in the air / radon gas (accept gases from rocks) / radiation used in medicine.
(Maximum 2 marks — 1 mark for each correct source.)
(ii) Some isotopes have very long half-lives (e.g. the half-life of caesium-137 is 30 years) so it will take a long time for the radiation levels in affected areas to decrease to a safe level ***(1 mark)***.
(c) (i) Beta ***(1 mark)***.
(ii) $^{137}_{55}Cs \rightarrow ^{137}_{56}Ba + ^{0}_{-1}e$ ***(1 mark)***

3 (a) (i)

Radiation type:	*Made up of:*	*Stopped by:*
Alpha particles	*2 protons and 2 neutrons* ***(1 mark)*** or helium nuclei ***(1 mark)***	*Thin paper*
Beta particles ***(1 mark)***	*Electrons*	*Thin aluminium*
Gamma rays	*Short-wavelength EM waves*	*Thick lead*

(ii) Alpha radiation is the most highly ionising radiation and so if emitted inside the body it can badly damage cells in a localised area ***(1 mark)***.

(b) (i) To make sure that the radiation dose they are getting at work is not too high as high doses can damage or kill body cells ***(1 mark)***.

(b) (ii) Any two from: e.g. limit exposure time / wear protective clothing / wear breathing apparatus. ***(2 marks available — 1 mark for each correct answer.)***

4 How to grade your answer:

0 marks:
There is no relevant information.

1-2 marks:
There is a brief explanation of how the method would detect cracks with no explanation of the type of radiation used.

3-4 marks:
There is an explanation of how the method would detect cracks and some explanation of the type of radiation or of an appropriate half-life. The answer has a logical structure and spelling, punctuation and grammar are mostly correct.

5-6 marks:
There is a clear and detailed explanation of how the method would detect cracks and the type and half-life are fully explained. The answer has a logical structure and uses correct spelling, grammar and punctuation.

Here are some points your answer may include:
The radioactive isotope will give out radiation.
The detector will detect how much radiation is reaching it as it moves along above the pipe.
If there is a crack, the count rate/amount of radiation will increase in the area above the crack.
The source used should be a gamma source.
Gamma should be used as it has a penetrates far into materials without being stopped and so will pass through the ground and reach the detector / Alpha and beta would be stopped by the ground as they have low penetrations, so they wouldn't reach the detector.
The source should have a short half-life.
The half-life should be short so that the source does not continue emitting lots of radiation for a very long time and so possibly harm people that come close to the pipes.

Physics 2.6 Nuclear Fission and Nuclear Fusion

1. Nuclear Fission

Page 328 — Fact Recall Questions

Q1 Nuclear fission is when an atomic nucleus splits up to form two smaller nuclei.

Q2 Uranium-235 and plutonium-239.

Q3 It must absorb a (slow moving) neutron.
If absorbing a neutron makes the nucleus unstable enough, the nucleus will split.

Q4 When a nucleus splits, two or three neutrons are released. These neutrons may be absorbed by other nuclei, causing them to split, which will release more neutrons that can go on to cause further nuclei to split... and so the process goes on.
This is a chain reaction.

Q5 a) In a nuclear power station, the energy from nuclear fission is used to heat a coolant, which in turn heats water to make steam. This is used to drive a turbine that is connected to an electrical generator.
b) E.g. Nuclear waste is difficult/expensive to dispose of safely. / The cost of the power plant/ decommissioning the power plant is high. / There is a risk of radiation leaks/major catastrophes like Chernobyl.

2. Nuclear Fusion

Page 329 — Fact Recall Questions

Q1 Nuclear fusion is when two nuclei (e.g. hydrogen nuclei) join to create a larger nucleus.

Q2 Nuclear fusion generates more energy.

Q3 E.g. Advantages: Fusion doesn't leave behind a lot of radioactive waste. / There is a lot of hydrogen available to use as fuel. / Nuclear fusion releases more energy for a given mass than nuclear fission.
Disadvantage: Fusion can only happen at really high temperatures, so at the moment it takes more power to get a fusion reactor up to temperature than the reactor can produce.

3. The Life Cycle of Stars

Page 331 — Fact Recall Questions

Q1 Gravity causes clouds of dust and gas to spiral in together and form a protostar. Within the protostar, gravitational energy is converted to heat so the temperature rises. When the temperature is high enough nuclear fusion begins, causing the star to give out heat and light. Smaller masses of gas and dust around the star may also be pulled together by gravity to form planets.

Q2 nuclear fusion

Q3 a) Main sequence stars are stable because the heat generated by nuclear fusion provides an outward pressure which balances the force of gravity trying to pull everything inwards.

b) Stars contain huge amounts of hydrogen — enough to support fusion for millions of years.

Q4 A neutron star.

Q5 a) Elements as heavy as iron are formed by nuclear fusion in stable stars, elements heavier than iron are formed in supernovae. Elements have been spread through the Universe by supernovae.

b) It will become a red giant. The red giant will become unstable and eject its outer layer of dust and gas as a planetary nebula. This will leave behind a white dwarf, which will eventually cool down to form a black dwarf.

Page 251 — Physics 2.6

Exam-style Questions

1 a) i) (nuclear) fission ***(1 mark)***

ii) a (slow-moving) neutron ***(1 mark)***

b) E.g.

Krypton nucleus
Uranium nucleus
Uranium nucleus
Particle
Particles / neutrons
Energy
Barium nucleus
Energy

(1 mark for showing small particles/neutrons being produced when the uranium atom splits, 1 mark for showing these particles going on to cause at least one more fission.)

c) E.g. the waste products are very dangerous ***(1 mark)*** and so they are difficult/expensive to dispose of safely ***(1 mark)***.

2 How to grade your answer:

0 marks:
No description of the star's life cycle stages are given.

1-2 marks:
Brief description of one or two of star's life cycle stages are given.

3-4 marks:
Several of the star's life cycle stages are clearly described. The answer has some structure and spelling, grammar and punctuation are mostly correct. Some specialist terms are used.

5-6 marks:
All life cycle stages are described in detail.
The answer has a logical structure and uses correct spelling, grammar and punctuation.
Relevant specialist terms are used correctly.

Here are some points your answer may include:
Star A is larger than the Sun and so will expand into a red super giant when it starts to run out of hydrogen.

It will expand and contract several times, forming elements as heavy as iron in various nuclear reactions.

Eventually it will explode in a supernova and throw its outer layers of dust and gas into space, leaving a very dense core called a neutron star.

If the star is big enough, the supernova will become a black hole instead of a neutron star.

Glossary

A

Acceleration
A measure of how quickly the velocity is changing.

Accurate result
A result that is very close to the true answer.

Acid
A substance with a pH of less than 7 that forms H^+ ions in water.

Activation energy
The minimum amount of energy that particles must have in order to react.

Activity (radioactive)
The number of nuclei that decay per second.

Aerobic respiration
The reactions involved in breaking down glucose using oxygen, to release energy. Carbon dioxide and water are produced.

Air bag
A bag in a car that inflates on impact to slow the passenger down more slowly and prevent them from hitting hard surfaces in the car.

Air resistance
The frictional force caused by air on a moving object.

Alkali
A base that dissolves in water and forms OH^- ions in solution.

Allele
An alternative version of a gene.

Alloy
A metal that is a mixture of two or more metals, or a mixture involving metals and non-metals.

Alpha decay
A type of radioactive decay in which an alpha particle is given out from a decaying nucleus.

Alpha particle
A positively-charged particle made of two protons and two neutrons (a helium nucleus).

Alternating current (a.c.)
Current that is constantly changing direction.

Amino acid
A small molecule that is a building block of proteins.

Ammeter
A component used to measure the current through a component. It is always connected in series with the component.

Amylase
A digestive enzyme that catalyses the breakdown of starch into sugars, in the mouth and small intestine.

Anaerobic respiration
The incomplete breakdown of glucose, which produces lactic acid. It takes place in the absence of oxygen.

Anhydrous
Doesn't contain any water molecules.

Anomalous result
A result that doesn't seem to fit with the rest of the data.

Asexual reproduction
Where organisms reproduce by mitosis to produce genetically identical offspring.

Atom
A neutral particle made up of protons and neutrons in the nucleus, with electrons surrounding the nucleus.

Atomic number
The number of protons in the nucleus of an atom. It's also known as proton number.

B

Base
A substance with a pH of more than 7.

Beta decay
A type of radioactive decay in which a beta particle is given out from a decaying nucleus.

Beta particle
An electron emitted in beta decay.

Bias
Prejudice towards or against something.

Bile
A fluid that is made in the liver, stored in the gall bladder and released into the small intestine. It aids digestion by creating alkaline conditions in the small intestine and by emulsifying fats.

Biological detergent
A detergent (e.g. washing powder) that contains enzymes to help break down stains.

Black dwarf
The remains of a star that are left behind when a white dwarf cools.

Black hole
An extremely dense object left behind after a supernova if the star was too large to form a neutron star.

Braking distance
The distance a vehicle travels under the braking force (after the brakes have been applied).

C

Carbohydrase
A type of enzyme that breaks down starch into sugars.

Carrier
A person who carries the allele for a genetic disorder, but who doesn't have any symptoms of the disorder.

Catalyst
A substance that can speed up a reaction without being changed or used up in the reaction.

Categoric data
Data that comes in distinct categories. E.g. type of fuel or metals.

Cathode ray oscilloscope (CRO)
A voltmeter that allows you to 'see' how the voltage of an electricity supply changes over time.

Cell membrane
A membrane surrounding a cell, which holds it all together and controls what goes in and out.

Cell wall
A structure surrounding some cell types, which gives strength and support. In plant and algal cells the cell wall is made of cellulose.

Cellulose
A molecule used to make strong cell walls in plants and algae.

Chain reaction
A reaction that keeps going (without any outside input) because the products of the reaction cause further reactions. E.g. nuclear fission.

Chlorophyll
A green substance found in chloroplasts which absorbs light for photosynthesis.

Chloroplast
A structure found in plant cells and algae, which contains chlorophyll. Chloroplasts are the site of photosynthesis.

Chromosome
A long molecule of DNA found in the nucleus.

Circuit breaker
An electrical safety device that breaks the circuit by opening a switch if the current gets too high.

Collision theory
The theory that in order for a reaction to occur, particles must collide with sufficient energy.

Compound
A substance made up of atoms of at least two different elements, chemically joined together.

Conductor (electrical)
A material in which electrical charges can easily move.

Conservation of momentum
In a closed system, the total momentum before an event is the same as after the event.

Continuous data
Numerical data that can have any value within a range. E.g. length, volume or temperature.

Control experiment
An experiment that's kept under the same conditions as the rest of the investigation, but doesn't have anything done to it.

Control group
A group that matches the one being studied, but the independent variable isn't altered. It's kept under the same conditions as the group in the experiment.

Control variable
A variable in an experiment that is kept the same.

Correlation
A relationship between two variables.

Cosmic ray
Radiation from space.

Covalent bond
A chemical bond formed when atoms share a pair of electrons to form molecules.

Covalent substance
A substance where the atoms are held together by covalent bonds.

Crumple zones
Parts of a car that crumple on impact, increasing the impact time.

Crystallisation
The formation of solid crystals as water evaporates from a solution. E.g. salt solutions undergo crystallisation to form solid salt crystals.

Current
A flow of electric charge. Measured in amperes (A).

Current-potential difference (I-V) graphs
A graph of current against potential difference for a component. The inverse of the gradient of the graph gives the component's resistance.

Cystic fibrosis
A genetic disorder of the cell membranes caused by a recessive allele.

Cytoplasm
A gel-like substance in a cell where most of the chemical reactions take place.

D

Decay
The breakdown of dead organisms.

Delocalised electron
An electron that isn't associated with a particular atom or bond and is free to move within a structure.

Dependent variable
The variable in an experiment that is measured.

Differentiation
The process by which cells become specialised for a particular job.

Diffusion
The spreading out of particles from an area of high concentration to an area of low concentration.

Diode
A circuit component that only allows current to flow through it in one direction. It has a very high resistance in the other direction.

Direct current (d.c.)
Current that always flows in the same direction.

Direct proportionality
When a graph of two variables is plotted and the variables increase or decrease in the same ratio.

Discrete data
Numerical data that can be counted in chunks with no in-between value. E.g. number of people.

Distance-time graph
A graph showing an object's distance from its starting point over a period of time.

Distribution
Where organisms are found in a particular area.

DNA (deoxyribonucleic acid)
The molecule in cells that stores genetic information.

DNA fingerprinting
A technique used to identify an individual based on their DNA.

Dominant allele
The allele for the characteristic that's shown by an organism if two different alleles are present for that characteristic.

Double covalent bond
Two pairs of electrons shared between two atoms.

Double insulated appliance
An appliance with a case made from an insulator that cannot conduct current. This type of appliance doesn't need an earth wire.

Drag
The frictional force caused by any fluid (a liquid or a gas) on a moving object.

E

Earth wire
The green and yellow wire in an electricity cable and plug that does not normally carry any current. It's connected to earth and protects devices and their users from surges in current.

Elastic object
An object that returns to its original shape after a force has caused it to stretch or change in shape.

Elastic potential energy
The energy stored in an elastic object when a force does work to change its shape.

Electrolysis
The process of breaking down a substance using electricity.

Electrolyte
A liquid used in electrolysis to conduct electricity between the two electrodes.

Electron
A subatomic particle with a relative charge of –1 and a relative mass of 1/2000.

Electron shell
A region of an atom that contains electrons. It's also known as an energy level.

Electronic structure
The number of electrons in an atom (or ion) of an element and how they are arranged.

Electroplating
A process that uses electrolysis to coat the surface of a material with a metal.

Element
A substance that is made up of only one type of atom.

Embryonic screening
Genetic analysis of a cell taken from an embryo before it's implanted into the uterus during IVF, in order to check that the embryo doesn't carry any genetic disorders.

Embryonic stem cell
A stem cell found in the early human embryo.

Empirical formula
A chemical formula showing the simplest possible whole number ratio of atoms in a compound.

Endothermic reaction
A reaction which takes in energy from the surroundings.

Energy level
A region of an atom that contains electrons. It's also known as an electron shell.

Enzyme
A protein that acts as a biological catalyst.

Epidermal tissue
A type of plant tissue which covers the whole plant.

Epithelial tissue
A type of animal tissue which covers some parts of the body. E.g. the inside of the stomach.

Evolution (of a species)
The gradual change in a species over time.

Exothermic reaction
A reaction which transfers energy to the surroundings.

Extinction
The process by which a species dies out.

F

Fair test
A controlled experiment where the only thing that changes is the independent variable.

Family tree (genetics)
A diagram which shows how a characteristic (or disorder) is inherited in a group of related people.

Fertilisation
The fusion of male and female gametes during sexual reproduction.

Force diagram
A diagram that shows all of the forces acting on an object, the direction in which they're acting and their relative size.

Fossil
The remains of an organism from many years ago, which is found in rock.

Fossil record
The history of life on Earth preserved as fossils.

Friction
The force that opposes an object's motion. It acts in the opposite direction to the motion.

Fullerene
A nanoparticle made from carbon. Its structure is based on hexagonal rings of carbon atoms.

Fuse
A tube containing a very thin wire connected to the live wire of an appliance. If the current gets too high, the fuse wire melts and breaks the circuit, cutting off the electricity supply.

G

Gamma decay
A type of radioactive decay in which a gamma ray is given out from a decaying nucleus.

Gamma ray
A short-wavelength electromagnetic wave.

Gas chromatography
A technique that can be used to separate and identify the compounds in a mixture.

Geiger counter
A particle detector that measures radioactive activity.

Gene
A short section of DNA, which contains the instructions needed to make a protein.

Genetic disorder
An inherited disorder that can be caused by an abnormal gene or chromosome.

Genotype
What alleles you have. E.g. Tt.

Geological activity
The internal and external processes that affect a planet. E.g. the movement of tectonic plates.

Glandular tissue
A type of animal tissue which makes and secretes substances like enzymes and hormones.

Glycogen
A molecule that acts as a store of glucose in liver and muscle cells.

Gravitational potential energy
The energy that an object has by virtue of its vertical position in a gravitational field.

Habitat
The place where an organism lives.

Half equation
An equation that shows the reaction that takes place at an electrode during electrolysis.

Half-life
The average time it takes for the number of nuclei in a radioactive isotope sample to halve.
or
The time it takes for the count rate of a radioactive sample containing the isotope to fall to half of its initial level.

Hazard
Something that has the potential to cause harm. E.g. fire or electricity.

Heterozygous
Where an organism has two alleles for a particular gene that are different.

Homozygous
Where an organism has two alleles for a particular gene that are the same.

Hydrated
Chemically combined with water molecules.

Hypothesis
A possible explanation for a scientific observation.

Independent variable
The variable in an experiment that is changed.

Indicator
A substance that changes colour above or below a certain pH.

Instrumental method
An analytical techniques that uses a machine.

Insulator (electrical)
A material in which electrical charges cannot easily move.

Intermolecular force
A force of attraction that exists between molecules.

Ion
A charged particle formed when one or more electrons are lost or gained from an atom or molecule, leaving it with a different number of electrons to protons.

Ionic bonding
A strong attraction between oppositely charged ions.

Ionic compound
A compound that contains positive and negative ions held together in a regular arrangement (a lattice) by electrostatic forces of attraction.

Ionic lattice
A closely-packed regular arrangement of ions held together by electrostatic forces of attraction.

Isomerase
An enzyme that converts glucose into fructose.

Isotopes
Different atomic forms of the same element, which have the same number of protons but a different number of neutrons.

Kinetic energy
The energy an object has because it is moving.

Lactic acid
The product of anaerobic respiration that builds up in muscle cells and can cause muscle fatigue.

Large intestine
An organ in the mammalian digestive system where water from undigested food is absorbed, producing faeces.

Light-dependent resistor (LDR)
A resistor whose resistance is dependent on the light intensity. The resistance decreases as light intensity increases.

Light-emitting diode (LED)
A diode that lights up when current flows through it in the forward direction.

Limit of proportionality
The point at which the extension of an object is no longer proportional to the applied force.

Limiting factor
A factor which prevents a reaction from going any faster.

Linear relationship
When a graph of two variables is plotted and the points lie on a straight line.

Lipase
A type of digestive enzyme that catalyses the breakdown of lipids into fatty acids and glycerol, in the small intestine.

Live wire
The brown wire in an electricity cable and plug that alternates between high positive and negative voltages.

Liver
An organ in the mammalian digestive system which produces bile.

Macromolecule
A large molecule made up of a very large number of atoms held together by covalent bonds.

Main sequence star
A stable star in the main sequence of its life, which lasts several billion years. Main sequence stars are stable because nuclear fusion in the star provides an outward pressure that balances the inward pull of gravity.

Mass number
The total number of protons and neutrons in the nucleus of an atom.

Mean (average)
A measure of average found by adding up all the data and dividing by the number of values there are.

Median (average)
The middle value in a set of data when they're in order of size.

Medical tracer
A radioactive isotope that can be injected into or swallowed by people. Its progress around the body can be followed using an external detector.

Meiosis
A type of cell division where a cell divides twice to produce four genetically different gametes. It occurs in the reproductive organs.

Mesophyll tissue
A type of plant tissue which is where photosynthesis occurs.

Mitochondria
Structures in a cell which are the site of most of the reactions for respiration.

Mitosis
A type of cell division where body cells divide once to produce two genetically identical cells.

Mode (average)
The most common value in a set of data.

Mole
A unit of amount of substance — one mole of a substance is the relative formula mass of that substance in grams.

Molecular formula
A chemical formula showing the actual number of atoms of each element in a compound.

Molecule
A particle made up of at least two atoms held together by covalent bonds.

Momentum
A property of a moving object that is proportional to its mass and velocity.

Monohybrid cross
Where you cross two parents to look at the inheritance of just one characteristic controlled by a single gene.

Multicellular organism
An organism made up of more than one cell.

Muscle fatigue
Where muscles become tired and can't contract efficiently.

Muscular tissue
A type of animal tissue which contracts (shortens) to move whatever it's attached to.

N

Nanoparticle
A tiny particle, made up of a few hundred atoms, that is between 1 and 100 nm in size.

Natural selection
The process by which species evolve.

Negative correlation
When one variable decreases as another variable increases.

Negative ion
A particle with a negative charge, formed when one or more electrons are gained.

Neutral wire
The blue wire in an electricity cable and plug. It is always at 0 V.

Neutralisation
The reaction between acids and bases that leads to the formation of neutral products — usually a salt and water.

Neutron
A subatomic particle with a relative charge of 0 and a relative mass of 1.

Neutron star
The very dense core of a star that is left behind when a red super giant explodes in a supernova.

Nuclear fission
When an atomic nucleus splits up to form two smaller nuclei.

Nuclear fusion
When two nuclei join to create a larger nucleus.

Nuclear model
A model of the atom that says that the atom has a small, central nucleus containing neutrons and protons and electrons moving around the nucleus, and that most of the atom is empty space.

Nucleus (of a cell)
A structure in a cell which contains genetic material.

Nucleus (of an atom)
The central part of an atom or ion, made up of protons and neutrons.

O

Organ
A group of different tissues that work together to perform a certain function.

Organ system
A group of organs working together to perform a particular function.

Oxidation
A reaction where electrons are lost.

Oxygen debt
The extra oxygen that needs repaying after anaerobic respiration in order to oxidise the lactic acid which has built up in the muscle cells.

P

Pancreas
An organ (and gland) in the mammalian digestive system which produces digestive juices.

Paper chromatography
A technique that can be used to separate and identify dyes.

Parallel circuit
A circuit in which every component is connected separately to the positive and negative ends of the battery.

Percentage yield
The amount of product formed in a reaction, given as a percentage of the predicted amount of product.

Periodic table
A table of all the known elements, arranged so that elements with similar properties are in groups.

Permanent vacuole (plant cells)
A structure in plant cells that contains cell sap.

pH scale
A scale from 0 to 14 that is used to measure how acidic or alkaline a solution is.

Phenotype
The characteristics you have. E.g. blue eyes.

Phloem
A type of plant tissue which transports sucrose around the plant.

Photosynthesis
The process by which plants and algae use light energy to convert carbon dioxide and water into glucose and oxygen.

Plum pudding model
A historic model of the atom that said that the atom was a positively-charged sphere with negatively-charged electrons stuck in it like plums in a plum pudding.

Polydactyly
A genetic disorder caused by a dominant allele where a sufferer has extra fingers or toes.

Polymer
A long chain molecule that is formed by joining lots of smaller molecules (monomers) together.

Positive correlation
When one variable increases as another variable increases.

Positive ion
A particle with a positive charge, formed when one or more electrons are lost.

Potential difference (p.d.)
The work done (or energy transferred) per coulomb of charge that passes between two points in a circuit, measured in volts (V).
Also known as voltage.

Power
The rate of transferring energy (or doing work). Normally measured in watts (W).

Precipitate
A solid that is formed in a solution during a chemical reaction.

Precipitation
A reaction that takes place in aqueous solution and leads to the formation of an insoluble precipitate.

Precise result
When all the data is close to the mean.

Predicted yield
The amount of product you would expect to be formed in a reaction. Also known as theoretical yield.

Prediction
A statement based on a hypothesis that can be tested.

Protease
A type of digestive enzyme that catalyses the breakdown of proteins into amino acids, in the stomach and small intestine.

Protein
A large biological molecule made up of long chains of amino acids.

Proton
A subatomic particle with a relative charge of +1 and a relative mass of 1.

Proton number
The number of protons in the nucleus of an atom. It's also known as atomic number.

Protostar
The earliest stage in the life cycle of a star. Protostars are formed when the force of gravity causes clouds of dust and gas to spiral together.

Punnet square
A type of genetic diagram.

Q

Quadrat
A square frame enclosing a known area which can be used to study the distribution of organisms.

R

Radioactive decay
The random process of a radioactive substance giving out radiation from the nuclei of its atoms.

Radioactive substance
A substance that gives out radiation from the nuclei of its atoms no matter what is done to it.

Radiotherapy
The treatment of cancer that uses ionising radiation (such as gamma rays) to kill cancer cells.

Random error
A small difference in the results of an experiment caused by things like human error in measuring.

Range
The difference between the smallest and largest values in a set of data.

Reaction force
A force that results from one object applying a force to another. It's always in the opposite direction and equal to the original force.

Recessive allele
An allele whose characteristic only appears in an organism if there are two copies present.

Red giant
A type of star that is formed when a star around the same size as the Sun expands as it starts to run out of hydrogen.

Red super giant
A type of star that is formed when a large star (much bigger than our sun) expands as it starts to run out of hydrogen.

Reduction
A reaction where electrons are gained.

Regenerative brakes
Brakes that put the vehicle's motor into reverse and turn the kinetic energy into electrical energy rather than heat.

Relative atomic mass (A_r)
The average mass of the atoms of an element measured relative to the mass of one atom of carbon-12. The relative atomic mass of an element is the same as its mass number in the periodic table.

Relative molecular mass (M_r)
All the relative atomic masses of the atoms in a molecule added together.

Reliable result
A result that is repeatable and reproducible.

Repeatable result
A result that will come out the same if the experiment is repeated by the same person using the same method and equipment.

Reproducible result
A result that will come out the same if someone different does the experiment, or a sightly different method or piece of equipment is used.

Residual current circuit breaker (RCCB)
A type of circuit breaker used instead of a fuse and an earth wire. It detects a difference in the current flowing in the live and neutral wires.

Resistance
Anything in a circuit that reduces the flow of current. Measured in ohms, Ω.

Resolution
The smallest change a measuring instrument can detect.

Resultant force
A single force that represents all the forces acting at a point. A resultant force has the same effect as all of the individual forces acting together.

Reversible reaction
A reaction where the products of the reaction can themselves react to produce the original reactants.

Ribosome
A structure in a cell, where proteins are made.

Rutherford scattering experiment
An experiment in which alpha particles were fired at gold foil to see if they were deflected. It led to the plum pudding model being abandoned in favour of the nuclear model of the atom.

S

Salivary gland
An organ (and gland) in the mammalian digestive system which produces digestive juices.

Seat belt
A belt in a vehicle that prevents the wearer from hitting a hard surface in the vehicle or being thrown out of the vehicle. It also stretches slightly, increasing the time it takes the wearer to stop.

Series circuit
A circuit in which every component is connected in a line, end to end.

Sex chromosome (humans)
One of the 23rd pair of chromosomes — together they determine whether an individual is male or female.

Sexual reproduction
Where two gametes combine at fertilisation to produce a genetically different new individual.

Shape memory alloy
A material that can be bent out of shape but will return to its original shape when it's heated.

Side impact bars
Metal tubes fitted into car door panels to protect the passengers.

Simple molecule
A molecule made up of only a few atoms held together by covalent bonds.

Single covalent bond
A pair of electrons shared between two atoms.

Small intestine
An organ in the mammalian digestive system where food is digested and soluble food molecules are absorbed.

Smart material
A material that has properties that change in response to external stimuli, like heat or pressure.

Specialised cell
A cell which performs a specific function.

Speciation
The development of a new species.

Species
A group of similar organisms that can reproduce to give fertile offspring.

Speed
A measure of how fast something's going with no regard to direction.

Starch
An insoluble molecule used as a store of glucose in plants and algae.

State symbols
The letter or letters in brackets that are placed after a substance to show what physical state it is in. E.g. gaseous carbon dioxide is shown as $CO_{2(g)}$.

Static charge
An electric charge that cannot move. It can form on an electrical insulator, where charge cannot flow freely.

Stem cell
An undifferentiated cell which has the ability to become one of many different types of cell.

Stomach
An organ in the mammalian digestive system where food is digested.

Stopping distance
The distance covered by a vehicle in the time between a hazard first appearing and the vehicle coming to a complete stop. It's the sum of the thinking distance and the braking distance.

Subatomic particle
A particle that is smaller than an atom. Protons, neutrons and electrons are all subatomic particles.

Successful collision
A collision between particles that results in a chemical reaction.

Supernova
The explosion of a red super giant.

Systematic error
An error that is consistently made throughout an experiment.

T

Terminal velocity
The maximum velocity a falling object can reach without any added driving forces. It's the velocity at which the resistive forces (drag) acting on the object match the force due to gravity (weight).

Theoretical yield
The amount of product you would expect to be formed in a reaction. Also known as predicted yield.

Theory
A hypothesis which has been accepted by the scientific community because there is good evidence to back it up.

Thermistor
A resistor whose resistance is dependent on the temperature. The resistance decreases as temperature increases.

Thermosetting polymer
A polymer that has cross-links between its chains.

Thermosoftening polymer
A polymer made of individual tangled polymer chains, with no cross-links between them.

Thinking distance
The distance a vehicle travels in the driver's reaction time (before the brakes have been applied).

Three-core cable
An electrical cable containing a live wire, a neutral wire and an earth wire.

Time period
The time it takes for a wave to complete one oscillation or cycle.

Tissue
A group of similar cells that work together to carry out a particular function. It can include more than one type of cell.

Transect
A line which can be used to study the distribution of organisms across an area.

Trial run
A quick version of an experiment that can be used to work out the range of variables and the interval between the variables that will be used in the proper experiment.

Two-core cable
An electrical cable containing a live wire and a neutral wire only.

U

Universal indicator
A combination of dyes which gives a different colour for every pH on the pH scale.

Valid result
A result that answers the original question.

Variable
A factor in an investigation that can change or be changed.
E.g. temperature or concentration.

Velocity
The speed of an object in a given direction.

Velocity-time graph
A graph showing an object's velocity over a period of time.

Voltage
The work done (or energy transferred) per coulomb of charge that passes between two points in a circuit, measured in volts (V).
Also known as potential difference.

Voltmeter
A component used to measure the potential difference across a component. Always connected in parallel with the component.

Weight
The force an object experiences due to gravity.

White dwarf
The hot dense core left behind when a red giant becomes unstable and ejects its outer layer of dust and gas as a planetary nebula.

Work done
The energy transferred when a force moves an object through a distance.

Xylem
A type of plant tissue which transports water and mineral ions around the plant.

Yeast
A type of single-celled microorganism.

Yield
The amount of product made in a reaction.

Zero error
A type of systematic error caused by using a piece of equipment that isn't zeroed properly.

Acknowledgements

Data acknowledgements

Data in the table of retention times on page 156 reprinted from Journal of Chromatography A, Volume 1218, Qun Gu et al. Evaluation of automated sample preparation, retention time locked gas chromatography-mass spectrometry and data analysis methods for the metabolomic study of Arabidopsis species. Pgs 3247-3254, © 2011. With permission from Elsevier & Research Institute for Chromatography.

Data used to construct stopping distance diagram on page 222 from the Highway Code.
© Crown Copyright re-produced under the terms of the Open Government Licence
http://www.nationalarchives.gov.uk/doc/open-government-licence/

Photograph acknowledgements

Cover Photo **Andrew Lambert Photography**/Science Photo Library, p 3 **Gustoimages**/Science Photo Library, p 4 **Tek Image**/Science Photo Library, p 5 **Philippe Plailly**/Science Photo Library, p 6 **European Space Agency**/Science Photo Library, p 7 **Andrew Lambert Photography**/Science Photo Library, p 8 **Gustoimages**/Science Photo Library, p 9 **Tony McConnell**/Science Photo Library, p 10 **Rosenfeld Images Ltd**/Science Photo Library, p 11 **Martyn F. Chillmaid**/Science Photo Library, p 16 **GODONG/Deloche**/Science Photo Library, p 17 **Pasieka**/Science Photo Library, p 18 **Dr. Martha Powell, Visuals Unlimited**/Science Photo Library, p 19 **Steve Gschmeissner**/Science Photo Library, p 20 **Power and Syred**/Science Photo Library, p 22 **Andrew Lambert Photography**/Science Photo Library, p 25 **Steve Gschmeissner**/Science Photo Library, p 26 **Dr Keith Wheeler**/Science Photo Library, p 29 (Fig. 1) **B.W.Hoffman/Agstockusa**/Science Photo Library, p 29 (Fig. 2) **Eye of Science**/Science Photo Library, p 32 **Eye of Science**/Science Photo Library, p 33 **Biophoto Associates**/Science Photo Library, p 35 **E. R. Degginger**/Science Photo Library, p 39 (Fig. 2) **Angel Fitor**/Science Photo Library, p 39 (Fig. 3) **36clicks**/iStockphoto, p 42 (Fig. 1) **Biophoto Associates**/Science Photo Library, p 42 (Fig. 2) **Wim Van Egmond/Visuals Unlimited, Inc.**/Science Photo Library, p 42 (left) **Angel Fitor**/Science Photo Library, p 42 (right) **Victor de Schwanberg**/Science Photo Library, p 43 **The Picture Store**/Science Photo Library, p 45 **Bob Gibbons**/Science Photo Library, p 46 **Martyn F. Chillmaid**/Science Photo Library, p 48 **Martyn F. Chillmaid**/Science Photo Library, p 54 **Clive Freeman, The Royal Institution**/Science Photo Library, p 59 **Martyn F. Chillmaid**/Science Photo Library, p 60 **Power and Syred**/Science Photo Library, p 61 **Eye of Science**/Science Photo Library, p 65 (Fig. 1) **Samuel Ashfield**/Science Photo Library, p 65 **Professors P. Motta & T. Naguro**/Science Photo Library, p 66 **BSIP, Laurent/B. Hop Ame**/Science Photo Library, p 68 **Gustoimages**/Science Photo Library, p 73 **David Parker**/Science Photo Library, p 74 **Tek Image**/Science Photo Library, p 75 (Fig. 1) **Sovereign, ISM**/Science Photo Library, p 75 (Fig. 2) **Michael P. Gadomski**/Science Photo Library, p 76 **Herve Conge, ISM**/Science Photo Library, p 78 **Adrian T Sumner**/Science Photo Library, p 80 **Paul Gunning**/Science Photo Library, p 81 **Pascal Goetgheluck**/Science Photo Library, p 83 Science Photo Library, p 84 **kutipie**/iStockphoto, p 87 Science Photo Library, p 88 **Bob Gibbons**/Science Photo Library, p 91 **Wally Eberhart, Visuals Unlimited**/Science Photo Library, p 95 **Sovereign, ISM**/Science Photo Library, p 97 **Pascal Goetgheluck**/Science Photo Library, p 103 (Fig. 1) **Sinclair Stammers**/Science Photo Library, p 103 (Fig. 2) **Natural History Museum, London**/Science Photo Library, p 104 (Fig. 3) **Dirk Wiersma**/Science Photo Library, p 104 (Fig. 4) **John Reader**/Science Photo Library, p 104 (Fig. 5) **Pasieka**/Science Photo Library, p 104 (Fig. 6) **Silkeborg Museum, Denmark/Munoz-Yague**/Science Photo Library, p 105 (A) **Josie Iselin, Visuals Unlimited**/Science Photo Library, p 105 (B and C) **Herve Conge, ISM**/Science Photo Library, p 105 (D) **Philippe Plailly**/Science Photo Library, p 106 **Photo Researchers**/Science Photo Library, p 109 **kojihirano**/iStockphoto, p 114 **Charles D. Winters**/Science Photo Library, p 119 **Andrew Lambert Photography**/Science Photo Library, p 124 (middle) **Lawrence Lawry**/Science Photo Library, p 124 (bottom) **Scientifica, Visuals Unlimited**/Science Photo Library, p 127 (top left) **Charles D. Winters**/Science Photo Library, p 127 (top middle) **Charles D. Winters**/Science Photo Library, p 127 (top right) **Charles D. Winters**/Science Photo Library, p 127 (bottom) **Pascal Goetgheluck**/Science Photo Library, p 129 **Friedrich Saurer**/Science Photo Library, p 130 **Victor de Schwanberg**/Science Photo Library, p 136 (left) **Pasieka**/Science Photo Library, p 136 (right) **Natural History Museum, London**/Science Photo Library, p 140 **Martyn F. Chillmaid**/Science Photo Library, p 141 **Andrew Lambert Photography**/Science Photo Library, p 145 **Andrew Lambert Photography**/Science Photo Library, p 149 **Martyn F. Chillmaid**/Science Photo Library, p 151 **Andrew Lambert Photography**/Science Photo Library, p 152 **Mark Sykes**/Science Photo Library, p 161 **Martyn F. Chillmaid**/Science Photo Library, p 162 **Andrew Lambert Photography**/Science Photo Library, p 163 **Andrew Lambert Photography**/Science Photo Library, p 167 **Trevor Clifford Photography**/Science Photo Library, p 168 **Andrew Lambert Photography**/Science Photo Library, p 170 **Charles D. Winters**/Science Photo Library, p 172 **Martyn F. Chillmaid**/Science Photo Library, p 173 **Andrew Lambert Photography**/Science Photo Library, p 174 **Martyn F. Chillmaid**/Science Photo Library, p 177 **Andrew Lambert Photography**/Science Photo Library, p 178 **Martyn F. Chillmaid**/Science Photo Library, p 180 **Charles D. Winters**/Science Photo Library, p 185 (top) **Martyn F. Chillmaid**/Science Photo Library, p 185 (bottom) **Martyn F. Chillmaid**/Science Photo Library, p 186 **Massimo Brega, The Lighthouse**/Science Photo Library, p 195 **Trevor Clifford Photography**/Science Photo Library, p 197 **Sam Ogden**/Science Photo Library, p 200 **Tek Image**/Science Photo Library, p 215 **Martyn F. Chillmaid**/Science Photo Library, p 216 **Sheila Terry**/Science Photo Library, p 219 **Gustoimages**/Science Photo Library, p 220 **NASA**/Science Photo Library, p 221 **Ria Novosti**/Science Photo Library, p 223 **David Woodfall Images**/Science Photo Library, p 226 **GIPhotoStock**/Science Photo Library, p 234 **Lee Powers**/Science Photo Library, p 238 **Pekka Parviainen**/Science Photo Library, p 240 **David Aubrey**/Science Photo Library, p 243 **Melhi**/iStockphoto, p 244 **Ria Novosti**/Science Photo Library, p 246 (Fig. 1) **Andrew Lambert Photography**/Science Photo Library, p 246 (Fig. 2) **Tony McConnell**/Science Photo Library, p 247 (Fig. 3) **Yves Soulabaille/Look at Sciences**/Science Photo Library, p 247 (Fig. 4) **CC Studio**/Science Photo Library, p 249 **Andreas Steinhart**/iStockphoto, p 251 **Sheila Terry**/Science Photo Library, p 259 **Andrew Lambert Photography**/Science Photo Library, p 260 **Trevor Clifford Photography**/Science Photo Library, p 261 **Ton Kinsbergen**/Science Photo Library, p 263 **Maria Platt-Evans**/Science Photo Library, p 264 **Andy Crump**/Science Photo Library, p 265 (Fig. 2) **Martyn F. Chillmaid**/Science Photo Library, p 265 (Fig. 3) **Martyn F. Chillmaid**/Science Photo Library, p 266 **Burwell and Burwell Photography**/iStockphoto, p 272 **221A**/iStockphoto, p 273 **Philippe Psaila**/Science Photo Library, p 282 **Tek Image**/Science Photo Library, p 285 (Fig. 1) **Hazel Proudlove**/iStockphoto, p 285 (Fig. 2, left) **Andrew Lambert Photography**/Science Photo Library, p 285 (Fig. 2, right) **Andrew Lambert Photography**/Science Photo Library, p 285 (Fig. 3) **Martyn F. Chillmaid**/Science Photo Library, p 286 **Martyn F. Chillmaid**/Science Photo Library, p 288 (Fig. 1) **Tek Image**/Science Photo Library, p 288 (Fig. 2) **Sheila Terry**/Science Photo Library, p 290 **Sheila Terry**/Science Photo Library, p 291 **Francesco Speranza**/iStockphoto, p 292 **Lawrence Lawry**/Science Photo Library, p 293 **Sheila Terry**/Science Photo Library, p 295 **Martyn F. Chillmaid**/Science Photo Library, p 303 **Emilio Segre Visual Archives/American Institute of Physics**/Science Photo Library, p 307 **C. Powell, P. Fowler & D. Perkins**/Science Photo Library, p 310 **Goronwy Tudor Jones, University of Birmingham**/Science Photo Library, p 313 **Trevor Clifford Photography**/Science Photo Library, p 315 **Lawrence Livermore Laboratory**/Science Photo Library, p 316 (Fig. 3) **Public Health England**/Science Photo Library, p 316 (Fig. 5) **Steve Allen**/Science Photo Library, p 319 **Josh Sher**/Science Photo Library, p 321 (top) **Martin Bond**/Science Photo Library, p 321 (bottom) **Oulette & Theroux, Publiphoto Diffusion**/Science Photo Library, p 322 (Fig. 3) **Dr P. Marazzi**/Science Photo Library, p 322 (Fig. 5) **Cordelia Molloy**/Science Photo Library, p 326 **Martyn F. Chillmaid**/Science Photo Library, p 328 **Patrick Landmann**/Science Photo Library, p 329 **EFDA-JET**/Science Photo Library, p 330 **National Optical Astronomy Observatories**/Science Photo Library, p 331 **European Southern Observatory**/Science Photo Library, p 334 **Science Photo Library**, p 340 **Andrew Lambert Photography**/Science Photo Library, p 342 **Science Photo Library**, p 350 **Photostock-Israel**/Science Photo Library.

Every effort has been made to locate copyright holders and obtain permission to reproduce sources. For those sources where it has been difficult to trace the originator of the work, we would be grateful for information. If any copyright holder would like us to make an amendment to the acknowledgements, please notify us and we will gladly update the book at the next reprint. Thank you.

Index

M

N

O

P

Q

R

S

T

U

V

W

X

Y

Z

Equations Page

If you're going to be tested on physics in an exam, you'll be given an equations sheet listing some of the equations you might need to use. That means you don't have to learn them (hurrah), but you still need to be able to pick out the correct equations to use and be really confident using them. The equations sheet won't give you any units for the equation quantities — so make sure you know them inside out.

The equations you'll be given in the exam are all on this page. You can use this sheet as a reference sheet when you're doing the exam-style questions at the end of each physics section.

Equations

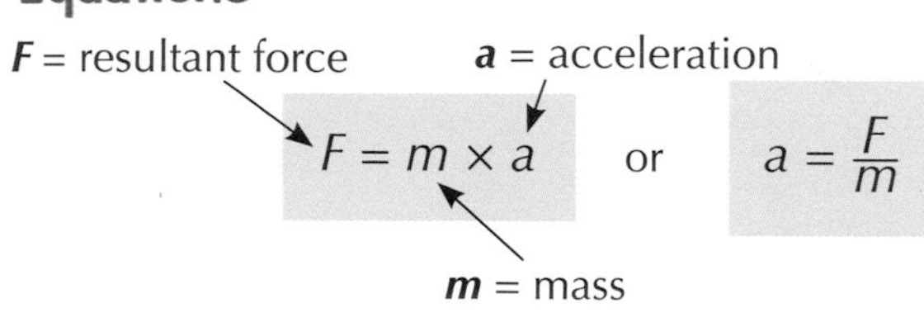

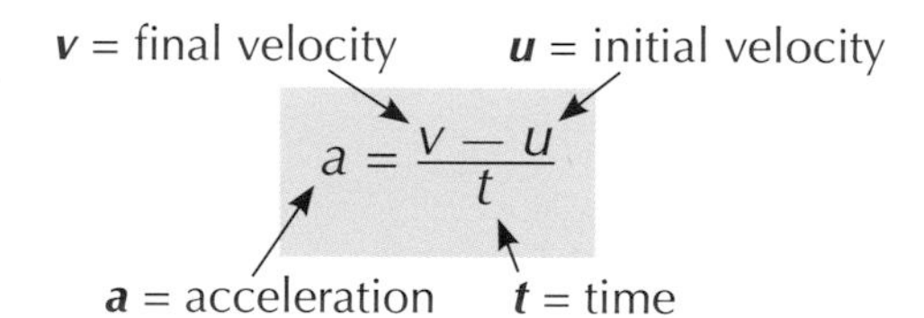

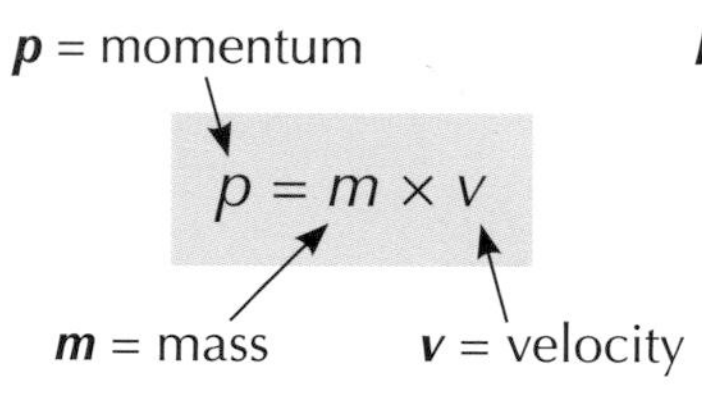

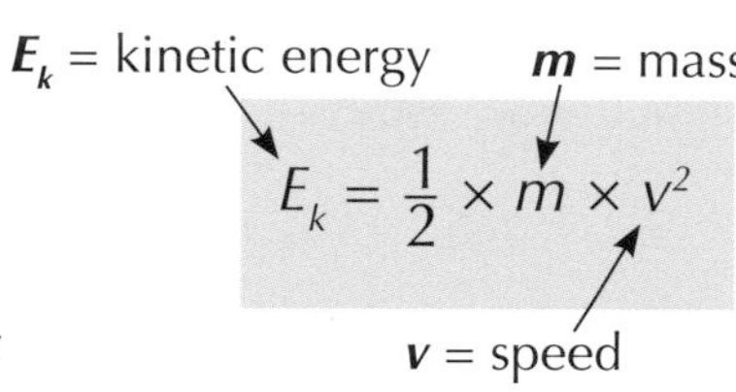

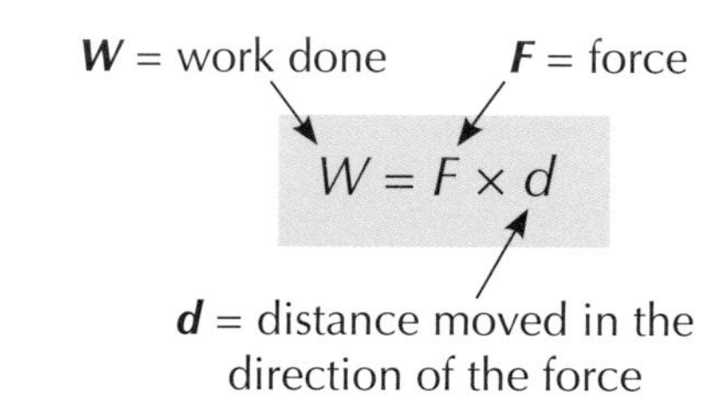

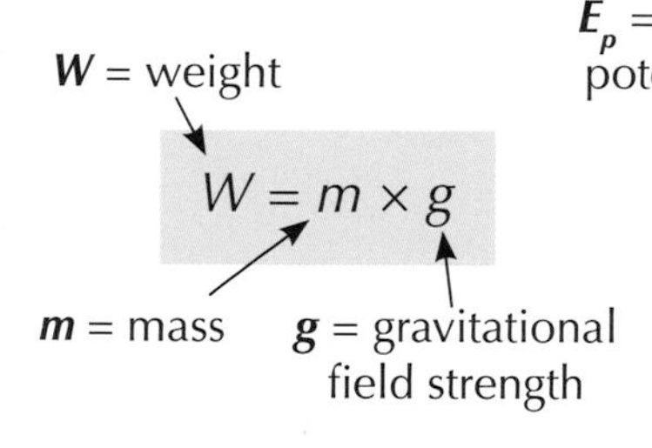

E_p = gravitational potential energy, h = height

$$E_p = m \times g \times h$$

m = mass, g = gravitational field strength

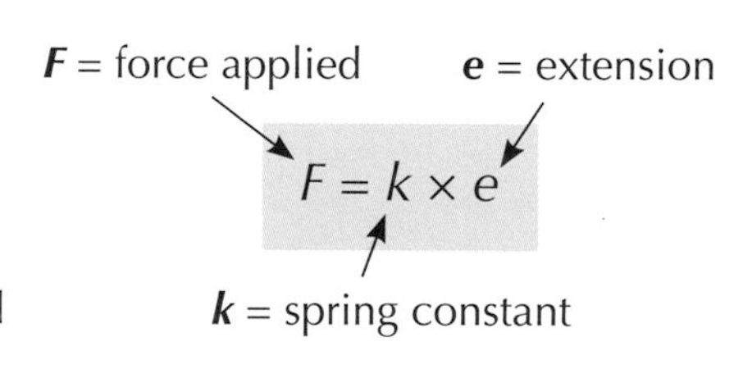

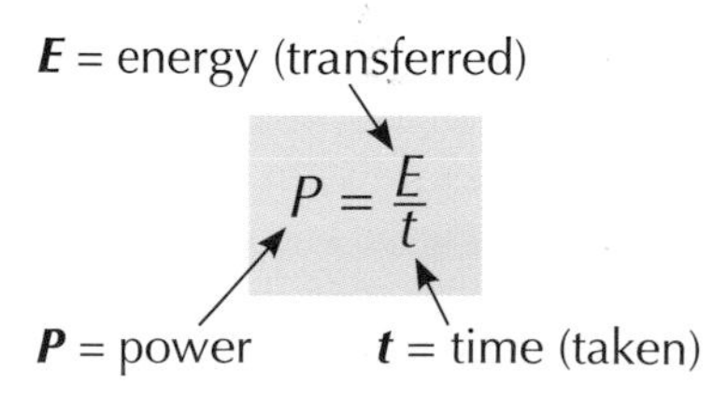

V = potential difference

$$P = I \times V$$

P = power, I = current

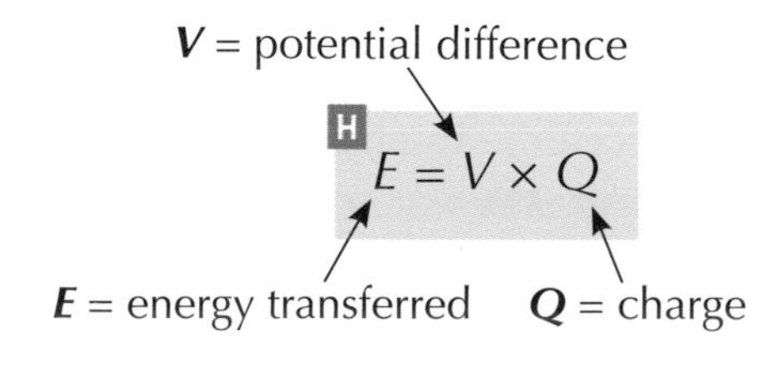

I = current, Q = charge

$$I = \frac{Q}{t}$$

t = time

V = potential difference

$$V = I \times R$$

I = current, R = resistance

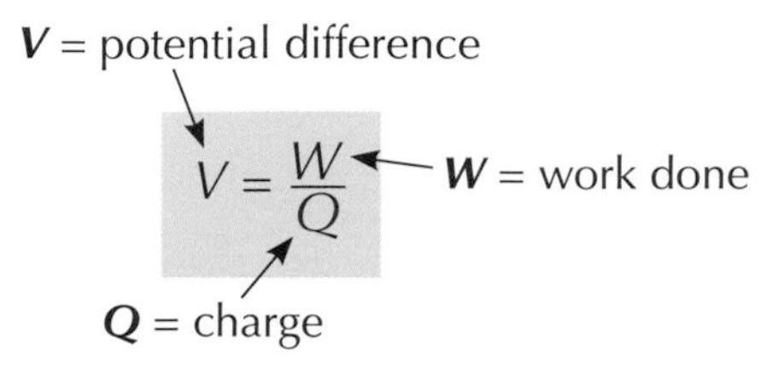

SQTB41